WORKS
AND BUILDINGS

BY

C. M. KOHAN, O.B.E., M.A.

LONDON: 1952

HER MAJESTY'S STATIONERY OFFICE

AND

LONGMANS, GREEN AND CO

First published 1952

Crown Copyright Reserved

HER MAJESTY'S STATIONERY OFFICE

London: York House, Kingsway, W.C.2 & 423 Oxford Street, W.1
Edinburgh: 13a Castle Street   Cardiff: 1 St. Andrew's Crescent
Manchester: 39 King Street   Bristol: Tower Lane
Birmingham: 2 Edmund Street   Belfast: 80 Chichester Street

LONGMANS, GREEN AND CO LTD
6 and 7 Clifford Street, London, W.1
also at Melbourne and Cape Town

LONGMANS, GREEN AND CO INC
55 Fifth Avenue, New York, 3

LONGMANS, GREEN AND CO
215 Victoria Street, Toronto, 1

ORIENT LONGMANS, LTD
Bombay, Calcutta, Madras

Price £1 12s. 6d. net

Printed in Great Britain under the authority of H.M. Stationery Office
by Sanders Phillips & Co. Ltd., London, S.W.9

CONTENTS

PART I: THE REARMAMENT PERIOD AND THE FIRST PHASE OF WAR, 1936–40

PART II: THE GROWTH AND CO-ORDINATION OF CONTROL, 1940–42

PART V: REFLECTIONS

NOTES AND APPENDICES

NOTES

EDITOR'S NOTE

THE preface to *British War Economy* mentioned some self-denying ordinances which the editor of this series accepted on his own behalf and that of his colleagues; in particular, it emphasised their obligation to respect the constitutional principle of ministerial responsibility and the impersonality of the civil service. Experience has confirmed, if confirmation were needed, the soundness of this rule; but it has also revealed one or two small difficulties in applying it. In *British War Economy* it was not found necessary—nor indeed was it always possible—rigidly to exclude the names of men, such as Mr. Arthur Purvis or Lord Keynes, who as temporary civil servants performed tasks which brought them prominently before the public. In succeeding volumes of the series a similar practice has been followed. However, the practice would create a lack of balance if it were followed too mechanically; for if an historian allows himself some relaxation in mentioning the names of the 'temporaries', while rigidly excluding those of the permanent civil servants, his book may give the impression that the former are to be credited with most of the achievement. In order to ensure that a sound rule is not spoilt by pedantry, I have reminded my colleagues of the following principles:

(a) There is no objection to stating that a certain individual held a certain office at such and such a period.

(b) Where there has been communication with the public on any matter, there is no objection to naming the civil servant who was the channel of communication.

(c) The objection to mentioning civil servants by name has less force if they were at the time acting in a representative or quasi-ambassadorial capacity abroad.

Consequently, in the present volume and those that follow, readers may detect some slight change of practice in the citing of names. They will not, however, observe any departure from the intention of the rule originally laid down. My colleagues and I remain bound to respect the constitutional principle of ministerial responsibility. We cannot indulge ourselves by giving good or bad marks to officials who are debarred from explaining or defending their actions. Sometimes we shall find ourselves compelled to record differences of official opinion within departments or between them, but we shall do this in an impersonal way; our concern is with the problems, the different attitudes and policies put forward for tackling them, the methods followed and the results achieved.

About the present volume this Note need say little, since the author explains its scope in his own preface. I should, however, make it clear that other volumes in the series will deal more fully with some of this country's war-time building achievements—for example, the provision of air-raid shelters. Major Kohan has indeed taken pains, especially in Part IV, to give his readers some idea of the wide front on which the resources of the building industry were deployed; nevertheless, the industry and its control have been the principal objective of his research and constitute the backbone of his book.

W. K. H.

PREFACE

A FUNDAMENTAL editorial decision requires the historians collaborating in this series to write the story not of particular departments, but of a number of selected subjects. Among the subjects chosen for investigation was that of Building; and because it was concerned mainly with war installations, Building was obviously on the margin of the war production field. There would have been logic in including this volume in the War Production series; there were rather better reasons for making it one of the General series of the Civil Histories.

In planning the contents the first question to arise was how far the theme of war-time building might in substance turn out to be inseparable from a history of the Ministry of Works as a department. For this Ministry, evolved in 1940 from its peace-time embryo the Office of Works, had been specifically charged with the co-ordination and control of the Government building programme. The limits of that assignment were proved by events to be conterminous with those of the building industry itself; and indeed in the war-time relations of the Ministry with the industry there was a distinct unity and a distinct interest. Was there not, then, a *prima facie* case for making Building an exception to the editorial ruling? Was there not even a likelihood that, in this particular instance, the history of a department might be found to fill the whole canvas of the subject selected?

Closer study did not support these assumptions. It was soon apparent that a departmental history of war-time building would have been misleading for two main reasons. The first reason is that although the Ministry of Works was set up as an administrative department of the first rank mainly in order to take charge of the building programme, it also absorbed and continued a number of the functions of the Office of Works which had nothing to do with the building industry, had no direct bearing on the Government building programme, and fell outside the field of war production. For, until the creation of the Ministry, the Office of Works had not only played a major role in the execution of the Government building programme: it had remained the guardian, and to a great extent the arbiter, of the architectural and ceremonial background of the State. As the holder of the largest estate in the country it was concerned, moreover, with problems of accommodation whose range was nation-wide, and whose character was extremely complex. The Office of Works had also had to exercise autocratic and unpopular powers of requisitioning; it had had to maintain a Supplies Division, and in that capacity to be a general provider for all departments on a scale not always realised. Further, it had not only had to safeguard and preserve historic buildings and ancient monuments, but to carry out some of the duties of a Ministry of Fine Arts. These multifarious functions of the Office of Works, and others of a like nature, now fell to the Ministry of Works; and it would have been impossible, within the limits of a single volume, to do justice to the war-time history of the Ministry, over the whole range of its activities, without doing injustice to the selected topic of building in war.

That brings us to the second reason why the subject of war-time building must overflow the confines of a departmental history. The Ministry of Works was not only new-born as a controlling and co-ordinating authority; it came as a newcomer among the older Ministries, each with its own building organisation and, particularly in the Service departments, a long tradition of virtual autonomy in planning and construction. Some of the constructional work of the other Ministries, it is true, was carried out by the Office of Works, and later by the Ministry, in its capacity of agent; but much of it, as Part IV of this volume shows, remained with individual departments. Consequently a history of war-time building cannot be restricted to the constructional problems of the Ministry of Works, but must also examine those of the Admiralty, the War Office, the Air Ministry, the Ministry of Aircraft Production, the Ministry of Supply, the Ministry of Transport, the Ministry of Home Security, and of the other civil departments engaged on building. A history of the Ministry of Works as a department would, on the other hand, have had to exclude, or only touch obliquely upon, this vital aspect of war-time building.

From the foregoing observations it will be seen that in planning the volume, the author had more or less rigidly to define the boundaries of his subject; and in so doing regretfully, but deliberately, to omit or cut down a number of topics which, though intrinsically important and often of absorbing interest, would nevertheless have obscured the outlines of the central theme—that of the co-ordination of the Government building programme and the control of the building industry. These observations are particularly relevant to the important topic of accommodation in general; for new war-time building, on however vast a scale, is but the half of a wider problem —that of accommodation in general for a nation at war. Plans for new building were conditioned by other plans for putting existing accommodation to the best use. Responsibility for making and carrying out these plans, during the rearmament period and the first year of war, rested with the Office of Works, and that responsibility was passed on to the Ministry of Works on its creation. The burden was a heavy one. Under the threat of war it became imperative to safeguard and secure the accommodation in which the Government of the country could be carried on under all conceivable conditions. This called for a scheme for the housing of Parliament—in itself a fascinating study; and for plans for the accommodation of the Government and the administrative machine. All these special tasks could not have been accomplished without the exercise of initiative and much technical ingenuity, often under conditions of great difficulty and urgency. To describe them in detail would have taken too much space from our central theme.

War requires the use to the best advantage of all existing buildings and of land. In co-ordinating the use of buildings and land by Government departments and other authorities, and in preventing overlapping and competition for accommodation, the Ministry of Works played an essential part. In so far as the best use could be made of existing premises, the diversion of resources to the erection of new buildings was reduced. When it dealt with problems arising from the provision of new buildings, the Ministry was starting afresh, but the development of existing buildings and their adaptation was a part of a process that had been planned and co-ordinated by the Office of Works for some years before the war began. Moreover, in addition to these co-ordinating activities, the Ministry of Works itself took over and adapted a vast variety of premises for all purposes both for the Service and civil departments and for Allied Governments and services in this country. The effort needed to prepare and adapt existing buildings was, for the whole war period, comparable in scale with the effort needed to erect new buildings. To have described this effort in detail would have taken the volume far beyond its prescribed limits, but the reader must be made aware of it, and of its effect on the perspective of the building programme.

Had this volume been as much a history of accommodation as of building, one topic to figure prominently in it would have been the scheme for the evacuation of Government departments, preparation for which began in 1936. That work was planned against the background of Air Staff estimates and probable damage from enemy bombing. It comprised both requisitioning and building, and under both headings secrecy was necessary and was maintained. The scheme changed from time to time as the Air Ministry's estimate of damage changed. Since the civil service had grown by 1942 from about a quarter of a million to three-quarters of a million the problem was immense. In peace-time accommodation was provided by building or leasing: in war-time power to requisition had to be used on a large scale, and was covered by the Defence Regulations. After the First World War, it had been recommended by the appropriate committee that the requisitioning power should be concentrated, that one central authority should requisition for all civil departments, though not for the Services. At the height of the Second World War, however, eighteen Ministries had requisitioning power. In addition, the Ministry of Home Security and the Ministry of Health, with their local obligations, had secured requisitioning power for about 1,600 local authorities. There was an obvious danger that the same premises might be requisitioned twice over or more by competing authorities. To some extent trouble of that kind occurred at the beginning of the war, but it was got over by the compilation and maintenance in the Office of Works (and later in the Ministry of Works) of a Central Register of Accommodation, which contained about 300,000 separate premises.

To give due prominence to each significant aspect of the building effort in a single volume would have been a vain endeavour, and the author has not attempted it. Where the relationship of departments with the building industry was part of a wider co-operation between Government and industry as a whole, he has tried to follow the practice of not pursuing a particular topic beyond the confines of his own subject. For that reason such aspects of the building programme as the decisive role of the trade union organisations in speeding up work on constructional sites, the improvement of welfare arrangements, the problems created by hours of work and working conditions and kindred problems with which the trade unions were closely concerned, are examined in outline as they become relevant, but they have not been grouped together as a separate part of the book or related to the broader industrial background.

Again, because personal sacrifice and devotion to the war effort were not the particular heroism of the building industry but were part of what was endured by the whole nation at war, much detail that might have added warmth and colour to this history has been left aside. That is not to say, however, that the rank and file of the building industry were not in the very forefront of the civilian battle. Moreover, it was a much diminished and ageing labour force on whom, at the height of the war, fell the heaviest burdens of the building programme. Under conditions of great hardship, often of considerable danger, these men, of whom many were elderly or unfit or both, fulfilled exacting tasks. In the final assessment of achievement their service and sacrifice rank high and will be remembered.

In the preparation of this volume the author has had the advice and guidance of many civil servants, permanent and temporary, both in the Ministry of Works and in other departments. He is precluded from mentioning their names, but to them all he would express his gratitude and indebtedness. Without their knowledge and experience he would often have been in danger of losing direction; and without their courtesy and kindliness his task would have been a harder one. Finally, he was fortunate in being allowed the privilege of nominating his wife for appointment as secretary and personal assistant. The appointment was on merit, for he already knew how well qualified she was to lighten his labours; and this knowledge was more than confirmed by the competence and devotion with which she carried out her tasks.

April 1952   C. M. KOHAN

PART I

The Rearmament Period and the
First Phase of War
1936–1940

B

CHAPTER I

REARMAMENT AND THE BUILDING INDUSTRY

(i)

Introductory

THE history of war-time building is the record of a joint enterprise by Government and industry under the stress of war. It is not so much a record of gradual progression as of ups and downs, periods of hesitancy and periods of success: nor were all the successes scored later in the war or all the blunders made earlier. If advance was not always from ineffectiveness to success it was at least from lack of organisation to organisation. Informal collaboration between the industry[1] and Government departments, begun in the uneasy rearmament period, changed under the mounting demands of war into a closely knit organisation—an organisation made effective, it is true, by State control, but control to which the industry for the most part had voluntarily submitted and under which all its resources were harnessed at last to the war machine. The attainment of that end meant also the transformation of the Office of Works,[2] with its limited responsibility, into an administrative department of full stature.

Implicit in the rearmament policy laid before Parliament in March 1936[3] was a massive programme of constructional work in every field of defence. Some of that work was already in progress. For the expansion of the Royal Air Force, the constructional industries were providing new airfields and air stations, storage and other accommodation, and training establishments on a large scale. Soon the expansion of naval and military installations, the limitless air raid shelter building of the Home Office and of the local authorities, and the multifarious building commitments of other Ministries, directly or indirectly linked with defence, were to make an ever-growing demand for men and materials. Through factory expansion

---

[1] Although in this narrative the term 'building industry' includes civil engineering unless otherwise stated, the two industries nevertheless differ in character and organisation and are in many respects independent of each other.

[2] See Notes and Appendices: Note I: 'The Functions of the Office of Works'.

[3] *Statement Relating to Defence*, Cmd.5107, 3rd March 1936.

3

and new factory construction capacity was to be created for the manufacture of the munitions of war. As a general principle the White Paper laid down that to meet Service and other assignments, industry was to be so organised that it could rapidly change over at the vital points from commercial to war production. To make such a change-over possible Government factories, and the factories of Government contractors who in peace manufactured various types of armaments, were to be called on to extend or duplicate existing capacity. It was clear from the White Paper that immense, though as yet undefined, building projects lay ahead.

That the building industry without straining its resources could carry through whatever emergency programme was likely to be laid on it was never doubted by its leaders. Of deeper concern both to workmen and employers was the need to safeguard the long-term interests of their vast industry. For building, though it held a key position in the modern economy and had comprised over the past fifty years, in spite of violent fluctuations in size, from eight to eleven per cent. of the total male population, remained in many respects unorganised.[1] Further, because great numbers of its workers were un-skilled or semi-skilled, the industry was peculiarly liable to be quickly caught up in alternations of general prosperity and decline;[2] hence a strong feeling in the industry that, as soon as the Government could define its building programme, the industrial organisations should be taken into the confidence of the departments and a detailed plan of co-operation worked out. Again and again, from the very commence-ment of rearmament, the industry's spokesmen asked to be brought into consultation with whatever official bodies were charged with the programme.

The Government's initial reserve in the face of these demands, although not justified by events, is readily understood. In retro-spect, one might expect a Government committed to rearmament to have formulated, at least in outline, a building policy linked up with the timing and co-ordination of the whole rearmament pro-gramme. Ideally the consumption or conservation of essential build-ing materials such as steel and timber, for example, should have been related from the commencement of rearmament to a definite programme in time; the supply of building labour should have been

---

[1] Robinson, H. W., *The Economics of Building*, 1939 (*passim*).

[2] Nevertheless, between the end of 1918 and the summer of 1939 the total number of insured building workers (including those in public works contracting) in Great Britain and Northern Ireland grew, after fluctuations in the early years, from little over half a million to nearly one million and a half, or just over one million for the building industry alone. Between the years 1932 and 1939 the gross output of the building and civil engi-neering industries (for Great Britain) rose in value from £303 millions in 1932 to £442 millions in 1939. See Notes and Appendices: Appendix 1, 'Activity and Capacity of the Building and Civil Engineering Industries in Great Britain (1932–45)'. See also *Recon-struction Survey*, October 1941. Cole, G. D. H., 'Training and Recruitment in the Building Industry' (Memorandum prepared for M.O.W. on behalf of Nuffield College).

planned to forestall the waste of manpower and the bidding of Government departments one against the other; an early and effective check should have been imposed on the drain of men and materials for non-essential civil building. Yet what of those economic and strategic factors that cannot emerge until war is well under way? In the uncertainties of the rearmament years to plan too much might have been as bad as to plan too little. Whether through the hesitancy and individualism of departments or the reluctance of the building industry to commit its resources blindly, the effectual co-ordination of the building programme, after a five years' process of trial and error, was not achieved until 1942, by which time a substantial part of the programme had already been carried out and some of the experiences of the First World War had been ingloriously repeated.

In that war large-scale building had fallen to the Service departments, the Ministry of Munitions, the Local Government Board (through local authorities) and the Office of Works. The Ministry of Munitions, with some help from the Office of Works, had carried out its building work through eleven separate departments, such as that of factory construction, the explosives supply department, the trench warfare department, and so on. Including the separate divisions of the Ministry of Munitions, Government building was under the control of no less than sixteen departments, with private work virtually at a standstill and ninety-five per cent. of all building in the country being done by the State or on its behalf. The worst evils of this divided control were the forcing up of prices of materials, of which there was a shortage, and the competition for labour.

The competition between departments for materials during the First World War had been notorious. Even worse in its results had been the competition for labour. Men had been drawn away from work under the control of one department to work under the control of other departments by the offer of increased wages, extra allowances and special facilities. Inevitably, as most of the work was urgent and important, the general level of wages and allowances had had to be brought up so as to avoid grave dislocation and delay. Indifferent work, too, had come of this competition. Inferior men had moved from job to job until they found the easiest one or the one most to their liking. On certain contracts, where the number of men employed ran into thousands, the labour had been entirely changed throughout the progress of the work within a period of eight to nine weeks. The creation late in 1915 of an inter-departmental labour committee had proved only a partial remedy, since the committee had no powers to enforce its decisions. Departments continued to follow their own lines, sometimes without reference to the committee, often in direct opposition to its decisions, and invariably at the cost of such departments as stood by its rulings.

Later chapters of this history will show how far the Government and the building industry, in the war of 1939–45, escaped the pitfalls of 1914–18. They certainly knew in advance what those pitfalls were. From an early stage of rearmament officials and industrialists were in almost continuous joint session; and all were clearly aware of the dangers in their path. It will be seen how, later, the dangers grew where co-ordination faltered and receded as it became effective and complete.

(ii)

Growth and Change in the Building Industry

With the growing volume of building in the twentieth century certain changes in its character had been taking place. For well over a generation the use of concrete, of iron and steel and of various methods of prefabrication had been developed side by side with older methods of construction. While as recently as the close of the last century building was still a traditional craft—carried out, broadly speaking, by the same methods and the same technique as were the buildings of the Middle Ages, and even of ancient Rome—scientific development in other fields had gradually crept into the equipment of buildings. On the large contracts (especially those carried out by great national contractors) lighting, heating, ventilation, lifts, escalators, telephones and other equipment drew more and more upon the services of specialists.[1] At the other end of the scale there remained the local jobbing builder, often a single craftsman who had set up his own business and whose whole capital might be little more than the tools he used.[2]

Between the great contracting firms at one extreme, with vast resources that enabled them to take contracts all over the country—firms which often owned their own works and quarries, employed thousands of men and could muster a great array of costly plant—and the local builder at the other extreme were many thousands of firms of varying size.[3] Contracts ranging from £100 to £20,000,

---

[1] Bennett, T. P., 'The Principles of Organisation and Management as Applied to the Building Industry', *The Builder*, 17th November 1944. Mr. (later Sir Thomas) Bennett was Director of Works in the Ministry of Works between 1941 and 1944.

[2] At least one such builder could be found in every village to carry out essential repairs; and every town had its force of building workers engaged almost entirely on maintenance and repairs. It is difficult to identify with accuracy the size of this labour force. One estimate puts it as high as 250,000 in 1939. See T. P. Bennett, *loc. cit.* Also M.O.W. Report, *The Placing and Management of Building Contracts*, H.M.S.O. 1944.

[3] A Ministry of Works census in 1942 showed that 80,000 firms in the building industry employed an average of six workers, varying from the ten largest firms, employing an average of 10,000 workers each, to 30,000 one-man firms employing no workers at all. The last figure presumably excludes many village 'handymen' doing odd building jobs.

simple in character and varied in requirements, fulfilled before the
war a very large part of the wants of the community—the simple
home, the small school, the block of retail shops, the village hall, the
small hospital or factory, and extensions and additions to all sorts of
existing buildings. Such works absorbed the bulk of the so-called
'small' builders. Above the £20,000 line, contracts rapidly became
more complex, and brought in, as has already been noted, specialist
firms and sub-contractors of many kinds.[1]

Not only on contracts for large modern buildings but even on small
building contracts similar problems cropped up, and the organising
and managing of such contracts was apt to become just as complicated
and difficult as those for single large buildings. Since, on the whole,
technical developments in building science between the wars had
outstripped architectural and building organisation, it became an
essential and vital function, both of the architect and of the contractor, to organise and co-ordinate the work of others.[2]

As Lord Simon of Wythenshawe (himself an engineer as well as a
leading authority on housing problems) has stressed, the building
industry, despite technical progress and in marked contrast with industries more capable of scientific organisation, operates under severe
handicaps.[3] The most notable is the percentage of the cost of the
building incurred in labour on the site. Moreover, the building contract has to be carried out on the owner's site, often far from headquarters and generally in the open air. Most of the work is exposed to
and at the mercy of the weather, and almost everything, especially in
house-building, is done by manual labour and with little more than
the simplest plant. Transport of the workers to the site, often over long
distances, adds greatly to the building costs, and as against factory
conditions transport of material on the job is often crude and
primitive.

The handling of bricks in building houses is an extreme example of
the impossibility of using modern methods. The bricks are generally
taken from the lorry by one labourer and transported to where they
are wanted by throwing them from man to man. The bricklayer
stands on the scaffolding, which has to be constantly moved as the
house gets higher and is only at the most convenient height for a small

---

[1] e.g.: (*a*) Craft firms. Firms or departments of contracting firms which confined themselves entirely to one or other of the building crafts such as plastering, plumbing, painting,
masonry, joinery, tiling. (*b*) Constructional firms. Firms which specialised in structural
steel, reinforced concrete, floors, and similar structural portions of buildings. (*c*) Firms
which specialised in the mechanical and other equipment of buildings such as electricity,
heating, ventilation, lifts, sanitary ware and similar work. (*d*) Firms which specialised in
decoration and other finishings, such as terrazzo, fibrous plaster work and mastic asphalt.
[2] M.O.W. Report, *The Placing and Management of Building Contracts*, H.M.S.O., 1944.
[3] Simon, E. D., *Rebuilding Britain—A Twenty Year Plan, 1945*. Between 1942 and 1944
Sir Ernest Simon, as he then was, was chairman of sundry committees in the Ministry of
Works, and of the Central Council for Works and Building. See Notes and Appendices:
Note X, 'Committee Organisation in Ministry of Works, 1940–45'.

portion of the time. The labourer carries the bricks to him on a hod up a ladder. It is almost incredible to an engineer that methods so wasteful of human effort should be employed to-day.[1]

As compared with the factory workers, regularly employed over long periods in the same factory, the building craftsmen's average period of employment on a single site has been estimated at no more than two or three months. The contractor for his part can only build up a small regular nucleus of key workers, since his contracts are likely to be in different parts of the country and the volume of orders on his books is subject to violent fluctuations.

There is a great difference in the position of the employer in the building industry in regard to technique, as compared with that of an employer in a factory or works.

If a manager in a factory decides that a certain job can best be done by a sequence of operations a–b–c, and even a sequence of movements within each operation d–e–f, he can simply direct the workers in the way in which the job has to be done. If a new method is involved, he may, it is true, have some difficulty over fixing with the shop steward the rate for the job, but once this has been settled there is no question of his leadership both as to operations and even as to movements. Something of the same sort is true in the civil engineering industry where new plant and new methods are familiar. In the building industry, however, craftsmen regard themselves as the experts on movements and to some extent on operations. They do not normally expect to be told in any detail how the job is to be done. If told, they are usually resistant to the change.

A new method in a factory may be adopted simultaneously by 500 to 1,000 workpeople. In the building industry it has to percolate, even for a single firm, from site to site.

Thus, the managerial task of arranging a sequence of operations logically is badly hampered in the building industry. It is difficult for the manager even to discover how much time can be saved by re-arrangements of a schedule of operations since he cannot rely on co-operation from the workpeople in any such rearrangements.[2]

Because of this handicap, and for other reasons inherent in the industry, managerial efficiency, except in some of the leading building firms, often appears to fall below the level of that of many other industries. On the other hand, from the point of view of the operative, the special characteristic which colours all industrial issues in the building industry is the high status still enjoyed therein by the traditional craftsmen. The importance of craftsmen and respect for good craftsmanship in the background of the operatives' mentality have had direct effect on the organisation of the industry.

---

[1] *Ibid.*

[2] Bowen, I. 'Incentives and Output in the Building and Civil Engineering Industries', *The Manchester School of Economic and Social Studies.* May 1947.

However widespread genuine craftsmanship may or may not have been, the tradition of this craftsmanship is still largely predominant. . . . It influences the employers into a rather negative attitude towards proposals for bonuses or incentives payments. The first influence is the pride in the quality of work usually shown and an anxiety to see that the unwritten codes of quality shall not be lowered. The second influence is fear that the privileged position of the craftsman will be undermined by improved or modern methods which will have the result of making his particular skill open to competition by the unskilled or semi-skilled labourer. Thirdly, there is a fear that the craftsman will be induced by the application of scientific methods to give more work for the same money, thus undercutting his own comrades.[1]

The conservatism of building craftsmen, and their fear of exploitation, proved for a time a retarding influence in the execution of the building programme; but at the height of the war both broke under the pressure of events. If the building employers were also unwilling to depart from traditional methods and traditional materials some of their reluctance can be traced to the same source.

(iii)

The Building Industry Seeks Safeguards

Before discussing the safeguards sought by the building industry at the commencement of rearmament some indication must be given of the many sections and branches that went to make up the building industry in the widest sense.[2] Many interests were affected by, or affected, building works construction. A great number of federations, associations, institutions, societies and groups claimed to speak for the industry as a whole or for one or other of its components. The extent to which any interest had organised representation varied widely: in some instances representation was almost complete, in others it was negligible or entirely absent. These widely varying bodies fell roughly into five sections: professional; building trade employers; building trade operatives; manufacturers; and distributors.[3]

The professional organisations were drawn for the most part from architects, surveyors and engineers. Of these the leading national organisations (apart from some eighteen local associations) were the Royal Institute of British Architects and the Architects' Registration Council of the United Kingdom; the Chartered Surveyors' Institu-

---

[1] *Ibid.*

[2] For a description of the joint negotiating machinery in the building and civil engineering industries see Notes and Appendices: Note II.

[3] B.I.N.C., 'Register of Organisations, etc., concerned with Building Activity', 1942. The Building Industries National Council (B.I.N.C.), a voluntary association of architects, builders, operatives, manufacturers and others, acted in an advisory capacity to the Ministry of Works but was not itself regarded as a representative body. See Chapter XVIII.

tion and four other national bodies comprising surveyors or architects and surveyors; and the Institute of Civil Engineers and twelve other bodies of engineers concerned with constructional work. Another important national organisation was the Reinforced Concrete Association concerned with that special form of construction.

The most important organisation of employers was the National Federation of Building Trades Employers, to which were affiliated some 300 regional and local associations. Other important bodies were the Federation of Civil Engineering Contractors and the Public Works Contractors Association. Some of the remaining national associations represented house-builders, slaters and tilers, electrical contractors, flooring contractors or specialists, plumbers and domestic engineers and many other trades. The national, regional and local associations of employers spoke with varying degrees of authority for that side of the industry, but the National Federation of Building Trades Employers was accepted by the industry and the Government alike as representing and speaking for the main body of employers.

The parent organisation of the workers was the National Federation of Building Trades Operatives, with whom were directly associated thirteen associations or unions representing a variety of trades, such as slaters and tilers, woodworkers, plasterers, painters, and so forth. Nine other national associations of operatives, including the Transport and General Workers Union and the National Union of General and Municipal Workers, represented the interests of various building workers. The Transport and General Workers Union organised workers in clay products, cement, iron and steel, paint, limestone quarrying and non-ferrous metals, and the National Union of Municipal Workers organised a number of similar trades. In the discussions on the building programme with Government departments, the representatives of the National Federation of Building Trades Operatives spoke for all the organised workers.

The manufacturers and distributors were organised respectively in 113 and 56 associations, national, regional and local. Included in the associations of manufacturers were the British Steelwork Association, the Cement Makers' Federation, the National Federation of Clay Industries, the Pressed Brick Makers' Association (of which the London Brick Company was a member), the Sand Lime Brick Manufacturers Association and the Timber Trade Federation of the United Kingdom. Other associations covered slate quarrying, non-ferrous metal products, paint manufacture, building stone products, building glass products, bituminous products, building lime, building hardware and a number of other products or services normally associated with the building industry.

Among the distributors' organisations were the National Federation of Builders' Merchants, the Builders' and Plumbers' Merchants

Association, and the Federation of Hardware Factors. Electrical retailers, scrap-iron and steel merchants, softwood and hardwood merchants and importers, and other branches of the timber trade were similarly organised in a number of associations. Some half-dozen important associations were for certain purposes linked up with an organisation known as the Distributors of Builders' Supplies Joint Council.

Of all the national associations not one could be said, whatever its claims, to speak for the building industry as a whole and in the widest sense. A claim put forward in 1940 by the Building Industries National Council that it should be brought into consultation by the Minister of Works as a Council representative of the industry was carefully examined but found unacceptable,[1] and in the rearmament period and the first year of war it was through the two principal national federations of employers and operatives that the industry made itself heard in its conferences with the Government.

In their approach to the rearmament programme both sides of the building industry, with the experiences of the First World War still vividly in mind, were agreed that, whatever the industry's ultimate share in the programme, certain broad objectives must predominate. They had to avoid or minimise the disturbing effects of the Government programme on the organisation of the industry; to safeguard its normal industrial and commercial growth; and, not least important, to ensure its long-term welfare. Nor would it be easy, they thought, for the industry to fall at once into step with a rapid change-over to war production. While, it is true, the 1929–31 depression had been left behind, and by 1936 trade was again active, the shadows of the darkening political scene also obscured the economic background. It appeared as though a slump might well follow on the boom in trade activity; and some economists saw in the high level of home investment the danger that industrial activity might reach proportions that would make a later decline inevitable. These fears were shared by leaders of both sides of industry. There were, at the same time, some fears of a different kind. Although the state of the building industry, as reflected in the unemployment figures at the beginning of 1937, had become satisfactory, there was some uneasiness because of the failure to train a steady supply of young skilled men; and when the requirements of rearmament were piled on top of the strong civilian demand the industry might be faced with a shortage of skilled labour and all the resulting difficulties of maintaining a steady level of wages.

It was with some such considerations in mind that the National Federation of Building Trades Employers, with a strong claim in the existing circumstances to speak for the industry as a whole, on 30th June 1936 laid their views before the Minister for Co-ordination

---

[1] See Chapter XVIII.

of Defence[1] and offered to co-operate with responsible Ministers in working out the building programme. But readiness to co-operate did not deter them from an equal readiness to put the blame for the prevailing uncertainty squarely upon the shoulders of the Government. Had not the problems of the industry been largely due to the inception, or accentuation, of alternating booms and slumps 'not by gradual or unavoidable economic processes but by spasmodic or avoidable movements, usually as the result of sudden political expedients'? Had not intervention or indifference on the part of Government departments made it impossible to keep up such a steady flow of work as might enable the industry to adjust its resources to the demands made upon it? Was it not, for example, because the country had been flooded in the years 1919 to 1921 with demands for house construction greatly in excess of the industry's resources that prices were inflated to an abnormal extent, discredit brought upon the Government housing schemes, and great and difficult problems left to the industry to solve at a later date? And, finally, was it not because of the Government policy of retrenchment in 1931 that the industry had passed through a slump of unprecedented proportions in the years 1931 to 1933?

Direct pressure on Government was reinforced by indirect assault through the press. Thus, in a letter to *The Times*, typical of others appearing in the press, the President of the Building Industries National Council wrote of the general anxiety of the industry lest the manner of carrying out the building programme might fail to provide defences against economic ills 'as worthy of the whole-hearted attention of Governments as the provision of defence against possible military enemies'. Over the past four years increasing building activity had brought with it enhanced prosperity. Any arbitrary interference with that activity, especially of a kind to lead to increased costs, would strike a blow from within at the very prosperity which armaments were designed to defend. Moreover, the probable armaments expenditure could not conceivably take the place of building activity as the basis of the industry's prosperity. It was the duty of the Government, therefore, so to plan public building works, both geographically and through time, as to ensure that the special works of military defence conduced to economic stability.[2]

In support of the letter, *The Times* in a leading article pointed out that the building industry was concerned less with theories than with facts which, if allowed, would speak for themselves. Upon an industry already made active by uncompleted housing programmes, a national slum-clearing campaign, and the capital expenditure of other indus-

---

[1] Sir Thomas Inskip (later Viscount Caldecote).
[2] *The Times*, 6th March 1937. See also letter to *The Times*, 9th June 1937, signed by leading Oxford economists.

tries on re-equipment and extension, the Government were imposing the large amount of constructional work required by the programme of defence. The industry would have to do the work without knowing the volume of the Government's orders or the time when they would be given. In order to avoid the loss of future idleness, there should now be a regulation of public works; and such regulation could not become effective unless the industry itself were brought into the Government's counsels.

> There still exists in some quarters an out-of-date departmental view that the Government's demands must be met just as and when made and that industry must take care of itself as best it can. . . . The proposed co-operation of the industry would bring about a new relationship with the State departments. Instead of being simply the servant of the departments, receiving their orders, the industry—that is to say, its higher councils—would be brought into consultation.

On 2nd February 1937 a second memorandum from the employers' federation was considered at a Conference of Ministers.[1] As a result new measures for inter-departmental consultation were devised. A committee, designated the Inter-departmental Committee on the Building Programme of Government Departments, was set up under the ægis of the Ministry of Labour, and held its first meeting on 8th February.[2] This was the first definite step in the long and often spasmodic progression towards full co-ordination of the programme. The new committee, with representatives drawn from the Treasury, Admiralty, War Office, Air Ministry, Ministry of Health, Board of Education, Ministry of Labour, Office of Works and the Scottish Office, and under the chairmanship of the Permanent Secretary of the Ministry of Labour, was charged with the duty of ascertaining the building programme of Government departments, whether undertaken direct or with financial assistance from other departments, and to consider possible measures, by priority or otherwise, for its completion. Any question of priority on which the committee found itself unable to reach agreement was to be referred to the Conference of Ministers. It was also agreed that once the committee had reported, but not before, the Minister of Labour (Mr. Ernest Brown) and the First Commissioner of Works (Lord Stanhope) should be asked to meet representatives of employers and workpeople in the building industry, and later representatives of employers in the building materials industries.

The first task to which the inter-departmental committee turned was to estimate the size and define the character of the building programme. The Service departments and the Ministry of Health, as

---

[1] The meeting was presided over by the Minister for Co-ordination of Defence.

[2] See Notes and Appendices: Note III, 'Inter-Departmental Committees for the Supervision of the Building Programme, 1937–40'.

well as the Office of Works and the Scottish Office, had already declared their labour demands for certain branches of building—such as the house-building programme of local authorities, house-building by private enterprise and works for Service departments in 1937 and 1938. But these figures were incomplete. They did not include town halls, asylums, hospitals, baths, schools nor the factory extensions which formed part of the defence programme. Apart from the incompleteness of the figures there was no indication of the special needs and resources of each district; and although problems of acute labour shortage in the skilled occupations were certainly national in character, more precise local information was wanted for each area throughout the country to help the inter-departmental committee in devising effective measures. The committee accordingly circulated to the departments schedules asking for particulars of their contracts and estimates of their labour requirements.[1] Before the end of February a rough preliminary picture of the building programme had begun to emerge. A sub-committee was appointed on 24th February to study the incidence of the programme in the various districts in the country, so that it could be seen what work was falling behind, and to devise means of easing the conditions in areas where the shortage of labour was likely to be most acute. As a further term of reference the sub-committee was charged with the investigation of questions of priority as between the Service and the non-Service departments.

Since the sub-committee, like the parent committee, was recruited entirely at the official level and was given no mandatory powers, it was a foregone conclusion that its recommendations were not likely to prove effective at long range; yet, although it was scarcely strong enough to make its intervention on wider issues either possible or desirable, it was certainly able by its advice to ease some difficult local situations.

Some five months after its inception[2] the parent committee made an interim report. The committee had held two meetings[3] and, on the main issue, its members were agreed that available labour might fail to overtake the building programme in the time allowed.[4]

---

[1] *Schedule A* called for particulars of contracts of £10,000 and over (£5,000 in the case of H.M.O.W. contracts); *Schedule B* for those under £10,000 (£5,000 in the case of H.M.O.W. contracts). Notes and Appendices: Appendix 2. In completing the schedules the Ministry of Labour administrative divisions were so far as possible to be followed.

For Ministry of Labour administrative divisions in operation before the war see Notes and Appendices: Appendix 3. Changes were made in the administrative divisions in August 1939.

[2] On 10th March 1937.

[3] On 8th and 24th February.

[4] An early analysis of the programme showed that in February 1937, for the Service departments and the Office of Works alone, 754 contracts had been let amounting to approximately £89 millions. Of this total 88 contracts for the Admiralty amounted to £10 millions, 142 contracts for the War Office to £29 millions, 117 contracts for the Air Ministry to £38 millions and 407 contracts for the Office of Works to £12 millions.

Ministers, they suggested, should no longer delay a meeting with representatives of the industry in England and Wales. In Scotland the labour position was easier. At the Conference of Ministers sanction had been given for an immediate meeting of the Secretary of State for Scotland with the industry in Scotland, and during February the Minister had first met the employers' federation and the trade unions separately, and later the representatives of the employers and the trade unions jointly. At further meetings of both sides of the industry, held under the ægis of the Ministry of Labour, arrangements were agreed for the supply of skilled labour for the defence and housing programmes in Scotland, and an immediate approach by the Minister of Labour to the Scottish building industry was not encouraged.

The self-sufficiency both of the Scottish Office and of the building industry in Scotland left the Minister of Labour free to concentrate on the labour problem in England and Wales. Here the difficulties of labour supply cut right across questions of policy on which decisions were awaited. These concerned the continuation of the Government's subsidy on housing, the grant for school buildings, the supply and prices of building materials and the need to restrict unessential building.

On the question of continuing the subsidy for housing, the interim report urged the Government to make an early pronouncement of intention. Although the existing authority ran up to March 1938, the question was in any case due for review in October 1937. Unless local authorities could be explicitly asked to postpone house-building, they were likely to speed up their own programmes and indirectly to retard those of the Service departments.

No less pressing was the need to clear up the question of school buildings. Would the period fixed for the grant of fifty per cent. towards loan charges on elementary school buildings erected by local authorities[1] be extended? Under arrangements with the Treasury the grant was payable for works authorised by the Board of Education during a three-year period ending 31st December 1938. If the duration of this grant were extended to the end of 1940 without the sum total being increased, the effect in slowing down and restricting capital expenditure on buildings by local authorities would be considerable. Moreover, the loan charges to be made out of central and local funds might be reduced, since authorities would no longer be compelled to enter into immediate contracts at what might prove to be peak prices.

As to the supply and price of building materials, these had been the subject of special investigations by the Ministry of Health and the Scottish Office. The conclusions pointed to substantial increases in

---

[1] Under the Education Act, 1936.

the prices, and actual or prospective shortages in the supply of certain classes of building materials, notably steel and timber. In so far as such supplies were subject to general consideration of priority in Government work, they affected many industries besides building; and it was beyond the authority of the committee to suggest effective action.

The restriction of non-essential building had been a matter of more or less academic discussion for some time, and the suggestion had been made with some seriousness that the nation might be roused to a high level of self-denial by an authoritative appeal to release labour and materials for the acceleration of the building programme. The committee, while alive to the need of restricting private building, thought it best to defer the question of a national appeal until Ministers had met the representatives of the industry.

(iv)

The Minister of Labour's Discussions with the Industry

While the inter-departmental committee stood by ready to give guidance on wider issues of policy, a deputation of the employers' federation made its own proposals to the Minister of Labour and the First Commissioner of Works.[1] This was the beginning of a series of meetings in which the representatives of the workers as well as of the employers were later included and at which the chief problems of the building programme, as they had so far shown themselves, were discussed and a plan for joint consultation worked out.

The employers' federation came forward with five main recommendations concerned respectively with supplies of labour, rates of wages, forms of contract, the administration of contracts and fluctuation clauses—all topics of importance which will be discussed in detail in this narrative in their appropriate context. For the present it is to be noted that on supplies of labour the employers urged the Government to consult with the accredited representatives of the industry; and on wage rates to seek in all their building operations the services of the National Joint Council for the Building Industry.[2] As to forms of contract, it was suggested that the standard form of contract of the Royal Institute of British Architects (1931) should be adopted by departments, and that in the administration of contracts specified action should be taken for improving contracts technique. The em-

---

[1] 23rd March 1937.
[2] Notes and Appendices: Note II, 'Joint Negotiating Machinery in the Building and Civil Engineering Industries'.

ployers also advised the inclusion of fluctuation clauses in all long-period Government contracts (that is, those that would endure for twelve months or more).

The Minister of Labour did not at this conference take up the detailed discussion of the federation's recommendations. He went no further than to draw a general picture of the demands of the building programme and to suggest ways in which the federation might help to meet them. He had received the first estimates of cost submitted by departments of building work in England and Wales for 1937, 1938 and 1939. These showed a total of some £200 millions, of which nearly £60 millions represented work for the defence departments, £84 millions for housing schemes of local authorities, and £56 millions for building work of certain other departments, including the Office of Works, the Home Office, the Ministry of Agriculture, and the Board of Education, as well as of the Miners' Welfare Fund Committee and of the Commissioner for Special Areas.[1]

The Government feared that the execution of so large a programme of building coming on top of a strong private demand would severely tax the industry's manpower. According to the departments' estimates the additional labour needed in the skilled occupations[2] in 1937, as compared with 1936, for slum clearance and rehousing and for the defence programme in England and Wales alone, was 11,500 skilled men,[3] and in 1938 probably not less than 19,000; and in the Ministry of Labour it was thought likely that they would be short of these totals by about 4,500 in 1937 and 12,000 in 1939.[4]

Three ways of bridging the gap were suggested by the Minister: to find new sources of manpower for the building industry, to restrict private building, and to find a way of determining priorities as between the work of the various Government departments. On the first two, as well as on the actual or prospective shortage of materials, the Minister invited the advice and co-operation of the employers' federation and in that appeal he later included the operatives.[5] All were asked to help in the timely completion not only of the defence but of the housing programme; and in seeking ways of bringing about a closer accord on labour supply and wage rates the Minister thought

---

[1] The statement did not purport to be an estimate of the total works over which the Government departments exercised control. The activities of all departments were not included and in some cases (e.g. Ministry of Health) only partial information was available. Housing programmes of local authorities were included but not hospitals, institutions and other public works. Service departments could only forecast their own requirements, including agency factories and a very small number of the extensions of private firms occasioned by the defence programme (see Chapters XIV and XV).

[2] Bricklayers, masons, carpenters and joiners, slaters and tilers, plasterers and plumbers.

[3] Including about 5,000 carpenters, 4,000 bricklayers and 1,100 plasterers.

[4] The estimates of additional demands on the industry, great as they were, excluded increased activity in industrial and commercial building and took no account of possible increase in the price of materials.

[5] At a conference between the Minister of Labour and the National Joint Council for the Building Industry, 27th April 1937.

that the National Joint Council might set up a small advisory standing committee to meet as necessary with the inter-departmental
committee. Meanwhile, to clear the air, the Minister asked for a joint
statement from the employers' and operatives' federations setting out
their views on labour supply and wages, as well as on machinery for
consultation between the industry and the building departments.

At the same meeting with employers on 23rd March the Minister
had said he doubted whether the industry was well enough organised
to make the work of the National Joint Council fully effective. If the
control over the industry was in fact inadequate, what would be the
effect on the large demands now being made on its resources? He
suggested that considerable unorganised sections within the industry,
even before the defence programme, had tended to create conditions
differing from those in agreements. If that lack of organisation could
be made good and all employers effectively organised, they could
impose a check on what might otherwise become uncontrolled competition for the classes of skilled labour most in demand—competition
which was increasing and threatened to make the joint machinery
unmanageable. Another reason for tighter organisation was that unchecked competition was apt to embarrass the administration of the
Fair Wages Clause.[1] There were instances where the payment of rates
higher than the agreed rates had caused them to become the 'fair'
rates and to be so recognised. If an obligation were put on Government departments to pay higher than agreed rates because that
happened to be the practice in a particular place, it was not properly
a matter for criticism if sometimes lower rates were found to be the
'fair' rates. The Government, the Minister added, would have been
willing to accept the nationally agreed rates in all building operations;
but agreed rates had no meaning if, even among organised employers,
rates were in fact settled by individual competition in different areas.
What did the National Federation of Building Trades Employers
mean when they asked that the National Joint Council rates should
be invariably recognised? And what would be the effect on contract
prices of all those other wages rates which in practice existed and
which departments were expected to pay under the Fair Wages
Clause?

On this and other topics the employers' and operatives' federations
made, in the joint memorandum they had been invited to submit, a
vigorous, if not always convincing, rejoinder. They traversed out-
right the Minister's assessment of the Government's demand on the
industry and of the industry's ability to meet it. Turning first to the
meaning of 'priorities'—in the proposed triple drive towards increased labour supply, the restriction on private building and the
determination of priorities—they asked whether that meant not

---

[1] Notes and Appendices: Note IV, 'The Fair Wages Clause'.

priorities as between Government and other work or even as between the works of one department and those of another, but rather as between the works currently contemplated in each department separately. Was it not the case that each department would determine which of its own works might be postponed? If a similar principle applied also to works for other public authorities (such as those requiring the approval of the Ministry of Health) might not the normal work of the industry, particularly industrial and commercial work, be accommodated only after the needs of all departments, as the departments might decide, had been assessed and satisfied?

As to labour supply, the industrial spokesmen maintained that a purely static analysis of requirements at any given moment could not —apart from the difficulties of computation—give a correct view of a dynamic situation. To this the successive drastic changes in employment in the building industry bore ample witness. Nor was there any reason to assume that the defence and housing programmes would alone give the building industry assured employment for years ahead. Not only was the existing situation uncertain but, after the bitter experience of the past, the industry was shy of that kind of guarantee. Definite Government guarantees for fifteen years, its spokesmen protested, had been given in respect of the Housing Act of 1924 and had soon been repudiated. Any improvement in the international situation might even now bring about a complete change in the Government's demand for building. If, at the same time, an economic policy like that of 1931 were pursued, the position of the building industry might again become desperate. That policy, and the economy campaign which followed it, did not incline the industry towards its repetition, or dispose them to risk the strangling of all non-Government work, industrial, commercial and domestic alike. Since 1940 had been fixed as the target date for the completion of the defence programme, unless there were a reservoir of building work controllable by the Government and intended for release as and when the defence and other Government programmes were completed, the industry might be left in 1940 without enough work to employ its existing resources. In that event was it not likely that a national campaign for the restriction of unessential building for the next few years would only aggravate the disaster?

The implication that organised employers and operatives in the building industry did not in fact control its wage rates was indignantly refuted. The National Joint Council's standard rates, so far from being a weakness, provided the only basis on which effective control could be exercised. Since the standard rates were fixed with care, there seemed no valid reason why the majority practice in any district should differ from them. In some departments there might have been a tendency to encourage departures from the regulated position; but lack of control, especially on airfield sites, was one result when enormous Government works were started in rural districts without giving the National Joint Council machinery any chance to fix appropriate rates beforehand and without allowing any opportunity for informing contractors as to the rates so fixed.

If the industry had some reason to feel ill-used, departments (as the Minister had insisted) also had their grievances, particularly over 'exceptional margins'[1] and increased costs. In their eyes increased costs of at least some classes of labour 'above that which was really necessary' had disturbed the generally accepted conditions in certain districts. Nevertheless the 'exceptional rate' machinery of the National Joint Council had not been devised to exploit the public need or to single out Government work for special treatment. Arrangements for exceptional margins had been part of the National Joint Council machinery for many years. From the industry's standpoint they were being used simply to meet exceptional cases (whether Government work or otherwise) where for a period there was an abnormally large project in an otherwise low-graded area. Their objects were, first, to enable the contractors to obtain a fair share of the labour available in the surrounding districts; secondly, to ensure that the surrounding districts were not unduly disturbed by being denuded of labour and, thirdly, to ensure that when the abnormal project was finished the district could revert to a wage-level consistent with its normal character. So far from being a hasty means of exploitation, the system was claimed to be a well-conceived means of maintaining balance and facilitating control. The industrial spokesmen felt indeed that the successful working of the system in the past (as, to quote two well-known instances, in the erection of the Royal Navy College at Holbrook, and of the Rettenden Mental Institution in Essex) had not been sufficiently appreciated by the departments.

In the course of negotiation it had been suggested by contracting departments, with an eye to the Public Accounts Committee, that they could not shed their responsibility for costs without proper assurances; and, since they felt that on the whole the existing method of administration had been in the interests of all concerned, they wished to know the probable effects of a change. To this the industrial spokesmen replied, on a somewhat sharper note, that if the existing method of administration by departments included the erratic interpretation of the Fair Wages Clause; if jobs in rural districts were to be left to improvisation and caprice, with departments refusing to give advance information to the National Joint Council or to notify contractors what rates were considered appropriate by the Council—then it must be said that such an attitude had not until recently been

---

[1] See Notes and Appendices: Note II, 'Joint Negotiating Machinery in the Building and Civil Engineering Industries'.

taken by any Government department and its results could not therefore have been proved to be in the interests of all concerned. So far
indeed from fostering economy, such unorderly methods had usually
led to unrestricted increases in costs and to much friction and delay
in the carrying out of works, with a further increase of costs in
consequence. It would be more satisfactory, it was urged, if a representative of the Treasury could sit on any inter-departmental committee charged with the supervision of the building programme.

It would be ingenuous to accept at their face value all the professed
doubts of a great industry invited to deploy the bulk of its resources in
the service of the State. The commanders of industry, like their
military counterparts in the field, must find scope to manœuvre for
position; yet beneath the adroitness of the industry's tactics was the
genuine desire to play a worthy part in the nation's emergency as
well as the genuine fear of a descent into the void once the emergency
was over or if it were in some way dispelled. To the demand to be in
the confidence of the Government was joined the need to co-operate
freely with the contracting departments. The employers' federation
had indeed already proposed that all questions of design, of materials
and methods of construction, of labour and the means of securing it,
should be remitted to an inter-departmental committee on which the
contracting departments and the Ministries of Health and Labour
would be represented, as well as the Treasury and the building industry, if its co-operation were genuinely desired. But the Minister
of Labour thought the situation would be met if a Government
committee could consider particular problems from the Government
point of view, aided by a small advisory standing committee of the
industry to be convened *ad hoc*. Delay in dealing with particular
problems could thus be forestalled, since such an advisory committee
would not be summoned merely to illuminate particular problems
but could also be brought in when the whole field had been surveyed.
The industrial representatives, however, stood by their original proposal. Past experience, they said, had shown that a small advisory
committee was unsatisfactory, especially if there were to be consultation between the two committees only when a department wished to
submit its particular problem for solution. To be of any real use there
should be a single committee, convened as and when required by any
one of the interests represented on it, whether Government or industrial, and with power not only to take decisions but give effect to them.

By 28th May, when the Minister of Labour once more met representatives of the industrial organisations, the way was clear for the
formation of a joint consultative body. It was now agreed that consultation with the industry should not take place merely through a
committee of the Ministry of Labour holding joint meetings with the
representatives of the National Joint Council. The Ministry of Labour

was accepted as the link through which the machinery would operate, and the National Joint Council was invited to nominate its representatives to sit with representatives of the interested departments, including the Treasury. Their first duty would be to examine the problems of labour supply and wage rates set out in the joint statement—problems, the industrialists were reminded, which did not always concern the same people, wage rates, for example, being a Ministerial responsibility, while other issues might be the concern of several contracting departments. Moreover, to take definite decisions and give effect to them was the prerogative of the Cabinet. Even a committee composed solely of representatives of the departments could only act under that authority; but to avoid delay in giving effect to the committee's decisions the Permanent Secretary of the Ministry of Labour was to act as chairman and a representative of the Treasury was always to be present at meetings.

Agreement having been reached on the foregoing principles, the Joint Consultative Committee on the Building Programme of Government Departments was duly set up. Both the national federations nominated a standing committee consisting of four representatives of employers and four representatives of operatives, together with joint secretaries, one for each side. Meetings of the Joint Consultative Committee with representatives of the departments, including the Treasury and of the industry were to be convened by the Ministry of Labour; but the industrial representatives also could ask for meetings to be convened. The Joint Consultative Committee could consider questions of detail as well as general principles.

Similar arrangements were later made for Scotland.[1]

---

[1] Notes and Appendices: Note III, 'Inter-departmental Committees for the Supervision of the Building Programme, 1937–40'.

CHAPTER II

THE DEMAND ON THE BUILDING INDUSTRY

(i)

The Estimated Cost of the Building Programme

IN the preceding chapter the early collaboration of contracting departments and the building industry has been briefly described. It has been noted how the inter-departmental supervision of the building programme, initiated in 1937, was later strengthened, or at all events augmented, by the appointment of joint consultative committees which brought both sides of the industry, in Scotland as well as in England and Wales, into direct and continuing conference with the departments. While the official field of vision was thus enlarged, and the industry was no longer kept waiting on the wrong side of the conference-room door, the inherent weakness of the arrangement remained, since the function of the several committees continued to be advisory. Each could recommend, but none had the power to act. The functions of the inter-departmental committee were now merged in those of the consultative committees. After holding four meetings in 1937 it was convened once more in 1939 to consider a particular problem.[1] After that it did not meet again.

While the joint committees applied themselves to urgent day-to-day difficulties, mainly those arising from labour supply, wage rates and working conditions,[2] discussion was apt to swing back to the root problem—how could the building programme be carried through without special measures which might embarrass the industry as a whole? Its leaders were determined to take the Government programme in their stride. If labour shortages developed they strove to limit their effect to individual enterprises and to stem any general repercussions on the industry. When in the spring of 1938 the Government had begun to expand and accelerate the rearmament programme,[3] and in the following year, when after the actual outbreak of war a further acceleration of the programme was demanded,

---

[1] Notes and Appendices: Note III, 'Inter-departmental Committees for the Supervision of the Building Programme, 1937–40'.
[2] See Note III and section (iii) of this chapter.
[3] H. of C. Deb., 24th March 1938, Vol. 333, col. 1410. Speech by the Prime Minister.

the industry still hesitated to put its resources unreservedly at the Government's disposal. By this time, as a later portion of this chapter shows, the materials supply position had worsened. It seemed to the departments as though the needs of the Government's building programme, to say nothing of other demands on the industry, might well be in excess of available materials and that a shortage of materials might in time create a surplus of skilled building labour. The industry, however, was not disposed to share these forebodings.

> We cannot see ourselves why there should be any difficulty in our meeting the whole of the requirements of the Government for building purposes. . . . The building resources of this country are enormous and ample for all the requirements of the Government departments whatever they might be. . . . There are the resources if we can only, I will not say divert, but if we can conduct them to the needs of the respective departments. . . . Difficulty may arise where building contractors, perhaps from over-willingness—I will not use a harsher word than that—assisted or perhaps encouraged by the respective Government contracting departments, take on more work than they are really capable of executing, with the result that they get a quantity of work which is in excess of their organisation and of their ability properly to carry out. Then they begin to squeal and attempt to attract labour from other places, and call upon the Government to bring into force some extraordinary measures such as priorities, perhaps dilution, something of that kind.[1]

The conviction that the Government programme alone could not absorb the building labour force was equally that of the operatives' leaders. Even after the outbreak of war the operatives' federation estimated that only about 350,000 building-trade workers (or a third of the remaining labour force) could be absorbed by the programme, and it was seriously contended that, after allowing for recruitment to the armed forces, and a movement of some of the skilled and semi-skilled men to other industries, as much as half the industry might become unemployed. That these fears were genuinely entertained is likely enough, and they were emphasised and reiterated in the argument against the restriction of civil building in the early months of war.[2]

In the absence of any agreed statistical basis such as was worked out after the creation of the Ministry of Works,[3] the wrangling on what the industry might or might not be capable of achieving went on endlessly up to the outbreak of war, and well beyond it. Until precise figures of the movement and allocation of labour became available,

---

[1] Sir Jonah Walker-Smith, N.F.B.T.E.

[2] Section (v) of this chapter. See also Chapter VI.

[3] Chapter IV. The first designation of the Ministry of Works was 'Ministry of Works and Buildings'. On 24th June 1942 it became 'Ministry of Works and Planning' and on 4th February 1943 'Ministry of Works'. Throughout this narrative the department is described by its last designation.

the departments could base themselves only on their own estimates of the cost of the programme and translate them as best they might into terms of labour and materials.

General estimates of the cost of the building programme were submitted by departments in June 1937, July 1938 and September 1939 and are summarised in the following table:

Government Building Programme: Estimated Cost
Great Britain

£ *millions*

Date of estimates	Civil departments (non-defence) £	Service and other departments (defence) £	All departments Total £	Programme to be completed by
June 1937	176	68	244*	1940
July 1938	317	150	467	1941
Sept. 1939	54	284†	338	1941

* £201 millions for England and Wales, £43 millions for Scotland.
† Includes £83·6 millions emergency building by civil departments (Home Office for A.R.P., £57·8 millions; Ministry of Health for emergency housing, essential building, etc., £25·8 millions).
Source: Joint Consultative Committee on the Building Programme of Government Departments (Ministry of Labour).

In later official computations[1] the total capacity of the building and civil engineering industries for Great Britain, as shown by gross output, was £421 millions for 1937, £455 millions for 1938 and £442 millions for 1939; so that had the volume of the building programme in fact been that suggested by the estimates of cost the confidence of the industry that the programme could be taken in its stride would have been fully justified. In the event, however, the estimated figures were found to represent little more than half the actual demand on the industry,[2] and the struggle for manpower and materials, which lay at the root of all war-time building policy, became even more desperate than the departments had foreseen.

Since the estimates of cost made in the rearmament years fell so far short of the Government's true commitments their detailed consideration is superfluous; but the allocation between non-defence and defence categories and their changing ratio between 1937 and 1940 are at all events worth noting. In the first estimates, produced in the Ministry of Labour in 1937, there was an allocation of £176 millions for the civil departments, for a programme to be completed in 1940. When, in March 1938, the Government decided to expand and

---

[1] Notes and Appendices: Appendix 1 (Table).
[2] Chapter IV.

accelerate the defence programme,[1] fresh estimates were worked out bringing the total State building programme to approximately £467 millions, with the figure for housing and other social services now swelling the building of civil departments to the total of £317 millions. The programme, it was now estimated, would take four years to complete and showed an allocation for defence building of £150 millions. In September 1939, after the outbreak of war, a fresh review of the position was made, which now took in the recently created Ministry of Supply. This showed the total building programme still to be completed by 1941 at approximately £338 millions. Of this total, the uncompleted defence building programme stood at £201 millions; emergency building by civil departments at £83 millions; and Government civil building, other than emergency, drastically cut at about £54 millions.[2]

The geographical distribution of defence building works in hand in the autumn of 1939 is summarised elsewhere.[3] The type of the main work and the cost as then estimated are summarised in this and the following pages. The Admiralty, for big new works and the completion of others already begun, estimated just over £25 millions. At Dean Hill, in Hampshire, an armament depot, with concrete and brick-lined tunnels for underground storage, and subsidiary brick buildings, had been commenced in April 1939 and was due to be completed by the end of 1941 at a total cost of £1,180,000. Sundry works at Exmouth and Plymouth, some begun as far back as 1937, were to be completed, also by the end of 1941, at a total cost of £3 millions. At Fishguard, a magazine depot in concrete and brick, at a total cost of £3,345,000, was to be ready by October 1941; elsewhere in Pembrokeshire a mine depot in concrete, brick and steel, begun as far back as 1935, was to be ready by June 1940; while oil storage facilities in concrete commenced in Pembroke in May 1939 were to be ready by October of that year. Another big Admiralty item was a factory at Caerwent, in Monmouthshire, commenced in July 1939 for completion in June 1941, at a total cost of £1,192,000; yet another was for an underground storage magazine at Benarty, in Kinross-shire, comprising a concrete-lined tunnel and chambers and brick and other buildings, due to be completed by September 1942 at a cost of £1,576,000. Protective works in heavy reinforced concrete at Rosyth, begun in March 1938, were to be ready by March 1940 at a cost of £1,147,000. In the Orkneys and at Invergordon other urgent works amounted to well over £2 millions.

---

[1] H. of C. Deb., 24th March 1938, Vol. 333, col. 1411.

[2] Notes and Appendices: Appendix 4, 'Summary by Departments of Estimated Expenditure on Building Works by Government Departments in the Four Quarters ending 30th September 1940'.

[3] Appendix 5, 'Summary by Counties of Estimated Expenditure on Building Works by Government Departments in the Four Quarters ending 30th September 1940'.

The War Office building programme, which in 1937 had included over £10 millions for barracks and a similar amount for munition factories, now totalled £40,599,000, of which a large part was for barracks, camps and hutments, the building of munition factories and extensions having been entrusted to the Office of Works and the Ministry of Supply under arrangements described in a later portion of this narrative.[1] Among outstanding items in this extensive programme were a number of barracks (mostly brick) and hutments at Shrivenham, in Wiltshire, commenced at various dates in 1938 and 1939, and due to be completed in 1939 and 1940, at a cost of about £1 million; a depot at Longtown, in Cumberland (steel shedding and concrete buildings) as well as a hutted camp for combined training, costing together some £1,600,000; a war camp at Barton Stacey and other contracts, mostly hutting, in Hampshire costing just under £2 millions; storehouses in brick and steel at Chilwell, in Nottinghamshire, to be completed by 1940 at a cost of £1 million and similar works at Donnington Royal Army Ordnance Corps Depot in Shropshire (April 1939–June 1940) at a cost of £1,200,000; underground storage in earthwork and concrete at Corsham, in Wiltshire, using direct labour and costing £1 million; and training-camp hutments in Pembrokeshire costing £2 millions.

The Air Ministry's building commitments were widespread and costly. The total of £70,635,000 was mostly for air stations, with £22,712,000 for factories and extensions to contractors' works. The air stations were being constructed at a cost in most cases of approximately £500,000, but for several of them £1 million or more was estimated. Among these were Carlisle, constructed in steel, concrete and brick, begun in June 1937 and now nearing completion, for which the total cost was estimated at £1,200,000; and Heywood, in Lancashire, which was of similar construction and had been begun in September 1938, for completion by June 1940, at a cost of £1,200,000. Storage units, equipment depots and training centres for the Royal Air Force were a heavy charge. For storage, estimates included Hawarden and Sealand depots in Cheshire at a cost of over £1 million; Kirkbride and Silloth depots in Cumberland at a cost of £1,200,000; Kemble (Gloucestershire) at a cost of £625,000; three depots in Shropshire (Cosford, High Ercall and Shawbury) at a total cost of just under £1½ million; and others. These depots were of steel, concrete and brick construction and due for completion at dates in 1940. A great repair depot at Warrington, begun in March 1939, was to be ready within twelve months and to cost £1 million; another at Abbotsinch, in Renfrewshire, begun in April 1939 for completion by March 1940, was to cost £1,050,000; another at Hartlebury, in

---

[1] Chapters XII and XV.

Worcestershire, begun in June 1937 for completion by December 1939, £1,150,000; and yet another at Stafford, begun in April 1939 for completion by April 1940, £1,050,000. Other big Air Ministry commitments included the training depot at St. Athan, also begun in July 1937 for completion by the end of 1939, at a cost of £1,550,000. All the foregoing were of steel, concrete and brick, and in the St. Athan depot of steel, concrete and timber.

The building commitments of the Ministry of Supply, which had been set up in April 1939, had reached by September £18,820,000, while much of the Office of Works estimate of £25,595,000 was directly for defence programme building. Under the ægis of these two departments, munition factories and extensions planned, and in some cases begun, at the commencement of rearmament were among the chief items of the building programme. The great filling factory at Chorley, originally estimated to cost about £4⅓ millions, but destined to reach a much higher figure;[1] the filling factory at Swynnerton, in Staffordshire, for which £5 millions was estimated; the great cordite factories at Bishopton, in Renfrewshire, for which the first estimates were about £3 millions; the Royal Ordnance Factory at Bridgwater, in Somersetshire, to be completed by November 1940, at a cost of £1,122,000; the Royal Ordnance Factories building at Bridgend, in Glamorganshire, at Glascoed, in Monmouthshire, and at Wrexham, in Denbighshire, represent but a part of the urgent demand on the building industry for armament factories.[2] Similar building on a lesser scale was going on or about to begin in a number of places; at Crewe, for example, where a small-arms factory, of brick and concrete, steel-framed and sheeted, was planned for early completion at a cost of £650,000; at Northwick and Runcorn, in Cheshire, where three chemical plant factories, of steel and concrete, were being completed at a total cost of £1,026,000; at the Royal Arsenal, Woolwich, where new constructional work was estimated to cost over £1 million; at Leeds, where a gun factory begun in August 1939 was due to be completed by June 1940 at a cost of £610,000; at Drigg, in Cumberland, where a Royal Ordnance Factory was to be erected by August 1940, at a cost of just under £1 million.

Estimates for brick and concrete construction for the Home Office air raid precautions programme in all parts of Great Britain amounted to £57,845,000 (apart from other air raid precautions such as, for example, those for which the Ministry of Health was responsible in respect of water undertakings, hospitals and first-aid posts; the Ministry of Transport in respect of railways, docks and harbours; the Board of Trade in respect of gas and electricity undertakings). These protective measures were a heavy drain on labour and materials in many

---

[1] Chapter XV.
[2] *Ibid.*

districts. Among larger allocations were those for Cheshire £1,400,000; Durham County £2,150,000, Essex £3,000,000, Southampton £1,200,000, Kent £1,800,000, Lancashire £8,100,000, London £8,200,000, Middlesex £4,000,000, Northumberland £1,150,000, Staffordshire £2,250,000, Surrey £1,250,000, Warwickshire £2,800,000; the three Ridings of Yorkshire £6,355,000, Glamorganshire £1,200,000, Lanarkshire £2,700,000.

*   *   *

In the preceding pages the character of the building programme has begun to show its general outline. Later parts of this narrative will describe in what ways costs had been under-estimated, why the dearth of materials was not always one of real shortages, and the way in which the supply of materials from time to time embarrassed the supply of labour. All these factors interacted one with the other in ways which were often confusing at the time but show themselves more clearly in retrospect. Although in this chapter they are viewed in the framework of the rearmament years and the early months of war, we shall look back on them again when we have witnessed the creation of the Ministry of Works in 1940 and noted the new ways in which the building programme was thereafter studied and controlled.

(ii)

The Problem of Labour Supply

From the very commencement of rearmament any local shortage of skilled labour which for a little time checked the defence programme was apt to give rise to a real or professed fear of a general shortage. Perhaps much of this anxiety was not disinterested. As early as 1936 it was being said that house-building and commercial building had been brought almost to a standstill by loss of skilled labour and could only go on with higher wage costs than were due under joint agreements; apprehensive critics of the building programme seemed already to detect the start of a vicious circle such as had appeared at the beginning of the First World War, with signs of the same type of unbridled competition for labour, and the same unrestrained offers and counter-offers of higher and higher wages, with a similar degree of demoralisation. It would have been true to say that there were some local shortages of labour and that delays in the delivery of materials, particularly steel, were causing some intermittent unemployment, so that the available amount of labour did not go so far as it should have done; that the industry as a whole was in a healthy condition, although in certain areas the position was deteriorating.

That was certainly the experience of the Service departments in 1937. Delays were worst in the Air Ministry's undertakings, which were generally situated in rural areas, were usually large and as a rule absorbed most of the labour in the district. Between May 1935 and June 1936 the Air Ministry's expansion scheme had gone ahead very fast, and by 1937 eleven of the twelve stations begun in 1935 were ready, but airfields started in 1936 had all fallen behind schedule, partly on account of the very bad winter of 1936–37. On some sites the delay was from four to six months, in several much more; everywhere the rate of progress had gradually slowed down. The first shortage to be felt was one of bricklayers, and as a counter-measure the Air Ministry had turned over, as far as it could, to concrete building, so that by the summer of 1937 about half its building work was in concrete. This change, however, in turn caused great difficulty in getting enough carpenters for shuttering. As a result, from labour causes alone, many contracts were considerably behind time.

Delays in the delivery of materials, especially steel, also began to be seriously felt by the Air Ministry in 1937. While in themselves worsening the position, they had the added effect of concealing shortages of labour from other causes. Faced in July 1937 with a budget for building of £18 millions and an increasing programme, the Air Ministry found it hard to get men to serve in country districts.

The experience of the War Office and Admiralty was similar if less general. A start had been made in 1936 on the War Office programme, part of which was in the hands of the Office of Works as agents; but as the first works called for the use of steel the contracts had fallen behind time. On the bigger contracts there had also been at the outset a shortage of bricklayers, and when this had been overcome a second shortage, in 1937, held up the contracts on Salisbury Plain. The works, still in their initial stages, on which the Office of Works was employed had not as yet made their full demands on the building industry. But, in the autumn of 1937, when that department was due to make a start on the large factory enterprises at Bridgend and in Scotland, it found itself faced with a deteriorating situation both as to labour and materials.

On the Admiralty contracts there had been some isolated shortages of labour, though no substantial delay because of them. But work was about to start on the huge magazine depot at Fishguard and the heavy works at Rosyth, and the Admiralty were entering on a period of difficulty through the shortage of materials and the consequent dislocation of labour supply.

There followed the acceleration of the rearmament programme in 1938. The supply of materials, especially of steel, now showed a marked improvement, with some assuagement of the Service departments' fears of persisting labour shortages. None the less the demand for labour was now heavier than ever. The debates on the Air Estimates[1] revealed that the number of squadrons was being increased from 52 to 123 and that the majority of them had been formed. The building programme had to keep step with the Royal Air Force expansion scheme and at the same time a great deal of temporary accommodation in timber hutting had to be provided for personnel. The temporary hutting enabled training to go on, and operational squadrons to form and function. At the same time space had to be found for technical and war-like stores of vital importance to meet the increased production of aircraft and munitions. Depots, too, were needed for the repair and maintenance of aircraft, and replacement had to be made of temporary living accommodation for personnel. In the previous year the shortage of steel had automatically reduced demands for labour, and in consequence labour shortages were less seriously felt than they would have been had steel been obtainable. In 1938, however, the prospect was that continuing improvement in the supply of steel would bring to the forefront difficulty in finding enough labour to maintain progress.

The shortage of steel in 1937 had also checked the growth of War Office building and thus helped to cover up the underlying labour supply problem. Now the department's accelerated programme brought to light labour shortages in the more remote areas, for example, on Salisbury Plain where six new buildings were being put up at a cost of £3,500,000.[2] Apart from undertakings in remote areas, there were at least ten building schemes, estimated to cost £2,500,000, for the replacement of existing barracks, and under the accelerated programme seven more building schemes costing £2 millions were to be added to War Office commitments. These undertakings, however, and those for the replacement of barracks, were all close to towns from which supplies of labour could be drawn.

Among the important works under construction by the Office of Works on behalf of the War Office the contracts for the Royal Ordnance Factory in Chorley were well in hand. By the summer of 1938 the number of men employed had risen to over 9,000. Substantial progress had been made and the work was at its peak. Other large contracts, almost all in South Wales, were being, or about to be, undertaken, including the contracts at Bridgend, Glascoed and Pembrey, and it was clear that labour supply would prove a decisive factor.

With the deployment of the accelerated programme, the danger of violent fluctuation in building activity, which the industry had been

---

[1] H. of C. Deb., 7th March 1938, Vol. 332, Col. 1555 et seq.
[2] The most serious trouble was on a Warminster site. Here the contractors were a federated firm which paid the recognised rates of wages, and the difficulties were due to the competition of non-federated firms in the district which were attracting labour by paying rates above those recognised for the district.

at such pains to assess and forestall, appeared imminent, and its spokesmen now pressed for deferment, at least of non-defence works. The argument advanced was that, since the estimates of expenditure, up to and including 1941, as revised in July 1938, showed an anticipated fall in the Government building programme of £8 millions in 1940 and a further decrease of £20 millions in 1941, it was surely better to defer some of the works contemplated for 1939 until 1940 or 1941, in order to provide a more even flow of work over the next few years. Defence works, they knew, could not be deferred, but less urgent items in the programme (for example, the building activities of the Commissioner of the Special Areas in England and Wales estimated to cost £4 millions in 1939 and £5 millions in 1940) might well, they thought, be spread over a number of years or even deferred until rearmament had been completed. These and kindred proposals carried little weight with the departments. Much of the expenditure of the Commissioner for Special Areas was for housing and formed a part of the slum-clearing programmes of the Ministry of Health; it was thus merely a matter of machinery whether the work was undertaken by the Commissioner or the local authorities. Similarly, because of the raising of the school-leaving age, school buildings had to be ready by the date when the scheme came into operation. The Board of Education would not contemplate reduction, knowing well that a policy of restriction might cause less essential items to be abandoned rather than postponed. In the face of such objections, the proposals for deferment were not pressed.

THE MILITIA CAMP PROGRAMME

By keeping a close watch on individual projects, labour shortages on the main defence works were not infrequently forestalled by the joint committees, and local disagreements resolved. The effect was often to ease the whole labour supply position. But in the summer of 1939 a new and more serious situation, with far-reaching effects, developed over the War Office hutting programme.[1] Militia camps had to be constructed on a large scale and against time to meet the expansion of the Army under the Military Training Act.[2] While on most of the hutting contracts (notably on Salisbury Plain, at Aldershot and at Catterick) labour supply was adequate, on certain sites —because of their isolated position or the competition of other contracts in the neighbourhood—there was a recurring lack of skilled workmen. In addition to the main contracts, local contracts, let through the War Office Commands, were scattered over the whole country. In the aggregate these contracts amounted to a formidable

---

[1] See Chapter XII.
[2] The programme was estimated to cost £10 millions.

item of the building programme; and not only did they draw off much of the local labour, but they aggravated the shortages on the main contracts.

The repercussions of the scramble for skilled labour were widespread and disturbing. The almost frantic speed and energy with which the militia camp programme had been tackled, the sudden demands for labour and the special inducements offered had begun to draw off in large numbers the men whom the Office of Works had relied upon to carry through other urgent undertakings for the War Office, more especially those in Scotland and South Wales. On Salisbury Plain and at Aldershot exceptional margins, subsistence allowance and unlimited overtime were being paid by contractors; and not only was subsistence allowance being paid to men who had been engaged by contractors in distant towns, but also to men engaged on the site who had come from a distance to apply for work. Advertisements appearing in the press offered every inducement, including Sunday work and the chance to earn wages up to £7 and £8 a week. This bidding for labour upset the orderly completion of other urgent and important contracts. At Bridgend, to take one instance, men were being drawn off to work on a militia camp fifty miles away.

A contributory cause of the bidding for labour was the fact that the militia camp contracts had been let on the 'prime cost' principle,[1] with provision for the repayment to the contractor only of the rates of wages as fixed by the National Joint Council, including overtime and subsistence allowance. It was now too late for the War Office to follow the practice of the Admiralty under whose contracts labour supply was less subject to spasmodic shortages because they were arranged on a fixed lump sum or definite schedule rate basis, so that the contractors had to shoulder the risk of uneconomical working. The main camps contracts were already let, and because of the extreme urgency of the work no change could be made; the contracts had to be left to work themselves out. Although in June 1939 the contracts still unlet under the programme were for some forty militia camps, at a cost of £2 millions, and although these were based on the 'target price' principle, with the programme spread over the whole of England in much smaller camps, they too were in effect 'prime cost' contracts and open to the same objections as the contracts already let.

Because of the urgency of the camps programme the War Office were able successfully to resist pressure from the Inter-departmental Committee on the Building Programme, specially summoned after an interval of eighteen months, to place the unlet contracts on a fixed price basis, with a limit imposed on overtime. The War Office stood firmly by the view that the remaining contracts could not be got out

---

[1] Notes and Appendices: Note V, 'Forms of Contract'. See also Chapter XI.

D

in time unless they were let on the 'prime cost' principle, although they undertook to do whatever was possible to reduce overtime. In resigning themselves reluctantly to the position that until the autumn all building work must inevitably suffer, the committee had little or no incentive to cut out subsistence allowance or overtime, or to work economically, though it did try to ensure that something more nearly approaching a lump-sum contract was adopted wherever possible.

THE CONTROL OF EMPLOYMENT ACT 1939

With the outbreak of war the whole problem of labour supply was radically changed. The introduction of the Control of Employment Bill cut across the joint committee's preparations for making obligatory the engagement of all building labour through employment exchanges, and the proposed line of action had to be changed.

It should be added that since the beginning of 1938 a clause had been inserted in all contracts of £500 or over issued by Government departments obliging contractors to notify employment exchanges of contracts. While this procedure had to some extent encouraged and strengthened co-operation between Government contractors and employment exchanges, it was none the less notorious that many firms had relied mainly on direct applications, had advertised their labour needs in the press, had restricted their applications to certain types of workers only or, while notifying their vacancies to the employment exchanges, had actually engaged labour direct.

The question of the engagement of labour through employment exchanges had accordingly been referred to the Contracts Co-ordinating Committee,[1] and at a meeting held on 23rd March 1939 that committee had agreed to recommend the insertion in Government contracts of a clause requiring contractors to engage their additional semi-skilled and unskilled, but not their skilled labour, through the employment exchanges. It had also been decided to retain the existing provision under which all additional labour requirements were to be notified.

This recommendation was considered by the contracting departments. Both the War Office and the Air Ministry were disposed to accept the recommendation only in respect of industries other than building, and only as to unskilled labour. The views of the Joint Consultative Committee were sought as to the terms of the clause and

---

[1] The Contracts Co-ordinating Committee, set up in 1920, was composed of Directors of Contracts of the Service departments, together with representatives from the Treasury, the Office of Works, the Post Office, and such other departments as might be called in. It was mainly concerned with the co-ordination of contract policy and procedure, but it was to some extent superseded by the Treasury Inter-Service Committee, established in 1936. Although the T.I.S.C. dealt with numerous problems in which contract and finance policy were inextricably mixed, the Contracts Co-ordinating Committee nevertheless continued to function as such mainly through its sub-committees, one of which was devoted entirely to works contracts.

whether the procedure should apply to skilled as well as unskilled workers.[1] In principle, both the industrial and official representatives approved the insertion in Government contracts of a clause obliging contractors to apply to employment exchanges for all labour other than controlling and supervisory staff, individual workers regularly or customarily employed by the contractor, and such 'suitable' workers as the labour exchanges could not supply within a reasonable period after receipt of the contractor's request. But on the outbreak of war, in view of the possible effect upon the engagement of building labour of the Control of Employment Bill, and all the circumstances prevailing, further action on the proposed clause (as has already been noted) was suspended and the position recorded in the minutes of the joint committee.

Under the Control of Employment Bill specified employers could no longer engage or re-engage certain classes of employed persons, specified in Orders to be made by the Minister, without the consent of the Minister, nor could they advertise for such persons—a provision intended to put a stop to the 'poaching' of labour almost openly practised in the building as in other industries. In the House of Commons the Bill met with a stormy reception. Organised labour through its representatives in the legislature made it quite clear that it was not prepared, at that stage of the war, to give anyone powers to prevent labour being sold to the highest bidder except under rigidly defined statutory conditions. The acceptance by the Government of a number of amendments deprived the Bill of all substantial authority, and its failure was evident as soon as it became law. Not until midway in 1940, after the passing of Emergency Powers (Defence) Act, 1940, did compulsion begin to be applied to the movement of labour.[2]

In the first (and only) Order to be issued under the Control of Employment Act carpenters, joiners and bricklayers were 'directed' to undertakings where they were most needed. This was in 1940. Shortly after, the whole position was fundamentally changed by the passing of the Emergency Powers (Defence) Act of May 1940. Regulation 58A of the Defence (General) Regulations made under the Act gave the Minister of Labour very wide powers to control employment, and on 5th June he made the Undertakings (Restriction on Engagement) Order 1940. This Order applied to the three industries where the dislocation due to the movement of workers seemed to be particularly severe, namely building, civil engineering contracting and general engineering. The Order provided that in those three industries employers should not engage workers or even try to engage them except through an employment exchange; and workers seeking

---

[1] No 'semi-skilled' category was recognised in the building industry by the National Joint Council.

[2] See Chapter VI.

employment were to register at an employment exchange and obtain employment by being submitted by the exchange to an employer. The effect of the Order was that employers could not advertise or seek by any other means to find workers except by telling the exchange what they needed. The worker retained his right to give notice and leave his job, but on becoming unemployed he was obliged to register at an exchange. Thus the exchange had full information about the supply and demand for labour in the appropriate industry and had an opportunity of picking out the most important jobs and filling them at once. Where a trade union had arrangements for placing workers in employment the Minister might approve these arrangements and the trade union, so long as it observed the Minister's directions, was treated for the purpose of the Order as an employment exchange.

(iii)

Wage Rates and Working Conditions

If during this period the committees appointed to supervise the building programme had little real control over the recruitment or movement of the labour force, they were somewhat more successful in influencing working conditions through methods of compromise and give-and-take expedients. Both the Inter-departmental Committee and the Joint Consultative Committees had set up sub-committees for dealing with local conditions in particular areas. Owing to the constitution of these sub-committees the official representatives were often able to make up for their lack of authority by personal contact with the industrial representatives at the conference table. But it remained the policy of the Government, as it had long been that of all British governments, not to interfere in the internal working of industry—a tradition which held the advantage for the industrial spokesmen that, although they had to seek for information, they were not obliged to submit to guidance. They asked only to be told beforehand what was being planned by the departments under the programme and to be given the longest possible notice of the main contracts. From this attitude they did not deviate so long as they remained free agents, and they were justified in so far as serious labour troubles did result from the lack of advance information on the timing and siting of large-scale contracts. The departments, it is true, agreed in 1937 to give advance information of contracts over £25,000. But from that year until the Ministry of Works was set up in October 1940, although there was a copious exchange of views, no accepted method of regulation was evolved. Unsatisfactory working conditions, when reported on, were dealt with *ad hoc* by the building department concerned, in some cases as the result of pressure by the Joint Consultative Committee, on information supplied by its sub-committees; but it was not until the Essential Works legislation was applied to the industry in 1941 and 1942 that there was any real control over the contractor on the site.[1]

On the costs of labour, and the related question of the attitude of organised building trades workers, the industry's sheet-anchor remained the machinery for fixing wages and conditions, coupled with the disputes machinery, under the National Joint Council.[2] Through that machinery the wage rates of the whole industry throughout England and Wales had been altered by reductions of $\frac{1}{2}$d. per hour five times between 1928 and 1933, and by increases of $\frac{1}{2}$d. per hour three times since 1933. These nation-wide alterations, it was claimed by the employers' federation, had been put into effect without the slightest dislocation of the industry, indeed without any real difficulty at all, 'thanks to the wisdom of the decisions of the responsible adjudicating body, the loyalty of the organised elements in the industry, and the fact that the non-organised elements also follow the decisions as being authoritative'.[3] Against this background the Joint Consultative Committee was able, in the summer of 1937, to give effect to three agreed provisions. First, that the contracting departments should notify the National Council of any building project of over £25,000 which it was proposed to put in hand as long as possible before the commencement of the work; secondly, that a representative of the contracting department concerned was to be free to attend the meeting of the National Council at which any exceptional margin for a particular building project was being considered and to take part in the discussion before the rate was fixed; and, thirdly, that, subject to the provisions of the Fair Wages Clause, exceptional margins fixed by the National Council were to be accepted by contracting departments as a basis upon which tenders for Government contracts should be submitted.

Not always was it found practicable to confine the application of exceptional margins to undertakings (for example, air stations) in rural or isolated districts. Occasionally special conditions brought in urban areas as well. This happened, to take a notable instance, at Chorley in December 1937. The arrangements for exceptional margins, intended to apply to districts graded B and below, did not in fact distinguish between one area and another, so that when application was made for exceptional margins for grade A districts at Chorley

---

[1] Chapter VI.

[2] Notes and Appendices: Note II, 'Joint Negotiating Machinery in the Building and Civil Engineering Industries'.

[3] On the other hand, apart from special rates, there were at least five different rates for the same job throughout the country, with London and Liverpool at the top and country areas, like North Devon, where 2$\frac{1}{2}$d. per hour lower was paid for the labourers, at the bottom.

and St. Athan, departments feared that if they gave way, especially at Chorley, there would be further applications in similar districts all over the country. The Grading Commission, however, granted the application at Chorley where, owing to the exceptional circumstances prevailing in December 1937, they awarded an additional 2d. per hour to skilled men, with the proportionate rate for labourers. The award was justified by the fact that labour for that contract was being recruited over a wide area and men employed were being compelled to meet heavy expenses for daily travelling to the site. Although arrangements had been made for cheap transport, these special facilities had been vetoed by the Regional Transport Commissioner in favour of the usual means of transport. For many of the men this meant an increase in travelling expenses of 1s. to 2s. 9d. per day. Moreover, during the winter months men could not work overtime owing to the shorter days, nor was the covered accommodation adequate for the 5,000 men then at work—all factors that made it harder to retain them on the job.

While Chorley was treated as a single exceptional case and the application for St. Athan was turned down, similar sets of circumstances in regard to the travelling of men to jobs of this kind applied to other contracts (for example, Bishopton, Rosyth and Bridgend) and means were later found within the industry to put travelling allowances on a more regular footing.

Up and down the country hours of work were a constantly recurring subject of concern and disagreement. In the summer of 1939 tendencies which had been present from the beginning of rearmament flared up with a new intensity over the militia camp programme. Contractors went to all lengths to attract men by the incentive of high earnings, made up of high hourly rates, daily subsistence rates, and exceptional overtime. Advertisements were common guaranteeing an 80-, 90- or even 100-hour week. Carpenters and other skilled workmen were receiving wages of £7 to £8 for a week of 70 to 80 hours. At Taunton, where some 950 men were employed and the working week was 88¾ hours, the average overtime was 42½ hours. The lowest average overtime at Ripon, where some 1,523 men worked a 66-hour week, was 12 hours. The War Office explained that there were wide variations in the total hours a week worked in the different camps, according to the date of starting work, unforeseen delays, broken time and similar factors, and such abnormal conditions as extensive site preparation, delay in delivery of hut sections, and so forth.

To protect the interest of the State financially, independent surveyors were employed by the War Office to supervise the working of the contracts. They were given the specific duty of keeping a constant watch on the output of labour and the power to curtail hours of overtime whenever output threatened to fall to an uneconomical level.

These investigations, it was claimed, showed that there was no difficulty in maintaining a good output of work for ten hours a day in
summer weather and that a maximum up to eighty hours a week could
be maintained for a short period, say of fourteen to twenty-one days.
There was evidence that work on Saturday and Sunday could be
limited with advantage to eight hours on each day, and that in exceptional circumstances a minimum of one half-day a week should be
observed as a rest period, but preferably a whole day. An average, it
was contended, of sixty-four to sixty-five hours a week was therefore
perfectly reasonable provided they were really working hours:[1] and
lost time through weather or other adverse circumstances was consequently to be made good by overtime.

The War Office, having consulted the National Joint Council
throughout in regard to overtime, rates of wages and other conditions
of work, pressed for a Government declaration, insisting that any
Ministerial decisions on curtailment of overtime should be promulgated through the National Joint Council and given the fullest publicity. When this demand came finally before the Ministerial Building
Priority Sub-Committee for decision, the number of full working
hours per week was limited to 60 hours as a maximum (but excluding
hours lost through weather conditions and other causes). It was left
to the Minister of Labour, after consulting other departments, to
evolve a precise formula for exceptions to the sixty-hour week. He
had, moreover, to find ways to prevent contractors from evading the
overtime limit through the exploitation of subsistence allowance and
the payment of wages higher than at local rates. The representatives
of employers and employed, in consultation with the Ministry of
Labour, agreed at last to the sixty-hour week, and later a public
announcement to this effect was made in the House of Commons.

The overlapping of building and civil engineering labour on many
of the important defence works was frequently a cause of friction and
delay, and it had long been foreseen that it would be essential to find
ways of securing greater uniformity. Although, as we have seen, the
building and civil engineering industries are usually included, for the
sake of convenience, in the term 'building industry' they had nevertheless always been separate, each with its own wage-fixing bodies
and differing conditions of employment. But civil engineering contractors often made use of building craftsmen, and it was obviously
desirable to ensure that normal peace-time divergencies between the
two industries should not be allowed to retard the war effort and
should be temporarily superseded. To enable departments to co-
operate on the building programme with both the building and civil
engineering industries, the Uniformity Agreement of 6th June 1940

---

[1] This view was not accepted by the industry, which later argued for an 'optimum' of
60 hours or even 55.

introduced uniformity on wages, hours and working conditions in the two industries. The agreement was between the National Joint Council for the Building Industry and the Civil Engineering Construction Conciliation Board and provided that, for the period of the war, on approved Government construction civil engineering and building contractors should observe the same conditions. Uniformity was applied to Government jobs specified by the Ministry of Labour and National Service as essential parts of the Government war programme. Before the Uniformity Agreement could be applied to a contract approval had to be given by the Uniformity Joint Board, consisting of representatives of both sides of the two industries. The ordinary industrial working rules in the two industries continued to apply, subject to the overriding terms of the agreement.[1]

(iv)

The Supply of Building Materials

During the summer of 1940 the licensing of civil building was at last agreed upon, and on 7th October became enforceable under Defence Regulations.[2] This new measure helped not only to relieve the labour shortage but also to regulate the use of materials. Although the use of timber, and later the purchase and use of steel, were already under quite stringent control, the restriction of private building was nevertheless needed to seal up a major source of leakage.

Before the war the general supply position of materials for the Government building programme was largely a matter of conjecture. Its rough outline could be traced only from the estimated cost of the contracts and the probable labour force that would be needed to

---

[1] The main provisions of the agreement were: (i) The rate of pay for all labour covered by the two industries should be the basic rates as prescribed from time to time by the National Joint Council and, including any exceptional margins that might be given to any job or area, was not to exceed the current rate for Grade A in the building industry. (ii) The hours to be worked before overtime rates applied should be $8\frac{1}{2}$ hours per day on the first five days of the week and $4\frac{1}{2}$ on Saturdays during the remainder. (iii) A minimum payment of not less than 30 hours per week if the workman had kept himself available for periods as defined in the agreement. (iv) Specific arrangements in respect of workmen travelling to and from the job. (v) For workmen required to live away from home a lodging allowance of 3s. 6d. per night was to be paid by the Ministry of Labour and National Service provided that the Ministry was satisfied that the workman was entitled to such an allowance. (vi) Free travelling facilities to and from the job to men travelling daily between 4 and 25 miles (if over 25 miles, the fare was to be refunded at the commencement of employment, and at the end of employment a railway ticket was to be provided back to the place of recruitment). If over 50 miles, in addition to the foregoing, after eight weeks of employment a man was entitled to a free railway ticket to the place of his recruitment and on return to the job was to be refunded his fare. That arrangement was to apply also at the end of each subsequent eight-week period of service). (vii) An allowance, varying according to distance, for travelling time for each day on which a man travelled over 10 miles to the job. It was laid down that the agreement should apply to all essential Government contracts but not to the A.R.P. shelter programme.

[2] Section (v) of this chapter.

carry them out. But in September 1939 departments were asked for estimates of the amounts of materials[1] (as well as of labour) needed for their contracts. Many of these estimates were later proved to have been put far too high; but for the time it was accepted (and was certainly true of timber) that the needs of departments exceeded supplies. The Works and Building Priority Committee, of which the Parliamentary Secretary to the Ministry of Labour[2] was chairman, now applied itself to working out a plan for the allocation of materials to departments. In the search for a solution Lord Chatfield, who had succeeded Lord Caldecote as Minister for Co-ordination of Defence, had put forward a memorandum[3] in which it was argued that since part of the demand was based on merely provisional requirements, in circumstances which were at that time conjectural (as, for example, in respect of air raid precautions) to release the whole of the programme would cause congestion and involve all departments in confusion and delay. Lord Chatfield gave his concurrence to the suggestion that for three months not more than forty per cent. of the aggregate contracts programme be released. The Works and Building Priority Committee were to determine (subject to Lord Chatfield's decision in case of dispute) the allocation of the forty per cent. among the different departments.

Any percentage restriction on materials, however, and especially on timber, was unacceptable to the departments; and the Office of Works used the occasion to press for a short-term, rather than a long-term, view of the programme and for the setting up of a central planning control over the whole field. The contention was that for the time being all hypothetical demands, such as those for air raid precautions and first aid, should be ignored, while all definite schemes should be planned on the basis of their geographical distribution and the character of materials and construction applicable to each. Intensive and systematic supervision by a controlling authority would enable the best use to be made of materials and labour. To release forty per cent. of total requirements for any period of three months, to be delivered at any time during the three months, might tend to aggravate the shortage rather than relieve it. On the other hand, if each month's requirements were to be taken separately the application of the forty per cent. would mean that a good deal of work would have to be stopped. The committee, though impressed by this argument, decided nevertheless to try out the forty per cent. restriction

---

[1] Timber, bricks, cement, roofing materials.
[2] Mr. Ralph Assheton.
[3] The memorandum had been prepared by Sir Connop Guthrie who, though not a member of the building industry, had earlier been charged by the Prime Minister (Mr. Chamberlain) to keep the industry under review on his behalf, but also with responsibility to the Minister for Co-ordination of Defence. The selection of Sir Connop Guthrie was presumably because of his assocation with industry, notably shipping, in the First World War.

provisionally for a three months' period and to limit it to the release of timber. But these tentative arrangements were dissipated by a wider scheme for the global allocation of materials to the committee.

On 16th October 1939 the Works and Building Priority Committee had under consideration proposals from a joint meeting of the Production and Materials Priority Sub-Committees[1] for the co-ordination of its work with that of the Materials Priority Sub-Committee. Two alternative methods were suggested: either for the Materials Priority Sub-Committee to make global allocations of raw materials to the Works and Building Priority Committee, or else for that committee to submit its proposed allocations to the Materials Priority Sub-Committee, which could then fit the recommendations into the general priority picture.

The Sub-Committee inclined towards the second alternative on the ground that if the first alternative were adopted the Works and Building Priority Committee might sometimes receive a smaller allocation than would otherwise be given. Mr. Assheton, on the other hand, thought that his committee could make effective recommendations for the completion of the programme of departments only if they first received some indication of the available amount of materials. This view was finally approved as the only practical procedure, and the Materials Sub-Committee were asked to make global allocations on the basis of returns that had been provided. This continued to be the procedure until a Controller of Building Materials was appointed by the Ministry of Works.[2]

Under the heading of building materials at least a hundred items might be listed. In the following pages it is possible to refer only to the most important: timber, steel, cement and tarmac, bricks and roofing materials (bituminous felt, corrugated iron and protected metal sheeting, asbestos cement sheeting and slates).

TIMBER

Before the war nine-tenths of the timber used in this country came from abroad and its consumption was increasing. From the outset it was therefore one of the materials for which methods of conservation had to be found. Immediately on the outbreak of war, and before there was time for a licensing system to be set up, the area officers of the Timber Control were given wide discretionary powers to limit the issue of timber to the minimum, and to refuse material where the end product did not justify its use. By 12th September 1939 the Control had already laid down a policy countering the use of timber in house-building. Timber was to be released only for houses which were

---

[1] These were sub-committees of the Ministerial Priority Committee. See Notes and Appendices: Note VI, 'The Central Priority Organisation'.
[2] See page 50; also Chapter VII.

almost complete, or in order to make the existing structure weather-proof; where only the foundations had been laid no timber at all was to be used.

After the introduction of licensing by the Timber Control, in order to ease the pressure on the licensing department of the Control consumers could obtain £20 worth of timber per month without a licence by signing a declaration that the timber would be used for essential purposes only. But this arrangement provided loopholes for certain users to consume timber for non-essential purposes, and the amount was therefore cut to £5 per month; later the arrangement was completely withdrawn. As from 1st January 1940 all consumers' stocks were brought under the control of the Ministry of Supply.

Meanwhile, at the outbreak of war, and before the Timber Control had been able to make a complete survey of existing stocks of timber in the country, the requirements of departments had been estimated at half as much again as the existing stocks of softwood and about one-third of the annual output. By mid-November the gravity of the timber situation was becoming fully realised, and strenuous efforts were made through different forms of official action to cope with the situation.

Of the economy measures initiated by the Timber Control, not the least important from the building industry's point of view was the substitution wherever possible of alternative materials in the place of timber construction. But in this respect the practice of the industry was not markedly progressive, and in the 1939 militia camp crisis contractors ignored the opportunity of adopting new processes.

A committee of representatives of leading contracting firms had been appointed[1] in September 1939 under the chairmanship of Sir Malcolm McAlpine to report to the Ministry of Supply on what types of hut construction should be adopted for future camps, having regard to the availability of the various materials and the need of making the most economical use of the nation's resources. In effect the committee were asked to find a satisfactory substitute for timber. Here was a chance, had the committee the mind and inclination to seize upon it, for a decisive swing from traditional methods of construction. Time, however, was not on their side. Since it was imperative to get the camps built with all speed, the members of the committee, drawn as they were from some half-dozen of the leading contracting firms, declined to look beyond the range of their own experience or advocate new methods and materials whose introduction would inevitably alienate the whole building industry. They were, it may be presumed, reluctant to read more into their terms of reference than conditions at that time dictated or to aggravate the labour situation both within

---

[1] On War Office initiative.

and outside the industry. In their interim report[1] they preferred, as alternatives to timber, materials already used in building small dwellings—bricks, concrete blocks, tiles and slates. The strength of their case was that the production of such materials and skilled labour for their manufacture were already assured; that distribution was well organised; that the most favourable applications and fields of use were known, and that there was, moreover, ample skilled labour for such traditional methods.

In seeking to put the problem in its true perspective, the committee recalled that for years past the house-building industry of the country had annually rehoused one and a quarter million people, which meant about £90 millions worth of building work each year. It employed, according to the committee, half the building operatives of the country[2] and used more than half the total output of bricks. Speculative house-building, because of the war, was closing down (builders completing the houses in hand but starting no more) and the committee presumed that no local authorities would be permitted to commence new housing programmes.[3] Thus a huge reserve, amounting to nearly half the building potential of the country, now became available for the national need. To that reserve was being added daily the very considerable section of the building trade normally occupied on such buildings as shops, schools, town halls, civil engineering works, roadworks, bridges, etc., as and when those jobs reached completion and no works of a similar nature were commenced. The total value of all this work was difficult to estimate, but on the basis of the 1935 census of production the figure of £90 millions already given might reasonably be doubled. Could the main hutting programme (to house under a quarter of a million men) have been spread over the reasonable period of twelve months, not nine months as proposed, and designed in the conventional brickwork in which

---

[1] An undertaking had been given that the report of the McAlpine Committee to the Ministry of Supply should first be considered by the Joint Consultative Committee, and accordingly the interim report, which was the only one made, came before it on 21st December 1939.

[2] Even taking this to mean craftsmen, and excluding entirely the civil engineering industry, it was of course an overstatement. About 350,000 new houses were built in the busiest years which employed about 350,000 men (craftsmen fifty-five per cent., labour forty-five per cent.) out of a building industry (including the halt and maimed, the sick and the unemployable) of 1,050,000.

[3] Ministry of Health Circular No. 1866, 8th September 1939 (in Scotland D.H.S. Circular No. 124/1939), addressed to housing authorities laid down the policy for the limitation of non-essential building. Quite a lot of building went on nevertheless. From 1st August 1939 to 31st March 1940 about 28,000 houses (22,000 subsidised) were completed under the Housing Acts, and over 60,000 houses by unaided private enterprise (H. of C. Deb., 10th July 1940, Vol. 362, Col. 1150). In Scotland (for the period 1st September 1939 to 31st March 1940) 8,283 houses were completed by local authorities (8,153 with subsidy) and 2,946 by private enterprise (2,870 without assistance).

In May 1940 powers were given to the Works and Building Priority Committee for the control of building contracts, and an obligation was put on all departments to obtain the committee's sanction for housing schemes for the building of 50 houses or more. In October of that year, too, the control of civil building was set up.

the civil population was housed, the building industry would have been able, in the committee's view, to take the work in its stride, without impeding its other activities or putting appreciable pressure on its resources.

The committee made some specific recommendations, most of which were endorsed by the Joint Consultative Committee. For economy in the use of timber, sleeping huts were to be simplified in design; sleeping accommodation was in the main to be in brickwork; other camp building was to be turned over so far as possible to the simplest and most economical form of brick construction; and professional aid was to be obtained to ensure the most economical lay-out of the camps. But the sum total of the building industry's advice for circumventing the timber crisis (in so far as the McAlpine Committee represented that comprehensive, diverse and complex aggregate of industries and trades commonly classed under 'building') was, in the light of subsequent events, timid and conservative.

Timber, it is true, remains the quickest and simplest of all building materials; but war had started, the Prime Minister had already announced that the War Cabinet were planning for a three years' war, and the timber position was likely to be quite desperate. That the strategic significance of this shortage was not yet realised by the industry is a point of major criticism. It was left to the Works and Building Priority Committee to meet the timber shortage as best it could by the global allocation of timber to building departments on an arbitrary basis wherever the committee were satisfied that timber was available for the purpose.

STEEL

A shortage of steel began to make itself felt during the early months of 1940. The estimated demand of the Government building programme for the calendar year 1940 was for 1,600,000 tons of finished steel,[1] a total which excluded steel requirements for air raid precautions. Against that demand the Production and Materials Priority Sub-Committees had given the Works and Building Priority Committee a global allocation of one million tons. (In practice this meant an allocation of 750,000 tons from 1st April to 31st December against requirements of 1,200,000 tons.) In a memorandum by the Works Co-ordination Section, based on information supplied by the Iron and Steel Control, it was made clear that the Control expected the Works and Building Priority Committee to make a separate allocation to each department for each of the three quarterly periods, so that the load on the steel mills in each of those periods might be calculated in advance.

It should be made clear that the global allocation to the Works and

---

[1] That is, excluding cast iron.

Building Priority Committee was intended to service four main categories: first, the direct building and civil engineering requirements of Government departments; secondly, the requirements of private enterprise building and civil engineering; thirdly, any railway work in connection with the construction of Royal Ordnance Factories and similar works undertaken for the departments by the railway companies; and lastly, the maintenance and repair of departments' own buildings and also of civil building.

It was left entirely to departments to choose the type of steel products they wished to use, and the Iron and Steel Control endeavoured so to organise the capacity of the industry as to supply, if possible, the kinds of steel needed by departments.

> They are even prepared to consider the case for the construction of new plants producing special products if by so doing substantial economies will be made possible in the consumption of ingot steel.

It should be added that in spite of difficulties at that time in the manufacture of certain steel products,[1] the policy of the Control was to route steel ingots in greater quantities to the mills making the products most in demand by the building departments, and by degrees (within the yearly global allocation of one million tons) to meet the needs of each department without delay.

For repair and maintenance of civil buildings steel was allocated in a different way from timber. Timber for those purposes was separately allocated by the Production and Materials Priority Sub-Committees and licences were issued direct by the Timber Control, so that departments did not have to scrutinise allocations for relatively small amounts. The Iron and Steel Control, on the other hand, had no unallocated reserve of steel that could be set aside for repair and maintenance. The Works and Building Priority Committee consequently adopted the principle of setting aside an amount for repair and maintenance out of its global allocation. Applications for steel under this heading were made direct to the Iron and Steel Control, not through departments.

The difference between the departments' demand of over 1,200,000 tons for the three quarters of 1940 and the 750,000 tons allocated was disturbing. It represented a three-eighths cut in the total estimate of requirements which, when priorities came to be examined, might sometimes mean a still larger cut. As a preliminary to asking that a larger allocation be made by the Production and Materials Priority Sub-Committees (and if need be referring the matter to the Ministerial Priority Committee) departments were asked by the Works and Building Priority Committee to give particulars of steel needed for

---

[1] e.g. heavy sections, boiler plates, reinforcing bars and rods under $\frac{1}{2}$ inch diameter and wire.

each type of undertaking and to say what saving of steel could be made through the use of alternative materials. In addition, they were to assess the effect of a three-eighths cut in the estimates, showing what undertakings or projects would have to be postponed or abandoned.

The information furnished by the departments and the representations of the committee persuaded the Ministerial Priority Committee to sanction a revised global allocation of 965,000 tons for the nine months beginning 1st April 1940. Actually the statements furnished by departments had shown no more than a possible total saving of some 100,000 tons on the total requirements of over 1,200,000 tons. As to the possibility of economising steel by the use of substitute materials, it appeared that not more than approximately 59,000 tons[1] could be saved in this way, chiefly through the use of reinforced concrete, timber and asbestos cement sheeting.

The estimates by departments of the effect of a three-eighths cut in their steel requirements showed that the requirements of some departments[2] had already been reduced voluntarily by the departments themselves or had been cut by the Government. In regard to all departments it was clear that any further reduction in the estimates could only be made by retarding the completion of the building programme. In some instances (for example, Air Ministry) the programme had already been delayed through tardy deliveries of steel.

Towards the end of June the Works and Building Priority Committee were called upon to consider proposals from the Ministry of Supply for the issue of an Order as soon as possible to prohibit the use of steel for building except under licence. The main object of the Order was to arrest the consumption of steel already in builders' hands and outside the scope of the existing steel licensing scheme; for although the sale and purchase of steel were already subject to licence, a conspicuous amount of private building was still going on without steel licences.

Substantial amounts of the steel for such building had doubtless been bought, as had the timber, before any licensing scheme was set up; or it had been obtained from stock-holding merchants who were not required to have steel licences. While the Control arranged to restrict supplies of steel to the stock-holding merchants, some margin was allowed so that they could supply the urgent needs of industrial consumers for various purposes in small quantities. The annual tonnage of structural steel in the hands of stock-holders was necessarily large, and one object of the Order was to prevent these large quan-

---

[1] Office of Works, 33,400 tons; Admiralty, 11,800 tons; Ministry of Health, 6,600 tons; Air Ministry, 4,000 tons; War Office, 3,000 tons.
[2] Especially War Office, Ministry of Home Security, Board of Education, Department of Health for Scotland and Government of Northern Ireland.

tities of steel from being sold to consumers for unnecessary building.

But the Control had also to review the purchases of steel for building already authorised by departments out of their allocations in order to defer, if possible, any not regarded as immediately essential. New applications for steel were discouraged through press publicity which left the public in no doubt that the Order stopped the use of steel in building except where licence had been obtained, and that licences would only be issued on the recommendation of a Government department that the work was in the national interest. As to steel already in the possession of builders, fabricators and others, or already covered by an authority to purchase, it was left to the Works and Building Priority Committee to sanction only applications of immediate importance, while a discretion was given the departments to sanction, without reference to committee, jobs of urgent importance where the amount of steel involved was less than 25 tons. The committee, too, had to co-ordinate the recommendations of the departments and to relate them to the total allocation of steel period by period. Where there were applications for authority to purchase and use (that is, new purchase) the procedure was similar: one authority covered both purchase and use, after approval by the committee, wherever more than 25 tons was in question. In order to cut off a whole flood of applications for small quantities of steel for repair and maintenance of factories and so forth, the Order exempted the purchase from a stock-holder and the use of quantities not exceeding one ton in one month for one building.

CEMENT AND TARMAC

The cement industry's capacity with all works functioning, as estimated by the Cement Makers' Federation and accepted by the Ministry of Supply, was from 700,000 to 750,000 tons per month, or approximately nine million tons per annum; but to a large extent production depended on weather conditions and was normally higher in the summer than the winter. This tendency was accentuated by the black-out.

On the figures available it seemed as though the ratio between demand and supply might become extremely narrow, and that the key to the position was to be sought in storage capacity and freedom from air attack. The cement producers had silos, with a capacity of 400,000 tons, or about four weeks' supply. In addition, stocks estimated at some 500,000 tons, were carried by builders' merchants in various parts of the country. Under the conditions imposed by the defence programme and the necessities of war it was unlikely that stocks in store would be allowed to deteriorate. The Works and Building Priority Committee were indeed well aware of the need for a system of turnover and replacement in order to keep stocks in good condition, and they made appropriate representation to the Ministry of Supply.

At first great concern was felt because of the apparent vulnerability of the industry in some areas, and one suggestion was that all cement makers should work to capacity between April and September 1940. Under such a scheme any surplus over actual demands would have been stored in kilns by builders' merchants and builders, and if necessary in specially adapted warehouses. The preponderant opinion, however, was that the danger from air attack was much exaggerated. A direct hit seemed a remote possibility, but even then it was unlikely that more than one kiln would be put out of action. Additional storage would have involved heavy cost in transporting cement from kilns to storage depots; and in any event capacity was already dispersed in various parts of the country, while kilns were distributed over a wide area.

By midsummer 1940 concern about vulnerability had given way to a wave of anxiety because of a feared shortage through the diversion of supplies to defence works.[1] Deliveries were now being made at the rate of thirty per cent. for emergency defence works, fifty per cent. for large Government contracts (airfields, Royal Ordnance factories, etc.), and twenty per cent. for other works. There were, moreover, a number of small demands for essential works or for urgent maintenance, for which no provision had been made in the priority list agreed with the Cement Makers' Federation and which could only be met on the intervention of the Ministry of Supply.

As an interim measure (intended to apply only until the adoption of a system of allocation similar to those for timber and steel) the Cement Makers' Federation were asked to observe the following order of preference in the distribution of supplies of cement:

(i) Emergency defence works (including Colonial defence works), contracts in the top urgency list (classed as W.B.A.),[2] any job certified as vital work by the Central Priority Department and the requirements of the asbestos industry.

(ii) Demands for small quantities of cement needed for other essential works or for urgent maintenance work on the representation of the War Materials Department of the Ministry of Supply.

By the beginning of August the supply position had appeared to tighten still further. Revised estimates for the rest of the year showed requirements for contracts in urgency list W.B.A. and equivalent priority at 1,856,209 tons, and requirements other than these at 1,709,050 tons. After making additional provision for August and September amounting in all to nearly 1,700,000 tons, the Works and

---

[1] Natural concern was fanned by popular agitation for political ends. These exaggerated fears about the sufficiency of cement supplies proved groundless. See Chapter VII.

[2] For definition of priority classifications see Chapter IV.

E

Building Priority Committee directed (the representative of the Air Ministry dissenting) that, in order to relate demand to supply, a flat ten per cent. cut should be made in the revised estimates of requirements for W.B.A. and equivalent contracts, and a cut of thirty per cent. in other requirements.

A short-lived coupon or voucher system was now set up.[1] The Cement Makers' Federation were instructed to deliver cement within the allocation to departments, against certificates from departments satisfying first those demands that were certified as being defence works, W.B.A. urgency contracts or works certified by the Central Priority Department as being vital works. On the other hand, the federation was itself given a discretion to release cement in quantities not exceeding four tons on individual applications which were shown to be urgent in the public interest (for example, maintenance and repair). In respect of such releases a report was to be made by individual cement makers to the federation.

The new expansion programme of the Air Ministry, having received War Cabinet sanction, was reinforced with revised priority arrangements. The construction of airfields was now given first priority, munition factories second priority, and the air raid shelter programme third priority. Allocation of cement had to be approved by the Minister without Portfolio;[2] and it had to conform to this decision. To meet the situation instructions were issued by the Minister of Labour that special attention should be given to the recruitment of labour for airfield construction, and new allocations of cement were made. These allotments added up to a total allocation for the six weeks' period ending 30th September in excess of actual supplies; but, as vouchers had already been issued on the basis of the allocations made, over-allocation was the only alternative.

To satisfy individual applications for more than four tons for unforeseen repair and maintenance, including repairs after air raid damage, the Ministry of Supply were asked to instruct the Cement Makers' Federation to release supplies at their discretion.

By the time the Ministry of Works was set up in October 1940 the uncertainty over cement was clearing up. The appointment in the Ministry of a Controller of Building Materials[3] and a Director of Cement[4] helped to restore confidence that the Government had the situation well in hand.

Because of the earlier uncertainties on the safeguarding of cement supplies, an investigation was made of the productive capacity of the tarmac industry. A point of special interest was whether it would be able to meet the existing and contemplated demands of the Air Minis-

---

[1] It was suspended before the end of the year. See Chapter VII.
[2] Mr. Arthur Greenwood.
[3] Mr. (later Sir) Hugh Beaver.
[4] Viscount Wolmer.

try, so that the amount of cement used for runways could be reduced. The report of a special sub-committee[1] showed the total productive capacity of the tarmac industry at some five million tons a year. There was no shortage of materials. Lack of labour in the industry itself and the absence of a co-ordinated demand by the Air Ministry were the only serious limiting factors; but there were minor difficulties because of inadequate rail and road transport or the distance of appropriate plant from the Air Ministry sites.

Early in October 1940 the Ministry of Transport were asked to organise the production of all materials needed for making runways and roads from tarmac; but it was objected by that Ministry that without more precise knowledge of the amount of tarmac wanted by the Air Ministry and its geographical distribution they were not justified in stimulating its production. The argument was cut short by the setting up of the Ministry of Works and the appointment of a Director of Cement. Tarmac did not come within his province. Its production and that of other road-making materials remained with the Ministry of Transport, an arrangement that perhaps reduced efficiency but was not vitally serious.

BRICKS

During the rearmament period the danger of a shortage of bricks was never seriously regarded.[2] But while, at the outbreak of war, the Works and Building Priority Committee were satisfied that the requirements of departments up to the end of June 1940 were well within the capacity of the industry, this view was not accepted by the Ministry of Supply which held that, although some expansion of production was possible, the estimated demand would absorb all the existing output. By mid-1940 the position was in fact disquieting. A sub-committee on bricks and cement, after studying the requirements of departments up to the end of the year, drew attention to the phenomenally large demand of the Ministry of Home Security for air raid shelter works. This amounted, for the September quarter alone, to 1,000 million bricks or two-thirds of the total requirements in that period, and it was feared that the number of bricklayers needed for so large a programme of shelter construction would not be forthcoming.

Even more alarming than the gigantic demand was the drop in brick output. In various parts of the country kilns had closed down because of the falling-off of demand in the preceding winter months;

---

[1] The sub-committee was appointed on 26th September 1940 and consisted of representatives of the Mines Department, Petroleum Department, Ministry of Transport, Ministry of Supply and Ministry of Labour.

[2] The economic problems of the brick industry came under closer consideration when a Director of Bricks was appointed in December 1940 in the Ministry of Works. These problems are discussed in Chapter VII. See also Notes and Appendices: Note VII, 'Types of Brick'.

but more recently the needs of the large-scale Government works at Chorley and elsewhere in the north-west of England had reversed the trend, causing demand (and also prices) to rise. Meanwhile the additional bricks already needed in July could not be produced for some six or eight weeks and the situation was being met by heavy withdrawals from stock.[1]

In order further to explore the demand-supply position and make sure of the industry's co-operation, the sub-committee on bricks and cement met in July representatives of the Pressed Brick Makers' Association (mainly the Fletton makers and in particular the London Brick Company) and the National Federation of Clay Industries.[2] The experience of these associations provided a valuable pointer.

The output of firms in the Association now was $85\frac{1}{2}$ million bricks per month, or about half the pre-war output. Existing stocks amounted to 191 millions, or two months' production, and at the rate of consumption then prevailing those stocks would have been exhausted in four to six weeks, that is by the end of August 1940. The maximum output that could be secured after a period of four to six weeks amounted to 125 million bricks monthly, an increase of fifty per cent. on production at that time. To obtain such an increase the labour force would have had to be augmented by 1,500 experienced workers (drawers, setters, etc.) from the prevailing total of 4,500 to 6,000; yet since the outbreak of war the pressed-brick manufacturers had lost 3,000 experienced workers.[3] True, the industry had been temporarily 'screened' from the calling-up of further men for the armed forces, but unless the protection thus afforded could have been permanently secured a fall in output was inevitable when the men were called up, and to obtain an increase in output men already serving would have had to be released. To increase output by longer working hours was impracticable, as a nine-hour day ($56\frac{1}{2}$ hours per week) was already being worked in the industry. Transport difficulties added to those of labour, and were mainly due to insufficient petrol.

The evidence of the National Federation of Clay Industries was similar. Returns received from 220 firms (out of a total of 500) representing about sixty per cent. of the output of firms in the federation, showed the number of workpeople employed before the war to be 13,300 as against 8,000 in the summer of 1940, a decrease of 5,300. Similarly the normal weekly output of 37,767,000 bricks was reduced to 23,242,000 bricks. The existing stocks amounted to 62 million bricks. About one-half of the decrease in the numbers employed was

---

[1] Thus, the London Brick Company were selling 4,250,000 bricks daily although their output was probably not more than two million bricks a day.

[2] The different outlook and production methods of the Fletton makers as compared with other sections of the industry are discussed in Chapter VII.

[3] About half of these had been called up for service with the armed forces. The remainder had obtained employment in agriculture, steel works and with building contractors.

attributable to call-up for the armed forces; the other half was made up of men who had been drawn into better-paid employment in other industries. Arrangements had only recently been made to defer until September 1940 the further call-up of men engaged in the production of bricks, and in order to increase output men serving would have had to be released.

The total output of bricks was at that time calculated at about 750 millions per quarter while the estimated requirements of departments were 1,500 millions in the September quarter (including those for air raid shelters) and 850 millions in the December quarter.

To arrange for an immediate increase in the output so as to ensure partial supplies, at least, to all vitally important Government work was imperative. There were two initial problems: first, the method by which enough confidence could be given to manufacturers and work-people in the industry to yield a full scale of production immediately; and, second, the machinery by which an order of preference should be operated until the supply of bricks was enough to meet all demands.

Inter-departmental discussion turned mainly on the suggestion that the Government should buy all, or a proportion, of the industry's output over a certain period. It was agreed that the Ministry of Supply, given time, had the experience to set up a controlling organisation on the lines of the Timber Control, but not the knowledge or experience to operate a central agency for the purchase of bricks. Since the time factor was all-important, the Office of Works, as it still was, could have appropriately acted as the central purchasing agent.

The Government were ready to give the brick-making industry an undertaking that they would buy every brick produced by the industry before 31st December 1940 at prices to be fixed in advance. In furtherance of this scheme a Government department, or some agency acting on behalf of the Government, was to arrange through the national federation with the local brick-makers' organisations for a schedule of prices of different types of bricks in the different localities; while the industry was to set up an organisation to control the routing of deliveries to brickyards, and to carry out as directed an order of preference during the immediate period of shortage.

After further meetings with representatives of the industry the Government agreed in August to take over up to one-third of the actual output of each firm if remaining in stock at 31st December 1940.[1] Subject to certain reservations over prices, agreement was reached in principle. The bricks to be bought were 'hard well-burnt common building bricks of the dimensions customarily used in the district' and 'sand lime bricks (class A building bricks)' of similar

---

[1] The guarantee was not to apply to the manufacture of Fletton bricks, as the firms making these bricks declined to come within the arrangement.

dimensions.[1] Final details of the machinery to be set up for giving effect to the guarantee were to be worked out by the Office of Works in conjunction with the federation. It was also proposed to extend the guarantee to Scotland.

Before effect could be given to these plans the Ministry of Works was set up and a Director of Bricks appointed. But not for another year could the full effect of the war on the brick industry be clearly seen nor could realistic action yet be taken to organise its war-time resources and save it from disintegration.[2]

ROOFING MATERIALS

Of the chief classes of roofing materials in demand for the building programme—bituminous felt, corrugated iron and protected metal sheeting, and asbestos cement sheeting—the first gave no cause for anxiety and the second very little until the heavy air raid damage of 1940, and the subsequent first-aid repairs, caused a temporary shortage of all roofing materials. Supplies of asbestos cement sheeting had threatened in 1939 to fall short of demand; but it is true of all these materials, as it is of cement, that the needs of the Service and supply departments were at times greatly over-estimated. No doubt, too, the demands of the air raid precautions department of the Home Office, and the prospective needs of the Ministry of Health and the Board of Education, added to the general fear of shortages.

Corrugated iron and protected metal sheeting. Soon after the outbreak of war the total capacity of the corrugated iron and metal sheeting industry, as estimated by the Ministry of Supply, was 70,000 tons a month. Of this total, 60,000 tons were being absorbed for shelter construction by the Home Office. Outstanding demands for 500,000 steel shelters, which would take some six months to complete, competed with the urgent needs of the War Office for supplies of corrugated iron for the protection of troops in the expeditionary force overseas—a demand that seemed likely to rise sharply in the near future. Similar requirements were stated by the Air Ministry, nor were either of the two Service departments able to accept for these materials the forty per cent. cut proposed by Lord Chatfield.[3] In these circumstances it was left to the Ministry of Home Security to agree with the two Service departments on whatever measures were practicable for meeting the demand out of existing production.

Asbestos Cement Sheeting. Early estimates of the ratio of demand and supply for asbestos cement sheeting and kindred products left it doubtful whether the needs of departments, even apart from hypothetical provision for air raid damage, could be met out of available supplies.

---

[1] See Notes and Appendices: Note VII, 'Types of Brick'.
[2] See Chapter VII.
[3] See page 41.

But when the industry was approached in October 1939 by the Central Priority Department of the Ministry of Supply, spokesmen of the manufacturing firms were confident (though they thought the demands of departments over-estimated) that the industry could meet all requirements up to March 1940.

At the beginning of November 1939 the demands of departments were approximately 6 million square yards for the December quarter, 4·6 million square yards for the March quarter, and 10·6 million square yards for the six months ending 31st March 1940.

Examining these estimates in December 1939, the Government's technical advisers found that, although there was a time-lag of about six weeks, the manufacturers had so far been able to meet the demands passed on by contractors and sub-contractors. The estimates received from departments were presumed to include every type of asbestos, i.e. corrugated sheets, flat sheets, asbestos slates and all asbestos fitments. They did not include the hypothetical requirements of the Board of Education and the Ministry of Health, previously estimated at some five million square yards for the December quarter and one million square yards for the March quarter. On the basis of their returns the estimated monthly requirements of the departments furnishing returns were 1,845,952 square yards a month (four weeks) for the December quarter and 1,419,176 square yards a month for the March quarter.

Figures of output obtained by direct enquiry from the firms concerned, including all types of asbestos except such items as pipes and rain-water goods, showed a monthly total of approximately two million square yards, including products imported from Belgium.[1] It was assumed that a firm making asbestos slates could turn over to flat or corrugated sheets if the demand for asbestos slates ceased and, on the other hand, that Belgian supplies were necessarily precarious. Excluded from the reckoning of supplies available for the building programme was an emergency reserve of asbestos sheets which was being collected and stored by the Office of Works.[2]

With these reservations output was approximately as follows:

	sq. yds.	sq. yds.
Total output from all sources a month of four working weeks . .		2,039,000
Deduct demands for war reserve, say, 117,000 sq. yds. a month . .	117,000	
Deduct Belgian supplies assuming delivery became too difficult . .	232,000	349,000
Estimated monthly output . .		1,690,000

---

[1] Practically three-quarters of the output was under the control of Messrs. Turners Asbestos Cement Co., Ltd. Belgian products accounted for 232,000 tons.

[2] Under Civil Defence Act 1939, Sec. 60. The Office of Works hoped to build up a reserve of 30,000 sheets before the end of March.

If the possible requirements of the Ministry of Health and the Board of Education and ordinary commercial needs were not taken into account the asbestos trades could give a monthly (four weeks) output of 1,690,000 square yards of all types, as against the estimated requirements of departments of 1,845,952 square yards per month for the December quarter, and 1,419,176 square yards per month for the March quarter.

From the above comparison of output and requirements it may be fairly assumed that the trade could have met the bulk of the demands upon it, provided additional demands were not made by the Ministry of Health and Board of Education and commercial firms. If, as seemed likely, manufacturing firms took too optimistic a view of their output and made no allowance for resting periods for machines over a long period, the departments for their part (in this as in other instances) tended to overstate their needs. None the less, even had the monthly output and demand been fairly well balanced, the trade could reasonably expect to meet demand only on the footing that an even flow of ordering was maintained. The asbestos firms received their orders monthly through building contractors and sub-contractors and had no trustworthy means of ascertaining the full Government demands for any period. If serious delays in the execution of the building programme were to be avoided, assuming that full supplies of raw asbestos and cement were assured, some method of central ordering appeared to them desirable.

A resolution in that sense was passed by the Asbestos Cement Association[1] and submitted to the Central Priority Department.[2] It was carefully scrutinised but proved unacceptable.[3] The main reason for its rejection was that there were no means of forecasting with any precision the departments' requirements over a period. Any such forecast, if it were to be of use to the industry for the purpose of advance production, would have had to be detailed among the various sizes of the different materials, and it would have been liable to considerable alteration owing to changes of policy. Nor did the departments wish to be committed to the use of asbestos cement goods while suitable alternatives might be available at competitive prices. They were confident they could get what they needed, whether in asbestos cement goods or in alternative products.

It had been suggested by the association that prices should be based on pre-war prices plus increased costs due to the war, but the depart-

---

[1] 1st November 1939.

[2] See Notes and Appendices: Note VI, 'The Central Priority Organisation'.

[3] On 22nd November 1939 the Production and Materials Sub-Committees decided to remit the recommendations of the trade through the Director of Army Contracts for the consideration of the Contracts Co-ordinating Committee. On 17th January 1940 the Director of Army Contracts notified the representative of the Asbestos Cement Association of the reasons which influenced the committee, after consulting the five departments concerned, to reject the proposals for central ordering.

ments preferred that their building contractors should obtain quotations from the trade in the usual way; nor were they willing to be committed to a particular price basis for the duration of the war, especially as they were already covered by statutory powers to ensure that prices charged were reasonable.

The trade were urged, as an ordinary business precaution, to maintain certain stocks of the classes of goods which they knew from experience that the departments often called for. Otherwise, as the goods took so long to manufacture and mature,[1] the departments would feel bound to use alternatives to meet urgent needs.

Recommendations along these lines were considered by the Works and Building Priority Committee on 9th May 1940. The committee concurred that, since the supply of asbestos cement goods was now in excess of demand, no further action should be taken on the proposal to allocate the output of manufacturers among departments.

On the setting up of the Ministry of Works informal control of roofing materials, in which the industries voluntarily acquiesced, was introduced.[2] Under these new arrangements the great demand for first-aid repairs after the air raid damage of the preceding months was more easily met. Central committees were now set up to allocate supplies not only of asbestos cement sheets but also of bituminous felt, and arrangements were made to increase the production of corrugated steel sheets by the standardisation of sizes. Since the building programmes of all departments were upset by the diversion of supplies of roofing materials to first-aid repairs, it became the first concern of the Controller of Building Materials to reduce to a minimum interference with construction programmes while the possible ways of increasing output were being explored.[3]

Slates. The first effect of the outbreak of war on the slate industry was to threaten it with disaster. The restriction of civil building, and especially of housing, had meant a steep drop in the demand for slates. In Wales, where the slate output constituted from three-quarters to four-fifths of the total home output and a still higher proportion of its value,[4] the situation deteriorated rapidly after the outbreak of war, and the percentage of unemployment rose from 6·6 on 11th September to 18·9 on 16th October. There was at that time no wholesale discharge of workers, and most of those affected by the depression in the industry remained on a reduced measure of employment. But the prospect was disturbing. Should the war be prolonged a large part of the industry, it was feared, would soon be at a standstill unless a way could be found of using slates in the building programme.

---

[1] Generally it takes about six months to make and mature asbestos cement materials.
[2] See Chapter VII.
[3] *Ibid.*
[4] M.O.W. Report, *The Welsh Slate Industry* (H.M.S.O. 1947). Most of the remaining slate production was in Scotland.

That view was forcefully advanced by the Welsh Parliamentary Party, by Mr. Ernest Bevin, on behalf of the Transport and General Workers' Union, and by individual quarries and public bodies in the affected areas; and at a meeting at the House of Commons on 28th November the Minister of Labour assured the members of the Welsh Parliamentary Party that the serious position of the quarries would be taken into account in pressing for a greater use of slates. In giving this assurance Mr. Bevin had the support of the chairman of the Works and Building Priority Committee, but it was none the less true that shortage of timber and the need for stringent economy severely limited the use of slates in the first year of war.

It is significant that at the end of the First World War the production of slates in North Wales had been only two-fifths of the 1914 output. The number of men employed had fallen during the war years from 8,634 to 3,234 and half the quarries had gone out of production. The industry never fully regained its pre-war position, and it was five years before it reached the level of output that was to be the average for the inter-war period.

In the Second World War the slate industry felt the effects of war earlier and more severely. New building came under stricter control and at an earlier stage of the war, while the outlay permitted for new repairs and alterations was within much narrower limits. By 1940 the output was already almost as low as the figure reached in 1918, and about 4,600 men had been obliged to leave the quarries. Since the total number of slate quarrymen who became members of the armed forces was about 2,000 (of whom only a very small proportion would have been called up by 1940) and since large-scale direction into war industries was then in quite an initial stage,

> it can be assumed that the original dispersal of half the labour force of the quarries was caused primarily by unemployment in the slate industry during the first year of war rather than by the direction of men straight from the quarries to the fighting forces or to war industries.[1]

Ultimately from its very nature the Second World War was to create an urgent demand for slates.

> The bombing of British cities and towns by the enemy from the autumn of 1940 onwards soon revealed the folly of allowing a skilled industry of this kind to disintegrate with the decline of the normal market. The existing stocks of slates were soon exhausted and steps had to be taken by the Government through the Ministry of Works to encourage the output of roofing slates and to economise their use, but irreparable damage had already been done to the production capacity of the industry.[2]

---

[1] M.O.W. Report, *The Welsh Slate Industry* (H.M.S.O. 1947).
[2] *Ibid.*

Although the fighting forces would probably have absorbed the same number of quarrymen, and some might have been directed to other industries, a well-considered policy for the slate quarries at the beginning of hostilities could have prevented the drift of a substantial number of men in older age-groups to unskilled occupations from which it became extremely difficult to reclaim them. On the other hand, the exceptionally individualistic character of the slate industry and its mediocre level of efficiency must also be recognised as retarding influences and a check to effective action. Under the Ministry of Works the slate industry was brought under Government control. The manner and effect of that control are discussed in a later portion of this narrative.[1]

(v)

The Restriction of Private Building

Proposals for the restriction of private enterprise building came before the Inter-departmental Committee early in 1937 but were considered on the whole premature and ill-advised. Not until the autumn of 1940 was it found practicable to call a halt to the manifest waste of labour and materials on 'luxury' building. Action had been delayed largely on the assumption that the shortage of building materials would in itself act as an automatic check. The timber shortage, as has been noted, was at the outbreak of war causing great anxiety, the steel position too was soon to become no less disturbing; and while it is doubtless true that in the pre-war period, and later, shortages of materials did here and there seriously retard the building programme, its effect on private enterprise building was not conspicuous. That was mainly because stocks of timber and other materials were already in the hands of contractors who were thus able to continue 'luxury' building well into the war period.

A specially appointed sub-committee of the Inter-departmental Committee, in considering what restrictions could be put on private building, suggested that merely to postpone individual items would not help materially in releasing labour for the Government programme. A small proportionate diminution, on the other hand, could be enough to make up the required labour, at least for England and Wales.

In support of the proposed restriction, it was urged that in 1936, on the basis of Ministry of Health estimates, approximately 113,000 skilled men (excluding painters) were employed in England and

---

[1] See Chapter VII.

Wales on house-building by private enterprise as compared with about 36,000 on the housing schemes of local authorities. Of the total of approximately 149,000 skilled men engaged in housing work, seventy-six per cent. were therefore employed by private enterprise and only twenty-four per cent. by local authorities.

It has already been noted[1] that the additional skilled building labour needed in 1937 as compared with 1936 for the housing and defence programmes in England and Wales was computed at 11,500; in 1938 the additional requirements promised to be even greater—certainly not less than 19,000 men in the skilled occupations. Now the surplus labour suitable and available at the peak period in 1936 was approximately 7,000 skilled men. If it could be assumed that the whole of that reserve of labour were completely mobile and that the arrangements of the industry were such that they could be freely absorbed, a deficiency of about 4,500 in 1937 and of 12,000 in 1938 was to be expected. It was suggested that those deficiencies could have been met by restricting the building of houses by private enterprise by four per cent. in 1937 and by eleven per cent. in 1938; but since complete mobility could not be assumed, a restriction of about ten per cent. in 1937 and of seventeen per cent. in 1938, representing 11,300 and 19,250 skilled men respectively, would have been needed. The sub-committee thought it undesirable to limit the restriction to the building of houses by private enterprise and proposed that it should also be applied to unessential building projects of a 'luxury' character such as cinemas, hotels and so forth. In that event the percentage restriction would have been reduced in proportion to the amount of industrial and commercial building which it was possible to postpone.[2]

In considering methods by which restrictions could be applied, the sub-committee thought that, because of the known shortage of steel and timber, the priorities between different classes of building could have been established by the control of supplies of these materials. The volume of building activity could have been related to the available labour supply by controlling supplies of steel and timber, and the sub-committee recommended that this possibility should be explored with the Board of Trade. On the other hand, should such indirect restrictive action have proved inadequate, direct restriction could

---

[1] Chapter I, Section (iv).

[2] In Scotland the position was more difficult. There the additional skilled labour needed for the Government's housing and defence programme was 4,280 in 1937 and 6,285 in 1938, while the surplus of skilled labour suitable and available at the peak period in 1936 was approximately 1,220. A deficiency of at least 3,060 in 1937 and 5,065 in 1938 was therefore to be expected. The most acute shortage was that of bricklayers. Even though local authorities were unlikely in any event to have been able to achieve their aim of 25,000 houses in 1937 or in 1938, it was clear that any acceptable proposals for the restriction of private building would have been quite insufficient in themselves to provide a solution of the problem in Scotland.

have been imposed, with the co-operation of the industry, on defined classes of private building.

The main objection to the sub-committee's proposals came from the Ministry of Health. That department doubted the wisdom of attempting to control or curtail private enterprise building, and indeed held that the expansion of that branch of the building industry had been accepted by the Government as a means of bridging the period of depression. Legislation on so controversial a matter would have been difficult to obtain, nor was the gap between building demands and labour supply such as to have made it necessary. Spacing-out the work would have sufficed: for example, the hardship would not have been serious if local authorities had been called upon to build 70,000 instead of 80,000 houses a year.

Influenced by these and similar considerations, the parent committee decided not to take up the sub-committee's recommendations since neither the indirect nor the direct restrictive measures suggested appeared to be practicable at that time. In concluding that no action was called for, they assumed that the desired diversion of labour and materials would follow from the restriction of local authority housing by administrative action, as well as by an announcement of Government policy at the appropriate time.

Although events did not fulfil these expectations, measures for the restriction of non-essential private building remained in abeyance. In 1939, however, and during the early months of 1940, the Ministry of Health and other departments (notably the Ministry of Food) were under close pressure to sanction several categories of private building more or less directly bound up with the war effort. It was debatable how such demands, especially in terms of materials, might be allocated between the interested departments. As listed in a proposed order of priority by the Ministry of Health, suggested categories were:

    1. Work which some department was prepared to certify as being essential to the war effort, e.g. houses for the Royal Air Force; houses for employees; a new factory to produce an essential drug only available from abroad.

    2. Work which served a useful public purpose not directly connected with the war effort, e.g. the completion of a new hospital block at a voluntary hospital; the completion of a new church; the completion of a public house needed to replace one being demolished for road widening.

    3. Work which had no public character, e.g. the completion of a boat-house at a school; the completion of houses for sale.

Meanwhile the Works and Building Priority Committee had taken up the loose threads of the problem and were applying themselves to its solution. The subject now ranged beyond the orbit of the individual departments; and in July 1940 the Production Council[1] was asked by Mr. Assheton to review suggestions for the closer control of all private enterprise building and to give directions.

In occupations in the building industry most in demand for Government work there was now virtually a state of full employment. For several months departments had been refusing licences for timber or steel for private building, and at the same time the Ministry of Labour had tried to steer available labour to Government works. Wherever possible the labour exchanges strove to obtain the release of workers from unessential work for transfer on a voluntary basis to urgent work, but the Ministry of Labour had not yet used the powers conferred on it in May 1940 to order such transfers under the Defence Regulations. A substantial amount of civil building had gone on and was still going on. Some of it no doubt was work for which money and materials had been made available months ago; on other work timber and steel might have been acquired by illegal means since the imposition of the Control Orders, but it was not easy, or indeed possible, to prove this. There were many buildings, too, where controlled building materials were not needed in the early stages of constructional work, and often buildings had been completed to wall height before the contractors applied for a certificate to purchase timber and steel. Where a Government department had had the strength of mind to refuse the application this had involved a sheer waste of money, labour and materials because the building would have to stand unfinished until the end of the war.

It was for the Production Council to determine whether the only certain method of preventing needless private building might not be to place upon the builder the onus of obtaining a licence either for the continuation of a job already started or for the beginning of a new job. The experience of the First World War gave a useful pointer. Then, as now, feeling at first had been against the control of civil building. Gradually the need to put all the national resources into the war effort had been seen to be inescapable, and in 1916 a licensing system had been introduced by the Ministry of Munitions to apply to all private buildings costing £500 or more, or using any structural steel. It would seem that once established a licensing system could succeed in bringing all private building work under control and stopping so much of it as need be. The essential underlying principle was that licensing should cover the whole act of building and assess it at a given moment from all its technical aspects. But the licensing system need not (and should not) automatically do away with the

---

[1] The Production Council was set up in June 1940. It replaced the Ministerial Priority Committee but retained the existing sub-committees, including those on materials and building. The Production Council was charged with the determination of priorities and was generally to oversee and direct the production drive. In June 1941 the Council was superseded by the Production Executive. See Hancock, W. K., and Gowing, M. M., *British War Economy (passim)*; also Notes and Appendices: Note VI, 'The Central Priority Organisation'.

specific controls over men, money, and materials. The licence should allow the intending building owner to go ahead with his plans only if, when the moment came, he had the money and the country had a margin of materials and labour over and above the Government's own programme.

On the basis of this argument Mr. Assheton, on behalf of the Works and Building Priority Committee, asked the Production Council whether control should be exercised

(a) by tightening up existing controls over the three aspects of building—men, by more drastic use of the Minister of Labour's powers; money, by tightening the Treasury's control over private and public authority borrowing; materials, by improving the machinery of the timber and of the iron and steel controls; or

(b) by instituting a system of building licences.

'With considerable regret, but with no hesitation', the committee recommended that the second course should be followed. To this the Production Council agreed. It decided that control by means of licensing should be applied at the earliest possible moment to all private building including private building already in course of construction; and it invited the Works and Bulding Priority Committtee to work out the details of the licensing system proposed, with a view to bringing it into operation as soon as possible.

At a meeting of the committee on 11th July the matter was taken further. Proposals earlier put forward by the Office of Works were accepted, and it was agreed in principle that there was to be one licensing authority. The machinery of control was to be under either the Office of Works, on behalf of the Works and Building Priority Committee, or of the Ministry of Works, should such a Ministry be established. All building and civil engineering works, whether in progress or not yet started, of which the total cost exceeded £500 were to require a licence, with certain exceptions;[1] and at the outset the scheme was to be put into operation by local officers of the Office of Works in the various regional headquarters towns. Such local officers were to have power to issue or refuse licences up to a total value of £10,000; but applications for licences to build dwelling-houses were to be referred to the representatives of the Ministry of Health or the Department of Health for Scotland for authorisation. The allocation of controlled materials for classes of building within the licensing scheme was to rest with the licensing authority. It was agreed further that a draft Order should be prepared by the Office of Works and that it should come into operation, if possible, in a month's time.

The estimate of one month for the completion of the arrangements

---

[1] These were: (i) Government works; (ii) duly authorised works carried out by local authorities; (iii) works carried out by railways, dock and harbour authorities, etc., and public authorities generally where duly authorised by a Government department; (iv) works of repair or maintenance and decoration.

proved optimistic, and it was not until October that the system came into force. Meanwhile, on 24th July 1940, the Works and Building Priority Committee had received a memorandum and draft Order prepared by the Office of Works and appointed a sub-committee to give it detailed consideration. On 23rd August a revised draft regulation to be known as Defence (General) Regulation 56A and various amendments were agreed. On 6th September the committee laid it down that because the licensing arrangements called for the transfer of responsibility for the issue of supplies of controlled materials from departments to the Office of Works as the licensing authority, departments were to inform the Office of Works of their allocations of materials for such transfer. The committee also ruled that allocations for materials in respect of civil building schemes below £500 should continue to be dealt with by departments under existing arrangements, but after the licensing scheme had been in operation for three months the Office of Works were to consider whether they could then assume responsibility for them.

On 7th October 1940, shortly before the creation of the new Ministry of Works was announced in Parliament, the licensing of civil building came into force under the Defence Regulations.[1] A building 'operation' costing over £500 could not be carried out except under the authority of a Government department or with a licence from the Ministry of Works. That limit was later reduced to £100, and finally in the London area to £10; this to meet special conditions arising in a later phase of the war.[2]

THE OVER-ALL PICTURE, 1936–40

Before this narrative turns to the circumstances in which the Ministry of Works was set up in October 1940, it is timely to ask what progress had been made so far towards the co-ordination of the Government's building programme.

Despite the absence of effective control over labour supply and working conditions, despite, too, recurring alarms over the shortage of materials—alarms which, as will be seen later, were at times needless—an impressive volume of new constructional work had been carried out by the departments. Labour shortages had at times been severe, but had been local in character, and the industry's manpower was not as yet seriously depleted. There was, on the contrary, in the first year of war a high level of unemployment[3] which gave some

---

[1] 56A. S.R. & O. (1940), No. 1678.

[2] The later developments of civil licensing under the Ministry of Works are described in Chapter VI.

[3] Up to October 1940 the figures of totally unemployed males aged 16–64 were: January 354,028; February 365,548; March 199,907; April 160,136; May 135,553; June 102,969; July 92,849; August 87,023; September 88,846; October 78,334. The unemployment was mainly due to the closing down of civilian building, and in particular because of the winding up of the housing programme in 1939.

colour to the oft-repeated claim of the industry that its resources of manpower were ample and that it was for the Government to provide an effective administrative organisation for its deployment.

The only administrative organisation provided so far, however, had been the Works and Building Priority Committee. Its positive achievement, up to the autumn of 1940, except for a certain measure of control over priorities of building materials and the rather belated limitation of private building, was not substantial; but it assiduously prepared the soil for new methods of control over labour which were to come later.[1] Nor, in assessing the Committee's achievement, should it be forgotten that the building programme was not the only activity in which the priority principle was to prove a failure. It failed, too, in other spheres of the war effort.[2] To give the Works and Building Priority Committee, or any similarly constituted inter-departmental body, the task of imposing a priority system on competing departments was unrealistic, since the committee could not give effect to its decisions or bind the departments to specific action. Returns and statistics obtained under such conditions were inadequate; they tended to obscure rather than illuminate the magnitude and complexity of the programme.[3] The committee, moreover, was heavily handicapped by having been allotted an absurdly small (albeit most efficient) staff which proved out of all relation to the vast interests they were called upon to regulate.

As to the industry, in the absence of a clear lead from the Government, its fears for future prosperity were not unreasonable. Up to the eve of war the doctrine of rearmament as a thing superimposed on 'normal trade', which was not to be disturbed, was the orthodoxy both of Government and industry in all spheres, and some elements of it remained even after September 1939. In all the political and economic conditions of those years it could hardly be maintained that the industry should have made an all-out effort, or indeed that it could have made it, unless the Government had also moved with at least an equal momentum. The initiative in pressing for joint conferences on the building programme had after all come from the industry. Once the principle of joint consultation had been accepted by the Government, the industry felt entitled to be taken fully into confidence.

In the information put before the industry there was nothing to suggest that the programme was not well within its capacity; nor does it appear, in retrospect, that within the limits of the commitments required from it, the industry failed to pull its weight. If at times indi-

---

[1] A system of allocations superseded that of priorities in the spring of 1941. See Chapter IV.

[2] Notes and Appendices: Note VI, 'The Central Priority Organisation'. See also Hancock, W. K., and Gowing, M. M., *British War Economy* (*passim*).

[3] See Chapter IV.

F

vidual firms seemed to take advantage of abnormal conditions, that was usually because they were quicker to recognise the position, and set out long before the industry as a whole to reorientate themselves to the new circumstances in which work was to flow from the Government. If now and again advantage accrued to individual firms, it was more likely to be a consequence of inter-departmental competition than of loose industrial discipline.

The building industry—let it once more be stressed—was not at any time well-knit or highly organised: its great size, the multiplicity of its trades, the diverse character and quality of the 80,000 or more firms of which it was made up, were intractable factors. The separate and parallel organisation of the civil engineering industry brought in a further complication. All the more reason, therefore, why the Government should have erected without delay a firm framework for the tasks it imposed on the industry; and until it had done so there were no means of applying its full authority in the execution of the programme. Meanwhile, the inter-departmental committees which from 1937 to 1940 successively advised the Government on the building programme were guided by the experience of the building departments, and more especially of the Service departments, each with its own building organisation and (at least in the Admiralty and the War Office) a long tradition of self-sufficiency. It was only after the Ministry of Works had been set up, and the Minister of Production had been given, more than two years later, an overriding authority over the building programme, that a satisfactory degree of co-ordination was achieved. But that was not to be until the war was in its fourth year.

PART II

The Growth and Co-ordination
of Control
1940–1942

CHAPTER III

THE CREATION OF A MINISTRY OF WORKS

(i)

Proposals by the Office of Works

UP to the outbreak of war, and well into 1940, the growth of the Office of Works had been within definite limits. Together with its functional expansion to meet during the nineteenth and twentieth centuries modern conditions in building and engineering, the Office of Works, standing close to the Court and its historic background, was charged with the care and physical maintenance of the cultural framework of the State. But that duty was not by any means the most arduous or exacting of its tasks, which took in increasingly the day-by-day needs of the expanding mechanism of administration. The department had not only to provide and maintain accommodation at home and abroad, to care for parks and palaces, embassies and museums; it had also to perfect a manifold and growing supplies division and to render other complex services essential for the civil functions of government.[1]

Because of its traditions and functions it is natural that the widening of the sphere of responsibility of the Office of Works should from time to time have been in the minds of governments. Towards the end of the First World War, when problems of reconstruction were coming under review, the Office of Works, at the instance of the Ministry of Reconstruction, examined proposals for placing with one department all the civil building work of the Government; and later[2] in a comprehensive memorandum it made out a persuasive case for a sole department of State for every kind of building—a claim which had been often put forward for the Office of Works itself since its reconstitution in 1852.[3]

In 1919, after the unhappy experience of the war years, that claim appeared better founded than ever before. The evils of the unchecked scramble for labour and materials, the individualism and jealousies

---

[1] Notes and Appendices: Note I, 'The Functions of the Office of Works'.
[2] June 1919.
[3] See Note I.

of the departments, to which reference has already been made,[1] had persisted despite each attempt to check them. An inter-departmental labour committee set up in 1915 was to have forced to the surface at least the most deeply rooted and malignant abuses in the industry. In that task it had failed; and by the end of 1916 disregard of the committee's decisions had been so rife that its meetings were condemned as a waste of time and suspended until its status could be more clearly defined. Later it had been agreed that departments should bind themselves to act on the findings of the committee; provided that if the head of a department found that he could not do so, he would before acting hear the views of the chairman and other members of the committee deputed for the purpose. This procedure, too, had failed to solve the problem.

Early in 1918, the whole question had been taken up *de novo* by the Ministry of Labour. It had tried to produce 'the next best solution' to what was described as the ideal one of a single Government building contracts department. Its method was to use the national conciliation machinery of the building industry for the settlement of general wages applications subject to certain conditions. That expedient, like the earlier ones, again had proved of little avail, and as a stronger measure a priority committee had been set up towards the end of the war—an admittedly empirical arrangement to clear up the chaos that by now had overtaken the constructional work of the Government. But the grading by that committee of various works had become quite impracticable because of competition between departments in the course of which the grades allocated to the several works were ignored by the departments concerned.

In view of this and other evidence, the advantages of concentrating in the hands of one department all Government building work received in 1919 much support. The concentration of building work during the war had been partial. It had caused very serious troubles, with much wasteful dispersal of effort, and a heavy loss to the exchequer, and the need for a co-ordinating authority was patent. At that time the Office of Works felt itself equal to the task should it be cast for the role; its organisation and procedure had proved equal to taking the strain of a great access of work, and it was confident that its pre-war activities were capable of almost indefinite expansion along the lines of its recognised functions. Nevertheless, the problems of unification did not get beyond the stage of discussion at the highest level until 1922, when a Cabinet sub-committee, after considering the specific proposition that the Office of Works should take over all building work for the other departments, turned it down.

A step towards a policy of greater co-ordination was attempted in 1932. The Select Committee on National Expenditure had recom-

---

[1] Chapter I.

mended a reduced standard in new construction for the three fighting Services; and a Defence Departments Building Committee, appointed by the Treasury in February, had reported in December of that year.[1] There was much similarity, the report stated, in the building needs of the three departments: it therefore urged closer co-ordination of general standards, whether by the already existing Inter-departmental Works Committee[2] or some other authority with wider powers. The idea of widening the powers of the Inter-departmental Works Committee was accepted in principle after a somewhat acrimonious correspondence between the Treasury and the Office of Works, but without any notable effect on the practice of the three departments.

Towards the close of the rearmament period, as has already been seen, the wider issues of building policy and its administration were again under review, both within and beyond the official sphere. But for the lack of concentration and co-ordination—an admitted evil— no remedy had been found, and at the outbreak of war at least twelve separate departments had direct or indirect control over building services of some £340 millions.[3] The programme, as we have seen, took in not only specific building services (such, for example, as those of the War Office for hutted camps) but also a vast and inchoate mass of shelter works by local authorities, commercial and industrial firms and private persons under the general authority of the Ministry of Home Security; and the equally undefinable contingent demand on building labour and materials for the repair of air raid damage, responsibility for which lay at that time with the Ministry of Health.[4]

Effective intervention by the State might have been in one of two ways: either for the State to bring the demand on the industry into closer relationship with production capacity; or else for the State to control the distribution of labour and increase the production of materials and manufactured goods. So far both methods had been pursued in the Government building programme but not overtaken, partly because of inter-departmental competition but mainly because no single authority had as yet been given the power to enforce decisions. Those who favoured the setting up of such an authority saw no reason why the building programme, at least on its specific side, should not be regarded as a whole. Did it matter after all whether temporary buildings were to be used as hutments for troops or for civil servants, to provide accommodation on airfields or to extend

---

[1] Cmd. 3920, 1931, par. 226.

[2] Notes and Appendices: Note III, 'Inter-departmental Committees for the Supervision of the Building Programme, 1937–39'.

[3] Of this total, work to a cost of £250 millions was due to be carried out within twelve months by an industry whose normal annual production was then calculated at roughly the same figure.

[4] See Chapter XVII.

ordnance filling factories? And on these specific programmes could not the placing of building contracts be so controlled in its timing, extent, geographical distribution and character as to bring the demands on the industry right up to its capacity to absorb them?

If it seemed reasonable to say yes to such questions in respect of one side of the building programme, other parts of it, notably work on air raid shelters and first-aid repairs, were less capable of central direction. Here State control, if it could be said to exist at all, rested on a narrow margin. Conditions might easily become chaotic. The call on the industry's resources for air raid works alone (though later found to have been exaggerated) was already quite alarming.[1] The total demand for materials was feared (mistakenly as it proved)[2] to have risen above production capacity; and though there were no statistics of the skilled building labour used on air raid precautions, it was obvious that substantial inroads were being made into the total labour force.[3]

The method so far evolved of the pooling of programmes for spasmodic examination in committee was incapable of solving the problems of the building programme as a whole, mainly because it left with the executive departments the responsibility for distributing specific building contracts. For these and other reasons, the Office of Works, in a vigorous and far-sighted memorandum, urged that if the varied demands on labour and materials were to be correlated, control would have to be systematic and intensive. But if there was to be no co-ordinating department how was that control to be exercised?

Suggestions for the routing of works in terms of time, locality and type of construction (as well as of demands on skilled labour and on materials) were now formulated by the Office of Works. They were put forward not because they were the best solution of the problem, but because they seemed at that time the only ones likely to be accepted by the departments. They were intended to forestall, or at least temper, grave difficulties and delays which would surely follow were the supply departments to go on launching unco-ordinated building schemes on the building market. On the other hand, any direct proposal by the Office of Works that it should itself assume control of the building industry and the Government building programme would doubtless have been strongly resisted by other departments. Meanwhile some speedy solution of the immediate difficulties had to be found.

---

[1] According to current estimates, the call for bricks was sixty-three per cent. of the total State demand, cement forty-three per cent., corrugated iron and protected metal sheeting seventy-three per cent.

[2] See Chapters VII and X. Also Chapter XVII.

[3] For such work, widespread as it was throughout the country, a skilled man would be snapped up in his own district despite the claims of work of greater strategic urgency elsewhere. Why, indeed, should he travel long distances, face discomfort, perhaps hardships, when he could do his bit, earn good money and yet sleep under his own roof?

In the protracted discussions on the possible creation of a Ministry of Works, planning and programme control were the vital issues on which, it was agreed, action was overdue. Responsibility for the execution of the programme, the Office of Works contended, was a secondary matter which, whatever form it might take, would surely engender inter-departmental difficulties and delays. Under those conditions the Office of Works was more disposed to continue as it was than be absorbed into a new Ministry.[1]

In May 1940 the Minister of Labour (Mr. Bevin) pressed for the creation of a Production Council to supersede the existing priority organisation. At the same time he urged the immediate need of a new department to absorb the Office of Works and henceforth plan and execute all building and civil engineering work for the Government. During the succeeding five months—that is, until the Lord Privy Seal (Mr. Attlee) announced in the House of Commons[2] the setting up of the Ministry of Works and Buildings[3]—the character and functions of the new department were hammered out.

The creation of a fully fledged central building department—even though it should, or perhaps because it might, be decided that this department should be the Office of Works itself—had found little favour with that department, not only for the reasons already given, but because it was proposed to make the change in war-time. In a private minute of 31st May 1940, one high official of the Office of Works wrote:

> There is nothing new under the sun. The idea of a central building department—which, N.B., should be the Office of Works—has been debated at different periods by a variety of committees. . . . But whereas the annual Government building programme in peace was of the order of £10 millions or so, it is now in the order of more than £100 millions; and centralisation of such a programme would run a risk of falling down under its own weight, even if months of cautious and unhurried preparation were available before it was attempted.

But that the existing system had glaring defects, that its lack of co-ordination in war-time was a positive danger was beyond dispute; and although the Office of Works protested that while they were all in mid-stream it would be impossible to reconstruct the several Government organisations administering individual building pro-

---

[1] A massive volume of building and other constructional work was already in the hands of the Office of Works in 1940, and, as it turned out, the new building and civil engineering work which fell to the Ministry of Works after 1940 was possibly not more than would have been undertaken by the department had it retained its former identity.

[2] H. of C. Deb., 24th October 1940, Vol. 365, Col. 1150.

[3] The first designation of the Ministry of Works was 'Ministry of Works and Buildings'. On 24th June 1942 it became 'Ministry of Works and Planning' and on 4th February 1943 'Ministry of Works'. Throughout this narrative the department is described by its last designation.

grammes, it was ready to accept a compromise through the creation of a Building and Civil Engineering Supply Board. The Board was to consist of some four or five members mainly drawn from outside, of high executive capacity and experienced in dealing with large-scale commercial operations. (Experience in the building and civil engineering industry in any of its aspects was regarded as useful, though not essential.) Such a Board could be entrusted with wide powers of decision and direction and could sit with representatives of the departments engaged in building to whatever extent circumstances demanded.

The proposed functions of the Supply Board covered a wide field akin to that already traversed by the earlier inter-departmental and joint committees and the Works and Building Priority Committee. In the view of the Office of Works the field might be widened here and there, but not extensively. The Office of Works was not in a mood to take to itself either the functions or the name of a new department. Nor did it seem logical to speak of a 'new' department which would be independent of the Office of Works. To quote one official of the department:[1]

> I am not clear why we talk of a new department. By trial and error over 200 years the Office of Works has built up a procedure and an organisation which is better calculated to stand the strain than any other. The old adage about swapping horses holds good. We could not risk the confusion attendant upon setting up a new department. By all means bring in outside people, but build up on the tried foundations of the Office of Works.

(ii)

Plans for a New Ministry

The views of the Minister of Labour remained unshaken by the arguments in favour of a Building Supply Board or by an alternative plea to strengthen the existing machinery of the Works and Building Priority Committee. The proposals would fail as half measures

> . . . because they do not provide for the effective control of the building activities of departments which remain independent. Only by placing the building and civil engineering work of the Government under a single responsible Minister can a single policy be enforced.

At that critical moment it was imperative to avoid the risk of delay on vital works through far-reaching administrative changes. The new Ministry, Mr. Bevin urged, should therefore take over the building

---

[1] 29th May 1940.

and constructional work of other departments in an ordered manner over a period of time and not all at once. Let them create immediately a Ministry with the title of 'Works and Buildings' under a Minister who should also be a member of the Production Council and who would take over at once the Office of Works, the sections of the Ministry of Supply concerned with new construction, and the section of the Ministry of Aircraft Production then under the charge of the Director of Air Ministry Factories.[1] In due course the new Ministry could take over the building and constructional work (other than repair and maintenance work) of the War Office and Air Ministry, and also possibly some parts of the Admiralty work. Meanwhile its responsibility should include much of the work of those departments as could conveniently and by agreement be transferred, for example, new building not of a highly specialised type. Any machinery set up for the control during war-time of civil building would appropriately fall to the new department.

Although some misgiving persisted within the Office of Works, and found an outlet in exchanges of views with the Treasury and other departments, plans went forward. At the end of August the Minister without Portfolio (Mr. Arthur Greenwood) was able to submit to the Prime Minister proposals first formulated by the Treasury at the end of June and now representing the greatest common measure of agreement that could be reached between the departments concerned. They were approved in principle by the Prime Minister. The plan fell short of the single Ministry controlling all Government building as contemplated by Mr. Bevin, and there was no agreement on the position of the Ministry of Aircraft Production. The view of the Ministers of Labour and Supply and the First Commissioner of Works was that plans of new factories or extensions for aircraft production[2] should be approved by the new Minister; but the Minister of Aircraft Production (Lord Beaverbrook) declined the tutelage of the new Ministry and insisted that if it were set up he should retain responsibility for buildings affecting aircraft production.

Despite the maturing of these plans, the Office of Works did not relax its somewhat rigid attitude. The First Commissioner of Works (Lord Tryon) added his caveat to that of his officials against the setting up of the new department, basing his argument mainly on the difficulties of carrying out the change under war conditions. He protested that on the hundreds of building schemes in all stages of planning and execution was being superimposed the demand for a degree of acceleration which the growing scarcity of labour and materials made it more than ever difficult to achieve. But if experience showed it to be in fact impracticable to centralise functions in war-time, they

---

[1] See Chapters XIII and XIV.
[2] M.A.P. built no factories for themselves.

could still go forward with the general control of the building programme for which the proposed Building Supply Board would, in his
opinion, be adequate.

The Office of Works, however, was making a losing fight. By mid-
July plans for the new Ministry were well advanced; and the department could only press for more time for adminstrative reorganisation
while deprecating too early a public announcement. On the assumption that the creation of a Ministry of Works was for political and
other reasons desirable, the First Commissioner now accepted the
main details of the Treasury's formulated proposals of the new Ministry's functions. Yet these functions, he urged, might well prove to be
unnecessarily restricted, since his department was already responsible
on an agency basis for more work than seemed likely to fall to the
new Ministry. Would not outside opinion wonder for what purpose a
Ministry had been set up at all? There was objection, too, to the terms
of the draft proposals which left it entirely open to the Service departments and the Ministry of Aircraft Production to decide whether or
not any work of any description should be entrusted to the new
department, although hitherto the Office of Works had always carried
a fair measure of responsibility for the building schemes of all the
Service departments.[1]

These fears were proved in the event to be well founded. The new
Ministry never acquired the whole of the territory to which it was
supposedly born the heir.

Although the main outline of the new Ministry's functions was
agreed by September, parts were left for settlement 'when', in the
words of the Minister-Designate,[2] 'the new man was on the job'. The
original plan had provided that specialised work, such as army defence works, work on airfields and naval works, should remain with
the departments already responsible for them, but that it would be
open to these departments to arrange with the new Ministry for it
to undertake non-specialised work of a civilian or 'architectural'
character. A revised plan by the Minister-Designate,[3] had meanwhile
been circulated by the Treasury to the three Service departments, the
Ministry of Supply, and other Ministries concerned, under which the
new Ministry would undertake all building 'not of a highly specialised
nature'; but it was evident from the replies of the departments that
they were not disposed to give the new Ministry discretion regarding
all works even though not highly specialised in character. The
Admiralty, for example, objected that such a grant of authority

---

[1] The responsibilities of the Office of Works, however, for Royal Air Force works had
in the past been limited to the design and construction of Cranwell Cadet College and the
sketch plans for a new staff college at Andover.
[2] Sir John (later Lord) Reith.
[3] For Lord Reith's own version of these discussions see his autobiography: Reith,
J. C. W., *Into the Wind* (1949), pp. 403 *et seq.*

would remove their own discretion as to whether or not work which was not of a highly specialised type should be given to the new Ministry or carried out by their own officers. The First Lord saw no reason for abandoning this discretion.

A rider added by Sir John Reith to the revised 'prospectus' provided that the Ministry should be ready to take up responsibility for other building, planning and construction arising from the requirements of war and the post-war period. This addendum had drawn a firmly-worded letter of objection from the Ministry of Health in which it was urged that either the last paragraph of the document should be omitted or that it should be amended so as to make it abundantly clear that the paragraph did not imply any actual decisions as to transfer of jurisdiction to the new department beyond what was stated in the earlier paragraphs.

In the final version of the 'prospectus', agreed on 22nd October, reference to reconstruction was retained in the final paragraph. The Minister was now 'charged with the responsibility of consulting the departments and organisations concerned with a view to reporting to the Cabinet the appropriate methods and machinery for dealing with the issues involved'. This concession to Sir John Reith's own conception of his responsibility for reconstruction, with its far-reaching implications, for a time obscured the Ministry's primary objectives. It was shortly afterwards to assume an undue prominence in Parliamentary debate, shifting the emphasis from the Ministry's immediate concern with vital war-time building to vague reconstruction talk in which the new Works Minister appeared for a time against a nebulous background in the role of Minister of Reconstruction-Designate. This is not to say, however, that Lord Reith (as he had now become) refrained during his fifteen months in office from fighting an endless battle to reserve to the Ministry of Works the authority and range which the Government statement envisaged.

(iii)

The New Ministry Launched

On 24th October 1940 the Lord Privy Seal (Mr. Attlee) made a formal statement in the House of Commons on the functions of the new Ministry.[1] It was, he said, to take over the whole organisation of the Office of Works and to be responsible for erecting all new civil works and buildings required by any other Government department. The Production Council would lay down the general order of priority of building work. The Minister would be a member of the Production

---

[1] H. of C. Deb., 24th October 1940, Vol. 365, Col. 1150. Notes and Appendices Appendix 6, 'Statement by Lord Privy Seal on Ministry of Works and Buildings'.

Council and responsible for the Works and Building Priority Committee. He would determine the application of the directions of the Production Council to the priority of particular buildings, subject to appeal, if necessary, to the Council.

Compromise and indefiniteness, Lord Reith complained, were still writ large throughout. In retrospect he has stated:

> The Service departments were to continue to do 'highly specialised' work; examples of this were the civil engineering works of the Admiralty, aerodrome buildings, fortifications and defence works. But none of these is highly specialised; a man or a company may specialise in this or that activity but that does not make a specialism of it; in any event the new Ministry could have engaged specialists wherever necessary. By agreement, the document continued, with the Service Ministries and aircraft production the new Ministry might erect works and buildings which were not 'highly specialised'. Ministry of Supply ordnance factory work was to be taken over. I was to be 'empowered to call' on all departments for information on present and prospective demands for labour and materials; to be responsible 'for such control or central purchase of building materials not at present controlled as may be necessary'—timber and steel being already controlled elsewhere. I was to institute research into the use of designs and specifications; to be 'empowered to call' on departments to satisfy me that they were putting the results into practice.
>
> Finally, there was this paragraph written by Attlee, agreement to which had eventually been wrung from the Ministry of Health:
>
> 'It is clear that the reconstruction of town and country after the war raises great problems and gives a great opportunity. The Minister of Works had, therefore, been charged by the Government with the responsibility for consulting the departments and organisations concerned with a view to reporting to the Cabinet the appropriate methods and machinery for dealing with the issues involved.'[1]

The functions of the new Ministry were more fully described by Lord Reith in the House of Lords on 13th November 1940.[2] It is a remarkable symptom of the confusion in the minds of members of both Houses of Parliament on the functions of the new Ministry that in the debate which preceded Lord Reith's statement, and on other occasions in the House of Commons, discussion returned again and again to post-war planning and reconstruction. On the completely unjustified assumption that a Minister of Works was *ex officio* also Minister of Reconstruction, some definite disclosure of post-war plans was demanded which, against the background of 1940 and 1941, would have been premature to the point of irony. But the question of

---

[1] Reith, J. C. W., *Into the Wind* (1949), p. 408.
[2] H. of L. Deb., Vol. 370, Col. 171 *et seq.* Sir John Reith was sworn First Commissioner of Works and Public Buildings on 4th October 1940 and Minister of Works and Buildings on 11th October 1940.

planning, as Lord Reith made clear in his reply, was relevant only in the limited sense of the last sentences of Mr. Attlee's statement in the House of Commons.

He agreed that sooner or later future post-war planning would be one of the functions of his Ministry, but meanwhile the immediate tasks that lay to hand were fourfold:

1. The continuing activity of the old Office of Works, now taken over by the new Ministry. This applied to Government buildings of all sorts; ancient monuments and parks; all civil buildings, including museums, diplomatic and consular buildings all over the world, post offices, employment exchanges, custom houses and such-like. The design, provision, care and maintenance of them all was a heavy responsibility. There was, too, agency work for Service departments not included above, and all supply services for civil departments such as furniture and general equipment.

2. The war-time additions to the responsibilities of the Office of Works. That expansion comprised office accommodation, particularly immense additions in London for bigger departments and new departments; considerable additions in the provinces; evacuation arrangements for departments, including not only the hiring but often the erection of temporary offices in the country; to some extent furniture and equipment; supply services covering furniture and similar equipment for offices, hospitals, camps and barracks and other equipment for the emergency fire services to an estimated value of £13 millions.[1]

3. New responsibilities of the Ministry, such as ordnance factories designed and erected for the Ministry of Supply, refrigeration and other stores for the Ministry of Food; hospitals for the Ministries of Health and Pensions—a total of about £50 millions. In addition there was the work that might or might not be transferred from other departments as defined in Mr. Attlee's statement. 'Highly specialised work', which was to remain with the Service departments, left room for discussion, Lord Reith explained. By and large it might be that Service departments would be inclined to interpret that expression as meaning that they should retain what in fact they were doing then and had for some time been doing.

4. General building control, that is, co-ordination of Government building and, in fact, of all building.

Lord Reith said he would discuss with the Service departments and the Ministry of Aircraft Production their programme in order to find out what services and what works and buildings they considered not to be highly specialised and could therefore be transferred to the new

---

[1] The Office of Works had already provided some 26,000 fire engines for use all over the country, 7,500 miles of hose, 10,000 office buildings and 3,000 stores. The rental payments amounted to nearly £4 millions. These figures were greatly increased as the war proceeded.

Ministry—in other words, what should be transferred and what would be. He added:

> There is what I have called general building control, that is, co-ordination of Government buildings and, in fact, all building. Mr. Attlee's statement was quite clearly intended to refer in the first place to priority, and the policy which dictates priority, and in the second place to national resources in terms of material and labour. . . . The statement indicates that the Production Council over which the Minister without Portfolio presides lays down the general order of priority for Government buildings. I am a member of that. I am responsible for the Works and Building Priority Committee on which all departments interested in any way in building are represented. As chairman of that committee I would determine to the best of my ability and with expert advice the application of the Production Council's priority decision in respect of particular buildings, and there may be an appeal.

Control, or the central purchase of building materials not at present controlled, was an important function of the new Ministry, and in defining this responsibility[1] Lord Reith explained that since it entailed an examination of all departmental building programmes and schemes, he had appointed a consulting engineer of eminence and experience, Mr. Hugh Beaver, to be Priority Officer for the Ministry and Controller of Building Materials. The only controls yet established were for cement and bricks. The Controller of Building Materials would as such be Controller of Cement and Controller of Bricks, but two special divisions of the department had been formed for these matters, each under a Director. The necessity for other control was being investigated, particularly with regard to material for roofing. The policy of the control would be to secure the maximum co-operation of the industry with the minimum interference; but it had been made clear that every power which might be necessary to secure the maximum output of which each industry was capable would be taken and used.

The creation of the new Ministry came at a time when the building programme was expanding rapidly towards its peak. The Works and Building Priority Committee continued its work under the guidance of Mr. Beaver; but it was not long before a completely new organisation within the Ministry was seen to be essential. The solution was found in the creation of the post of Director-General in May 1941. Sir Hugh Beaver (as he had now become) undertook in that capacity wider duties which were administrative at a high level but called also for extensive technical and civil engineering experience.

Almost simultaneously with the appointment of the Director-General, the office of Permanent Secretary had become vacant. As

---

[1] H. of L. Deb., 13th November 1940, Vol. 370, Col. 171 *et seq.*

the newly-appointed Permanent Secretary[1] was in Australia and had to finish his work there and await his successor, the vacancy continued for a period of six months. During this interval the Deputy Secretary[2] acted as Secretary, but it was not possible at first to complete the reorganisation of the office, nor to define precisely the respective spheres of the Director-General or the Permanent Secretary. Later the Permanent Secretary and the Director-General strove together to ensure the smooth running of a somewhat improvised organisation. While on paper this did not conform in various respects with normal civil service practice, it did efficiently conduct the very large and complicated Government programme. Under the Director-General the 'Sixth Floor Organisation', as it came to be called, was a notable effort to fuse 'business method' and civil service practice in a way which, while not always pleasing to either of the elements that contributed to the amalgam, nevertheless achieved a great measure of success.[3]

Following a formula laid down by Lord Reith, the Permanent Secretary and the Director-General were to be jointly responsible for the administration of the department, leaving the Permanent Secretary supreme in regard to finance. In practice the Permanent Secretary (the accounting officer and recognised official head of the Ministry) and the Director-General maintained the closest possible contact and each was kept fully aware of the activities of the other. In the main the Director-General was responsible for the direction (in the fullest sense) of the Government building programme, and in addition there was a weekly 'Secretary's meeting', attended by the Secretary, the Director-General and the Deputy Secretary, at which current questions were discussed, decisions were reached, and the advice to be tendered to the Minister was determined.

The organisation developed was the creation of a series of directorates and divisions, each of which was responsible directly to the Director-General. The circumstances which provided its background must next be examined.

---

[1] Sir Geoffrey Whiskard. He was later succeeded by Sir Percival Robinson.
[2] Mr. (later Sir William) Leitch.
[3] See Chapters IV and XVIII.

G

CHAPTER IV

PROBLEMS OF CONTROL

(i)

First Steps towards a Co-ordinated Control Policy

ROM the outset the essence of the policy laid down by the Ministry of Works was to avoid statutory control if the various industries would agree to some form of 'voluntary' control—that is, a control residing in the industries but embodying the directions of the Ministry. This agreement was forthcoming. By 1942 the freedom of all industry had come to be controlled in many directions by Defence Regulations, but these did not include, for the building industry, more than three or four Statutory Rules and Orders.[1] It may be fairly claimed, in fact, that the control established in 1941 used a minimum of regulations at what were admittedly key points. Within the framework of general control over materials such as iron, steel and timber, the controls applying specially to building fell into five main groups:

1. Control over the building programmes of Government departments.
2. Administration of the building and civil engineering industries.
3. Co-ordination of the repair of air raid damage.
4. Control of building materials.
5. Control of plant.

Some account of how the main controls were applied under these headings is given in a later portion of this narrative.[2] In the present chapter the development of Government policy over the building programme of departments as a whole is first examined.

On 17th October 1940 the Works and Building Priority Committee met for the last time at the Ministry of Labour and under the chairmanship of Mr. Ralph Assheton. Its next meeting on 2nd December (the thirty-third since its creation in 1939) was at the Ministry of Works and was presided over by the committee's new chairman, Mr. George Hicks, Parliamentary Secretary to the Ministry. The Priority Officer (Mr. Beaver) was present for the first time, together with the newly-appointed Directors of Cement and Bricks; and it was now announced that, with the committee's concurrence, the Priority

---

[1] These are described in Part III, 'Methods of Control'.
[2] *Ibid.*

Officer would act as deputy chairman of the Priority Committee and chairman of the Contracts Sub-Committee.[1]

It was not the Minister's immediate intention to impose statutory control of building materials not then controlled. He wanted the co-operation of manufacturers and merchants and the least possible disturbance of existing industrial organisation. From the most recent investigation and analysis of the building programme it was now evident that the volume of work included in the programme in hand was greater than the labour resources of the industry could carry out with full efficiency. On the whole, materials were sufficient for the labour that would be available; the priorities problem was becoming more and more a problem of labour. How could the new Ministry correlate the building programmes of departments with the available supplies of labour?

The first essential was that departments should supply advance information of projects at an earlier stage. As a rule the first notification received from departments was the application made to the Contracts Sub-Committee for permission to place a contract. Since, in 1940, it was expected that the labour force available for building work in the following year would be smaller and that severe cuts might have to be made in the programmes of departments, each department was exhorted to use its labour to the best advantage, to determine its own order of priority of the various projects in its own programme, and to keep the Controller advised of such internal priority.

The last general indication of policy by the Production Council had been in June 1940. At that critical hour it had been sought to press on with all speed on works that could be made effective against the enemy by the end of September 1940. On priority as between different classes of Government work decisions had been taken at the highest level. The War Cabinet had already directed that aircraft, the training of pilots and crews, and anti-aircraft equipment (such as Bofors guns) should be accorded priority, a decision that had been embodied in the Priority of Production Direction dated 31st May 1940. That direction had also given effect to the War Cabinet's decision that all jobs which would contribute to the war effort in the critical months of the summer of 1940 should receive special acceleration. Moreover, the War Cabinet had allowed overriding priority to airfields and special defence works.[2]

In interpreting the application to building of the direction to give priority to air training and anti-aircraft equipment, and to jobs which

---

[1] The original intention was that the Priority Officer should be the new chairman, but on the advice of Mr. Assheton it was decided that the chairman should be a Minister. At that stage the decision was probably wise, but in fact, in the end, it was found that the best chairman of a committee of officials was an official.

[2] See Hancock, W. K., and Gowing, M. M., *British War Economy*, pp. 282, 283.

would make an early contribution to the war effort, the Works and Building Priority Committee had compiled a list (W.B.A.) of Government works that it was proposed should be accelerated and, after defence works, given first priority, and a list (W.B.Z.) of jobs from which labour and materials could, if necessary, be drawn. There was also an intermediate ('neutral' or N) category, but not listed, of works of less urgency than those on the W.B.A. list of immediacy.

The priority list had included works and factories which were to come into use by the end of September, and also some which could not become effective until later in 1940. It had taken in works and factories regarded by the departments as vitally urgent, but it was not limited to the products or services which had been given first priority by War Cabinet decisions. The list had therefore included a very substantial part of the Government programme, particularly of the programmes of the Air Ministry and Ministry of Supply. Since it represented as much as £30 millions of work it had appeared likely to diminish its effectiveness as a priority list, particularly as the value of works on the W.B.Z. list from which labour and materials could have been drawn amounted to only £17 millions, and some of these had not, in fact, started.

It had been at that time the intention of the Works and Building Priority Committee that in the first instance labour and materials should be diverted, first from all non-essential civil work, next from Government jobs on the W.B.Z. list, and only as a last resort from jobs on the neutral list, but there was clearly a risk, unless the W.B.Z. list could be increased, that works on the neutral list would suffer by deprivation of materials and labour.[1] The committee had accordingly asked the directions of the Production Council as to whether they were right in including in list W.B.A. for acceleration works of the following types:

(*a*) establishments for the training of air pilots and crews which would not come into use until after the end of September;

(*b*) factories or special plant required for products other than those already given priority by the War Cabinet or the Production Council which would not come into operation until after the end of September;

(*c*) wheat silos and stores for essential foodstuffs being erected for the Ministry of Food and due for completion by 31st December 1940.

Apart from these specific issues the Works and Building Priority Committee had also raised a question of general principle in regard

---

[1] Probably the most important of these 'neutral' works were the refinery at Heysham for the production of 100 octane fuel which the Director of Air Ministry Factories classed as a job of the highest urgency but which was not due for completion till April 1941, and underground storage for oil fuel and ammunition then being got ready by the Admiralty and maturing after the end of September.

to any priority directions. They had pointed out that the terms of the Priority of Production Direction, dated 31st May 1940, had been drawn up by a sub-committee of Principal Priority Officers representing the Admiralty, Ministry of Supply and Ministry of Aircraft Production. The terms of the first paragraph appeared to be directed specifically to acceleration of actual production of the fighting equipment scheduled, but the terms of the second paragraph were much less specific and were being read by manufacturers, or at least by some of them, as giving priority to the orders of all fighting services at the expense of any other departmental orders. In consequence, engineering equipment for certain building works regarded as vital to the war effort had sometimes been delayed. The Works and Building Priority Committee had therefore suggested that a supplementary direction should be issued instructing contractors that orders included in list W.B.A. by the Works and Building Priority Committee should rank equally with any orders from fighting services referred to in the second paragraph of the Priority of Production Directions.

It was also desirable, in the committee's view, to ensure that priority directions were determined on a uniform basis, and with due regard for all aspects of the war effort, and it was suggested that on any sub-committee of Principal Priority Officers appointed to enquire into the types of requirement to which priority should be given, the Works and Building Priority Committee should be represented.

(ii)

The System of Priorities

The Production Council on 14th June 1940 agreed that the Works and Building Priority Committee should be asked to scrutinise building proposals on behalf of the Production Council. On the basis of the committee's decisions the Central Priority Department would certify the services in question as essential and issue priority certificates. The committee would naturally continue to give the highest possible priority to buildings whose completion directly helped the maximum production of Service requirements 'capable of being used against the enemy within the next three months'. At the same time it was essential to make sure that works and buildings urgently needed by the Services should be completed, even though they would not be in use within the next three months; and that the vital importance for the defence of the country of certain works of a civil character, such as emergency food stores or oil storage, should not be overlooked.

The Production Council at this meeting approved the issue of revised Priority Directions and adopted as a guide for the immediate future the line of policy summarised in the preceding subsection. Machinery for putting these instructions into effect was now set up by the Works and Building Priority Committee.

1. When a department wished to let a contract, as part of a new scheme costing £25,000 or more or involving the construction of more than 500 houses, it was required to submit an application to the Works and Building Priority Committee, stating whether it was desired that the contract should be a W.B.A. or a neutral job. A similar procedure applied when it was desired to change the category applying to an existing job.

2. Copies of W.B.A. lists had to be sent on to the Central Priority Department, which then issued to the Works and Building Priority Committee a certificate for the works and building projects so listed. The schedule to the certificates was not to state in detail the projects set out in W.B.A. lists, but the document was to be in the following form:

'The Central Priority Department hereby certify that the work referred to in the schedule to this certificate is vital work for the purpose of para. 2 (ii) of the Directions given by the Minister of Supply dated 14th June 1940 and headed "Priority of Production".'

The schedule read:

'Works and Building projects specified in W.B.A. List No. . . ., dated . . . submitted by the Works and Building Priority Committee, including the machinery and the equipment required for the effective operation of such projects.'

3. Departments were to be informed by the Works and Building Priority Committee when each certificate was received from the Central Priority Department and to what contracts it applied. Copies of the W.B.A. lists certified by the Central Priority Department were to be sent to the Iron and Steel Control, to the Timber Control, and to the Divisional Controller of the Ministry of Labour.

4. It was laid down definitely by the Production Council that departments were to be informed that the only body to whom the Production Council had delegated the allotment of priorities as between various building projects was the Works and Building Priority Committee.

To obtain steel supplies for jobs covered by the omnibus certificate of the Central Priority Department, the symbol 'Q' was to be used.[1] In respect of other materials, a statement that the Central Priority Department had certified the contract as vital work under the Priority of Production Directions was sufficient.

An important innovation was that on instructions from the War

---

[1] This was the identification symbol for steel priorities.

Cabinet 'super-priority' ranking ahead of W.B.A. could be awarded temporarily to defence works being carried out by the War Office and Air Ministry to secure the country against invasion.

5. Departments were obliged to inform their contractors whenever a job they were carrying out had been put on the W.B.A. list. It was then for the department concerned to discuss with the contractor all aspects of the work (availability of materials, transport, lodging accommodation, and so on) in order to arrive at the figure of additional labour needs. That statement of firm demand for labour was to be passed to the manager of the employment exchange nearest to the job for suitable action.[1] If after a reasonable time there were still outstanding demands for labour, the regional representative of the contracting department was to get into touch with the appropriate divisional officer of the Ministry of Labour.

6. With regard to steel and timber, the contractor was to be notified by the department concerned that the job he was doing had been placed on list W.B.A. and that the symbol 'Q' was to be used in addition to the contract number when ordering steel or making inquiries from the Iron and Steel Control. The Control was to be informed as soon as jobs were placed on the W.B.A. list. If steel deliveries were slow, the matter was to be taken up through the local officer of the Control and finally through the liaison officers representing each department attached to the Control in London.

Normally it was not necessary to apply priority procedure to timber, provided that the timber could be found from allocations made to departments and the procedure laid down by the Timber Control was followed.

(iii)

From Priorities to Allocation

While the priority system was still in force, the enemy's blitz tactics between September 1940 and May 1941 created a new problem with many unpredictable implications. More and more often the War Cabinet were driven to the expedient of prescribing 'super-priority' for air raid damage repairs, work on air raid shelters, the dispersal of factories, special work on airfields and similar jobs, and it was soon apparent that the existing priority system was breaking down.

The breakdown was inevitable, partly because it had never been intended to be a long-term policy, and partly because it had never been really based on a true computation of available labour and

---

[1] As laid down in M.L. Circular 28/257.

materials. The programme of work in hand was too large for the labour and material resources of the country and correspondingly inefficient and dilatory in its execution.

The time had come for a stocktaking. For the next critical few months a new policy would have to be adopted and would have to take account not only of the fact that the building programme then in hand appeared to be at the rate of about £700 millions a year, as compared with previous estimates of £350 millions, but that the existing capacity of the industry, unless greatly improved efficiency could be devised, did not exceed £350 millions a year.[1] Moreover, the labour force in 1941 would be seriously affected by withdrawals for the Services and munitions, and air raid damage repairs to war factories and houses were then absorbing something like fifty per cent. of the entire production of roofing materials in the country and would make increasing drafts on the labour force.[2]

On the assumption that it was more important to keep existing war factories at work than to complete new factories, the dominating problem during those four winter months would be to keep factories roofed and the labour housed and to prevent or minimise wastage in the nation's war effort. It was also realised that dispersal of factories involved a cumulatively large total not allowed for in any programme and that the air raid shelter programme required at least a quarter of the resources of bricks and bricklayers in the country.

In a memorandum submitted by Mr. Beaver to Lord Reith, and circulated by him to the Production Council, these considerations were forcefully presented. It was clear that not only had the priority machine become completely top-heavy, with arrears piling up for certain building materials as well as labour, but that the various special and overriding instructions issued, with or without real authority, by the different departments had reduced suppliers to despair—and now new demands which were a result of air attacks on industry struck right across all previous priorities. It was for the Production Council to lay down a priority policy on broad but definite lines which the Minister could apply in practice; and a tentative order of priority for building and construction was suggested as a basis for discussion.[3]

Mr. Beaver followed up his initial thrust by bringing together in informal meeting the chief technical officers of the main contracting departments. The true position of the building programme had been obscured or distorted by the lack of adequate statistics, nor was it yet certain how large a building force was available. Whereas there were some 1,389,000 persons in the building and constructional engineer-

---

[1] It was doubtful if it had exceeded that rate even during the peak of the building season in exceptionally good building weather during the past summer.

[2] See Chapter X.

[3] Notes and Appendices: Appendix 7, 'Tentative Order of Priority for Building and Construction'.

ing industries at the outbreak of war, there had been a reduction by July of 353,000, and a further reduction to 806,000 was now asked for by the Manpower Committee. As the last figure included some 50,000 persons who were more or less unemployable, the total effective labour force was assumed to be approximately 750,000; that meant a maximum building effort of about £350 millions. On the basis of these figures, what procedure would reduce the monthly rate of building to a level at which all jobs could be so pushed forward as to make the fullest use of the country's resources?

The answer, the technical officers were agreed, was a planned direction of the location of jobs, of their timing, and of the distribution of labour, materials and transport. Control, it was suggested by the representatives of the Admiralty and of the Ministry of Supply, should be along lines of allocation of capacity rather than along lines of priority.

This proposal was revolutionary and fundamental, and it was adopted. The difficulties in the way of dividing the resources of the building industry were fully realised, but here at least was a more promising direction for experiment than any system of establishing a series of priorities. In its simplest form the plan was to make the most careful assessment, in terms of monthly expenditure, throughout the year, of the capacity of the building industry and the building programmes of departments. Including allowance for the amount of work to be carried out on air raid precautions and air raid damage repair work, the total was to be divided among departments in such a way as would best fulfil the instructions of the Production Council as to strategic priorities of functions. At first the system of allocation was worked out on a money basis, but later, as will be seen, it was fixed on a labour basis.

Various modifications were made in the existing procedure. The W.B.A. list was given up, and all jobs which were permitted to start were regarded as being of equal importance, with the exception of a very small proportion—say, five per cent.—of special jobs carried out on the express instruction of the War Cabinet. These were to be such jobs as were capable of completion within two or three months and were specially favoured in respect of labour and materials.

As soon as a department had decided on any new project in principle—and before any plans or estimates were ready—application was to be made to the Works and Building Priority Committee for general permission to proceed. That enabled the necessary contracts for such material as steel or special plant (for example, cold storage plant or boilers) to be placed in good time. When contracts documents and drawings—or if that were not possible, at least preliminary sketches—were ready, the department could report that constructional work was ready to begin. A date might be fixed on which work could start or, if the quota were already full, the job would be placed on the waiting list until room for it could be found.

In a statement in the House of Commons on 19th March 1941 the Parliamentary Secretary of the Ministry of Works (Mr. George Hicks) gave a clear explanation of the new system in these terms:

> We have, therefore, instituted a new system which is just coming into operation, whereby we first estimate the total quantity of building of which the resources of the country are capable in each given period. We measure this by value and, in accordance with the instruction of the Production Executive, we allocate it between departments so that each department knows what share of the building capacity of the country it will have at its disposal for a given period—three, four, or six months, whatever the period may be. It is the job of the departments to arrange within their own allocation which jobs are to be speeded up, which to be stopped, and so on. We are limiting the programme so that the amount of construction work to be undertaken will be as closely as possible related to the labour and materials available, and, as far as possible, only those works which will be effective before or by the end of the summer are being proceeded with. Works requiring a longer period for their completion, or new works, are only being permitted if they are of great strategic importance. Let me say here that the more efficiently departments use their labour, the more of their programme can be completed.[1]

Certain implications in Mr. Hicks's statement on the development of the allocation system must be underlined.[2] Thus, there can be no doubt that at March 1941 the idea of allocating work by value, rather than by a labour allocation or labour ceiling, was still firmly entertained. One principle of the labour allocation had, however, already been adopted: to give each department a 'ceiling' (or allocation) of work and to leave the division of this capacity between projects to the discretion of the department. The principle was basic to an orderly form of devolution.

> It put an end to long and feverish meetings of officials when list upon list of projects had to be gone through one by one, with a view to determining their A, N, or Z priority. From time to time in the war, later in 1941 and thereafter, similar attempts to 'vet' detailed lists of projects at inter-departmental meetings of officials were revived, but either had to be abandoned, or resulted in long, fruitless, and frequently adjourned discussions.[3]

---

[1] H. of C. Deb., 19th March 1941, Vol. 370, Col. 177.

[2] Bowen, I., 'The Control of Building', in *Lessons of the British War Economy* (Cambridge University Press, 1951). In the following pages of this section Professor Bowen's direct evidence on the working of the allocation system during his war-time service as Chief Statistical Officer at the Ministry of Works is by permission fully drawn upon and often liberally quoted.

[3] *Ibid.*

Another point in Mr. Hicks's statement which calls for comment is the reference to the Production Executive.

It must not be thought that the ancient and proud Departments of State like the Admiralty and War Office, nor the new and 'go-getting' ones, like the Ministry of Supply and of Aircraft Production, welcomed any tutelage on building plans from the newest department of all (Works). Quite clearly no one department, and certainly not the most recently formed, could be expected to lay down the law to all other departments of Whitehall, especially as some of the prohibitions or restrictions on construction cut right across the policy and plans of the staff and Ministers of nearly all the other Ministries. The prestige of the Production Executive, and at a later period of the war, of the Lord President's Committee, were indispensable to the successful working of any programme. Every decision taken, after inter-departmental consultation, in the Ministry of Works, had to take the form of advice to this higher authority. Because of this 'all-powerful sanction', this 'court of appeal of unquestioned authority and decisive judgement',[1] which was fully accepted both by Ministers and (perhaps more important) by their officials, the new system had a special chance of success.

The 'value allocation' ideas of March 1941 were soon superseded by a thoroughgoing labour allocation system. Statistically, money allocations were unworkable. Money expenditure from month to month—a quarterly check-up being regarded as too crude a basis of control—could not be reckoned accurately, while labour employment might be. Moreover, some five months of planning had convinced the new team of administrators that since labour was the commodity in short supply, a direct allocation of that article was logically, as well as practically, the best procedure.

Faced with the bleak prospect of a complete absence of statistics for long periods at a time, and, furthermore, with the fact that the Ministry of Labour statistics gave no indication of the nature of employment, or whereabouts, of the building labour force, the Ministry of Works set up its own statistical organisation. In so far as this statistical system was used to operate the labour allocation scheme it must be briefly outlined.

The labour allocation system was worked by a threefold statistical

---

[1] These phrases were applied to the Lord President's Committee in a letter to *The Times* of 8th April by Sir Hugh Beaver which emphasised the point made here. It should be observed, however, that while the prestige of the Lord President's Committee possibly justified the phrases used, it is doubtful whether that of the Production Executive stood at a comparable level outside the building sphere. Thus, on 21st October 1941, in a private memorandum Sir Hugh Beaver refers to 'general agreement apparently that the Production Executive was not functioning as an executive, that it was only a consultative body. If the Ministers agreed, well and good—if they did not, nothing happened . . . the Lord President is carrying out an investigation into manpower and the Manpower Committee is reporting to him and not to the Production Executive'.

control which is described by Professor Bowen as extremely simple in principle, as were the statistical returns inaugurated for the purpose.

First, in order to assess the new work coming forward, all projects had to be notified to the Ministry of Works on a form known as B.P.2. This asked for details of the project, its value and material requirements, and the labour that it would need during its lifetime. In practice the value figure given was only of use as the basis of a rough check on the labour estimate; and because by totalling the values some useful controls could be worked out. The materials' requirements were practically valueless, since they were put in as estimates only and were not always based on quantities. Throughout the whole war the supply of materials went through the normal trade channels, and there were rarely any shortages since the market steadily declined.[1] The value of the B.P.2 was emphatically as a basis for estimating future labour demand rather than that for materials.

The second statistical control was the monthly check-up on the departments' labour force. Here, again, the responsibility was put on the departments to make, on Form W.B.1, a monthly return of labour for each job of over £5,000 in value, and a summary return for all jobs of less than £5,000 in value. So began, in April–May 1941, a record of the monthly labour employment of the building labour force of Great Britain. The departments fulfilled their responsibilities in regard to these labour returns with varying degrees of completeness. Some departments preferred to use their own forms. Others were persistently late with their returns. The system began haltingly, but gradually improved. By 1942 it was possible to circulate a figure of labour employment by departments, at the end of any month, by the 21st or 22nd of the following month. This did not mean, however, that all the detailed returns were in by that date, and it was some weeks before an analysis by types of work or by place of employment could be issued.

The third statistical control was the result of Defence Regulation 56 AB, whereby all building and civil engineering undertakings were compelled to register with the Ministry of Works.[2] Under this regulation the Minister of Works was empowered to make Orders requiring

(*a*) the keeping of such records relating to the carrying on of the said activities[3] as might be specified by or under the Order;

(*b*) the making of such returns, at such times, in such manner and containing such particulars, whether as to number, qualifica-

---

[1] Cement was an exception. The Cement Control based its policy on a statistical forecast of demand obtained through the programming and statistical sections. Even here, however, the B.P.2's as such were ignored.

[2] See Chapter VI.

[3] i.e. building and civil engineering activities as defined earlier in the Order.

tions or otherwise, regarding persons employed in any of the said activities as might be specified;

(c) the production of such books or other documents, and the furnishing of such information, relating to the carrying on of the said activities as might be so specified.

Development of statistics under these powers put into the hands of the Minister of Works the tools for regulating the war-time building programme, but the use of the statistics was not left to economists or statisticians. Full responsibility for the building programme lay with the Director-General, who was charged with substantially the whole administrative, as well as executive, responsibility for the Ministry's affairs, except for the reservations as to finance already noted.[1] The Director-General appointed a Director of Programmes, and this officer operated the scheme of control, the sanction for which, as has already been explained, was received from an inter-departmental body with Cabinet backing, such as the Production Executive.

The Director of Programmes drew up a balance sheet of labour for each month. On the one side was the total labour estimated to be available for two to three months ahead; from it were deducted such items as the probable numbers to be used on civil building for maintenance purposes, the number of unemployed, men in transit between jobs, and clerical workers. The net figure represented the total number of operatives likely to be available for the programme. This was then subdivided between the departments. So far the planning represented paper operations only, even though the allocations were agreed one by one between the Director of Programmes (or the Director-General himself) and the departments concerned, or were referred for a decision to the Production Executive. It may well be asked, first, how these paper operations were transmuted into some kind of reality and, secondly, on what principles the allocation as between the departments came to be fixed, or were fixed at the start.

Translation of allocation into reality was by way of the Ministry of Labour machine. A building labour division had been set up in the Ministry of Labour in 1937, and this division had to work in daily contact with the programming division of the Ministry of Works. The Ministry of Labour represented operational tactics, while the Ministry of Works represented headquarters strategical planning. If, after a few months, by which time the statistical checks were in working order, the Ministry of Works discovered that any department was employing a considerably larger amount of labour than it had been allocated, instructions were given through the Ministry of Labour to the local employment exchanges that requests for labour from contractors working for that department should not take precedence over

---

[1] See Chapter XVIII.

the requests of any other department. This began by being, and always remained, the most effective of the administrative measures that could be found to keep each department within its allocation limits.

The original basis of the actual allocations allotted to departments was fixed as roughly equal to the actual labour which each department was employing at the time when the allocation system began.

This was, in fact, the only practicable course. Grave as was the future outlook for an extensive building programme, there would have been little sense in, and enormous political and administrative opposition aroused by, cutting down the level of employment already enjoyed by the departments. The best that could be hoped was that the wilder fancies of the building planners would be pruned as time went on, so that projects became completed more rapidly, and so that dates of completion could be given to the Cabinet with some fair chance of their being realised. As things were, when the allocation system began, none of the major projects started in 1939 or 1940, and still in course of construction, seemed certain of finishing before the end of 1941. Nor was immediate success attained on this particular point. It was at least another two years before constant pressure, and querying from the highest level, induced departments to put in realistic forecasts of the dates when projects would be completed.[1]

(iv)

Corollaries to the Allocation System

Much close and laborious investigation was needed to estimate the capacity available and make a true assessment of the departments' programmes in terms of labour; so that although it had been intended to put the allocation system into operation by 1st March, it did not in fact get to work until 1st May. Meanwhile Lord Reith had repeatedly pressed the recently-appointed Production Executive, which had taken over the functions of the Production Council, for further powers, since it was clear that a system of allocation could not be made to work without thorough-going control and direction of the building and civil engineering industries.

In the almost complete absence of precise statistical information, and while the Ministry of Works had still to proceed by estimate and guess and to 'chance its arm',[2] a Note prepared jointly by Mr. Bevin and Lord Reith for the guidance of the Production Executive helped to clarify the position at Cabinet level. The total building labour

---

[1] Bowen, I., 'The Control of Building', in *Lessons of the British War Economy* (Cambridge University Press, 1951).

[2] Private note by Sir Hugh Beaver.

force in the country, as has been noted, was then thought to be of the order of 750,000 men. This estimate, which was frequently quoted in Ministers' speeches as late as the autumn of 1941, was based, as Professor Bowen has pointed out, on knowledge of one figure only—that 1,023,000 men had been insured at July 1940; this figure represented a decline of 359,000 on the figure for July 1939. No one knew with certainty how fast the call-up or the drift to other industries had affected the industry since July 1940.[1]

The joint Note showed in some detail how the figure of 750,000 to 800,000 for the estimated existing labour force had been obtained.[2]

I. Returns as at February 1941 (in reply to questionnaire sent out by M.O.W.):

Contractors	465,648
Local authorities—direct labour	52,033
Public utilities—direct labour	16,070
	533,751

II.
Unemployed—since absorbed	40,000
Unemployed—as at May 1941	18,603
	592,354

III.
Outstanding returns from a number of contractors and builders—estimated May 1941	25,000
Outstanding returns from local authorities—direct labour—May 1941	30,000

IV.
Small builders, not yet tapped and to be brought in by registration (estimated)	70,000
Private companies (collieries, steel companies, estate companies, hotels, etc.)	50,000

V.
Government departments—direct labour	15,000

VI.
Northern Ireland	20,000

Total	802,354
Less: Call-up (about 10,000 per month), say	28,500
	Approx. 775,000

---

[1] 'It is worth observing that a technical point of great importance affected the procedure of the administration. It normally took several months to complete the count of insured workers, classified by industry groups, at the Ministry of Labour. No figures for July 1941 were to be expected until October. Thus up to October 1941 all that could be known was the number insured at July of the *previous* year. Hence administrators were forced to make their own guess at wastage from the industry, and 750,000 was the net remainder at which they arrived. It is easy to be wise after the event, and to point out that the actual numbers of men insured at July 1941 were 919,000' (Bowen, I., 'The Control of Building').

[2] Civil engineering and building in the approximate proportions of 40 : 60 respectively.

Allocations had been on the basis of a total labour force of 750,000 men. The first allocation made to the principal departments for new construction work was 439,289 men; the balance of 320,711 men was allocated to the needs of other departments and for the general maintenance work of the country. Returns had not at that time been received from all departments. Some of them claimed shortages, but from the returns to hand, and from other information, some 400,000 men appeared to be actually at work for the principal departments, which were thus already in possession of nearly all their labour allocation. The reason why some departments were still short of labour on various contracts was that 50,000 or more men were at work on air raid damage repair over and above the figure of 100,000 which had originally been allowed.[1]

Mr. Bevin and Lord Reith were agreed that, in order to succeed, the allocation system must be based on a scheme for the stricter direction of the building industry, of which the core would be the application of the Essential Work Orders, the creation of a mobile labour force, the registration of all builders and the restriction of unessential work. The Ministry of Works was already moving in that direction. It was rigorously applying the restriction on civil building; where necessary it was using the existing powers of direction to curtail unessential work and decoration, to stop the reconstruction of cinemas and banks and kindred classes of building, and so divert contractors and their labour to essential work. Men were prevented from leaving the building industry by means of Ministry of Labour instruction to the employment exchanges not to place building trade workers outside the industry. Small contractors too were being so grouped as to increase the number of men needed for essential work, especially in urban areas; and the Ministry investigated special shortages whenever it was notified of them by departments in order to direct men from less urgent work.

In the further action planned by the two Ministers, the first step was to set up what were described as clearing-house arrangements under the Ministry of Works and the Ministry of Labour. Men who could not be fully employed on any contract were to be released immediately and diverted under these clearing arrangements to other urgent work, not necessarily for the same department. A system of joint inspection by the Ministries was to be introduced for securing the most effective use of available labour; and it was also intended to inquire into the way in which labour was being used by local authorities, statutory bodies and private companies in order to see what men could be withdrawn without impairing the maintenance of the mini-

---

[1] This particularly affected Admiralty (3,000), War Office (3,000), Ministry of Supply (20,000) and Ministry of Aircraft Production (4,000) who had each been given a portion of the A.R.D. reserve to the extent of the figures in brackets shown after each.

mum of essential service. Finally, there was the question of applying to the building industry the principle of payment by results, possibly through an Essential Work Order specially adapted to the industry.[1]

The Production Executive had before them, on 27th May, in addition to the joint Note by Mr. Bevin and Lord Reith, memoranda by the Secretaries of State for Air (Sir Archibald Sinclair) and for War (Mr. Margesson). Both these Ministers urged that more stringent powers to control and direct building and civil engineering labour should be taken immediately and used in such a way that the allocations made for essential work were at once realised. The Air Ministry's allocation of labour for the period April to September 1941 had been agreed at a figure of 87,000—an allocation based on an examination of the scope and urgency of its programme—but its estimated labour force was not more than 76,000, and there was much delay on a number of sites through shortages of labour. In particular, work on forty bomber stations and twenty-six fighter stations was being retarded, and the deficiency of labour could not be made up without adequate powers of control and direction of building workers. Essential work was being held up, Sir Archibald Sinclair protested, because labour was still neither properly controlled nor directed. Squadrons were already congested for lack of airfields; congestion entailed risks from attack and loss of efficiency in operation. To let the matter drift was to affect directly the power of the Royal Air Force to hit Germany and to defend the country.[2]

In backing up the Air Ministry's demand for more men Mr. Margesson claimed that in some respects the War Office was even harder hit by the failure to control and direct building labour.

Actually the Minister of Labour already had full powers to direct labour where needed and those powers were being frequently exercised in respect of building labour. Under existing conditions, however, they had to be exercised with discretion in order to avoid directing men to work under unsatisfactory conditions and with no certainty of continued employment.

The Production Executive, in approving of the proposals in the joint Note, invited the further co-operation of the Ministers concerned. They were agreed that in principle payment by results was acceptable to the most important section of the workers; but should it be rejected, the Minister of Labour, with the approval of his colleagues, could 'schedule' the most urgent building works, after consultation with departments, and then introduce on those works a guaranteed day and week and payment by results.

By mid-June 1941 the first Essential Work (Building and Civil

---

[1] See Chapter VI.

[2] The Air Ministry's 'lost 11,000' became for a time the cause of much bitterness between the Secretary of State for Air and the Minister of Labour; and largely influenced the latter in his revolt in 1942 against the allocation system. See Chapter V.

Engineering) Order had been made and undertakings or sites could be scheduled under this Order.[1] The application of payment by results was shortly to follow.[2] The next step was to press for the registration of builders and contractors, and for power to obtain returns from all building employers, including local authorities, public utility undertakings, companies, corporations, and so forth. In that way it would become possible to get full information of the size of the labour force and how it was employed, in order to concentrate builders, particularly smaller firms who belonged to no federation, on essential work. Action was already being taken in certain areas to co-ordinate builders and contractors; but registration was necessary to enable this work to be done adequately. Lord Reith also desired to set up at once a war-time Central Building Council as the first step to general co-ordination of the industry.[3] The Production Executive supported Lord Reith's proposals for registration and the furnishing of returns as well as the setting up of the Council. These decisions were endorsed by the Lord President's Committee on 20th June; and by 15th July 1941 the draft Defence Regulation for registration[4] was in order.

On that date the Production Executive returned to the consideration of Lord Reith's proposals for the establishment of a clearing-house system for labour and for joint inspection. These proposals, after some revision, were finally approved and later confirmed by the Lord President's Committee as follows:

1. Some restriction was clearly necessary on starting new works in areas already overburdened or likely to be so. Jointly with the Minister of Labour, the Minister of Works was given the right, under the Production Executive, to declare certain areas temporarily prohibited for new works. Thus, to take one notable example, in the Wiltshire triangle lying between Swindon, Salisbury, Bristol and Gloucester, where the labour shortage was acute and billets and transport were difficult, to bring in new labour meant the provision of hostels. Thousands of workers were required by existing works and, in the interests of all, no new works, or material extensions, were to be started there in the next three months. Such a prohibition did not apply, however, if the Minister for the department responsible for a proposed new building had personally satisfied himself that its erection in the area in question was urgently necessary on strategic grounds.[5]

---

[1] S.R. & O. 1941, No. 822. This was amended by S.R. & O. 1941, No. 2067 and superseded by S.R. & O. 1942, No. 2044. See Chapter VI.

[2] See Chapter VI.

[3] See Chapter XVIII.

[4] S.R. & O. 1941, No. 1038, 18th July 1941.

[5] Cp. a decision of the Production Executive *re* steel for building purposes. 'Before the work on the building of any new factories or stores is begun the Controller-General of Factory and Storage Premises (in the Board of Trade) shall be consulted and the work shall not be begun unless a certificate has been given by the Controller-General, or *the Minister for the department responsible for the building has personally satisfied himself that no suitable existing building can be made available.*'

2. A right of veto could be exercised by the Minister of Works. The Minister of Works, in his capacity of chairman of the Works and Building Committee (as it now came to be known) was given the right, subject to appeal to the Production Executive, not merely to 'question', but to veto the starting of any work if, in the locality chosen, there was an acute labour shortage and no immediate means of meeting it.[1]

3. Advance information was to be given by departments to the Ministry of Works. In order to give effect to the proposals in the preceding paragraphs, departments were to inform the Ministry of Works in advance of all new works and extensions of existing works.

4. No long-term works were to be begun. No work taking more than eight months to complete was to be begun unless the Minister for the department responsible for the work personally certified it as of urgent strategic importance.

5. On the combing of remaining sources of labour, the Minister of Works had suggested that, after 1st September, building operatives under the age of 35 employed by private companies, local authorities or public utilities should not be classed as protected, but be subject to military service—unless enlisting in the recently-formed mobile body of builders.[2] This proposal had been considered by the Production Executive as too drastic, since it might have led to a serious loss of labour to the building industry, and it was not approved.

The Production Executive had already approved the powers taken by the Minister of Works to compel employers of building labour to make returns of such labour. After consultation with the departments concerned, he was now to submit to the Executive his proposals for the reduction of building labour held by them. If consultation did not lead to agreement. the decision was to be with the Production Executive.[3]

In July 1941 the Production Executive approved in principle further measures. These included the registration of builders' merchants and the registration of plant hirers.[4]

---

[1] The chairman of the Works and Building Committee undertook to give decision within seven days on such proposals. In the event of an appeal to the Production Executive, arrangements were to be made for a decision to be given without delay.

[2] See Chapter X.

[3] The Minister of Works had already agreed with the Ministers of Health, Home Security and War Transport, and with the Secretary of State for Scotland, the principles for the withdrawal of labour from local authorities. The Ministry of Supply declined to accept any such further restriction.

[4] See Chapter VIII.

(v)

The Prime Minister Intervenes

While the Minister of Works had pressed persistently for further powers, and in a succession of memoranda to the Production Executive had outlined his proposals to that end and obtained sanction for many of them, the manpower situation as a whole remained a grave source of anxiety to the War Cabinet.

What reserves of manpower, needed for the armed services and for industries directly engaged in war tasks, lay within the labour force of the building and civil engineering industries? That question, never out of sight throughout the war, assumed in the summer of 1941 an inescapable insistence.[1] In July 1941 the War Cabinet, alarmed at the demands of the Services, had set up a Committee of Ministers under the chairmanship of the Lord President to examine the whole manpower position anew; and in the late summer the Minister of Labour had made the following estimate of requirements up to June 1942:

	Men	*Women*	*Total*
Armed forces and civil defence services	829,000	462,000	1,291,000
Munitions and other industries (including clerical labour).	315,000	460,000	775,000
	1,144,000	922,000	2,066,000

Even before these figures were out, the aircraft programme had been raised by another 100,000 men and women, and other additional labour requirements of 200,000 had come under discussion.[2]

Against this forbidding background, viewed with misgiving and pessimism by the departments concerned, the dissipation of resources on building tasks of doubtful urgency was conspicuous.

On 26th August 1941 the Prime Minister in a personal Minute addressed to the Production Executive expressed his concern. He wrote:

I am concerned at the great amount of manpower and raw materials which are still being directed to constructional work. The works and building programme is using $2\frac{3}{4}$ million tons of imported materials a year (iron, steel and timber) and three-quarters of a million men.

---

[1] In the grouping of war-time industries, building and civil engineering fell into Group III, with other industries and services (such as distribution, the food trades and textiles) which normally were chiefly engaged on production for civilian consumers. This Group was therefore a recruitment reservoir for Group I, comprising the engineering and chemical industries, and for Group II, comprising the chief basic industries such as shipping, land transport, coal, agriculture and the public services.

[2] Hancock, W. K., and Gowing, M. M., *British War Economy*, pp. 139, 202, 203, 290, 291, *et. seq.*

Has not the time come to disallow all new projects of factory construction, save in very exceptional cases? Can we justify further expenditure when so much existing plant is only half employed? Could not building resources be better used in providing hostels and amenities for the labour needed to man extra shifts in the existing plant?

The utmost economy should also be sought in Service requirements, which are apt to be on a more lavish scale than the needs of the moment or the available resources justify.

I trust that there is some machinery for preventing designs being accepted which are wasteful of imported material.

Please inform me what safeguards you have to ensure—

(*a*) that new factories or building undertakings are really essential;

(*b*) that the plans and designs for such undertakings are of the most economical character;

(*c*) that building labour is used to the best advantage.

W.S.C.

The Production Executive agreed that the constructional proposals of the departments as they then stood could not be carried out. There was not enough labour to meet demands; and each department was enjoined to examine critically its own projects in order to see which of them could be cut out with the least damage to the national effort. A Note, prepared by the Secretariat of the Production Executive, was to be the basis of the reply to the Prime Minister's Minute. This was referred to the departments for their observations; and the attention of the Service departments was in particular invited to the Prime Minister's reference to Service requirements.

The Production Executive was careful not to trespass on matters which were already the responsibility of separate departments: why, for example, a large factory programme was still necessary, or what were the checks within a department on non-essential constructional works and on too lavish a scale of planning.

In the investigations carried out by the Secretariat, the total effective building force was estimated at 800,000 or over, of which number approximately 479,000 were being employed on new works. In these calculations the term 'new works' covered all the departmental programmes, including the construction of air raid shelters; it did not cover air raid damage repair and reconstruction work, private new works under £100 in value, maintenance and the work of local authorities other than on shelters and highways.

The existing consumption rates of steel and timber for building were respectively 762,000 tons per annum, and 1,250,000 tons per annum.[1] New works were being started each month to a value of

---

[1] Recent allocations of steel for all purposes had been at the rate of approximately $11\frac{1}{2}$ million tons per annum.

approximately £15 millions, and new factories at the rate of thirty a month.

Building and other constructional work was going on at the rate of about £22 millions per month. The principal classes of work were roughly as follows (the figures were in some cases estimates):

	£
Airfields (excluding R.N.A.S.) . . .	6,000,000
Ordnance and filling factories . . .	2,750,000
Other new factories and extensions of factories	2,200,000
Air raid shelters	2,500,000
Storage	900,000
Hostels	920,000
Army camps	730,000
All other work including Admiralty work, hospitals, defence works, transport, electricity work, harbour works	6,000,000
	£22,000,000

The total could also be divided up between departments as follows (some of the figures were estimates):

		£
Air Ministry		6,435,000
War Office		2,515,000
Ministry of Supply—		
Royal Ordnance factories .	£2,380,000	
Other work . . .	1,885,000	
		4,265,000
Ministry of Aircraft Production . . .		1,995,000
Admiralty		1,310,000
Ministry of Home Security		2,500,000
Ministry of War Transport		1,040,000
Electricity Commissioners		840,000
Ministry of Works (so far as not included under other heads)		290,000
Ministry of Health Emergency Hospitals . .		120,000
Other departments, etc.		690,000
		£22,000,000

In the last paragraph of his Minute Mr. Churchill asked a specific question as to safeguards for ensuring that new building undertakings were really essential. In reply the Note prepared by the Secretariat recalled that building programmes had been submitted by departments considerably in excess of the capacity of the building industry. Accordingly all the programmes, except that of the Air Ministry,[1] had been scaled down to bring them within the available resources. Once the allocations had been made each Minister had remained fully responsible for deciding what building work should go forward and for seeing that only essential work was put in hand. Nevertheless, because work had been started beyond the capacity of the industry, the combined demand of the departments for building labour was

---

[1] See Chapter XIII.

well above the total of the allocations made to them. That new buildings for factories or storage should not be undertaken if accommodation could be found in existing buildings was, as the Note recalled, an accepted principle, and it had been arranged that the Controller-General of Factory and Storage Premises in the Board of Trade should be consulted as to what existing buildings could be used.[1]

It had been agreed, however, that works should be allowed to go on wherever the Minister for the department responsible had personally satisfied himself that no suitable existing building was available. It had also been agreed that the Minister of Works should have the right to raise objection to any building proposal that could not be completed within eight months or which was to be erected in any area where there was an acute shortage of labour. If the Minister responsible disagreed with the Minister of Works, the matter was to be referred for decision by the Production Executive or the Lord President's Committee.

In reply to Mr. Churchill's question on safeguards to secure that plans were of the most economical character, the Note explained that the Minister of Works had set up a Directorate of Construction (Economy) Design. That department rigidly examined departments' steel and timber requirements; sometimes it checked structural design and also prepared standardised economic designs which the departments would in due course require to use.[2]

As to safeguards for securing that building labour was used to the best advantage, each Minister was already fully responsible that within his own allocation resources were devoted to the most essential projects; and in a recent memorandum by the Lord President of the Council, the Minister of Labour's overriding authority on this point was defined. He had written:

> In many cases it is, no doubt, convenient to allow labour released by the completion of one contract to be transferred to another contract for the same department, within the department's allocation of building labour. I am satisfied, however, that the Minister of Labour must himself retain control of the movement of the personnel of the building industry, and that he must be free to move men from the work of one department to that of another, as he thinks right in the national interest, although this power will, of course, only be exercised with great discretion and after the fullest consideration. Unless the Minister possesses this power he cannot discharge his responsibilities to all departments under the scheme for the control of building labour and secure the most economical use of the labour force available.

---

[1] See Hargreaves, E. L., and Gowing, M. M., *Civil Industry and Trade*, in this Series.
[2] See Chapter XIX.

So far as it was a question of the conditions under which labour was employed, that matter had not recently been considered by the Production Executive, but was likely to be discussed in connection with the reports on the progress of the Government building programme.

On 13th September 1941 the Minister of Works, as chairman of the Works and Building Committee, submitted an interim report setting out the departments' proposals for curtailment of building programmes.[1] Lord Reith explained that the value of works stopped was about £2½ millions, the value of programmes curtailed at least £12½ millions. That meant ultimately about 40,000 persons less in new allocations. On the other hand, there were demands for increases of allocation amounting to more than that; but it seemed unlikely that these would be accepted, except for such as arose from new policy decisions.

In addition to the departments' proposals, a complete re-survey was in hand of programmes existing and proposed, on which new allocations would be based. The Minister proposed to ask departments to reconsider certain works. At the same time, as soon as the Ministry of Works knew the balance of building labour employed by commercial undertakings, local authorities, statutory companies and similar bodies, they would consider with the Ministry of Labour possibilities of reduction. As to the restriction of private work, a new draft Defence Regulation was to be circulated to the Home Policy Committee, designed drastically to curtail demolition, repair, maintenance and interior decoration. Discussions were in progress on the possibility of reducing standards.

In view of the terms of Mr. Churchill's Minute, it is not surprising that the Production Executive found in Lord Reith's proposals no basis for a satisfactory reply to the Prime Minister. Departments were asked once more to reconsider their building programmes and to suggest more drastic cuts.

The Production Executive could adduce the pressing demand of the Army for men in general and for skilled men in particular. The demands of the mining industry too had to be met, and heavy labour had to be found to replace men in the metal trades who were being withdrawn for service in the Army or in the mines. The Minister of Labour looked to the building trades to obtain these men. Nor was there any doubt that better use could be made of the existing labour force if it were concentrated on finishing a limited number of jobs and if the application of piece-work were pushed with greater vigour. Successful as such efforts might be, however, the manpower situation still made it essential that the amount of building work should be drastically cut down and every effort made to use existing buildings.

---

[1] Notes and Appendices: Appendix 8, 'Lord Reith's Interim Report on Departments' Proposals for Curtailment' (13th September 1941).

The Production Executive asked that the revised proposals for curtailment should be co-ordinated by the Works and Building Committee. It was also agreed that all proposals for new factory or storage buildings should be submitted to the Lord President, nor were they to be begun without his authority.

(vi)
New Proposals for Curtailment of the Building Programme

This was a very black period in the progress of the war, and it was also a period of great struggles between departments. The Ministry of Works had accepted the policy of progressive reduction of the building force in the country and accordingly continued to press for reduction of the programmes of departments—a hard demand which was resisted with particular determination by the Ministry of Supply. At the same time the Ministry of Works was resolutely seeking ways to extend its authority in the direction of the real control of building. While, during September and October 1941, the Production Executive, in consultation with Lord Reith and other Ministers, concerned itself with curtailment of the building programme, there were simultaneous discussions at a high level on action to speed up the additional bomber programme, and on the creation of a small Production General Staff. Both these topics had an immediate bearing on curtailment and the reply ultimately given to the Prime Minister's Minute of 26th August.

THE ADDITIONAL BOMBER PROGRAMME

A committee[1] appointed to report to the Lord President of the Council on the possibilities of releasing labour by the curtailment of the building of war factories, did so rather inconclusively on 11th October. The position now was that the Lord President did not propose to institute individual investigation of projects by himself; he wanted to see an effective procedure and he accepted the allocation system as the chief means of controlling construction. As to the machinery for reducing labour engaged on non-vital work, clearly it had to include means for securing that it was transferred to vital work (whether within or without the building industry) and that it did not drift to other non-vital work. On its new programme the Ministry of Aircraft Production was alive to the need of making every use possible

---

[1] Three representatives of the Offices of the War Cabinet, two of the Ministry of Works, and one of the Board of Trade.

of existing buildings, of double-shifting and other expedients. None the less, in the eyes of the Ministry of Works, with its responsibility for the equitable allocation of labour, the demands made for building labour for the additional bomber programme appeared extravagant and far beyond true requirements, and the Ministry of Aircraft Production's methods of planning and estimating were also the subject of criticism. But the Ministry of Works was hardly firm enough in the saddle to take a strong line. It was still cautiously feeling its way; and although it was aware that the Ministry of Aircraft Production was putting the allocation picture out of perspective, the full needs of that Ministry, if not its full demands, were promptly met. Some 80,000 building operatives had been asked for, whereas ultimately it was found that the maximum that could be absorbed was 35,000. But, since the Ministry of Works was anxious that any delay or failure to attain the new bomber programme should not be capable of being ascribed to shortage of construction labour, the number actually given was at peak 45,000.[1]

PROPOSED PRODUCTION GENERAL STAFF

On 8th October the First Lord of the Admiralty (Mr. A. V. Alexander) submitted for the consideration of the Production Executive the proposal that a small Production General Staff should be set up and should stand in the same relation to the Production Executive as the Chiefs of Staff Committee stood to the War Cabinet. In a preliminary discussion of this proposal on the official level it was explained on behalf of the Admiralty that Ministers were often called upon to take important decisions on production matters without adequate information. Thus they were not able to form a clear picture as to the effect of proposals from one department on the production programme of the others or upon the manpower position.

Discussion showed that, in general, the establishment of a formal body of the kind proposed by Mr. Alexander was not acceptable. On the whole, it was thought that such a body, whose functions were already largely fulfilled by the Production Executive, could only work effectively if it possessed a large staff and were directed by a single Minister with overriding authority over the three Supply departments —a development immediately condemned by the Admiralty representative himself[2] as undesirable and impracticable.

The view advanced by the Ministry of Works in these discussions was that, in relation to the building programme, the department's functions were ancillary. Its officers were not principals because to a large extent they had to accept facts stated by other departments. It

---

[1] See Chapter XIII.
[2] Admiral Sir Bruce Fraser, Third Sea Lord.

had been their experience that, while in theory departments were the best judges of the urgency of works and what they could carry out, in practice this had not necessarily proved to be so. Decisions were taken without full consideration and knowledge; and there were not, in fact, at that time enough men in the country, or at least not enough men in the right place, to man the factories that existed or were being built. The Ministry of Works had introduced the system of labour allocation as the only way of controlling priorities; and now, in despair of getting departments to agree that only the really urgent work should be done, it proposed to make a drastic reduction in labour and so force departments willy-nilly to contract their projects. That, it was felt in the Ministry of Works, might seem illogical, but it was the only way. The creation of a Production General Staff seemed to offer no help.

Although the proposed Production General Staff proved still-born, the discussion served to show that with the increasing stringency in manpower there seemed to be only two solutions of the priorities: either the creation of a Minister with complete authority or the application of a labour allocation system on the lines adopted by the Ministry of Works. The Admiralty paper was accordingly withdrawn.

Throughout the autumn of 1941 the search for the solution to the labour curtailment problem went on. There was much overlapping and every predisposition to disorganisation. The allocation for the next six months was being worked out and was to be put to the Production Executive on 28th October. It involved an initial cut of labour—by 60,000 on new works and by 70,000 on maintenance—with departments establishing their own internal priorities. It was also based on the general principle that work which could not be made effective within eight months should be prohibited. In these matters the Minister of Works had the right of objection. At the same time the Ministry of Aircraft Production was to be given a 'super-priority' over other departments in regard to allocation (whether open and admitted or not) and for it the eight months' rule was not to operate. Yet the Ministry of Labour and the Ministry of Works had started to apply an embargo on new works in certain areas and the same ground appeared to be partially covered in the recent proposals by the First Lord of the Admiralty. Meanwhile the Production Executive was working out a procedure for the 'vetting' of new factory proposals, the Ministry of Labour had independently arrived at the figures to be withdrawn from the building industry, and the Lord President's Committee was dealing with all or some of these matters, either in principle or detail.

In the discussions and consultations which preceded the Lord President's report to the Prime Minister, Sir John Anderson, Mr. Bevin and Lord Reith kept in close touch. Writing to Mr. Bevin on

28th October (the day on which the Production Executive were to
consider Lord Reith's proposals for the curtailment of the building
programme and the allocation of the building labour force for the
period October 1941 to April 1942), Sir John Anderson defined his
own responsibility for curtailment jointly with that of the Production
Executive. This arose, he wrote, partly because of the Prime Minister's
specific instructions to him to consider how far factory construction
could be curtailed, but also because of his own responsibility for a
general review of the manpower position; and the review showed that
there would have to be a considerable release of manpower from the
building industry to meet the needs both of the forces and of the
munitions industries. Under those conditions allocations could not be
stabilised up to April 1942. There would have to be a drastic revision
(which should not exclude questions of policy) designed to reduce
building requirements, and consequently labour allocations, to the
essential minimum. Sir John Anderson added:

> You will understand, I know, that I am not seeking to impose my
> views on you or your Executive. As, however, I have been giving some
> thought to this question and have had before me the results of certain
> enquiries which have been made into it on my behalf, I thought it
> only right to let you know the provisional views which I have formed.
> The Prime Minister has asked me to report to him what help we
> could give to the bomber programme by curtailment of building
> activities; and, although he referred specifically only to new factory
> construction, I do not think that any recommendation I made to him
> could reasonably be based only on a review of that limited part of the
> field. I should like, therefore, to be able to let him have a report on
> the economies which might be made on the whole of the building
> programme; and, if you were agreeable, I think it would be con-
> venient if we made a joint report on this subject after your discussion
> this afternoon in the Production Executive.

The Production Executive agreed that there should be a general
review of all the allocations before February 1942. The Minister of
Works was also invited to submit as soon as possible proposals for
controlling miscellaneous building work as yet outside the allocation
system, such as maintenance, work by local authorities and public
utilities, miscellaneous small Government works, private building and
kindred activities.

Sir John Anderson's draft reply to Mr. Churchill, submitted to
Lord Reith and agreed by Mr. Bevin, embodied the proposal that in
order to ensure a proper balance of civil and military needs there
should be a controlling body under a 'neutral' Minister, linked on the
one hand with the machinery of the Civil Committees under the Lord
President's Committee and, on the other hand, with the Defence
Committee under the Minister of Defence. This Minister was to be

responsible for allocating building labour between the departments within the total laid down from time to time by the Prime Minister's directives, his specific sanction being required for individual building projects costing more than, say, £50,000 and for new policies in voting large or continuing commitments in the use of building labour. It was the intention that the controls administered by the Ministry of Works should be maintained and linked up with the new machinery; and it was to be the duty of the proposed 'neutral' Minister to apply in detail the broad general principles laid down in directions issued to him from time to time, as, for example, in regard to the siting of new factories or, after consultation with the Minister of Defence, in regard to specific questions of strategic policy.

The proposal to create a new Minister to allocate building labour was distasteful to the Ministry of Works, where it was deemed retrograde and unworkable. That there was no co-ordination of the departments' programmes from the point of view of production was not questioned; nor that this lack was due to defects in the existing system. No doubt new works were decided on—particularly factories —without full consideration of what would be the position when they were completed, or of their effects on other projects and works. It was true, too, that there had not always been enough authority to enforce a definite policy. That had been partly because both the Works and Building Committee and the Production Executive were bodies of interested parties and, moreover, had insufficient connection with the armed services. None the less it was felt that the Works and Building Committee could still be made to function, had in fact already functioned to a large extent. The curtailment of labour had been the policy of the Ministry of Works since the previous December. The Ministry of Labour had not had, nor had it yet, the machinery to implement the reductions suggested by the Ministry of Works or even to know the numbers of the industry.

The Director-General of the Ministry of Works insisted that the efficient and scientific use of the building labour force required the closest study of all the programmes, item by item and region by region.

> The problems cannot be solved by the statisticians talking globally and making precise deductions from approximate data which contain large errors. The machinery of the Works and Building Programme Division must continue and in fact must be extended. The Ministry of Works are the only people in a position to assess the real needs of a department to carry out a programme.[1]

In Lord Reith's view the issue was indeed a narrow and clear one. The only way to control building was to control labour. That had

---

[1] Private Minute by the Director-General, 14th November 1941.

been done by the Ministry's allocation plan. Allocation between departments involved decisions on production policy, and that must
depend on strategy. The system had been worked under the Production Executive which, however, had been unable to give strategic
guidance to the Minister of Works.

What the Minister of Works had not hitherto been able to do was
to say whether there would be, say, twenty airfields or not; whether
they must be in certain regions or not; and whether they must be
completed by a certain date or not. If some machinery were set up
to give him that information, or if the Minister were enabled to get
that information himself, he felt confident he could do the rest; and
that no one else could. Even without that information the Minister
could claim that he had, on the whole, successfully allocated labour
in the past and initiated all 'cuts', and it appeared that a change in
the existing machinery could only be justified if there were a very
certain and large improvement. That depended on whether there was
to be real and greatly increased authority as to information, decision
and enforcement, and on who was to be the 'neutral' Minister. If new
machinery were set up there should be very considerable delegation
to the Minister of Works to work within broad limits. But was there
need for a new Minister after all?

> We recommend a drastic reduction of labour next year. You agree
> and adopt almost unaltered my proposals which P.E. accepted. There
> is nothing for new machinery or new Minister there. But some co-
> ordination of production policy is needed. You propose to make a
> connection with Defence to cover strategy, and that is excellent. We
> have tried to get this help. But does it need a new Minister on the job?[1]

The building programmes and the allocation system were the
responsibility of the Minister of Works under the Production Executive. The machinery was dual. The Works and Building Priority
Committee provided consultation with departments. The Building
Programme Division and the Statistical Office of the Ministry were
working out programmes and individual projects of departments,
labour demands, the relation to the regional labour position, the inter-
relation of the departments' programmes, super-priorities, the restriction on new works in certain areas, the obtaining of returns of labour
and the preparation of statistics, checking the departments' use of and
demand for labour. All that and more was needed for control; and,
against many difficulties, and even obstructions, it had now been
made pretty efficient. In the words of Lord Reith:

> This must all go on, and under P.E.; I am sure you don't want any of
> it moved elsewhere. I don't know where else is the knowledge, or
> experience, or machinery.

---

[1] Letter from Lord Reith to Sir John Anderson, 14th November 1941.

Either, then, I might be given the information and authority now missing, or, if P.E. is to be responsible, surely its chairman should have it. I cannot understand why there should be introduced between myself and P.E. a new Minister, in order that he may have information on strategy and policy which could (and I think should) be available either to Bevin or me.

He could understand it if appeals on matters which the Production Executive could not decide were to go to the Prime Minister or the Lord President. But the suggestion was that control should still be under the Production Executive. Then, he suggested, the logical and simple plan would be to appoint, in addition to the Works and Building Committee, a small committee of impartial departments, as Sir John Anderson proposed, with a Defence member and, if a ministerial chairman were desirable, the Minister of Works as chairman (or even the Minister of Works alone should a committee after all not be thought necessary). Or they could confirm and reinforce the authority of the Production Executive and arrange to add to it, or to its chairman, the necessary information on strategy.

And in a postscript Lord Reith added:

> Confirming what I said yesterday, the Ministry of Works is really impartial. It does not compete with other Ministries for labour allocations. The allocations are given to departments, including the Ministry of Works client departments. The only competition that might take place is in getting the Ministry of Labour to produce the labour which the Ministry of Works has been allocated by its client departments.

In his reply to Lord Reith, Sir John Anderson wrote that, although he understood Lord Reith's view, he still thought it would be difficult for him, with his departmental responsibilities as a large user of building labour, to exercise the kind of central control he (Sir John Anderson) had in mind. He had made clear to the Prime Minister the grounds on which he and Mr. Bevin took a different view, but he also recognised that their proposals were built on foundations laid by Lord Reith and the Production Executive. In forwarding his report to the Prime Minister Sir John Anderson added three comments:

First, the report adopted and developed methods and proposals worked out by the Ministry of Works under the Production Executive. Though much remained to be done, he believed that the Ministry had made substantial progress during the last year in bringing order into the departmental building programmes.

Secondly, the report proposed a supplementary control under the authority of a 'disinterested' Minister. Lord Reith thought that he should be authorised to exercise that control. The Minister of Labour and Sir John Anderson held that the function of weighing competing demands of departments could not be discharged effectively by the Minister of Works, since he was an interested party as a substantial user of building labour. Further, they thought that such control should be exercised by someone occupying for that purpose a central position—with access on the one side to the Production Executive and on the other to the Defence Committee.

In their view that control should be modelled on that exercised in respect of materials, where a junior Minister was in charge. But, if Mr. Churchill approved the general scheme proposed, they naturally left it to him to decide whether he would appoint a 'disinterested' junior Minister or would authorise the Minister of Works to undertake those duties.

Thirdly, the report was based on the programmes as they stood at the beginning of October, though it took account of decisions reached to date on the bomber programme. Since it had been drafted he had heard that the Ministry of Supply were about to notify substantial new demands. They were planning new groups of explosives factories and chemical plants, together with hostels for some part of the labour force involved; they might wish to construct additional capacity for steel stampings and machine tools; and the tank programme might call for further extensions of existing factories and increased rolling-mill capacity for armour place. Some of these demands were because of the expanded bomber programme, and others because of the diversion of equipment to Russia.

If all those new projects were to proceed, the Ministry of Supply would need between 30,000 and 45,000 additional workers; and they were therefore claiming that they could not make do with the building force of 78,000 provisionally allocated to them by the Production Executive, which involved a reduction of about 21,000 on the numbers employed by them in September 1941.

If those projects were found to be necessary, the result would be to diminish the aggregate release of men from factory and storage building from about 60,000 to about 15,000–30,000.

The report itself declared that building *must* and *could* be curtailed. It *must* be curtailed because it was using 920,000 adults—about 490,000 on new building for Government departments, the rest on civil building, maintenance and the repair of air raid damage. New building was a double drain on manpower because of the large additional number engaged in the production of building materials and ancillary equipment. They must, therefore, look to building to make a substantial contribution to the labour demands of the expanding war effort.

New building *could* be curtailed, because they had now reached a stage at which much constructional work was no longer of primary urgency.[1] The programme of factory construction was tailing off rapidly, and apart from aircraft factories and a few other large projects (mainly Royal Ordnance factories), a high proportion of the new building in progress or approved would be completed within the next few months. While it was true that only about one-ninth of the total labour force was engaged in factory construction, in many other fields (for example, air raid shelter and emergency hospitals) the bulk of requirements ought by now to have been met, and there should be room for considerable contraction.

Sir John Anderson and Mr. Bevin, in considering their recommendations, had decided that in order to enforce curtailment they should not at that stage press for detailed modifications of the departmental programmes, but rather for reduction in the departmental allocations of building labour. They therefore proposed:

1. That the global amount of labour which might be employed on all building work over the next year should be fixed at a progressively declining figure.

2. That arrangements should be made for this labour force to be allocated between departments on the basis of certain broad decisions of principle which would take into account the general strategic factors affecting the balance of the war effort.

3. That departments should be invited to submit, after successive allocations, reports showing how they proposed to modify their building programmes to accord with the new allocation of labour. These reports, while leaving with the departmental Minister the responsibility of deciding where cuts must fall, were expected to ensure that the reduction was made effective.

In the supervision of the building programme it was recommended that the 'disinterested' Minister should be assisted by a small central secretariat drawing its data mainly from the Ministry of Works. Within a total laid down from time to time by the Prime Minister, this Minister was to be responsible for determining the allocation of building labour between departments.[2] In addition, new policies involving large or continuing commitments in the use of building labour were to be referred to him for examination in the light of other departmental programmes; and his specific sanction was to be required for any individual building project costing over, say, £50,000.

The report proposed further that the existing control administered by the Ministry of Works should be maintained and linked up with the new machinery.

In a Minute to the Prime Minister of 20th November 1941, Lord

---

[1] The entry of the United States into the war soon nullified this assumption. See Chapter XII.

[2] Subject to appeal in the event of disputes to the Production Executive and, if necessary, to higher authority.

I

Reith returned to his claim that the proposed 'neutral' Minister should be the Minister of Works, urging that his Ministry had been set up to co-ordinate building programmes, carry out new works for departments, and administer priorities. On his advice the old system of priorities had been abandoned for that of allocating labour to departments. It had succeeded.

> There were no adequate statistics. All action to get at building labour facts—numbers and where employed—began here. We are at last in sight of effective control of the whole building programme, acceptable to departments.
>
> I have always advocated the allocation system to control and curtail programmes, and the proposals put forward by the Lord President are, as he says, mine. To implement them, and to secure the best use of remaining labour, demands the close technical and statistical control established and operating in this Ministry. Assessing departments' labour needs and dove-tailing programmes cannot be done as effectively elsewhere.

But they lacked one thing—authoritative guidance on strategy and production policy. Now that this was to be supplied, was not the logical and simpler plan to give it to the Minister who had, in fact, lacked it, rather than to a new Minister without knowledge of this difficult subject? If it were said that, being a user of labour, he could not be impartial, he was not a competing principal but an agent only, using labour allocated to others. And the Lord President had referred to his department as a 'neutral'.

> In his covering note he recognises that you might prefer to authorise me. I hope you will.

(vii)

Mr. Churchill's Second Directive

In a memorandum issued on 27th November the Prime Minister embodied the recommendations of the Lord President of the Council, but at this stage a 'disinterested' Minister was not appointed. The supervision of the building programme was left to the Minister of Works under the authority of the Production Executive. Close contact with the Defence Committee was, however, to be preserved by the Minister, and he was to determine the allocation of building labour within the total laid down from time to time according to the Prime Minister's directives. The Prime Minister also laid it down as fundamental that offence came before defence and that precedence was to be given to works which improved the striking power of the forces. The detailed directions issued by him for the guidance of all departments, which had been drawn up with the advice and collaboration of the Minister of Works, were:

A. LIMITATION

1. (*a*) The total numbers of insured adult workers in the building industry should be progressively reduced from 920,000 to 792,500 during the first three months of 1942.

    Departments should aim at making this reduction effective very soon after 1st January 1942.

    (*b*) Our general manpower policy assumes that the building industry will be able to make a further contribution by the end of June 1942. By then the total numbers should be reduced to 770,000; and departments should aim at getting down towards that figure soon after March.

    (*c*) Our further objective should be to secure that, after the end of the 1942 building season, the numbers employed on new building are reduced to 250,000. The total labour force in the industry should then be about 600,000.

    Departments should plan their programmes on this basis.

    (*d*) Further reductions will be possible on the completion of the programmes for aircraft factories and airfields, which in their last phase will be employing about 150,000.

    For the time being departments should proceed on the basis that by mid-1943 the labour force of the industry will be reduced to 500,000.

2. Departments whose allocations have been reduced or who are now employing numbers in excess of their allocations should submit reports to the Minister of Works by 15th December next, showing how they propose to modify their existing programmes in order to get down to their new allocations by 1st January next.

B. SUPERVISION

3. The existing machinery for scrutinising the departmental building programmes under the Ministry of Works will continue to operate under the authority of the Production Executive. As and when necessary the Minister can consult a military officer in the War Cabinet Secretariat in order to preserve close contact with the Defence Committee. The Minister will be responsible for determining—subject to appeal, in the event of disputes, to the Production Executive, and if necessary to higher authority—the allocation of building labour between the departments within the total laid down from time to time by the Prime Minister's directives.

4. The Minister's policy will be based on the following considerations, subject, of course, to existing ministerial responsibilities:

    (*a*) In any clash between the requirements of different projects the bias should be to give precedence to those which tend towards the improvement of the striking power of our forces, e.g. the essential munitions of war are of more importance than the air raid precautions; the bomber programme takes precedence over food storage.

(*b*) Even for the most urgent requirements every effort must be made to make do with existing premises rather than build new factories or extensions.

(*c*) No new factory should be constructed unless it can be shown that the fullest practicable use is being made of all existing capacity, including double-shift working.

(*d*) The standards of construction demanded must be reduced to the lowest efficient level.

(*e*) Departments must exercise the greatest possible economy of building labour, and do all in their power to avoid wasteful use of labour by insistence on uneconomically early dates of completion.

(*f*) The sites of new factories and extensions must, wherever possible, be so chosen as to reduce the demand for hostels or housing to a minimum. Full use must be made of compulsory billeting and every other practical expedient before recourse is had to building.

(*g*) The standards of storage must be the lowest that are consistent with avoiding serious waste.

(*h*) The force of building labour available for maintenance, air raid precautions and air raid damage must be reduced to the minimum required on the assumption that any stricken area will be able to obtain the maximum aid from all neighbouring sources, including labour employed on Government building work.

(*i*) When the present programme for providing static water is completed, any further constructional work in connection with air raid precautions (including hospitals and shelters) must be limited to that which can be carried out during lull periods by this minimum maintenance force.

On 4th February 1942 it was announced from Downing Street that Lord Beaverbrook had become Minister of Production, and in a White Paper, which was later withdrawn, the new Minister's position and functions were defined.[1] In relation to the building programme the Minister of Production took the place of the Production Executive and it was to him that Lord Reith had now to refer decisions. Lord Reith promptly pointed out that some departments had not been able to reduce labour to the agreed figures required under the Prime Minister's directive because they had more work in hand than their allocations covered and their cutting estimates had been over-

---

[1] This appointment followed the Anglo-American conversations in Washington after Pearl Harbour, and was stimulated particularly by the need for close United Kingdom-United States co-ordination in the war-economic sphere. Lord Beaverbrook held the appointment for a very brief period, being followed by Mr. Lyttelton. See Chapter V.

optimistic. To secure reductions, what was in effect an embargo would have to be put on all new works, except those of the Ministry of Aircraft Production, for the next two, in some cases three, months. The effect on the Air Ministry and the Ministry of Supply would be the derangement of forward planning. The alternative course was to revise decisions altering allocations. There were also the new factors of the entry of America into the war and reduced Irish labour,[1] as well as the needs of the scrap metal programme[2] requiring 25,000 men mainly from building and civil engineering. These factors were liable to upset original calculations, and other serious factors were involved in the regional transference of labour.[3] Lord Reith asked for instructions as to whether the policy in the Prime Minister's directives was to be modified to meet the programmes of departments—particularly the Ministries of Aircraft Production and Supply and the Admiralty—or whether 150,000 men were to be withdrawn by June, as directed, to the Services and to munitions, come what might.

If, to carry out the existing programmes, extra labour had to be provided, Lord Reith suggested that it should be by some internal redistribution of allocated quotas which would, however, only go a short way to meet the difficulty and would take some months; secondly, by the slowing down of the intake into the Services (which need not seriously affect the numbers for the Services) and munitions, no labour being taken that could be used on major Government works; and thirdly, by the temporary release of 25,000 unskilled men from the Services for six months, since unskilled labour had been excessively called up in the past two and a half years, thus unbalancing the industry.

If, as appeared, the maximum volume of work in the next eight months was essential, no solution could be found unless more labour, particularly unskilled. were temporarily made available. Labour taken off air raid precautions, shelter and other such work would only meet a small part of the Air Ministry's and other heavy civil engineering needs.

Were not the next eight months of paramount importance to the building programme? Could they afford to close down or delay much of the departments' programmes, with the result that works would not be ready until the end of the year instead of that summer? The proposed modifications would be temporary. If there were no major

---

[1] The Eire Government were embarking on an ambitious building programme of their own which was expected to affect the exportation of labour. The result threatened to be a partial drying-up of this source and even some loss of manpower through the return of men to Eire. The threat, however, was less serious than appeared, since these men could earn very much more in the United Kingdom than they could expect in Eire.

[2] See Chapter X.

[3] The labour shortage was most acute in the North-Western Region (mainly on Ministry of Aircraft Production works), in the Eastern Region (mainly on Air Ministry works) and in the North Midland Region where both these departments were competing for labour.

changes of circumstances the industry could still be reduced by the end of 1942 to 625,000 or so, as originally recommended by him.

But Lord Beaverbrook was adamant. The Prime Minister's directions must stand with regard to the position at the end of the year, although there was cause for intermediate alleviation. The Minister of Works was immediately to tell departments that the reduction in building labour to the figures in the Prime Minister's Directive of 27th November must be carried out, and that they were therefore required to work to the allocations fixed in October by the Production Executive. Where the building labour employed by a department was in excess of the allocation programme no new approvals were to be given except when authorised by the Minister of Production. Reconsideration of individual quotas was to be pressed forward as promptly as possible in order to make the best use of available building labour. With regard to the release of men from the Services, in order that current work might be completed as rapidly as possible the Ministry of Works was to arrange any slowing down of intakes into the Services that might suit the Minister of Labour's plans. Fresh building labour demands caused by the presence of the American Army were to be assessed and considered independently. If American labour could not be provided the Minister of Production was ready to take up the question of temporary release of unskilled men from the Services for the purpose. Any enlargement of the Army or Air Force demands was to be met by the use of their own available manpower.

CHAPTER V

THE CO-ORDINATION OF THE BUILDING PROGRAMME UNDER THE MINISTER OF PRODUCTION

(i)

Direction of Policy by the Minister of Production

O N 23rd February 1942 Lord Portal succeeded Lord Reith as Minister of Works, and on 12th March Mr. Oliver Lyttelton, who from 1940 to 1941 had been President of the Board of Trade and subsequently Minister of State in Cairo, took over from Lord Beaverbrook the office of Minister of Production. To him fell the duties hitherto discharged by the Production Executive, among them the specific task of determining, with the help of the Minister of Production's Council (on which the Minister of Works also sat) the scope and extent of the building programme.[1] Against the background of these changes, America's entry into the war, which had in part brought them about, was making its first demands on the building programme, and before long the full extent of these demands began to be realised.[2]

The works in hand during that summer were indeed of vital importance, but the withdrawal of men from the building industry for the Services and munitions had to go on. That could only be done if drastic measures were boldly taken, and if with renewed energy, adaptability and co-operation all concerned—departments, contractors, workpeople—combined in a supreme effort to complete the scheduled programme.

When, on 9th April, the Minister of Production's Council met for the first time it approved the policy submitted to them by the Minister and, with the concurrence of the Ministers of Labour and

---

[1] H. of C. Deb., 12th March 1942, Vol. 378, Col. 1205. Statement by the Prime Minister. It should be understood that only through the authority of the Minister of Production was it possible for the Minister of Works to get any more powers or to ensure action by other departments. On the other hand, the Minister of Production was necessarily guided in his decisions by the Ministers of Works and Labour, and building policy was fashioned through the close collaboration of the three Ministers.

[2] See Chapter XI et seq.

Works, Mr. Lyttelton invited concentration of effort on the following:

1. Payment by results.
2. Standardisation of design and construction.
3. No unauthorised change in lay-out or design.
4. Intensive scrutiny of all new works to meet labour curtailment.

Payment by results. The Essential Work (Building and Civil Engineering) Order 1941 already provided for the application of a system of payment by results on all scheduled sites 'where practicable and desirable'.[1] Such a method of remuneration had always been recognised in civil engineering and always strictly prohibited in the building industry, except in speculative house-building. It is related in another portion of this narrative[2] how the Minister of Labour and the Minister of Works jointly invited both sides of the building industry to put forward their own scheme, which it was promised would be for war-time only, and how there was a complete failure to reach agreement. It was left to the Ministry of Works to produce a scheme and schedule and to impose it by regulation. The industry co-operated loyally and helpfully in carrying out the scheme, which was at first restricted to civil engineering operations and to bricklaying and only extended later to other trades.

Reports had shown that while most satisfactory results had been obtained where payment by results had been adequately operated, it was by the beginning of 1942 not yet in force on many sites where it could and should have been applied. Less than half the operations to which the system could be applied were subject to bonus, and on many contracts only about ten per cent. of the total work was in that category; on many others no attempt had been made to introduce payment by results. Works could not be regarded as of prime importance where the department and contractor failed to operate the system, and it was Mr. Lyttelton's intention, of which he gave due warning, to give weight to that factor in the placing of labour.

The very incomplete use of payment by results was mainly due to the reluctance of contractors to apply it. Their objection can be traced to a variety of reasons—sometimes to inexperience, sometimes to dislike of the new technique, sometimes to perplexity over the method or the staff required, sometimes to misgivings over the financial results.

Mr. Lyttelton left it in no doubt that payment by results was the definite policy of the Government. In placing contracts, departments were to insist that the system was applied to the full. It was for them to consider whether the refusal of any contractor might not be met by terminating the contract, since the Ministry of Labour could not maintain the scheduling of a site under the Essential Work Order

---

[1] See Chapter VI.
[2] *Ibid.*

if payment by results were not adequately operated upon it. Delay in such scheduling, too, caused undue postponement of payment by results, and a new procedure was therefore to be put into immediate operation.

In future every job passed as W.B.A.[1] was to be automatically and immediately scheduled.[2] It had been found that new contractors and sub-contractors coming on to a site some time after the site was first scheduled had been unaware—or had ignored the fact—that the Essential Work Order applied. It was for contracting departments to inform the Ministry of Labour immediately any main or direct contracts were placed by them. At the same time all main contractors were now to be required to notify the Ministry of Works of any sub-contracts let by them, so that the sub-contractors might be reminded of their obligations under the Essential Work Order, and in particular of the necessity to introduce payment by results without delay.

The Minister of Production affirmed that the general control of the system of payment by results was in the hands of the Minister of Works, and the final decision as to whether 'bonusing' was in any case practicable or desirable would rest with him; while the recognised methods of bonus payment were as laid down by him in consultation with the Joint Industrial Panel established for the purpose.

Standardisation of design and construction. On many contracts the standards in design and construction were considered to be still too high for purely war purposes. They often called for the excessive use of labour and materials, and that could no longer be permitted. It will be remembered that the Prime Minister, in his Directive of 27th November 1941, had laid down that 'the standards of construction demanded must be reduced to the lowest efficient level' and the Production Executive on 23rd December 1941 had directed that

> new schemes should conform to the standards of economy laid down or to be laid down by the Ministry of Works, and that in preparing designs there should be full co-operation with the Directorate of Construction (Economy) Design of that Ministry.[3]

In order to give effect to these directions it was essential that design and standards of construction should be jointly investigated by the Ministry of Works and the contracting departments; and the Minister of Production directed that the allocation of building materials (including steel and timber) by the Ministry of Works should be fixed

---

[1] Although the priority system was abolished, the old symbol W.B.A. was maintained as a label for approved jobs to enable the regional officers of the Ministry of Labour to recognise them.

[2] Such scheduling took effect forthwith, but was regarded as preliminary. The contract was inspected within six weeks of starting and the scheduling was confirmed if payment by results was being properly operated.

[3] See Chapter XIX.

accordingly.[1] The Ministry was to be responsible for seeing that all designs and specifications (other than those for purely operational requirements) conformed with whatever reduced standards it laid down, and was to take such reduced standards into consideration when arranging the labour allocation.

No unauthorised changes in lay-out or design. Many of the delays in completing contracts had been because of changes in lay-out or design after work had been begun on the site. The Minister of Production now asked that all departments concerned should be instructed that no major variation was permissible without the specific authority of a high official of the ordering department, if not of the Minister himself.

Intensive scrutiny of all new works. All departments had to realise that the demands for release of labour from the building industry would increase. They had to accept the position that there could be no material deviation from the Prime Minister's direction that the total labour force should be reduced to 600,000 by the end of 1942, and to 500,000 by the middle of 1943. Future programmes of construction were not to be prepared on the assumption that the existing labour allocation would be maintained after September 1942. All departments were asked to review their future programmes accordingly, and the scrutiny in regard to all new works was to be increasingly strict.

> I have informed the Minister of Works to this effect (Mr. Lyttelton wrote) and have requested that no projects that will not contribute quickly to our war effort should be approved without reference if necessary to me. Further, any project which may carry a department outside its labour allocation will be referred to me by the Minister of Works for approval.

(ii)

Reversion to a System of Priorities

Within a few weeks of the new Minister of Production's policy instruction the situation was changed completely by the disclosure, for the first time, of the full extent of the programme of requirements for the accommodation of the American forces, a new programme subsequently known by the code-word 'Bolero'.[2] The additional building labour requirements were estimated at 90,000 men for the War Office and 46,000 for the Air Ministry; there were to be further requirements, not yet established, for aircraft and vehicle assembly depots and other schemes.

---

[1] A special section of the Ministry dealt with the scrutiny of all proposed uses of steel and timber.

[2] See Chapters XII and XIII.

Clearly some new course of action, far more drastic than anything envisaged at the time Mr. Lyttelton issued his policy instruction, was now incumbent.

The Minister of Labour's view was that on the basis of existing arrangements the additional demands being put forward could be met only by stopping the withdrawal of men from the building industry to the Forces; yet in the existing war situation the adoption of that course was unthinkable. Somehow or other available resources had to be used to carry out all essential work, including the new requirements for the United States forces, without holding back men from the Army. Too many jobs were going on at once without any being finished to time; transfer of labour from one job to another was far too slow; and payment by results was still inadequately enforced. To overcome these shortcomings Mr. Bevin suggested the creation of a single pool of labour for all Government work, operated by the Minister of Works under the authority of the Minister of Production through a directorate, so to speak, formed of the chief officers responsible for the constructional work of the various departments. That organisation, he thought, should be able to handle the whole Government building programme and see that resources were concentrated on the most urgent jobs; whereas, in the existing circumstances, non-urgent work could not be stopped if the department concerned was within its labour allocation. To concentrate on the most urgent requirements would mean temporarily shutting down some other work, but in the long run even such work would benefit by the full weight of the available resources when the more urgent work had been finished. If such a scheme were brought into operation and a national labour pool were formed, Mr. Bevin for his part undertook to impress on the trade unions the need for regarding as fully mobile all building labour apart from the 'garrison' force.[1] He also undertook to transfer to the Government building programme 250,000 men from other building work.

An informal Conference of Ministers, on 5th May 1942, endorsed Mr. Bevin's views. It was then agreed that he and the Minister of Works should jointly submit proposals to the Lord President's Committee for ultimate reference to the War Cabinet. The main feature of the proposals, as formulated by the two Ministers, was the substitution of a new scheme for the existing scheme under which, after an examination of programmes, a head of labour was allocated to each department for a specified period.

As will be recalled, under that procedure allocations were proposed by the Ministry of Works and discussed at meetings of the Works and

[1] The 'garrison' labour force consisted of men, above military age or otherwise ineligible as mobile building labour, employed on maintenance, etc. See Notes and Appendices: Note XI, 'The "Garrison" Labour Force'.

Building Committee. The placing of contracts over a certain size was approved by the Contracts Allocation Sub-Committee of that Committee, and a dissatisfied department could appeal to the Production Executive (in whose place the Minister of Production now stood). The main difficulty hitherto in controlling labour under this system had been this—that once a department got an allocation of labour it was inclined, if the urgent work for which the allocation was made did not come to hand, to use the labour on works which were not really urgent, so that when the urgent work arrived it could readily be transferred.

The new scheme provided for an examination of each job; but departments themselves were first to be classified A, B, and Z on the footing that, in the main, the work of a department in category A was more urgent and important than the work of a department in category B and that the work of a department in category Z, and some of the work in category B, could be postponed until the job of departments in category A had been completed. The system was in some ways similar to that in use before the Ministry of Works introduced that of allocations. Contracts—not departments—were then categorised A, B, and Z, A having the first call on labour, B the second, while labour was taken from Z, the contracts in that category being postponed or abandoned.

Under the revised application of priorities, all building and civil engineering labour was to be pooled and all resources were to be carefully ascertained, including the available labour in the Services (which itself formed part of the pool for Service work). The rigid barrier of separate allocations was to be broken down, and the allocation system modified to the extent that departments were to be entitled not to a certain amount of labour but to the completion of certain contracts. In the process means were to be found to procure the maximum fluidity and mobility of labour: for example, by using craftsmen as labourers, where necessary, at the craftsmen's rate of pay, and by widespread use of directions to cause men to work away from home wherever they might be required.

The priority of contracts was to be laid down and effectively enforced. The first step in that direction would be for the priority of constructional requirements to be settled by the Minister of Production; the second for the priority of major jobs to be assessed and determined by a new Directorate. Payment by results was to be strictly enforced to the utmost, nor were objections arising from the idiosyncracies of contractors and builders to be tolerated; and the supply of building materials was to be fully assured so as to enable production to keep going at full speed.

In the classification of departments under categories A, B, and Z, Class A comprised the six main departments in need of war buildings

—Admiralty, War Office, Air Ministry, Ministry of Supply, Ministry of Aircraft Production and Ministry of War Transport. Much of the work of these departments (with their essential ancillary services) was on operational undertakings and was entitled to first priority.

Work which was indirectly essential for a Class A job (for example, on roads) came into the same category, although it might be carried out by one of the departments not normally included in the Class A. In such special circumstances the Minister of Production had authority to award classification A, and also in appropriate circumstances to remove a specific job from Class A.

Class B comprised the remaining departments engaged on work of importance for the conduct of the war, but of a less urgent kind than Class A, and was subject to postponement in the interests of urgent operational work.

Class Z covered the balance of those departments at that time in Class B for allocation, and their work could be curtailed or temporarily postponed. Z jobs, and so much of the B jobs as were postponed, could be resumed after the A jobs were completed.

Labour could thus be taken off category Z jobs and to some extent off category B jobs. Use could also be made of labour directly employed on work for local authorities, public utility companies and private employers, by including it as might be necessary in the general pool for allocation to A jobs. Similarly labour on maintenance work was included in the general pool. Civil departments were assured that immediately men were released from war requirements they would be made available, under a similar organisation, to make good any delay through cessation of existing contracts.

The Conference of Ministers directed that during the summer of 1942 there was to be a maximum concentration on the A contracts. The sole criterion in according labour supply was the maximum efficiency of output from the labour supplied. Departmental claims for labour based on allocations now ceased to have validity for that period, except in so far as they were related to the new priorities. The Ministry of Works was itself to carry out as much of this total constructional programme as it could satisfactorily control, except operational works, and it was also called upon to tighten its control by the Ministry of Works over contractors' plant.[1]

The release of labour for the Forces was to proceed according to programme, but the release of labour to munitions industries was cancelled.

For the scheme to function with success it was essential, while accepting the overriding authority of the Minister of Production, to bring the whole Government constructional programme under one

---

[1] See Chapter VIII.

control. The expedient suggested for this purpose was the creation of the special Directorate, with the Minister of Works himself as chairman, and including the Parliamentary Secretaries as representatives of the principal departments concerned.[1] The Directorate was to be fully empowered to give decisions, subject to the authority of the Minister of Production; and its purpose would be to act, not as an interdepartmental committee but as a body responsible for determining the intensity with which programmes or portions of programmes, operational or otherwise, should be completed according to the needs of war strategy. The Directorate's first duty was to be the completion at the earliest moment of all items of capital construction in the priority list, and there was to be absolute concentration on works that could be completed at the earliest possible date. Questions of general policy in the allocation of contractors were also to be the concern of the Directorate.

It might here be appropriately recalled that in the earlier stages of the war, when building work was governed by a system of priorities whereby certain departments had been able to claim first priority for all their building work, one result had been that works of importance to the war effort, if sponsored by departments whose work as a whole was less directly connected with the war, had fallen into arrear. On the other hand, the system of departmental allocation of labour, though it had remedied this defect, had resulted, it was said, in much labour being employed in an uneconomic manner on work that could have been much more quickly completed. The defects of both the earlier schemes were this time to be avoided. The urgent need for tackling large new building schemes could only be met by rigorously concentrating resources and effort upon them.

The proposed procedure under which the six main departments requiring war building were to be put under category A was not welcomed by all departments. Ministries such as the Ministry of Home Security or the Ministry of Food, which were outside that category, objected that they had jobs of equally urgent priority which should qualify for category A—among them the provision of static water, the completion of the shelter programme, the replacement of civil defence depots destroyed by enemy action, and the provision of cold storage depots. Was it not inconsistent to put departments in category A when the emphasis should be on priority for particular jobs?

These claims, however, though not without substance, could not match in urgency claims of immediate operational importance—for tasks which the industry was called upon to approach in the spirit of

---

[1] The proposal to appoint a single Directorate was modified later in the month, when two Directorates were created at ministerial level, together with two corresponding Committees at official level.

a war offensive and with the resolve that they should be completed by the due dates, come what might. That priorities for each individual major work should be decided by reference to a body on which all departments were represented would have led to endless discussion and wasteful delay. The alternative was to set up a second Directorate at a lower level of urgency comprising departments not, as it were, in the front line. There was already a useful precedent for such a course. In the procedure for the allocation of raw materials the corresponding committee had been divided into two bodies comprising respectively the representatives of the main users (few in number) and the representatives of the other departments,[1] and it seemed appropriate to the Lord President's Committee that a similar separation should be made of the building Directorate.

The second body thus recommended to be set up was, like the first, to be presided over by the Minister of Works and to comprise representatives of the departments other than the six main users. The departments represented on this second body had to select one of their number as an additional member of the first Directorate to represent their interests. It was stressed that the scheme did not connote that *any* work put forward by the six main departments requiring war building should automatically be granted a category A priority; and it was recognised that the Minister of Works would preside over the two representative bodies as an impartial Minister and not as Minister in charge of the department responsible for carrying out works services.

Subject to the modifications described, the Lord President's Committee, on 15th May 1942, gave its general approval to the scheme and took note that, in the altered circumstances, some amendment would have to be made in the Prime Minister's Directive of 27th November 1941. Mr. Lyttelton accordingly undertook to ask Mr. Churchill for his approval.

At no time since the creation of the Ministry of Works had the older Ministries, and especially the Service Ministries, accepted with conspicuous good grace the tutelage over building plans of this newcomer among the Ministries. The present occasion was no exception. Thus, the Air Ministry, while welcoming the proposals in principle as a great gain if they gave more effective labour mobility, objected to a Directorate presided over by the Ministry of Works:

> The Air Ministry and other Class A departments, in which all operational work is of first priority, will be suppliants to a Civil Minister who has a very large stake in the civil building programme. This arrangement appears to be open to serious objection. . . . There is also to be absolute concentration on works which can be completed

---

[1] See Notes and Appendices: Note VI, 'The Central Priority Organisation'.

at the earliest possible date. This may militate against the satisfactory completion of the Air Ministry's phased works programme; for example, we may well prefer a large number of uncompleted aerodromes from which, in an emergency, squadrons can operate under field conditions to a small number of completed aerodromes with a consequent limitation of operation.

It was not clear to what the phrase 'available labour in the Services, as part of the labour pool for Service work' referred.[1] The Air Ministry could not pool the Royal Air Force Works Squadrons, which were established as an insurance against war damage to airfields.[2] Indeed they had no Service labour to offer at all.

The War Office, too, found difficulty in giving a precise interpretation to this phrase. If it referred to Constructional and Pioneer Companies which were to be brought into the reckoning in fixing the general disposition of building labour for Service work, then there was no question of making them available for other Service departments at the expense of Army needs; nor yet of counting for this purpose building operatives already in the Forces who were employed in other capacities. Moreover, in accordance with its existing practice, the War Office expected to retain the power to place contracts up to £20,000 locally, and asked that constructional jobs below that limit should not be brought within the purview of the new Directorate except as representing bulk labour needs.

The references to control by the Ministry of Works over contractors, and to general policy in the allocation of contractors, were interpreted by the War Office as meaning that they would continue to consult the Ministry freely as hitherto.

> There can, of course, be no question of the Ministry having the final word on the allocation of contractors to the War Office. For example, I wouldn't dream of allowing the firm of XY, whom we have knocked off our list, being wished on to us.[3]

It was of obvious importance to the War Office that the Secretariat of the new Directorate should be closely linked with its own Bolero Secretariat;[4] and that responsibility for planning American accommodation in the United Kingdom (so far as concerned the United States Army) should remain with the War Office. These demands were forcefully pressed; moreover, the War Office required that, should the new Directorate desire to give decisions contrary to any War Office instructions, then the War Office representative must

---

[1] See p. 124.
[2] It should be realised, however, that the Works Squadrons were also very fully occupied at this time on construction as well as repair.
[3] Sir P. J. Grigg to Mr. Lyttelton, 9th May 1942.
[4] See Chapter XII.

bring the point to notice so that it could be settled by the Minister of Production.

The attitude of the Ministry of Health was more co-operative. Provided its urgent work were placed in the right category, it accepted the new scheme as better on the whole than the existing one of allocations. Under the original priority system for the building programme many Ministry of Health contracts—such as, for example, housing, water and sewerage schemes required in connection with vital factories, airfields and hospitals—had been placed in category A; repair of war damage had been given a super-priority. The Ministry had never been unduly interested in allocation as such; its object had been to get the urgent jobs approved by the Contracts Sub-Committee, and so far approval had not been refused for any really urgent job. Why, indeed, asked its spokesmen, should departments be categorised? Would it not suffice if the jobs only were examined and placed in category A, N, or Z? Unlike other departments, the Ministry did not itself place contracts, but was concerned with the placing of contracts by local authorities and public utility undertakings. Most of the public health work of local authorities was carried out in fulfilment of Government policy; and much of it was of the highest priority. Then there were all the urgent special tasks tied up with the transfer of population under war conditions, which, like the first-aid repair of war damage, demanded an overriding priority and involved the temporary transfer of labour from other urgent Government work. In all these classes of constructional work a claim to the highest priority was inherent and had been admitted. If, however, categorisation by departments were indeed insisted upon, the Ministry of Health's place was surely in category A and, it was urged, it should be represented on the Directorate.

(iii)
The Building Directorates

The proposal to appoint a single Directorate was modified; and on 21st May 1942 the Minister of Production formulated the system which was to give effect to the decisions of the Lord President's Committee. He had meanwhile consulted the Prime Minister and had obtained his agreement in the necessary amendment to his Directive on 27th November 1941.

Two Directorates were now set up on the ministerial level, both presided over by the Minister of Works. In addition, there were two Committees of Officials presided over by the Parliamentary Secretary.

K

The two Directorates and the two Committees were constituted as follows, on both levels:

1. Admiralty, War Office, Air Ministry, Ministry of Aircraft Production, Ministry of Supply, Ministry of War Transport, Ministry of Labour, and a representative of the departments in (2) below.

2. Ministry of Health, General Post Office, Ministry of Food, Board of Trade, Ministry of Agriculture, Scottish Office, Home Office and Ministry of Home Security, Board of Education, and Ministry of Labour.[1]

The function of the Directorates was to deal with (a) laying down of broad programmes; (b) settling of appeals and apportioning labour globally, as might be necessary, to categories of work; (c) directing matters of policy.

The function of the Committees of Officials was to deal with (a) all programming and progressing of approved works; (b) the 'vetting' of new works in the first instance; (c) the co-ordination of the use of contractors; (d) the transfer, on the instructions of the Directorates, of labour from unessential to essential work; (e) the pooling of plant; (f) the enforcement of economy in materials; (g) the enforcement of payment by results.

If the Directorates failed to reach agreement, decisions were to be taken by the Minister of Production.

(iv)

The Minister of Production in Effective Control

The reversion to a system of priorities was regretted by responsible officials of the Ministry of Works; they were convinced that without an upper limit it would be impossible to prevent the total volume of building from increasing until it once more far exceeded the capacity of the industry. Nevertheless, they did their utmost to make the new system work.

The first act of the Directorates was to call for complete lists of all major works in hand or proposed. Details were to be given of the value of such works, their purpose and the progress achieved. They were then to be examined individually and their urgency decided. The lists were duly provided by the Building Programmes Directorate.[2] They proved to be so bulky, however, as to make it at once

---

[1] Other departments, such as the Ministry of Information, not mentioned here, were to furnish the Committees with their programmes and were to be allotted priorities accordingly. They would be asked to attend if necessary to put their case.

[2] The Building Programmes Directorate was a branch of the Ministry of Works set up in 1940 to operate the allocation system; it continued in existence until the end of the war. It should not be confused with the Ministerial Directorates. See Chapter XVIII.

obvious that a detailed scrutiny would take more time than could be spared by committees of Ministers. Even so, scrutiny would have been quite futile since the position in hundreds of contracts would have changed materially in the time needed to collate and investigate the returns. None of the departments would admit that their works were unimportant. On the lists no action at all was in fact taken by the Directorates. Instead of down-grading the priority of less urgent works the easier course of up-grading the priority of the most urgent works was followed. The symbol W.B.A. continued in use, but all the more urgent works were now given the designation 'first urgency'. Specially vital works were put in a higher category, called 'super-preference' to distinguish it from the earlier 'super-priority'.[1] At first only a limited number of individual projects was given this higher priority. Super-priority had previously been applied as sparingly as possible and only on the direct authority of the War Cabinet for jobs of the first strategic importance. Under the new regime the scope of super-preference was rapidly extended until whole categories of work were given 'blanket' priorities.

The Bolero works[2] were very slow in getting under way; meanwhile, under the reborn priority system there was again no upper limit to the amount of work the departments could commence. The bad practice arose for labour combed out of non-essential work by the Ministry of Labour to be used on new works that were not truly part of the Bolero programme. To compete with existing contracts the new works had to be given super-preference too, and when the Bolero contracts started to flow, in the summer of 1942, the position was that all the available labour was already employed on super-preference works and there was no higher priority that could be accorded.

The process of combing out labour from less essential building work never produced even a fifth of a large number of men the Ministry of Labour had predicted. Nothing like the numbers talked of really existed. Even such as were in theory available for redirection to more urgent work proved mostly to be immobile—and, therefore, not available for Bolero tasks, most of which were sited in areas far from the big centres of population. Meanwhile, the large-scale withdrawals of men from the building and civil engineering industries had perforce to continue. The release of labour to munitions (though not to the Army) was theoretically suspended; but normal wastage not replaced by new entrants continued. Nothing could prevent the continual drift out of the industry to more remunerative work in the armament factories.

By early autumn the worst fears of the officials of the Ministry of

---

[1] Notes and Appendices: Note IX, 'Forms and Symbols Employed by Building Programmes Directorate'.

[2] See Chapter XII.

Works had been realised. More and more jobs were being imposed on an ever-shrinking labour force, and there were long lists of further jobs still waiting to start. Most of the works in progress had been given super-preference, but this was no longer a guarantee that the labour requirements of a job would be met; indeed, nearly all jobs were below strength, with little hope of building up. The volume of work in hand was, in fact, once more hopelessly in excess of the capacity of the building industry.

The departments pressed for a new priority category above super-preference with which to overcome their labour shortages, but by November they were beginning to realise, at least at official level, that the only hope was a reversion to the allocation system.

Nevertheless, yet another comb-out for the Forces became impera-tive. Late in November 1942 it was announced that there had to be a further call-up at the rate of 15,000 men a month as from January. At a meeting of the Service and Supply Committee of Officials it was generally felt that the new call-up would torpedo the Bolero pro-gramme since the labour needed in the immediate future would be short by a number which the Ministry of Works estimated, and the Committee accepted, at the figure of not less than 115,000 men. This view was brought to the notice of the Minister of Production and referred to the War Cabinet. The Minister of Works in pointing out the failure of the attempt to operate priorities, urged a return to allocations, to be called 'ceilings',[1] drastic cuts of all programmes and an embargo on new works for six weeks. The War Cabinet had to act promptly. In mid-December the Air Ministry and other Bolero re-quirements were cut down, and the Minister of Production was asked to review the whole situation on the basis that 225,000 men would be withdrawn from the building industry during 1943.

As an interim measure, to check further deterioration while he prepared his review, the Minister of Production put an embargo on the starting of new works.

The wheel had gone full circle. The recommendations of the Minister of Production were accepted by the War Cabinet in January 1943. Control of the building programme now took the form of labour 'ceilings' limiting the maximum volume of work to be undertaken. Individual projects were to be jointly scrutinised by the Ministry of Works and the Ministry of Labour, and were not to be approved un-less they could clearly be undertaken without unbalancing the pro-gramme. Cases of difficulty were to be referred to the Minister of Production.

By the middle of February the departments' allocations were finally confirmed. The Minister of Works, under the Minister of Pro-

---

[1] The term 'ceiling' was coined to meet the Minister of Labour's objection to 'allocation', but it was simply a play of words.

duction, was at last arbiter of the building programme. The Minister of Production occupied the position formerly held by the Production Executive and was the authority before whom the departments bowed when a decision went against their wishes. The operative work of the building programme continued, however, to be the function of the Minister of Works, both on paper and in fact. To him and his department fell all the administrative work of checking the allocations, and of submitting reports and recommendations for authorisation by the Minister of Production. Although the Minister of Production had discretion to question any recommendation of the Minister of Works, in practice that discretion was rarely exercised.

After December 1942 the Directorates did not meet again, nor were any meetings held of the Official Committees after that date. Throughout 1943 and 1944 the building programme was administered without committees, but in accordance with policy laid down. All doubtful cases and questions arising out of policy decisions were referred to the Minister of Production. Allocations for each period were submitted to the War Cabinet by the Minister of Production advised by the Minister of Works, while the Building Programmes Directorate itself carried out detailed investigation of the demands of departments and made recommendations on allocation of labour.

The imposition of ceilings was virtually a reversion to the former allocation system. The theoretical difference between an allocation and a ceiling was that the one was the labour force to which a department was entitled, while the other was merely an upper limit beyond which a department could not go. In practice, as it turned out, there was no essential difference, but the word 'ceiling' had a certain psychological value as a substitute for the word 'allocation'. It proved more acceptable not only to the Ministry of Labour but to the Service Ministries, on whom Ministers, as has been seen and as will appear in later chapters,[1] had found great difficulty in imposing allocation.

When the labour ceiling allocation system finally superseded priorities, super-preference was also abolished as a 'blanket' category covering whole programmes, but from time to time specially urgent works continued to carry this label. Ceiling allocations remained the normal method of controlling the building programme. There were several important occasions, however, when the method had to adapt itself to operational needs. One was in October 1943 when allocations had to be modified for the new programme of works known as 'Phoenix'.[2] This was the construction of the great floating caissons of reinforced concrete which, when sunk, formed the breakwaters encircling the

---

[1] See Chapter XI *et seq.*
[2] See Chapter XV.

Mulberry harbours. The building industry's role in the execution of the Phoenix programme was made possible only through the urgent transfer of large bodies of men from all parts of the country to the Thames, Solent, Mersey and other port areas. In the space of two months some 20,000 men were transferred. Another special occasion was in April 1944 when, for the impending Second Front operations, the volume of rail haulage of building materials had to be severely cut so as to free the railways for operational traffic. That meant a ten per cent. cut in allocations combined with an embargo on the starting of new works.

Another adaptation of the ceiling allocation system was because of the flying bomb attacks on London and south-east England in June 1944 and the following months.[1] For the repair of the damage, on an unprecedented scale, a large labour force had to be assembled, partly at the expense of the building programme, and many men transferred to London from the provinces. Under these conditions formal allocations to departments would have been unrealistic, and no formal allocations at all were in fact made from the period July to September 1944, but the Ministry of Works saw that essential works received the labour. To restrict the use of labour as far as possible for work other than war damage repair, the War Cabinet put an embargo on all new works in the London area except those of operational or equivalent importance.

By this time the impartial administration of the building programme by the Ministry of Works had been at last accepted by the departments. All questions were settled inter-departmentally without any meetings of the official committees and without even threats of appeal to the War Cabinet. Although the allocation system was centrally directed, its detailed operation was decentralised to regional allocation officers, who were in close touch with the Ministry of Labour representatives and with all the important contracts in their areas. The system was elastic enough to take these major operational changes in its stride, and even to dispense for a time with fixed allocations without endangering any of the really vital building projects.

---

[1] See Chapter X.

PART III

Methods of Control

CHAPTER VI

THE CONTROL OF THE BUILDING AND CIVIL ENGINEERING INDUSTRIES

(i)

The Basis of Control Policy

WE have seen how, by a process of trial and error over six years, co-ordination of the Government building programme as a whole was substantially achieved by the beginning of 1943. We have also recorded what was salient in the relations between Government departments and the building industry.

The means by which control over the industry was made effective have yet to be described.[1] That control began in 1940. Much of it, as has been noted, was voluntarily accepted by the industry in its endeavour, jointly with Government, to meet the successive economic problems which the building programme presented.

At the root of most of them lay the struggle over manpower. The crucial fact for the industry during the war was that it had to sacrifice sixty-four per cent. of its labour strength[2] to the forces and to other industries. The necessity for control arose from this fact: that the steadily diminishing labour force had to be used to the best advantage in the gravest years of the war. That the method of control was successful is sufficiently proved by the volume of work that was done on Government account under very difficult working conditions by this depleted operative force.[3]

Almost every control, as Professor Bowen testifies, was forced on the Government, and was carried out by very inadequate staffs who had not the slightest desire to increase their sphere of influence. The various regulations which are to be noted were not arbitrarily imposed on a refractory industry, but built up within a single framework of consistent policy.

The situation, as seen in the new Ministry of Works in the autumn

---

[1] See Bowen, I., 'The Control of Building', from which the writer freely quotes in this chapter by permission.

[2] This figure refers to the percentage decline in the insured male labour force in July 1939 (1,362,000), which force was reduced to a minimum, e.g. July 1944 (496,000).

[3] Bowen, I., 'The Control of Building'.

of 1940, before the allocation system had been worked out, was somewhat paradoxical. The object of the Ministry was specifically to secure that a balanced production programme should be laid down for the industry, so that its labour and material resources could be used to the full, and to the best advantage. There was unemployment still in parts of the country; yet there were labour demands unsatisfied elsewhere. The total volume of building and civil engineering work in hand did not seem to be perhaps much over half the volume in 1937—but no one knew for certain whether or not this was true, in the absence of any even partially complete statistics. The efficiency of labour was already believed to have fallen. One guess, Professor Bowen recalls, which had some currency at that period was that an average of fifty bricks laid per hour before the war had perhaps declined to thirty by 1940. There was a dispute as to the optimum number of hours that could be worked weekly in the industry; 'experience' was said by some employers to 'show' that fifty-four hours per week was an optimum—but whose experience this was, and over what period was not made clear.[1]

Meanwhile the Schedule of Reserved Occupations, amended though it was to include building labourers, had left the industry badly out of balance. By the summer of 1941 there was a shortage of at least 50,000 labourers. Moreover, the decline in the total labour force (overestimated as it then was) alarmed the Government.

> In July 1941, as a result of an even more alarming decline in the number of men in coal-mining, a registration of all men who had since 1935 done six months work in the mines was made by Statutory Order. It was natural that a similar idea should be discussed in connection with the building industry; and the possibility of individually registering each man who had been in building, or at least each one who was now in the industry, so as to put a 'tab' on each of the individuals needed for the programme, was entertained very seriously, and, indeed, the idea was always simmering in the background until 1945. The strongest objections to such a plan were the administrative inconvenience of dealing direct with some three-quarters of a million not highly literate operatives, and the floating nature of the labour force in the industry. An industry such as building and civil engineering has unaccountable entries and exits going on continuously, even in war-time.[2]

The two main instruments of control, apart from the Schedule of Reserved Occupations, were the registration of employing firms[3] and

---

[1] Bowen, I., 'The Control of Building'.

[2] *Ibid.* From mid-1942 to mid-1943 it was estimated, on the basis of a sample, that 137,000 men left the industry for other industries, but that over the same period, 99,000 *entered* the industry *from* other industries.

[3] Under S.R. & O. 1941, No. 1038. See Section (iii) of this chapter.

the scheduling of sites under the Essential Work Orders,[1] both of which first applied to the building industry in July 1941. Though less drastic than the proposed registration of individual builders, the registration of firms was equally thorough since, as Professor Bowen observes, the administrative control of labour in the industry is after all organised, at any given moment, most easily through the firm. 'The *raison d'être* of the firm is as an organisational nucleus'. Not only were all building and civil engineering firms compelled to register with the Ministry of Works and to make returns to the department, but the Essential Work Orders became the basis of the scheduling of particular sites.[2] Labour was tied to these sites, and men could neither be dismissed nor resign without the agreement of the National Service Officer of the district. Scheduling of contracts under the Essential Work Order was the second new weapon of administrative control; the only loophole left was that contractors, once they had engaged men, could move them from contract to contract without reference to the employment exchange, and in this way labour was found for a certain amount of low priority work. This was stopped by the Restriction on Transfer Order of 18th December 1941, which became effective on 12th January of the following year.[3] These Orders were the instruments through which the allocation system was operated in practice.

Against the background of the struggle for manpower the regulations accepted by the industry fall into place. They are examined in greater detail in this chapter and the ones that follow, and we begin by reviewing some of the chief categories under these headings:

1. The Restriction of Civil Building.
2. The Regulation of Contracting Undertakings.
3. Forms of Contract and Contractors' Records.
4. The Control of Employment.
5. Payment by Results.

(ii)

The Restriction of Civil Building

Apart from the general restrictions on civil building whose introduction is discussed in an earlier chapter,[4] and later regulations which are the subject of this section, action was taken on the outbreak of war by the Ministry of Health and the Department of Health for Scotland

---

[1] S.R. & O. 1941, No. 2067: 1942, Nos. 2044 and 2071. Registration was used as a means of grouping some of the smaller contractors, and great efforts were made to see that these groups were employed for sub-contract work in Government jobs.

[2] See Section (v) of this chapter.

[3] S.R. & O. 1941, No. 2068.

[4] See Chapter II.

to regulate the normal housing work of local authorities. In a Circular to housing authorities in England and Wales, on 8th September 1939,[1] the Minister of Health referred to slum clearance and housing schemes then in varying stages of progress. The broad effect of the Circular was that, in view of the possible destruction of housing accommodation by air attack, clearance schemes should stop short of actual demolition; and that the erection of further houses would not be approved save in exceptional circumstances, such as, for example, where houses were needed for the employees of new factories or for agricultural workers generally. Local authorities were to concentrate only on houses in an advanced stage of construction and not to continue work on houses in an early stage or to start foundations for new houses. In May 1940, after powers had been given to the Works and Building Priority Committee for the control of building contracts, all departments were obliged to obtain the committee's sanction for housing schemes of fifty houses or more.

On 7th October 1940, shortly before the creation of the new Ministry of Works was announced in Parliament, the licensing of civil building came into force under the Defence Regulations. Licensing had two clear objectives:

1. To stop all private building not essential for the war effort or for the upkeep of the morale of the civil population;
2. To ensure, for permitted civil building, the most economical use of labour and materials.

A building 'operation' as defined by the new Defence Regulation[2] costing over £500 could now only be carried out under authority of a Government department or with a licence from the Ministry of Works. This provision, it was soon seen, did not go far enough. Much of the work still being carried out below the £500 limit was unessential, and as from 14th April 1941 the limit was reduced to £100.[3]

Even the amended Regulation was found to be too narrow. It still did not control work on demolition, repair, maintenance, decoration, or protection of premises against enemy attack. Under all these headings labour and materials were being wasted on non-essential works. To bring under control such work when carried out by a private firm or person, an entirely new Regulation[4] was substituted for the original 56A and came into force on 1st January 1942.

---

[1] Ministry of Health Circular No. 1866 (in Scotland D.H.S. Circular No. 124/1939).

[2] Regulation 56A (S.R. & O. 1940, No. 1678). This followed the procedure adopted in the First World War.

[3] S.R. & O. 1941, No. 437. As a consequence of the flying bomb attacks in the summer of 1944, and in order to concentrate labour and materials on urgent repairs, this limit was reduced to £10 for the London Civil Defence Region with effect from 3rd October 1944, S.R. & O. 1944, No. 112). The £10 limit was extended to specified areas in south-eastern England with effect from 5th February 1945 (S.R. & O. 1945, No. 105) and later to the whole of Great Britain.

[4] S.R. & O. 1941, No. 1596.

The effect of the new Regulation was twofold. It ensured, in the first place, that no single operation of more than £100 was carried out without licence. In the second place, it limited to an expenditure of £100 the amount of building work of all kinds that might be done on a single property in any period of twelve months.[1] A new departure was that, instead of a fixed financial limit of £100 in the Regulation itself, the Minister could fix the limit by Order which he could vary (again by Order) as circumstances might from time to time require.

The Minister also had power to regulate the size and type of building materials and the manner in which works were carried out: for example, to regulate the size and type of glass in the replacement of windows; to alter proposed construction from reinforced concrete to structural steel and vice versa; to order building in brick or building blocks instead of timber, roof covering in asbestos instead of tiling or slating, etc.

Works carried out by a Government department or by a local authority or by a public utility undertaking in discharge of its functions were excepted from the Regulation. Although for the last two categories no licence from the Ministry of Works was needed, the work had to be authorised by the appropriate Government department[2] and consequently had to be covered by the authorising department's allocation of labour.

The interpretation of the Regulation was stringent. In the first place the complete cost of a proposed building operation had to be stated. This included the cost of all labour and materials (whether secondhand or already existing on the site or already the property of the owner or contractor), builders' overheads and profit, hire of plant, fees charged for professional and technical services and any other charges paid by the party for whom the work was being done.

It was not permissible to avoid the obligation to obtain a building licence by carrying out in stages a building operation the total cost of which exceeded £100: for example, by erecting a portion at a cost of £100 or under year by year. In calculating the amount spent on any property within the preceding twelve months, the cost of all work had to be included whether it took the form of a single building operation or a series of building operations or maintenance work, whether it was licensed or unlicensed, whether it was carried out by or on behalf of the owner or occupier. The cost of all work carried out on

---

[1] Property for the purpose of the Regulation was defined as the Schedule A unit or, in default thereof, the rating valuation unit.

[2] For example, the Ministry of Health and the Department of Health for Scotland authorised municipal houses, water and sewage schemes; the Board of Trade gas undertakings; the Ministry of War Transport railways; and so forth.

the property by a local authority, including first-aid repairs after damage by enemy action, had also to be included. The term 'preceding twelve months' did not mean any calendar or financial year, but the twelve months up to and including any day on which work was being done.

The precise meaning of maintenance under the new Regulation was a source of difficulty. On the one hand, before any building operation or any combination of such operations could be carried out in excess of £100, a licence was required. Maintenance, on the other hand, was not an operation as originally defined in Regulation 56A and was not in fact subject to licence as an operation. Left undefined in the Regulation, it might have been interpreted in various ways. At one end of the scale the renewing of a washer or a tap might be maintenance, while at the other end of the scale it might equally well be applied to the reinstatement and decoration of industrial and commercial buildings. The practice, therefore, was to grant annual maintenance licences limiting the amount spent during a period of twelve months. A maintenance licence having been granted, the building owner was free to give effect to it at his own discretion.

To avoid abuse of such licences it was important to ensure that no operation for which an individual licence was properly required, and which was subject to close scrutiny as to its necessity, should be carried out under the cover of maintenance; and since there was no appropriate legal definition of maintenance a workable list of items had to be classed by the Ministry under that heading and used as a rough-and-ready index.[1]

Decoration, often regarded by owners as maintenance, was not so interpreted except when it was incidental to an item of maintenance work. Decoration was classed an operation, and a separate application had therefore to be made for a licence to carry it out. To have left decoration under the heading 'maintenance' would have debarred licensing officers from the discretion of postponing a proposed work of decoration as unnecessary.

Although works carried out by Government departments were exempted from the provisions of Regulation 56A, a substantial proportion of the works licensed were in fact sponsored by departments: for example, factories working for the supply departments. The labour so employed on such works was counted against the department's allocation.

When labour allocation proposals were being drawn up a proportion of the labour was always reserved to cover civil building; and the total volume of civil licences had to be progressively reduced as the total labour force diminished.

---

[1] Notes and Appendices: Appendix 9, 'Maintenance Items'.

The Regulation was unavoidably somewhat complicated; it took some time to impress it upon the industry and the public. There was a good deal of evasion, nor was the attitude of the Courts at the outset conspicuously sympathetic towards enforcement. The Ministry of Works had to keep a vigilant eye on offences and could not always leave the decision to the Public Prosecutor. The Ministry formed its own views as to 'intent' and moral culpability, and the papers were sent to the Public Prosecutor only after a suspected offender had had an opportunity of putting the whole case to the Ministry, and the department had determined as to whether it was a bad case. The Public Prosecutor merely decided whether the evidence was adequate or not. Prosecutions were never allowed to become automatic or vindictive.

(iii)

The Registration of Contracting Undertakings

The registration of employing firms took effect as from 1st October 1941. No person could now carry on a building or civil engineering contracting undertaking, as defined in the Regulation, unless he was registered by the Ministry of Works and held a certificate of registration.[1]

In addition to its primary object in getting accurate information of the personnel in the building and civil engineering industries, the Regulation had the equally important purpose of preventing a steep rise in the cost of building while labour was short and demand plentiful. That purpose was to be achieved, first, by stabilising the wages and conditions of employment in the industry at the level fixed by joint industrial agreement; secondly, by controlling maximum hours of employment (including Sunday work) so as to prevent uneconomic use of labour through the working of excessively long hours; and lastly, by ensuring that the resources of the industry as a whole were used to the best advantage in the national interest.

While it was not the Minister's function to fix rates of pay and conditions of work (matters to be settled by joint agreement within the industry), it was his duty to safeguard terms and conditions of employment and working hours in registered undertakings and to issue certificates of registration, provisional and otherwise. Power to revoke

---

[1] This Regulation was added to the Defence (General) Regulation 1939 by S.R. & O. 1941, No. 1038, as from 18th July 1941, as noted earlier. The date for the operation of the above provision was fixed by S.R. & O. 1941, No. 1162. It also applied to Northern Ireland, but was administered there originally by the Minister of Commerce and later by the Ministry of Labour, Northern Ireland.

certificates was given; and the Minister could also call for releases of labour employed by registered undertakings.

To provide himself with help in administering the Regulation the Minister appointed, in January 1942, an advisory panel, with the Director-General of the Ministry as chairman and ten industrial representatives nominated by the National Federation of Building Trades Employers and the Federation of Civil Engineering Contractors.

It is noteworthy that while wage-fixing in any industry has commonly been the fixing of a minimum, both sides of the industry now unanimously agreed to fix a maximum as well as a minimum. The minimum was fixed by the Fair Wages Clause, and it was not permissible to pay any wage above the industrially fixed rate. The provision was rigorously enforced and very effective.

As originally made, the Regulation was intended to create a register of contractors operating at 1st October 1941; it was not designed to provide for the registration of new firms set up after that date or as a continuing instrument of control of entry to the industry. In practice, until the summer of 1944, registration was only granted to applicants who had previously been in business in the industry, and this did in fact provide a check on the entry of unwanted newcomers into the industry at a time when war conditions were throwing many builders out of business. But more difficulties seemed likely to arise from a refusal to grant admission than from conceding it, especially as many applications came from men recently discharged from the Services. Under political pressure, provision was ultimately made to widen the conditions of registration and to include new applicants.

By an Order in Council on 29th June 1944[1] registration was granted as a right where the Minister was satisfied that an applicant had carried on a building or civil engineering business at any time between 1st May 1939 and 1st October 1941; or that the application for registration was made for the purpose of reviving or carrying on a business in respect of which a certificate of registration had been issued to any person.

Where these conditions did not exist the Minister was empowered to issue a certificate of registration if it appeared to him expedient and in the public interest. To advise the Minister in the exercise of his discretion an independent committee of three persons was formed, with instructions to take into account the views of all sections of the industry and to give sympathetic consideration to applications from ex-Service men.[2]

---

[1] S.R. & O. 1944, No. 745.

[2] Despite all precautions new building firms (many of them old businesses which had been closed down early in the war and now revived) sprang into existence in tens of thousands, greatly reducing the efficiency of the industry, at all events for the time being. See *The Builder*, 17th November 1944, p. 394. Letter from a correspondent.

(iv)

Forms of Contract and Contractors' Records

It was hoped that the State could check waste and extravagance by regulating war-time contracts and sub-contracting. Normally, the accepted dividing line of responsibility between the Treasury and the contracting departments had been this: it was for the Treasury to lay down principles for the placing of contracts, to regulate procedure and to deal with any unusual conditions; but it fell to the departments themselves to take complete responsibility for contract administration in detail and to see that financial provisions were prudent and economical.[1] However, as the Government building programme came more fully under direction by the Ministry of Works, contract practice, both to secure uniformity and to secure economy, became the subject of discussion between the Ministry and the building and civil engineering industries. The discussion took place both at the Joint Consultative Committee and also inter-departmentally at the official level, but the vital link of the Contracts Co-ordinating Committee in securing uniformity of contract practice still remained.[2]

It has already been noted that in building contracts the price to be paid by the building owner is usually determined, subject to a number of variations, in one of two ways: by a 'fixed price' or a 'cost plus' contract. Of these alternatives, fixed price contracts are obviously the more desirable. But it is doubtful if the full advantage of placing contracts on the basis of fixed prices could be secured unless there were some way of stabilising the general level of prices of building materials and of wages and other payments to the building operative on what is a practically fixed price basis; on the other hand, the device of Variation of Price Clauses does enable most of the advantages of fixed price contracting to be secured even in time of instability of prices and wages.

A cost plus or cost reimbursement contract is appropriate only where the character or scope of the work is undetermined at the time of the contract; but fluctuation in cost of materials, wages, output of labour and similar circumstances, which might make a fixed price contract difficult to negotiate, are not alone always considered sufficient justification for resorting to cost plus contracts.[3]

In this respect the Ministry of Works endorsed and preached the Treasury's general policy. While contracts for Government works ser-

---

[1] Notes and Appendices: Note V, 'Forms of Contract'.

[2] See p. 34 (footnote).

[3] In the War Office, for example, fluctuating labour output was not so accepted, and where prime cost contracts were used the reason was that extreme urgency made the negotiation of contracts at fixed prices impossible.

L

vices, for which tenders were normally invited by competition, were in appropriate cases on a fixed price basis—for example, in regard to new construction, especially of a repetitive type, and for alterations and adaptations of existing buildings—cost plus contracts had to be used for first-aid repairs following air raids, for maintenance work where it was not practicable to use a schedule of prices, for alterations to existing buildings where it was not practicable to contract on any other basis, and for specialist work which from its nature required details to be settled as the work proceeded.

The letting of fixed price contracts was made easier by the use of the Ministry of Works Standard Schedule of Prices,[1] a list containing prices of work in each of the customary trades. Such prices were fixed with reference to stated rates of pay for tradesmen, labourers and navvies, and to basic prices of the principal materials. Using these constants, with various allowances, rates were built up to ensure uniform overhead charges and profit in each trade. The schedule was thus used for the pricing of bills of quantities to be issued to contractors as a basis for tenders quoting on or off percentages. It could also be used where no bills of quantities were prepared, but where a bill of preliminaries or some similar arrangement was made to cover the charges. In these ways the schedule obviated the use of the cost plus form of contract for specified categories of work and simplified the preparation of bills of quantities.

The evolution of the Standard Schedule of Prices was the work of the Central Council for Works and Building[2] and was carried through despite professional criticism and denunciation, based apparently on the quite mistaken assumption that the use of the schedule would deprive quantity surveyors of their livelihood. The view was held in the Ministry of Works (but not necessarily shared by other building departments[3]) that as there was more work on offer than could be done and a vast amount of extensions of contracts, really competitive tendering had ceased to have any meaning. Even if one secured a firm price it might be too high. The schedule provided a yardstick. A small committee worked out the actual cost of work based on an efficient contractor applying the system of payment by results and including all overheads, profits, etc. The schedule became universally used and was an effective check on prices. A contract could be let without plans simply on plus or minus tendering against the schedule of prices. Its use, too, was a powerful force in extending

---

[1] A comprehensive schedule of prices had existed in the War Office for many years and formed the basis of a large volume of measurement contracts.

[2] See Chapter XVIII.

[3] War Office experience, for example, did not confirm the view that really competitive tendering had ceased to have any meaning. Even in the busiest periods of the war, provided time could be allowed to frame the contract on which competitive tendering could be based, reasonable (and often keen) competition was obtained for War Office contracts.

payment by results, because the prices could not be achieved without payment by results.

The role of the *specialist* sub-contractor, to which reference has already been made,[1] was less prominent in war-time than under normal peace-time conditions, but in determining the scope of building contracts for new construction the Ministry of Works was able to ensure that they included as provisional services heating, lighting and other engineering services. The Ministry could require competitive offers to be sought for this work and nominate sub-contractors to carry it out.

Quite different considerations applied to the *non-specialist* sub-contractor. In order to stimulate the use of local resources, and bring in the small builders, it was a condition of the majority of contracts over £60,000 that not less than twenty per cent. of the general building work (as distinct from sub-letting of trades) should be sub-let to local firms. In default the Ministry had the right to appoint nominated sub-contractors for this percentage of work. In this way more labour was made available, and something was done to save the building industry from disintegration through the disappearance of smaller firms unable to take direct part—for example, in the huge Bolero contracts.[2]

THE CENTRAL AND REGIONAL CONTRACTORS' RECORDS

In addition to the register of building and civil engineering undertakings under the Defence Regulations already described, a Record of Contractors was maintained by the Ministry of Works as a clearing-house for all Government departments concerned with the placing of building and civil engineering contracts. Inclusion in this record was not compulsory, but under pressure of the Bolero programme it was introduced, with the co-operation of the industry, to minimise waste of effort, to spread the work over as many suitable firms as possible, to prevent the over-loading of individual contractors, and to provide a rough-and-ready estimation of the unemployed capacity of contractors.

At the outset, in 1942, the Central Contractors' Record consisted of contractors already registered under Defence Regulation 56AB who employed not less than 100 men on 1st July 1941 (in Scotland seventy-five men) and whose average turnover for the three years 1939, 1940 and 1941 was not less than £40,000. The test for inclusion in the Record was later amended to £60,000 (in Scotland £45,000) average turnover or more.

Firms on the central record were eligible to be invited by the con-

---

[1] See Chapter I.
[2] See Chapter XII *et seq.*

tracting Government departments to tender for works over £25,000 (£18,000 in Scotland). When the total amount of the uncompleted work on hand (Government or otherwise) of a firm reached sixty per cent. of the value of their average annual turnover they were placed on a 'temporary suspension' list and were automatically excluded from the Government's 'invitation to tender' list until their uncompleted work on hand fell to forty per cent. of their average turnover.

A firm was regarded eligible to tender (provided it was not otherwise disqualified) for any service which would not increase its load to more than twenty-five per cent. above its average turnover. In calculating this margin for permissible additional load, account was taken of the *rate* of working represented by average annual turnover.

In addition to the central record, Government contracts under £25,000 (in Scotland under £18,000) were dealt with by means of regional contractors' records on similar lines. Moreover, for the purpose of tendering it was permissible for a number of firms to combine to form a group. Such groups operated either under one firm appointed as a leader or as a group registered under Defence Regulation 56AB, whether as a limited liability company or not.

Additions to the Central and Regional Contractors' Records of firms which were not operating during the years 1939, 1940 and 1941, or for only a part of that period, were made on the recommendation of the Contracts Allocation Sub-Committee and the Building Programme Joint Committee.[1]

(v)

The Control of Employment

Within the general regulations for the control of employment, some special restrictions, which have already been referred to, were applied to the building industry. It is timely to recall that under the Emergency Powers (Defence) Act 1940, Regulation 58A gave the Minister of Labour absolute control over employment as from 22nd May 1940. Under these powers he had made a number of Essential Work Orders under which persons employed in certain scheduled undertakings could not leave their employment or be dismissed without permission. On the other hand, such persons, while so employed, received a guaranteed wage, but were subject to control in regard to absenteeism, lateness and the disobedience of orders.[2]

---

[1] See Notes and Appendices: Note X, 'Committee Organisation in Ministry of Works, 1940–45'.

[2] The principal Order of the Essential Work (General Provisions) (No. 2) Order, S.R. & O. 1942, No. 1594. The Essential Work Orders dealing especially with building and civil engineering and with electrical contracting were, as already noted, S.R. & O. 1942, Nos. 2044 and 2071.

The broad effect of the Order specially applied to building was that the Minister of Labour was empowered to schedule both sites and undertakings where essential constructional works were being carried out. Subject to conditions, certain classes of employees could no longer be dismissed from, or leave, the undertaking without the permission of a National Service Officer; they also received guaranteed wages and were paid by results.

Certificates of scheduling were issued by the Ministry of Labour showing the grades or classes of labour covered by the Order. A scheduling notice had to be posted on all sites or undertakings scheduled under the Order.

On scheduled undertakings, as distinct from scheduled sites, scheduling was in practice limited to plant yards, plant offices, plant-hiring firms and a few specialist firms.

The extension of the Essential Work Order to building brought in its train new and immensely difficult problems, not only for the Ministry of Labour and the other departments called upon to administer the Order, but for the workpeople too. Under the parent Order a man was tied to a factory, which would normally remain in continuous operation for the whole of the war. In the building industry the Essential Work Order tied a man not to a firm but to a site, which in due course he would leave as the work became completed and move to another scheduled site. The system worked well, but required cumbrous machinery; nor did it put an end to the vast fluctuations in all building labour or absenteeism. The real 'waster' slipped through the meshes of the net; prosecution was ineffective and dismissal meaningless. On the other hand, it must be realised that in the very large movement of building and civil engineering labour from one place to another, the workpeople as a whole accepted with considerable good will and patience the necessity for constant transfer under very difficult and uncomfortable conditions. They, too, they felt, were in the first line and were helping to win the war.

Where a site or undertaking had been scheduled certain main conditions applied. Most of them were common to the Essential Work (General Provisions) Order and the Essential Work (Building and Civil Engineering) Order. Such common provisions were:

1. The conditions of employment of the workers had to conform to the recognised conditions applicable to the job.
2. Satisfactory arrangements had to be made for the welfare of workmen, including the provision of meals.
3. The employer could not dismiss a workman (except for misconduct) without permission of the National Service Officer of the Ministry of Labour.
4. A workman could not terminate his employment without approval of the National Service Officer.

5. At least seven days' notice of termination of employment had to be given by either employer or workman.

6. The employer or the employee could appeal through the National Service Officer to the appropriate Appeal Board against the granting or refusal by the National Service Officer of permission to discharge or leave.

7. A workman might be summarily dismissed for misconduct, but had the right of appeal through the National Service Officer to the appropriate Appeal Board. Where the appeal was successful, the workman could be redirected to the job and receive payment for the period of absence.

8. A workman might be suspended without pay for disciplinary reasons for three consecutive days. He might appeal through the National Service Officer to the local Appeal Board and, if successful, was entitled to the payment of wages for the period of suspension.

9. If a worker failed to comply with any reasonable order given to him (including orders as to working of a reasonable amount of overtime) the employer could report him in writing to the National Service Officer, who might issue directions to the worker.

Differences between the general provisions and those applying specially to building and civil engineering were:

GENERAL PROVISIONS	BUILDING AND CIVIL ENGINEERING
1. Scheduling	
By undertaking only.	(*a*) By site, generally.
	(*b*) By undertaking in certain special cases.
2. Guarantee	
(i) (*a*) *Week*. Hours obtaining in the industry. (Applied to a person on a time-rate basis.)	(i) (*a*) *Week* = 44 hours. (Applied to a person on a time-rate basis.)
(*b*) *Day*. Hours obtaining in the industry. (Applied to persons paid otherwise than on a time-rate basis.)	(*b*) *Day* = 8 hours (4 on Saturday). (Applied to a person paid otherwise than on a time-rate basis, including all persons on work to which payment by results was being applied, whether or not they in fact earned a bonus.)
Overtime counted at ordinary plain-time rate.	*Overtime* counted at ordinary plain-time rate.

(ii) *Sundays*

Hours worked on a Sunday were not normally counted in the guaranteed week but were taken into account at plain-time rate in calculating whether any sum was payable under the guarantee.

(ii) *Sundays*

Excluded from the guarantee. Workers required to attend on a Sunday were therefore not entitled to any guarantee for that day under the Order (as distinct from the practice of the industry). Any earnings on a Sunday were not taken into account in calculating whether anything was due under the guaranteed week.

3. *Payment by Results*

No special provision, but not prohibited if agreed within the industry.

Required wherever practicable and desirable. Any bonus paid under the scheme was additional to the guaranteed day.

4. *Absenteeism*

Cases of absenteeism had to be referred to the works committee or other joint council in the undertaking (if any) before prosecution was initiated.

Special provision was made for setting up committees to deal with absenteeism. Where such a committee was set up cases had to be referred to it before prosecution.

(vi)
Payment by Results

The importance of applying the Essential Work Orders to payment by results in the building industry has already been noted. The system of fixing wages by the National Joint Council was to settle them on a basis of time-work with adjustments to changes in the cost of living. An hourly rate of wages was agreed for each separate district of the country. Before 1939, in the civil engineering industry, the National Working Rule provided for the payment of bonus in addition to time-rates on individual sites, but there was no general bonus scheme applicable throughout the industry. In the building industry, the National Working Rule did not accept any system of payment by results, and in some local rules it was expressly prohibited.

In practice, however, private enterprise builders worked largely on a piece-work basis by means of special arrangements between private building firms and their workers. The trade unions had always officially opposed piece-work on the ground that it led to shoddy work, operated unfairly between one workman and another and gave employers a chance to obtain more work for less pay.[1]

---

[1] Bowen, I., 'Incentive and Output in the Building and Civil Engineering Industries', in *The Manchester School* (May 1947).

The Government building programme during the first year of war had proceeded almost entirely on a time-work basis except for occasional bonus schemes in the civil engineering industry. These were mainly rewards for increased output unrelated to any measurable quantity of work.[1]

By the beginning of 1941 the Government had come to the conclusion that output per head in the building industry had fallen and, as we have seen, were greatly dissatisfied with the progress of the building programme, which was failing to keep pace with strategic needs. These difficulties were aggravated by the drawing away of a substantial part of building labour to the forces or munitions, leaving behind mainly the older and slower workers.

Negotiations between the Ministry of Works and the employers' and operatives' federations during the early months of 1941 for the acceptance of the principle of payment by results failed to secure agreement.[2] That failure was due in the main to the unreservedly hostile reaction of the leaders of the operatives' unions to the imposition of the payment by results system. Even after it had been reluctantly accepted by them, Mr. Luke Fawcett, President of the Amalgamated Union of Building Trade Workers of Great Britain, is reported as saying:[3]

> Payment by results will, from now onwards, be applied to selected building jobs. What must be our method of dealing with the system? We are opposed to it. That opposition has been expressed by the executive council of the Union and by the executive councils of the other unions in the building industry and by the National Federation of Building Trade Operatives. It has been emphasised in conference with the employers, and in consultation with the Ministers of Labour and Works, and other representatives of the Government departments concerned.

Nevertheless the representatives of the unions collaborated with the Government in drawing up some of the schedules of trades to which the system was applied, though continually criticising the system of piece-work. The military situation in Europe, however, made it imperative to accelerate the rate of construction in the industry, and both the employers' and operatives' organisations bowed before the Government's expressed determination to introduce a system of payment by results related to some measurable quantity of work, and one which would be applied on all works regarded as essential for the prosecution of the war.

---

[1] M.O.W. Report, *Payment by Results in Building and Civil Engineering during the War*, H.M.S.O. 1947.

[2] The course of these negotiations is outlined in *The National Federations' Defence of the Plain-Time Rate System*, published by N.F.B.T.O. (1941).

[3] *The Builder*, 18th July 1941.

In announcing their intentions to the representatives of the industry the Government gave the following assurances:

1. They would reconsider the scheme if at any time an agreement were reached by representatives of employers and operatives in the industries which was likely to be more effective than the official scheme in attaining its objects.

2. The scheme would be as flexible as possible, but no departure from its principles and no unauthorised bonus methods would be permitted on any Government work.

3. So far as the scheme affected branches of the industries previously remunerated solely on a time-rate basis, it would constitute a recognised 'change of practice' and would be operative only during the war unless continued by joint agreement.

4. No worker under the scheme would receive less remuneration than he would receive under existing agreements or under the guaranteed pay provisions of the Essential Work Order.

The representatives of the industries, though not actively supporting these arrangements, acquiesced in them, and in July the Essential Work (Building and Civil Engineering) Order 1941 made the introduction of a system of payment by results obligatory in all undertakings or sites scheduled under the Order, where considered (by the Ministry of Works) to be practicable and desirable.

The drawing-up of a scheme of payment by results appropriate to the building and civil engineering industries fell to the Ministry of Works. In this task the department had the advice of a joint advisory panel representative of the industry. This panel was presided over by the Director-General (Sir Hugh Beaver) and included representatives of the employers' and operatives' federations, both for England and Wales and for Scotland, who throughout co-operated in the administration of the scheme, though without prejudice to their views on the principles involved. The panel obtained technical advice on all aspects of the trade operations to which the bonus system could be applied, and as full information as was possible on trade practices and standards throughout the country before rates were fixed for general use. In determining the rates, it was taken into account that most of the younger men had been called to the colours, that the standard of workpeople available in the industries under war-time conditions had declined, and that standards of war-time building work, too, were reduced. The scheme provided definite targets of output for specified trade operations and, when those were exceeded, the additional output achieved entitled workers to bonus payments which were normally distributable in the proportion of five shares to foremen, four shares to craftsmen and three shares to labourers.

When the system was introduced in 1941 it was first applied to the trade operations of machine and land excavation, stone hardcore, concreting and bricklaying. The results were on the whole satisfactory and there was a demand for extending the system to other branches of constructional work. On 30th October 1941, it was accordingly applied to a number of additional operations, namely, pipelaying, reinforcing steel, carpentry and joinery, hutting, plastering, painting and glazing. There were by the end of 1942 some twenty-six schedules to all the main trade operations of the constructional industries to which payment by results was applied. These were listed in a consolidated memorandum issued in December 1942. In November 1944 the erection of temporary bungalows[1] was added to the list, and in the 1944–45 edition of the memorandum special provision was included for bonus payments in open-cast coal production, which had been operating successfully from its introduction in June 1943.

Bonus payments in respect of permanent housing was first discussed by the joint advisory panel in July 1943. The question came up in regard to the programme for the construction of 3,000 agricultural cottages for which special provision had been made during the war.[2] Since, however, this work could not be regarded as limited to the war period, and would have involved the post-war period by making bonus payments obligatory, the panel advised against its inclusion in the scheme. In their decision they were influenced by the assurance already given by the Ministers of Works and Labour that there would be no interference with industrial arrangements when the war was over. If, however, employers and operatives on any particular site wished to apply payment by results to those operations to which the scheme was suitable, they were left at liberty to do so. In any event the existing scheme was not suitable to permanent house construction.

The question of applying it to permanent housing was certainly considered in relation to the post-war position; but since the panel concluded that this would involve the whole issue of payment by results in the post-war period, the scheme was not applied to this work, whether scheduled under the Essential Work Order or not.

It was important that problems arising on sites should be promptly disposed of. To achieve this and to give guidance where there had been little or limited experience in working the system, payment-by-results advisers were appointed by the Ministry of Works in six regions which covered the whole of Great Britain. These advisers were qualified to give assistance in the practical application of the scheme. They were apprised of decisions reached on general principles as well as of specific cases of difficulty; and it was for them to apply the code of practice established by the headquarters of the Ministry of Works for general adoption throughout the country. They were thus able to help contractors to apply the system on any particular site; and were ex-

---

[1] Seco, U.S.A., Tarran, Phoenix, Arcon, Spooner, Universal.
[2] See Chapter XVII.

pected to visit every new site scheduled under the Order, within a reasonable time of the commencement of work, to make sure that the requirements of the system were understood and properly applied.

While the success of the scheme in increasing output lay with the operatives, responsibility for its application fell mainly upon the contractors.[1] They in turn relied upon their site staffs to make weekly measurement of the work completed by each gang. This work varied in extent with the type and size of contract and with the organisation of the contractors concerned. In the large civil engineering jobs where firms often had in existence systems of time allocation and weekly measurement for costing and bonusing, the extra work involved in operating the scheme often lay in the actual computation and distribution of the bonuses. On the smaller building contracts, however, the system might be a complete innovation and, at first, a tax on the available staff. The success of the scheme thus depended to a great extent on adequate and efficient bonus staff, and this became increasingly recognised as the industry gained experience in its operation.[2]

An important factor in the application of payment by results was that the men should have full confidence in the fairness of the bonus rates. The fact that these had been agreed by an advisory panel representing both sides of the industry carried much persuasion. The men were encouraged, too, by notices showing the target figures in operation and the bonuses earned. Bonus records had to be readily available for reference by the men's representatives; and this was particularly important where men on bonus work failed to reach basic output and were therefore ineligible for bonus. Further, the full value of the scheme as an incentive to increased production became apparent only if men consistently earned a reasonable bonus for a good day's work. In the building and civil engineering industries, where work was carried out under widely varying conditions, adjustments to the rates had to be promptly made, otherwise men might have been unable to earn a reasonable bonus and become discouraged. Clearly, close co-operation between the contractors' bonus staff and the men's representatives was essential. As to the effect of the varying working conditions on the output in relation to the basic outputs laid down and the consequent effect on bonus earnings, it is reported that there was surprisingly little real trouble on this score[3] and a great deal of give-and-take on the part of employers and operatives.

These matters were usually handled on behalf of the men by the card stewards of the respective trade unions. If the business to be discussed was considered of sufficient difficulty, a payment-by-results adviser and the area secretary of the men's union concerned were

---

[1] M.O.W. Report on *Payment by Results*. H.M.S.O. 1947.
[2] *Ibid.*
[3] *Ibid.*

asked to attend, and were generally able, by their wider experience, to contribute suggestions as a basis for settlement of any dispute. On the smaller contracts the procedure for agreeing site adjustments was on a more simple basis, often taking the form of direct agreement between the foreman and the men.

Among good examples of successful collaboration between contractors, operatives and payment-by-results advisers were the Phoenix and Beetle components of the Mulberry Harbour scheme,[1] and other forms of reinforced concrete floating structures for which special bonus rates were agreed to suit the unusual nature of the work; the runways and camps built for the use of the British and Allied forces; the Fido scheme for the dispersal of fog on airfields; and the Pluto project which involved the laying of vast lengths of pipeline through the land.

From 1942 regular returns were obtained by the advisers when visiting sites, and from these reports national statistics were derived, particularly of the output achieved in relation to the basic output laid down and the bonus earned. The table below summarises all the main trade schedules and shows the average level of output achieved in relation to basic output. The figures are based on data taken from the advisers' reports over a period of three years—1943 to 1946—and cover many millions of man-hours and machine-hours worked.[2]

Average Level of Output in Relation to Basic in the Main Trade Schedules

Operation	Average actual output expressed as percentage increase over basic	Operation	Average actual output expressed as percentage increase over basic
	%		%
Unloading materials .	62	Asbestos cement sheeting	48
Machine excavation .	50	Painting . . .	28
Hand excavation . .	7	Glazing . . .	48
Hardcore . . .	18	Air raid shelters . .	— *
Concreting . . .	39	Hutting (13 types) .	67
Reinforcing steel . .	35	Brick chimneys . .	— *
Scaffolding . . .	55	Slating and tiling . .	— *
Brickwork . . .	38	Slating and tiling (Scottish trade practice) .	— *
Pipe-laying . . .	27	Hollow tile floors and roofs	41
Tarmacadam . . .	41	Track-laying . .	51
Kerb fixing . . .	47	Pre-cast concrete floors and roofs . . .	— *
Carpentry and joinery .	29		
Wall and ceiling linings .	23	Pavings . . .	28
Plastering . . .	36	Opencast coal production	63

Average actual output on all operations covered by scheme, weighted by volume of work recorded = 34 per cent. over average basic output.
* Insufficient statistics on which to base an average.

[1] See Chapter XV.
[2] M.O.W. Report on *Payment by Results*. H.M.S.O. 1947. (Table B in this report.)

In arriving at the basic outputs, allowance was made for the special war-time classes of work and the lowered efficiency of building labour during the war period. The operations least affected by these conditions were machine excavation and trades such as bricklaying and plastering; the opposite is true of operations carried out by labourers in which heavy manual work was called for—a tendency no doubt accentuated by the use of 'designated craftsmen' on this kind of work, to which they were unaccustomed.

There are also figures in respect of temporary housing schedules, based on reports made by advisers over the period 1944 to 1946. In these figures the value of payment by results as an incentive to increased production is strikingly reflected.[1]

In order to assess the general influence of payment by results on output and cost, one would have to compare the output with that achieved on work not subject to a similar incentive. Unhappily there were no national records of output in the building and civil engineering industries in the pre-war period, nor was such information available in the early years of the war, although it was known that output in the industry was dropping, particularly in those operations most affected by the loss of the younger men to the armed forces and to other industries, and by the abnormal conditions under which the work on the whole was carried out.

The general question of output was, however, considered on several occasions by the Payment by Results Joint Advisory Panel, and in the autumn of 1943 a special committee was set up to consider the general effect on output and cost of the scheme.

Evidence was obtained from representative contractors throughout the country on output achieved in 1939, immediately before the introduction of payment by results in 1941, and at the time of the inquiry. The special committee's report showed that, while it might be unwise to draw too specific conclusions from this inquiry, it had demonstrated that the decline in output compared with 1939 had in general been arrested, and that the 1943 output figures reflected an improvement against 1941 for which a slight increase in labour cost had had to be paid. But the committee found, too, that the success of the scheme as a means of increasing output and reducing costs varied, fairly widely, according to the extent to which it was applied on individual sites. Where the scheme was fully operated with enthusiasm by both contractors and operatives it was very effective in increasing output, and this was particularly so on work of a straightforward nature. In concreting and bricklaying, increases of upwards of twenty-five per cent. to thirty per cent. were common, and often enough the effect on output of applying the scheme was considerably greater.

While it was difficult to measure factually the effect on output of

---

[1] M.O.W. Report on *Payment by Results*. H.M.S.O. 1947.

the scheme on the industry as a whole, it was possible to measure the effects of the scheme on specific classes of work. Details of these are given in the Ministry of Works 1947 Summary Report.

The effect of a bonus incentive on quality of work generally, and on site organisation, was carefully examined. It was sometimes alleged, stated the 1947 Report, that 'bonusing' tends to have an adverse effect on the quality of the work.

> Bad workmanship, however, is not necessarily the result of high output. A good workman can be expected to maintain a reasonable speed of production without in any way affecting the quality of his work. With regard to the effect on craftsmanship, it is generally accepted that the objects of a bonus incentive are not so much to increase the speed of working as to encourage the men to work with efficiency and increase their overall output by avoiding waste of time and overcoming causes of delay.

Since the question is almost entirely one of supervision and inspection of the work in progress, whether in an aircraft factory or on a building site, the fact that the men themselves were interested in overcoming minor delays relieved the supervisory staff of a good deal of work and left them free to give more time to watching the quality of the work in progress.

The advisory panel held that where unsatisfactory work did not show itself until after completion one might fairly conclude that supervision by the contractor was inadequate, and that he was responsible. Where supervision was efficient and the work was checked while in progress (the workmen's attention being drawn to defective work immediately it was detected), the quality was maintained; and because bonus was not payable on work condemned at the time the effect of the scheme on quality gave little cause for complaint.

The output achieved and the proportion of men engaged on bonused work varied with the efficiency of the site organisation and the facilities offered. Even the condition of tools supplied—such as picks and shovels in excavating—the provision of suitable material for concrete shuttering or the method of hoisting materials affected output in varying degree. In trench work, if timber was short and timbermen inefficient, output was low and no bonus was earned. It was often found, too, that a large number of non-bonused hours were accounted for by periods of waiting for materials where site transport was inadequate, by plant breakdowns, and by excessive movement of gangs either because of late delivery of materials or because of delay in receiving instructions.

An efficient bonus staff making frequent reports to the agent or foreman on the output achieved on the bonused work, and the manner in which the remaining time was spent, was often of immense assistance to the contractor. From such reports he could judge where weaknesses in the organisation lay, and it became evident that the regular measurement of output under the scheme formed a sound basis for the efficient organisation of the job.

That there should be much criticism of a scheme imposed by Government on the industry, even though the industry had accepted it for the time being, was inevitable. Some contractors found that while output had certainly increased, costs had also risen; but that was more a criticism of the targets fixed in relation to the standards of workpeople available in the industries under war conditions than a valid objection to payment by results as such. A more real disadvantage for the contractor was that, since clerical staff was necessary for the measurement of trade operation details, he had to shoulder a loss where output did not reach the basic rates. From the operatives' point of view, it is noteworthy that the standard of basic output rates was not common for various occupations and the system did not provide an equal bonus opportunity in all trades. All men on scheduled sites could not participate in bonus, since every class of work could not be measured, and men who were employed partly on 'bonusable' work and partly on other work tended to exaggerate the time spent on work on which bonus was payable so as to qualify for increased earnings. Another difficulty was that while the war-time scheme was welcomed by unskilled men, it always remained suspect in the eyes of the craftsmen, who considered that it led to scamped work.[1] Moreover, in the measurement of the work, the ganger could not be relied on to give accurate figures where he himself was sharing the bonus. Then, again, gangs where the workers were elderly or unfit sometimes did not achieve even the basic output, and this led to discontent with the bonus scheme. All these practical points had to be met and overcome, but underlying them was the fundamental objection of many operatives to bonuses worked out at sites or at regional conferences. Unless *ad hoc* bonuses could be kept roughly in step all over the country they threatened to cut across the trade unions' hard-won principle of national-level negotiations.[2] To quote the General Rules of the National Federation of the Building Trades Operatives:[3]

> The plain-time rate method of payment constitutes a vital and well-established principle of the Federation, and the Federation Branch is the guardian of that principle.
>
> Should piece-work or any other deviation from plain-time rates operate, the Federation Branch should at once write to affiliated

---

[1] Bowen, I., 'Incentive and Output in the Building and Civil Engineering Industries', in *The Manchester School* (May 1947).

[2] *Ibid.*

[3] Rule 12 (i). There was nothing, however, in the joint industrial agreement of the building industry to preclude the operation of payment by results, except in one or two regional agreements which specifically excluded it.

branches with a view to an immediate withdrawal of labour for the enforcement of plain-time rates. . . .

On the other hand, once the stubbornly resisted innovation had been agreed as a war-time measure, payment by results undoubtedly acted as a strong incentive to output. The rivalry between gangs became as important a factor as the financial aspect. The time and trouble taken by contractors in measuring work was repaid in the speeding up of the job. Contractors had also to take more trouble than they would otherwise have done in forming their gangs, since one slow worker in a gang might reduce output out of all proportion to his own slowness and antagonise the other workers, who resented their output being pulled down.

CHAPTER VII

THE CONTROL OF BUILDING MATERIALS

(i)

A System of 'Voluntary' Control

REFERENCE has been made in an earlier chapter[1] to shortages of building materials—some real, some illusive—during the rearmament period and the first year of war. It was then noted that in its handling of the materials problem the Works and Building Priority Committee had been more successful than in its efforts to control the supply and movement of labour; but that the committee lacked the authority to lay down a firm policy. That authority was later conferred upon the Minister of Works. In his statement to the House of Commons on 24th October 1940[2] the Lord Privy Seal had stated:

The Minister will be responsible for such control or central purchase of building materials not at present controlled as may be necessary.

Although this provision gave the Minister of Works wide powers, it became the consistent policy of his department to avoid control of building materials by any system of rationing or allocation which was likely (as the early attempts to ration cement demonstrated) to create an artificial scarcity through overbidding and subsequent hoarding. The Ministry's aim was always to ensure that the quantities of materials produced should be just sufficient for the labour-strength of the industry, and then to ration the labour by means of the allocation system. Steel and timber were exceptions because they were used not solely by the building industry but by nearly all industries. These materials could only be acquired and used for building by the authorisation of the respective Controllers, although small quantities of certain products could be acquired without authorisation from stock-holding merchants.

Of the other materials used in building works the most important were bricks, cement and roofing materials. As we have seen, each category was put under a Director at the Ministry of Works in 1940

---

[1] See Chapter II.
[2] H. of C. Deb., Vol. 365, Col. 1152.

and a number of regulations were later made to bring them under control. But the 'control' was not absolute in the ordinary sense, except over cement, for which a statutory control, imposed in a mood of unwarranted over-anxiety, remained—merely, however, as a paper control.[1] For the greater part of the war the Ministry of Works operated its system of 'voluntary' control, using only small staffs. The Director of Roofing Materials, for instance, had a staff of four or five people to cover his considerable and miscellaneous field.

(ii)
The Control of Bricks

Although in the first year of the war, as has been noted,[2] there was much uncertainty on the position of the brick industry, no shortage of bricks was apparent until the summer of 1940. In those weeks of crisis and suspense the demand for bricks rose steeply. Part was for the vast programme of air-raid shelter works, part for the direct building contracts of Government departments. There were difficulties, too, of labour, transport and fuel which helped to open a temporary gap between supply and demand. This tendency had been obscured mainly because there were large stocks to draw on, but also to some extent because shortages of cement had delayed the demand for bricks. The appointment of a Director of Bricks in December 1940 sharpened official awareness of the problems of the industry and was followed in September 1941 by the appointment by the Minister of Works of a Committee on the Brick Industry, with wide terms of reference.[3] The decision to set up the committee was not taken because there was in the Ministry of Works any real anxiety about the war-time supply of bricks, but because it was feared that the whole post-war reconstruction programme might collapse if the brick industry were allowed to disintegrate as it had done after the First World War. The Committee, under the guidance of its chairman, Mr. Oliver Simmonds, did a remarkable work in getting an agreed report and establishing a sense of research and efficiency.

The various types of product that constituted the brick output are examined in some detail in the first and third reports of the Simmonds Committee and are briefly described in another part of this volume.[4]

---

[1] See Chapter II.

[2] See *Ibid.*

[3] Referred to as the Simmonds Committee, this body met under the chairmanship of Mr. (later Sir) Oliver Simmonds. The brick industry was fully represented on it. The committee issued its final report in October 1942.

[4] See Notes and Appendices: Note VII, 'Types of Brick'.

Of the total output of the brick industry of Great Britain in 1941 approximately ninety-three per cent. could be classified as 'common bricks'. Within that broad classification the type and quality of product varied considerably: there were important differences, too, in the methods of manufacture and distribution.

To understand the problems of the common brick industry it is fundamental, as the Simmonds report insists, to regard the undertakings which comprised it as falling into either the Fletton group or the non-Fletton group.

The non-Fletton section of the industry, made up of a large number of highly diversified undertakings spread throughout the country, produced about two-thirds of the national output of common bricks. Many of these undertakings were relatively small and followed traditional methods of manufacture; others were skilfully and efficiently managed and, so far as their raw material permitted, used modern machinery and production methods. But one accepted idea prevailing in this section of the industry was the conception of the brick market as essentially a regional affair.[1] On the other hand, some of the Fletton group of undertakings, which produced the remaining one-third of the common bricks in the country in the Bedford and Peterborough areas under favourable natural conditions, rejected the idea that a brick undertaking should confine itself to a limited market, and much to the dismay of many other undertakings in the industry set out boldly to develop the marketing and distribution of their product on a national basis. The divergent trends in the non-Fletton and Fletton groups were widened by the development of the sand-lime group of undertakings in which mass production by modern methods, combined with an economic fuel consumption, enabled sand-lime bricks[2] to be delivered at a price competitive with Fletton bricks.

The war affected the two groups of the industry in different ways. A reduction in the total annual demand from some 7,000 million bricks in 1938 to not much more than half this figure by the end of 1941 had caused 384 undertakings in both sections of the industry to close down. Many of the undertakings which remained in production in the non-Fletton section of the industry had to meet severe difficulties. Facing bricks[3] were required only in very small quantities in war-time, and in some parts of the country particularly exposed to enemy air attack there was little building of any kind, so that the local market for bricks virtually disappeared. In other places, as has already been noted,[4] labour was a serious, sometimes desperate, problem. In some undertakings, too, the lack of any sales organisation, such as had

---

[1] *Second Report of the Committee on the Brick Industry* (H.M.S.O. 1942), Section 90.
[2] See Notes and Appendices: Note VII, 'Types of Brick'.
[3] *Ibid.*
[4] See Chapter II.

been developed by the larger companies, hindered the search for new markets to replace those lost through war conditions. Often large stocks of bricks remained on hand, and to find stacking-room became an acute problem.

For the Fletton section of the industry, the restriction of long-distance transport in war-time was the most serious check. Although most of these undertakings had large road transport fleets, the permitted mileage had to be drastically cut in order to economise fuel. On the railways, too, which had always carried the greater part of the Fletton supplies, similar restrictions were in force.[1] The net effect of the war conditions was to place Fletton producers somewhat at a disadvantage compared with the rest of the industry,[2] except for the non-Fletton producers in the south-eastern part of the country where, owing to special circumstances, the decrease in production was even greater.

It was only through the influence of the Simmonds Committee that the two groups of the brick industry, which until then had declined to meet, were induced to study each other's views and problems. The committee, not only in the interests of the brick industry but also in the public interest, saw to it that their reconciliation within the industry did not suffer any avoidable shock.

> The policy which we have kept before us has been to place the national interest as an overriding consideration, and therefore to seek the greatest practicable equity in meeting the interests of the two sections of the industry and of the undertakings which they comprise.[3]

The committee had to determine the means by which brick production could be reduced to the desired level. They laid down this broad principle: bricks should be drawn only from such works as could ensure the production and delivery to site with a minimum demand on national resources that could be used to greater advantage. In the application of this principle information and advice from representatives of the Ministry of Labour and the Mines Department did not give the committee the help they had looked for; but the Ministry of War Transport, by its insistence on the need to restrict the length of hauls, gave a definite impetus to the committee's policy. It was made evident that brick undertakings whose products must pass through congested routes on the railways were best shut down; while others which did not need to use these routes were kept in production, even though their consumption of manpower and fuel might be relatively

---

[1] In November 1941 the Ministry of War Transport ordered that no building bricks should be transported more than seventy-five miles by rail without a special licence.

[2] According to information given to the Simmonds Committee, the Fletton section of the industry manufactured during 1941 only sixty-one per cent. of its 1938 output as compared with sixty-eight per cent. in non-Fletton undertakings.

[3] *Second Report of the Committee on the Brick Industry* (H.M.S.O. 1942), Section 95.

heavy. While in some areas it might prove a clear advantage to release labour by shutting down a brickworks, in others—particularly in those where a brickworks was associated with, or was close to, a colliery—the balance of advantage might be in keeping open the works despite the need to transport the bricks some distance, thus retaining workers who might otherwise be absorbed by other industries. But the whole problem was beset with difficulties. Not the least was the dearth of accurate information, of a strictly comparable kind, on manpower and fuel consumption in the various undertakings, except such as was supplied by the undertakings themselves. The committee, since its members were mostly members of the brick industry, felt that it could not itself appraise the relevant issues in individual cases. It did, however, determine that further reduction on demand should be met—whether by the closing of works or otherwise—upon the basis of sharing the contraction of output as equitably as possible at the expense of all sections of the industry. That could be done in one of two clear-cut ways—either by the appointment of a controller of quotas with plenary powers or through the firm allocation of a quota on a predetermined basis. The committee thought that if it chose the second method, it would stereotype the pattern of the industry and thus prevent the changes which under war conditions were essential. To appoint a controller of quota, on the other hand, might be undesirable for two main reasons: first, because the structure of the industry was so complicated that its own experience in working out any scheme of contraction should not be side-tracked; and secondly, because it was one of the chief aims of the committee to foster within the industry a corporate sense and to set up an appropriate organisation. To appoint a controller with plenary powers would have run counter to this object; and the committee preferred to recommend the appointment by the Minister of a controller who was to work in close touch with the industry. He was also to have discretionary powers, but within stated limits.

Among other specific recommendations of the committee were schemes for the fixing of minimum prices and for compensation for loss of sales. For the war-time control of these schemes they recommended that a controlling authority, under the statutory authority of the Ministry of Works, should be set up, with the title National Building Brick Council. This body was also to be the controlling authority for a contributory scheme for the care and maintenance of closed works; and it was to co-operate with the Ministry of Works and the appropriate organisations in continuing the programme of technical investigation initiated by the committee. The Council in effect was to provide a suitable framework within which a permanent national organisation for the brick industry might subsequently be built up.

It was a matter for decision whether the control of the industry's production and sales, under the proposed quota plan, should fall to the industry, to the National Building Brick Council, or to the Minister. It was represented to the committee that to place these important duties in the hands of an official nominee would affront the industry. On the other hand, since the State was almost the only customer for bricks in war-time, would it not be logical for the Government to control the allocation of the output of the industry without reference to the industry itself? The balance of advantage, it was thought, lay between these two extremes. It is true that the Directorate of Bricks could rely on a considerable fund of current statistical information and experience; and that an official nominee might strike a balance between the often conflicting points of view of other departments. The industry had, however, immense experience of the problems of brick production and distribution and had learned in a hard school to assess them at their correct value. In contrast to this, no officer of the Directorate of Bricks had other than a war-time knowledge of the industry, and although from many points of view such relative detachment was desirable, what was wanted was a close relationship with the industry. The immediate outstanding need of the industry was a strong national organisation. To create such an organisation and to give it no part in these vital questions of current sales and production would have been unthinkable.[1]

The Committee accepted this reasoning, and recommended that the Minister should appoint the Director of Bricks as his representative to the National Building Brick Council. It would be his duty to direct the operation of the quota plan in particular and to consult the Council on all matters affecting the brick industry. For area organisation the controller of the quota plan was to make use of the organisation of the area councils of the National Council, so that the existing organisation of the Directorate of Bricks in the regions would fall into the background.

The committee's main specific recommendations were:

1. The reduction of the current national output of common bricks by ten per cent. as from 1st June, and by an equal number by 1st July, 1st August and 1st September 1942. This reduction was to be brought about by shutting down certain brickworks under compulsory order, or by lowering the productivity of the larger works.

2. A quota plan for the allocation of trade.

3. A scheme of statutory minimum area prices.

4. The control of maximum prices.

5. A scheme of compensation for loss of sales on the basis of a compensation datum.

---

[1] *Second Report of the Committee on the Brick Industry* (H.M.S.O. 1942), Section 121.

6. The creation of a National Building Brick Council for the wartime control of specific measures under the statutory authority of the Ministry of Works.

Effect was given to these recommendations. The National Brick Advisory Council was set up by the Minister of Works, with an independent chairman. Under Defence Regulation 55 the Minister made the Bricks (Control) Order 1942,[1] with effect from 4th May of that year, enabling licences to manufacture bricks to be issued to all producers. This was followed at once by the Bricks (Charges) Order 1942,[2] made by the Treasury. Under this Order a levy of 3s. per 1,000 was charged on all brick sales. The revenue collected was applied in making payment for the care and maintenance of brick-producing works which, by reason of the Brick Control Order, or by agreement with the Minister, had ceased or might cease production.

Under the new organisation, information on brick supplies was obtainable from the Director of Bricks. Permits were not needed to get supplies, but for the delivery of bricks beyond specified distances a permit had to be obtained. It was an advantage that stocks were widely distributed, and in consequence long haulage could often be avoided even in taking bricks to contracts in distant or isolated areas. Bricks were normally drawn, so far as possible, from works nearest to the building site, subject to safeguards for price, quality and delivery. Where suitable supplies could not be drawn from works within a radius of twenty-five miles of the site, the Director of Bricks nominated a supplier or suppliers and gave a permit for transport.

Permits for road transport were not given for deliveries beyond thirty-five radial miles of works unless the railway could not handle the traffic. For shorter distances rail had also to be used in preference to road transport wherever practicable.

In a third report, submitted to the Minister of Works in October 1942, the Simmonds Committee surveyed some of the technical aspects of the brick industry. Long-term considerations and the post-war organisation of the industry form the background to this report. What the committee contemplated was brick manufacture as a modern industrial process, and the report made specific suggestions for setting the industry as a whole on sound lines of technical development.

The work of the Simmonds Committee was a valuable contribution to the technique of the voluntary control of industry in war-time. Lord Portal, as Minister of Works, invited the National Brick Advisory Council to continue the technical work inaugurated by the committee. He asked them especially to promote research on a national basis at the expense of the industry, by means of a levy or

---

[1] S.R. & O. 1942, No. 675.
[2] S.R. & O. 1942, No. 915.

otherwise. Among other proposals made by the committee, those for standard technical conditions of purchase and uniformity in carrying out tests of bricks[1] were to prove far-reaching in their effect, and from the first were closely studied in the Ministry of Works.

(iii)
The Control of Cement

Reference has already been made in an earlier chapter[2] to Government concern and public alarm during the critical summer of 1940 about the supply of cement. It was then thought that the abnormal demands of the armed forces would exhaust stocks, and a short-lived voucher system had been set up which in itself had added to the shortage it was supposed to cure. After that system had been recognised as unnecessary and had been suspended, a working arrangement was made with the industry.[3] Meanwhile, agitation inside and outside Parliament—much of it partisan and political—had confused and obscured the true position.[4] As late as the end of November 1940 the Prime Minister himself[5] wrote with disquiet, not so much of the shortage of cement, which was no longer regarded as serious, though reserves were small, but of the indication it gave of how far the programmes were falling behind the approved scale. On no account, he wrote, must any capacity be idle that winter.

The alarm had been caused in some degree by a misunderstanding of the true position, which was that in 1939 and 1940 the cement consumed[6] (excluding exports) was:

	1939	1940
Portland cement .	7,455,231[7]	6,581,049
Blast furnace cement .	251,000	183,000 (approx.)

The heaviest months were September 1939, 762,245 tons and July 1940, 834,741 tons. The reduction in use was mainly because of the almost complete loss of from four to five weeks in January and February 1940, and because of reductions in available labour.

---

[1] *Third Report of the Committee on the Brick Industry* (H.M.S.O. 1943), Appendix III and Appendix IV.

[2] See Chapter II.

[3] See p. 50.

[4] See p. 49.

[5] In a Personal Minute to the Minister without Portfolio (Mr. A. Greenwood) dated 30th November 1940.

[6] For classification of cement see F. M. Lea, *Cement and Concrete* (Lecture at Royal Institute of Chemistry, 1945). Classified according to the raw materials used, there are three main types of cement, namely, Portland cement, Portland blast furnace cement and high-alumina (or aluminous) cement. Only the first two are discussed in this section: the control of aluminous cement during the war is referred to in Notes and Appendices: Note X, 'Types of Cement'.

[7] This includes 135,772 tons imported mainly from Belgium.

The maximum capacity of the industry was 800,000 tons a month, that is, at the rate of 9,600,000 tons a year. To have attained that maximum rate would have meant very heavy pressure on the plant, which would have had to go for long periods without adequate overhauling and repairs; it would only have been justifiable in an emergency and for a period.

The actual economic and commercial output was estimated to be between $8\frac{1}{2}$ and 9 million tons. In war-time, because of lighting restrictions during black-out, air raids, labour shortages, bad coal, limited transport, delays in getting spare parts and other checks, the maximum capacity was estimated at about $7\frac{1}{2}$ to 8 millions.

The Ministry of Works instituted a system of weekly returns and regular inspection, the industry was steadily kept to maximum output, and by the beginning of 1941 there was already a reserve of over 900,000 tons of cement and clinker.

Viewed as a whole, the capacity of the industry was well in excess of all probable—if not all possible—demands. But a direct hit on a kiln, it was feared, might put it out of use for six months. The kilns were perhaps more vulnerable than the grinding plant, although experience showed that both stood up well under air attack and that the danger from the air was less formidable than had been supposed. Cement works were indeed often bombed without any loss of output.

It was right, however, for the Ministry of Works to foresee and prepare against the danger of a shortage, and this was done at the risk of some rise in the cost of manufacture. (Maximum working through the winter, however, was economically unjustifiable; so too was the expenditure of public money on the extension of works.) In the end, the Controller thought, it might be found that there was a large excess of cement and manufacturing capacity, but on strategic grounds that risk had to be accepted.

After the short-lived coupon system was suspended, working arrangements were agreed with the industry under which manufacturers and merchants were allowed to deliver cement, without vouchers or other restriction, to Government departments, local authorities and public utility undertakings. Cement could be delivered, too, to any civilian users in lots up to two tons at a time. But cement manufacturers were not to supply contracts of more than 1,000 tons total until a form giving detail of requirements had been rendered by the contractor to the manufacturer and to the Director of Cement.

Subsidiary arrangements affecting chalk and chalk lime, sponsored for certain purposes by the Director of Cement, were also agreed with the industry.

The soundness of the cement industry was demonstrated after the Ministry of Works had appointed, on 4th January 1941, a Committee on Cement Production, under the chairmanship of Mr. George Balfour, M.P. The committee was a particularly strong one, and in no way connected with the cement industry. It was to consider and report whether (bearing in mind the probable demands for cement in meeting cement needs and in post-war reconstruction, and taking into consideration economic, strategic and other factors affecting the allocation of cement) new cement works should be established, existing ones extended or old plant modernised; and if so what general considerations—financial, geographical and economic—should apply.

The committee reached unanimous conclusions, and reported on 23rd April 1941.[1] The evidence of witnesses on the probable demand for cement during the war period confirmed what was already apparent—that the consumption of cement would be automatically limited by the size of the labour force in the building and civil engineering industries and the amount of work it could deal with. The committee also reaffirmed that, because of the special character of the work, war-time consumption would be at the annual rate of about six million tons, and it appeared unlikely that the consumption of 6,764,049 reached in 1940 would be attained again until after the war.

The provision of bomb-proof shelters on a large scale, for which there was popular agitation, would have meant the diversion of labour and materials (including cement) from works essential to the prosecution of the war and was therefore not included in the committee's estimates.

Because of war-time handicaps the output per man in the cement industry was now less than in peace-time. With the number of men left in the industry it seemed likely that the output of cement during the war would be about $7\frac{1}{2}$ million tons a year as against the calculated consumption of six million tons. The committee concluded that there was an ample supply of cement to meet all needs (including an allowance for exports[2]) during the war period.

Although there was no reason to fear a general shortage of cement, the chance of local shortages remained. These were the more likely if coastwise shipping continued to be restricted, as it then was, and all transport from south-east England confined to road or rail. To ward off local shortages the industry was asked by the Controller of Building Materials to add to stocks of finished cement and of cement clinker, and thus ensure larger reserves for the summer months, when demand was always at its maximum.[3]

---

[1] *Report of the Committee on Cement Production.* Cmd. 6282, 1941.

[2] During the ten years before the war the maximum export of cement was 1,092,000 tons in 1929 and the minimum in any year 399,000 tons. During the war period exports fluctuated between 7,000 tons and 72,000 tons per month.

[3] As a result, stocks rose between 1st September 1940 and 27th March 1941 by 805,000 tons.

Under the ill-starred (or at least ill-considered) voucher system of 1940 some contractors had no doubt been allotted too many vouchers and others too few. Inequality and delays in delivery gave colour to widespread reports of a general shortage of the cement urgently needed for air-raid shelters. This fear was exploited (if indeed it had not been created) for purposes of political propaganda by extremist agitators. Pamphlets and leaflets were disseminated attacking the Government, the 'capitalist system' and the 'Cement Ring', and the public were told that if they could not get their air-raid shelters the reason was that the 'Cement Ring' had deliberately restricted the output of cement in order to swell their own profits. A number of well-meaning persons, among them the Bishop of Birmingham and Professor J. B. S. Haldane, were credited with the belief that a monstrous crime against society had been committed, and the subject was brought up more than once in Parliament.[1] Since, as the cement companies claimed, the output of cement had been trebled between the wars and the price halved, while labour conditions had been greatly improved, these attacks were deeply resented; and a number of leading cement firms took action in the High Court in order to clear the reputation of their industry.[2]

In the forefront of the attacks on the 'Cement Ring' was the allegation that the industry had failed to foster the manufacture of blast furnace cement, and sanguine estimates were put forward by Professor Haldane and others of how far cement production might be increased by the manufacture of blast furnace cement. English cement makers, it is true, had been mildly criticised[3] for not having pursued the manufacture of blast furnace cement in Great Britain as had been done on the Continent; but there were good reasons for the omission. The points of difference between Continental and British cement production may be summarised as follows:

1. In England there was an abundance of the cheapest materials for making Portland cement, that is, chalk and clay, to a degree that did not exist in certain parts of Europe.

2. Few of the iron ores used in England produced a slag which made the best blast furnace cement, whereas such slags were available to a greater extent on the Continent.

3. On the Continent iron and cement works were closer to each other than they were in England.

The only part of Great Britain where conditions resembled some

---

[1] See, for example, H. of C. Deb., 11th June 1941, Vol. 372, Col. 201.

[2] On 9th May 1941 damages amounting to £1,600 were awarded by Mr. Justice Wrottesley to sixteen cement companies, plaintiffs in a slander action against the Bishop of Birmingham.

[3] Building Research Station: Report by Dr. F. M. Lea.

parts of the Continent was in Scotland, where chalk and limestone do not exist. For that reason, blast furnace cement had been manufactured in Scotland for some thirty years before the Second World War,[1] but it had to be sold at a lower price than Portland cement, since it could not be sold otherwise.

In view of the conditions prevailing in the summer of 1940, the Ministry of Supply ordered an investigation into what amount of blast furnace cement could then be made in England. A report submitted on 12th November 1940 suggested that it would be possible to manufacture blast furnace cement to yield 400,000 tons per annum of additional cement, that is six per cent of the whole cement output. When the control of cement was transferred to the Ministry of Works on its formation in October 1940 its manufacture was fully examined. A special committee was appointed by the Controller of Building Materials in the Ministry of Works; and it was decided to manufacture blast furnace cement out of those slags on whose suitability the two technical members of the committee were agreed.[2] A programme was drawn up under which slag from the following iron works was to be used to make blast furnace cement at the cement works shown in the opposite column:

Iron works	Cement works
Barrow Haematite Steel Co., Ltd., Barrow-in-Furness	Ribblesdale, Lancashire
Millom and Askam Haematite Steel Co., Ltd.	Hope, Yorkshire
Consett Iron Co., Ltd., Durham	Casebourne, Durham
Pease & Partners, Ltd., Normandy Works, Yorks	Earles, Humber
Guest, Keen & Baldwin Iron & Steel Co., Ltd., Cardiff	{ Aberthaw, Cardiff Penarth, Cardiff

The agitation in Parliament continued, and on 31st December 1940 the Parliamentary Secretary to the Ministry of Works made a statement in the House of Commons defending the industry from the attacks that had been made upon it.[3] On 19th December 1940, in reply to a further question, he told the House that it was hoped to commence manufacture in time for the spring.[4] The Ministry of

---

[1] The cement clinker was brought from the Thames by ship.

[2] The members of the committee were Mr. Hugh Beaver, Controller of Building Materials, Viscount Wolmer, Director of Cement, and the two experts, Dr. F. M. Lea, of the Building Research Station, and Mr. N. M. Jensen, who was chairman of the only English company with practical experience of the manufacture of blast furnace cement, through its subsidiary in Scotland.

[3] H. of C. Deb., 3rd December 1940, Vol. 367, Col. 405.

[4] H. of C. Deb., 19th December 1940, Vol. 367, Col. 1358.

Works was faced, however, with difficult practical problems. The Treasury had asked that, before any further commitments were undertaken, detailed estimates should be prepared. That involved lengthy tests in granulating[1] slag, and it was not until August 1941 that the Director of Cement at the Ministry of Works received a full report from the Building Research Station on the main sample of granulated slag. Meanwhile, the Balfour Committee closely investigated the conditions of slag cement production and the chances of increased supply from this source. After taking evidence and studying the report of the committee appointed by the Controller of Building Materials, the Balfour Committee thought it questionable whether in war-time labour and materials should be used upon the construction of granulating plants at steel works, and of drying plants at cement works, until there was positive evidence that it had become a matter of urgency to secure additional output of cement.

Although the terms of the Balfour report did not bind the Ministry of Works, the Director-General was guided by its recommendations. The blast furnace programme was modified by indefinitely postponing the plans to manufacture blast furnace cement at all works except at Ribblesdale in Lancashire and Aberthaw in Wales.

The manufacture of blast furnace cement was not seriously developed through the rest of the war years. Results were disappointing and the cost of production uneconomic. It had been intended from the first that the product of all works should be sold at a price to cover the average cost of manufacture, and that the expenses of the various companies should be pooled. The principle still held good after it was decided to restrict manufacture to Ribblesdale and Aberthaw. No other course was indeed open. Blast furnace cement cost more than Portland cement to manufacture at Ribblesdale, but less than Portland cement at Aberthaw; and the average cost of making blast furnace cement at the two works proved to be greater than the price of Portland cement. It was an added embarrassment that blast furnace cement from the Aberthaw works was markedly inferior to that from the Ribblesdale works, and customers were expected to accept both at the same price. Since, however, during the war the demand for blast furnace cement was entirely for Government contracts, the dilemma was more academic than real; but it served at least to explode the myth, so sedulously fostered as political propaganda, that a potential source of supply had been wilfully sealed off by the 'Cement Ring'.

It was not only about blast furnace cement that the 'Cement Ring'

---

[1] 'Granulation' is a process by which the molten slag is split up into small particles by a jet or stream of cold water being poured on to it as it leaves the furnace, or alternatively by a blast of compressed air, or again alternatively by a mixture of both. Different methods of granulation are suitable for different slags. No two slags are exactly the same.

was often taken to task by its critics. The control of cement prices was almost as thorny a subject and one on which the 'Cement Ring' was equally open to attack from many quarters.

All manufacturers of Portland cement in the United Kingdom were members of the Cement Makers' Federation which controlled *inter alia* the price policy of the industry and the operation of the related quota agreements.[1] The Federation grew out of the Inland Cement Makers' Alliance and came into being in 1918. Complete federation was not reached, however, for some sixteen years: by that time the industry's price structure in its mature form was at work. In the past competition had been intense and selling prices uneconomic, and it was because of these conditions that complete federation had become possible in 1934. Only through an orderly and stable price structure, the Federation urged, could they ensure that reasonable confidence in the future without which they could not expect large sums to be laid out on costly capital equipment for expansion and improved efficiency.

The primary function of the Federation was the fixing of prices, and this was done through the votes of the members. The voting power of the individual firm or group varied each year in proportion to the tonnage of cement delivered by that firm or group in the preceding year. But the voting rights were weighted in such a way that the number of votes did not increase automatically with the increase of deliveries. In years when the total output of the industry was low, the preponderance of voting power of the largest group was greater than in years of high over-all output. No decision could be taken without the support of at least four members or groups. In general, it would be fair to say of the exercise of voting power, that to carry a resolution against the largest group would require the votes of all, or most, of the remaining members. On the other hand, it would never have been possible for the largest group alone, even in a year when its votes were together more than those of all the other members, to carry a resolution by itself. Resolutions amending the quota arrangements were specially dealt with and required unanimous approval.

Apart from the question of price fixation, the existence of the Federation had been a great indirect benefit to the industry as an agency through which information on technical and business matters was quite freely exchanged. As one witness for the Federation put it, a most valuable part of the Federation was the periodical meeting of the chairmen of the thirteen companies to work out measures useful to the consumer—as, for example, by the elimination of cross-transport and wastage.

---

[1] M.O.W. Report, *Cement Costs* (H.M.S.O. 1947). This report was made by a committee of which Sir Arthur fforde was chairman and is subsequently referred to as the Fforde Report. The findings of the committee were unanimous.

The detailed conditions governing the relationship between manufacturers, merchants and consumers in Great Britain and Northern Ireland were contained in price schedules that covered all towns of any consequence. The schedule prices were always minimum prices and normally covered delivery to site. Although the prices were stated as minimum prices, in practice they operated as fixed prices. The delivered-to-site price in any locality was based on delivery from the nearest works or coastwise importing centre and applied whether or not the cement was in fact delivered from that works or coastwise importing centre.

Two elements contributed to the building-up of the delivered-to-site prices:

1. The 'base price'. The price showed little variation as between different works or coastwise importing centres in England, although small allowances had been made in particular cases. For example, a works which used limestone instead of chalk had a slightly higher base price, the limestone being harder and more costly to process.[1]

2. A series of circles, the first with a radius of five miles, and each subsequent circle having an additional five-mile radius, was drawn round each works or coastwise importing centre. Within the first circle the base price operated without addition as the delivered price. Thereafter each circle represented an addition of 1s. to the base price to arrive at the delivered-to-site price. The resulting price operated for the whole of the additional area enclosed by the circle, unless the circle was intersected by another circle radiating from a different centre, in which case the lower of the circle prices prevailed. The operation of the base price for the Thames and Medway works was not limited to a radius of five miles, but also operated in the Greater London area. To that extent the above principles were modified.

The chief ports into which the cement was 'imported' from other parts of the country were treated as 'works' with a base price and radiating circles.

The system operated automatically. Thus, if a new works was opened, the price of cement was lowered in the area adjacent to the works, and that applied whether or not the works could supply the full demand to the locality. Any cement brought in to satisfy the excess demand was sold at the same price as if it had come from the nearest works or coastwise importing centre.

From 1939 onwards the industry accepted on a voluntary basis Government control over its profits and selling prices. Between September 1939 and March 1945 increases in prices, all of which received approval of the appropriate Ministry, were from 2s. per ton to 6s. per ton as follows:

---

[1] For a list of base prices 1934, 1938 and 1945 see the Fforde Report, Appendix VI.

				Increases of price
				per ton
October 1939	.	.	.	2s. 0d.
December 1939	.	.	.	2s. 0d.
May 1940	.	.	.	3s. 6d.
June 1940	.	.	.	1s. 0d.
January 1941	.	.	.	6s. 0d.
October 1941	.	.	.	1s. 0d.
*August 1942	.	.	.	1s. 6d.
March 1945	.	.	.	6s. 0d.
Total increase		.	.	23s. 0d.

*This increase did not apply to Scottish blast furnace cement, but, upon the application of the Scottish manufacturers, 1s. 6d. per ton was sanctioned in March 1944.

If the average of these increases is weighted to take into account the inclusion of the London area in the specimen prices selected, the increase is forty-eight per cent. as compared with the September 1939 levels.

In examining the principles on which prices were fixed, the Fforde Committee gave weight to the fact that when the Federation was formed it took over a position which had developed over a long period. Various stresses of open competition had been a cause of a price-cutting which not only harmed individual interests, but was a check to economy of transport and to the long-term planning of production or distribution over the country as a whole. The committee added that it was also important to bear in mind that between the year 1934, when the Federation first really got control of the problem, and the post-war period came four normal years (1935–38), one year (1939) which was probably regarded as having on the whole been normal, six years when the governing factor was the war effort, and one year during which the industry was partially emerging from the war stresses. The committee's view was that the system set up a rational method of varying the prices according to the remoteness or proximity of a delivery point from the nearest source of supply. It did not appear to the committee that the profits in the past had been excessive. They found, too, that there was nothing in the system as a system to check or hamper the achievement of an economically sound and fair delivered price for cement within the United Kingdom.

The quota system used in the cement industry, first introduced in the year 1934, was based on a series of agreements made in that and later years. The war-time pooling agreement was quite distinct from the normal quota system and was terminated by the industry on 31st December 1945. Although the quota system was in abeyance during the war, its effect on the industry in the rearmament period, and again in the reconstruction period after the war, nevertheless colours the over-all picture of the war-time control of cement; and in itself gives the answer to much biased or ill-formed criticism of the 'Cement Ring' in the war years. Its principal features, as defined by the Fforde Committee, should therefore be briefly noted.

The object of the quota arrangements was, in the first place, to establish that each firm in the industry quoted for delivery at any given point a uniform price for standard Portland cement with differentials for rapid hardening cement. In common with other industries, the experience of this industry, as the Fforde Report points out, was that the setting up of a price scheme was not enough in itself to solve the problems which had made such a scheme necessary. There was, therefore, superimposed upon the agreement about prices an agreement about quotas. The basis on which quotas were fixed was essentially one of bargaining; and its background was the turnover of the several parties to the negotiation. Once a quota was fixed a firm that delivered cement in excess of its quota was penalised, and a firm that delivered cement below its quota advantaged. Had the position been allowed to become static it could have undermined the industry. But, as the scheme worked out, the firm that relaxed its efforts tended to find the more energetic firms applying to it for transfers of quota; and, in the revision of quotas at the end of the agreement period, firms which had taken over deliveries were apt to be in a stronger position both within the industry and in the connections established with customers. There was no prohibition as to the point at which deliveries could be made. Thus, the energetic maker could, if he wished, deliver at any point which he could economically reach within the agreed maximum price for delivery at that point.

Although there was a very strong bar to the establishment of new businesses independently from the Cement Makers' Federation, for reasons set out in the Fforde Report, the industry did set itself and achieved the aim of making supplies available at all places at prices 'calculated to absorb the cost of affording that service to the public at all places'. Competition from an outside interest concerned only to supply the localities best suited to it, without sharing in the less profitable deliveries at greater distances from the convenient point, might well be classed as unfair competition. The committee regarded this as a reasonable and logical answer to criticism, provided always that the protection which the Federation thus gave its members was not used so as to increase prices above what was reasonable or to allow the survival of inefficient work.

N

(iv)
The Control of Roofing Materials

The supply of roofing materials up to the first year of war has already been discussed in an earlier chapter.[1] It was there noted that of the chief classes of roofing materials in demand for the building programme—bituminous felt, corrugated iron and protected metal sheeting, and asbestos cement sheeting—only the last-named gave cause for concern, and this largely through over-estimation of demand by departments. The voluntary submission of the various industries to the control of the Ministry of Works has also been recorded; and it is now only necessary to add a brief account of the measures in force at the climax of the war for the control of these materials.

Under Defence Regulation 55 the Minister of Works made the Control of Roofing and Other Materials Order 1942[2], under which he controlled asbestos cement products, roofing and damp-course felts, plasterboard[3] and natural slates for roofing and damp course. As with bricks and cement, a Director was appointed to take charge of roofing materials.

Asbestos cement products. Under the Order it was illegal to manufacture asbestos cement sheets or other asbestos cement products (for example, asbestos cement slates) or to deal in them except under licence issued by the Ministry of Works.

Quantities not exceeding 480 square feet of flat or corrugated sheets could be obtained without a certificate, but such a sale could be made only for an essential purpose or for air-raid damage repairs; it was not to form part of a larger transaction involving more than 480 square feet. The merchant was expected reasonably to assure himself that these conditions were complied with by the customer, who had to complete and sign a form.

The placing of other orders for asbestos cement sheets was regulated according to whether they were for:

1. Government or Government-sponsored contracts; or
2. First-aid repairs of air-raid (and fire or storm) damage.

Government contracts. Orders of more than three tons were placed through the convenor of the Asbestos Cement Industry Operating Committee at the Ministry of Works and supplied by the manufacturers to the merchant, roofing contractor, building contractor, etc.

---

[1] See Chapter II.

[2] S.R. & O. 1942, No. 2017.

[3] This included gypsum plasterboard, ceiling board and baseboard, but not wallboard of the pulp or fibrous type, which was under the Paper Controller at the Ministry of Supply.

Orders of less than three tons were placed through the Ministry of Works representative in the area in which delivery was required and were executed either from the Ministry of Works emergency stocks or from dispersal stocks which had been placed in the hands of a number of builders' merchants throughout the country.

First-aid repairs. Orders for asbestos cement sheets required for first-aid repairs of air-raid damage (or damage caused by fire or storm to essential buildings) might be met, irrespective of the quantity of material needed, from dispersal stocks or Ministry of Works emergency stocks on certificate from the appropriate officer of the Ministry of Works.

Similar conditions for the control, licensing and the placing of orders applied also to Scotland and Northern Ireland, the functions of Ministry of Works officers being fulfilled in Northern Ireland by representatives of the Ministry of Commerce.

The general procedure for the placing of orders and for the use of asbestos cement slates was as for asbestos cement sheets, except that for the sale of quantities of less than fifty slates the procedure was the same as for natural slates.[1]

Roofing and damp-course felts. The control of the Director of Roofing was exercised through the Roofing Felt Industry Executive Committee. The control did not cover flax felts and hair felts or fluxed pitch saturated felt, but included damp-course, whether manufactured from bitumen or pitch, or whether the base was of fibre, woven fabric or metal.

Specified authorities could certify the purposes for which roofing felt and damp-course were to be sold when essential for work of national importance. These included Government departments, local authorities, public utility companies, railway companies, Government contractors quoting contract reference and priority numbers, builders and contractors quoting civil building licence numbers and references, and certain officers of the Ministry of Works.

A consumer requiring one roll or less of fluxed pitch felt could obtain it on completion of a form without the supporting certificate of a competent authority.

The control applied also to Scotland and Northern Ireland. (In that country certificates were issued by a duly authorised officer of the Ministry of Commerce.)

Plasterboard and wallboard. The control over plasterboard was exercised by the Director of Roofing. This material could only be used where it was essential, and in no circumstances for such purposes as blacking-out windows. Plasterboard manufacturers were permitted to execute orders only from merchants whose names appeared on the approved list.

---

[1] See pp. 54 *et seq.*

Government orders received first priority from manufacturers. They had to be substantiated with accurate Government contract numbers and departmental symbols. Orders within this category for quantities greater than 600 square yards were delivered direct from the manufacturers to the site, but smaller quantities had to be supplied from merchants' stocks, if any.

Orders for air-raid damage repairs, essential maintenance work, storm damage and other work of national importance, where these exceeded 480 square feet, were supplied against an original certificate issued in a similar manner and by the same officers as for natural slates.[1]

No certificate was needed for requirements below 480 square feet for essential purposes or air-raid damage repairs; the purchasers completed a form with the merchant supplying the plasterboard. The control extended to Scotland and Northern Ireland (Ministry of Commerce).

Wallboard (pulp or fibrous, hardboard, insulation and laminated wallboard) was under the Paper Controller at the Ministry of Supply, in consultation with the Director of Roofing at the Ministry of Works. Licences were granted by the Paper Controller to building board producers and importers for the delivery of wallboard to users for specific purposes, and for delivery to merchants empowered to hold stocks.

The categories of wallboard used in building and building repairs were category 'C' (all hardboard and insulation board in thicknesses of $\frac{1}{2}$ inch or more) and category 'D' (insulation board in thicknesses of less than $\frac{1}{2}$ inch and laminated wallboard). The stocks of category 'C' materials were especially meagre and could only be released for use on essential work. Category 'D' materials were issued primarily for air-raid damage first-aid repairs, for other emergency damage first-aid repairs, and for works certified by certain Government departments (Admiralty, War Office, Air Ministry, Ministry of Aircraft Production, Ministry of Works and Ministry of Supply) and Royal Ordnance factories. Limited quantities of category 'D' materials were also issued for approved uses in factories engaged on Government work, hospitals and other public institutions.

Natural slates. Natural slates, under the control of the Director of Roofing, could be used (with some exceptions) only on certification by the appropriate officer of the Ministry of Works or other Government departments for such purposes as repairs made necessary by enemy action, essential maintenance and storm damage repairs, building of vital national importance and similar essential purposes. Certain slates, however, could be obtained without certificate. These were all slates quarried in Scotland, for delivery and use in Scotland; all slates quarried in Westmorland or Lancashire, but only for de-

---

[1] See p. 57 *et seq.*

livery into, and use in, the counties of Cumberland, Durham, Lancashire, Northumberland, Westmorland and Yorkshire; slates 14 inches in length and downwards from any quarry; 'scantle' and 'moss' slates (irregular sizes); and small sales by merchants from stock, that is, for small isolated jobs requiring not more than fifty large slates.

Slates for use in Cornwall and Devon could be obtained only from the Cornish quarries, nor was it permitted to supply Cornish slates to Wales or the North of England. Scottish slates could not be supplied to England and Wales. These restrictions and other restrictions and recommendations to merchants were designed to avoid unnecessary transport.

No slates could be imported into England, Scotland, Wales or Northern Ireland except under the authority of the Director of Roofing and subject to such conditions as he might impose.

CHAPTER VIII

THE CONTROL OF CONTRACTORS' PLANT

(i)

The Need for Control

THE control of contractors' plant began in August 1941 when the Minister of Works, under powers specially conferred on him under Defence Regulation 55, made an Order for the control of rates of hire.[1] Since, in the execution of the building programme, departments (with the Admiralty as the most notable exception) generally let the work on a cost plus basis and were contracting with numbers of different firms, there was need for a standard schedule of plant hire rates to be applied to the settling of all cost plus accounts. The Ministry of Home Security had been one of the first departments to recognise this need; and, after consulting the Federation of Civil Engineering Contractors, it had published on 14th December 1939 a schedule of plant hire rates which covered a limited number of types of plant. The rates had as a rule been accepted by other departments, but after the outbreak of war the demand for plant began to exceed supply, with departments competing for plant and sometimes departing from the rates laid down.

In December 1940 the subject was raised at a meeting of the Works and Building Priority Committee.[2] In the succeeding months there were discussions between the Ministry of Works and other departments, as well as with industry, and it was finally agreed that the observance of the new schedule should be made compulsory with effect from 1st June 1941.[3]

During the inter-departmental discussions in the early months of 1941 it had become evident that because of the heavy demands of the Service departments for new contractors' plant, progress on the building programme of civil departments could be maintained only if plant already in possession of the industry, and any new plant not already

---

[1] S.R. & O. 1941, No. 1277, entitled 'The Control of Rates of Hire of Plant'.
[2] At the request of the Industrial Capacity Committee of the Production Executive which invited the Works and Building Committee to submit a scheme for the control of contractors' plant. In applying the scheme the Ministry of Works later worked with the Industrial Capacity Committee, which regulated new construction on lease-lend import.
[3] In these and subsequent negotiations Mr. R. M. Wynne Edwards, later Director of Labour Requirements and Plant at the Ministry of Works, played a decisive part.

appropriated by the Service departments, were brought within some system of control. This was important not only because in the event of invasion the military authorities responsible for defence had to know what plant was available, but also because the control of plant was vital to the Government building programme. The successful execution of the programme indeed demanded that every class of plant should be kept fully occupied and also that it should be used in the most efficient manner. The advantageous and economical use of existing plant was all the more necessary since the Ministry of Supply insisted that the manufacture of new plant should be kept down to a minimum, thus making more room for the production of war weapons; and that everything should be done to make the fullest use of existing plant, to safeguard maintenance and to provide spare parts.

The considerations which influenced the plans of the Ministry of Works for the control of contractors' plant in the summer of 1941 may be summarised as follows:

1. There were several types of owners of plant: that is, public works contractors and builders; Government departments; public and statutory bodies; private corporations and firms not engaged in public works contracting work; and plant hire firms who owned plant which they hired out to contractors and firms.

2. Certain types of plant were used by both the building and civil engineering industries. Most of the heavy plant, however, was used exclusively by civil engineering contractors and, in war-time circumstances, on Government work.

3. Contracting firms did not ordinarily let out their plant to other firms. In the first place, plant was not so well cared for by those who were not its owners, and secondly, the decision as to whether or not to tender for work depended largely on the amount and type of plant available or becoming available. As plant represented a large capital expenditure, there was a strong incentive to keep it fully employed.

4. Plant hire firms made their income out of hiring out their own plant or as middlemen. It was therefore to their advantage to have a wide knowledge of the whereabouts of plant so that they might hire it out whenever it was idle.

5. An important cause of shortage was the lack of spare parts or their faulty distribution.

If those were the conditions to be met, it was clear that war-time control in the national interest meant not only that there must be the fullest possible information of the existence and availability of all types of plant needed for the Government building programme, but also that measures had to be devised to deal with scarcity of plant wherever it might occur. Means had to be found, too, for the production of new plant and spare parts, and for making sure that the plant was kept fully employed.

(ii)
Schemes for the Co-ordination of Plant

At a meeting of the Industrial Capacity Committee on 13th October 1941, a memorandum prepared by the Production Executive in conjunction with the Ministry of Works was adopted subject to certain amendments. This placed on the Ministry of Works responsibility for:

1. The co-ordination of the use of contractors' plant by Government departments.
2. The appointment of plant inspectors.
3. The submission of plans for production to the Ministry of Supply.
4. The 'permitting' of the purchase of new plant.
5. The registration of contractors' plant.

All plant other than plant in direct ownership of Government departments came within the orbit of this scheme.

There followed numerous meetings between departments on the working out of the details of the scheme. Many of the points covered were included in a fresh memorandum prepared by the Ministry of Works and considered at the thirtieth meeting of the Industrial Capacity Committee on 2nd February 1942. This important document was accepted with one or two reservations. One of its proposals was to set up an Allocation Committee; and, as the future of the Industrial Capacity Committee was uncertain,[1] it was agreed that the chairman of the Allocation Committee should be nominated by the Ministry of Works and that he should speak for the civilian departments as a whole.

The Allocation Committee played a vital part in the war effort, and will be referred to again later in its role of Engineers' Stores Assignment (Special Plant) Sub-Committee of the London Munitions Assignment Board. The Ministry of Works scheme involved a change-over from the Board of Trade and Ministry of Supply to the Ministry of Works of certain functions which had been performed by those departments up to the end of 1941. Press notices of the new arrangements began to appear on 19th February 1942, and by 1st March 1942 the Ministry of Works was fairly launched in its capacity as the accepted co-ordinator of contractors' plant.

Treasury approval for the appointment of six Regional Plant Inspectors (a title later changed to Regional Plant Advisers) was given in October 1941, and in the summer of 1942 assistants to the

---

[1] Because the Ministry of Production was soon to be set up.

Advisers were engaged for each region. The Regional Plant Advisers were responsible throughout to the Director of Labour Requirements and Plant at headquarters. These arrangements remained in force throughout the war.

The registration of all plant, except that held by Service departments, began soon after the adoption of the Ministry of Works proposals by the Industrial Capacity Committee on 13th October 1941. Some returns had already been made voluntarily at this time, but it was thought that without legal backing further requests for information might be ignored by some owners of plant. An Order entitled 'The Owners of Contractors' Plant (Returns) Order 1942', dated 17th January 1942,[1] was accordingly made by the Minister of Works to enforce the submission of returns. The first returns called for were of excavators, mechanical trenchers, mobile cranes, tractors, portable air compressors, dumpers, concrete mixers and road rollers. Thereafter regular returns were only asked for at intervals for excavators and tractors, both of which were particularly scarce. From the time the forms were sent out until the card indexes were ready a return took from two to three months to complete. As soon as one return of tractors and excavators was completed it was time to start on the next one. Changes of location were notified by the Statistical Division of the Ministry of Works to the Director of Emergency Works, who needed the information in the first place for the taking of anti-invasion measures, and to the Regional Plant Advisers, whose duty it was to see that the plant was kept at work and evenly distributed.

The circumstances which had led to the making of the Control of Rates of Hire of Plant Order,[2] and in particular the problem of shortage of plant at that time, had clearly proved the need for control over the prices paid for second-hand plant. Contractors' plant and agricultural tractors were changing hands at excessive prices since there was not enough new plant to satisfy all needs. In May 1942, after consulting the Ministry of Agriculture and the industry, the Minister of Works made the Second-hand Plant (Control of Prices) (No. 1) Order, dated 18th June 1942.[3] The price limit under this Order, which came into force on 29th June 1942, was the retail price for an equivalent new machine specified in a price list at that date or in the latest price list published before that date or the price paid when new. Despite this liberal allowance the control price was frequently reached in public auctions, and there were always willing buyers at prices exceeding the control price. At the time of the making of the Control of Rates of Hire of Plant Order it was thought that a register of plant hirers might be advisable as a safeguard against abuse of the Order.

---

[1] S.R. & O. 1942, No. 57.
[2] S.R. & O. 1941, No. 1277.
[3] S.R. & O. 1942, No. 1163.

This proposal was, however, found to be unworkable, since plant was often offered for hire by firms who owned plant but were not in business as plant hirers—a practice which the Ministry of Works thought it best not to discourage. Yet a number of plant hirers did decide, in May 1941, to form the Contractors' Plant Association. Although its membership did not take in the whole of the plant hire trade, it was none the less a useful body with which officials could confer on plant problems.

Control of plant by the Government also brought about the formation of the Federation of Manufacturers of Contractors' Plant; their advice was often sought by the Ministry of Works to gauge the opinion of the trade on questions of policy.

In the original proposals by the Ministry of Works for co-ordinating the use and supply of contractors' plant there was emphasis on the need to ensure that plant was well maintained, and that enough spare parts were to be had. In a letter to the Federation of Civil Engineering Contractors dated 16th October 1941, the Director of Labour Requirements and Plant invited the co-operation of the industry; and a comprehensive survey of shortages of spare parts was made by the leading contractors and plant hirers. On 27th November 1941 he wrote to the leading caterpillar tractor agent in the country asking his firm not to accept orders for spare parts for stock. In December 1941, under the ægis of the Ministry of Works, informal meetings were begun between users and manufacturers; they made a joint study of their problems and put forward proposals for alleviating the shortages. The meetings led to a determined effort by the manufacturers to make up some of the deficiencies; but time was needed if supplies were to improve. Meanwhile owners of plant were asked to take precautions against avoidable wear of the machines. Some owners were also persuaded to share their plant and reconditioning facilities, and they did in fact set up a clearing-house to achieve this aim. But most firms treated their plant and repair shops as part of their stock-in-trade; and the clearing-house system, although it contributed to the spirit of co-operation which the Director of Labour Requirements and Plant was trying to foster at that time, proved not more than a moderate success.

After 1941 meetings between the manufacturers and users began to fall off, and in the spring of 1942 ceased altogether. The manufacturers now put into voluntary use 'certificate of need' for spare parts to be filled in by the purchaser.

In December 1942 the Director of Plant appointed a full-time headquarters adviser to deal with the demand for spares. By keeping a register of all known stocks of parts—whether in the hands of manufacturers, agents, contractors or plant-hiring firms—he was able to meet many of these requirements satisfactorily. Another useful innovation began in June 1943 when the Federation of Civil Engineering Contractors, the Federation of Manufacturers of Contractors' Plant and the Contractors' Plant Association, with the advice of the Ministry of Works, jointly produced a guide entitled 'Servicing Organisations', which gave lists of repair shops throughout the country and the kind of work they undertook.

The meetings with the manufacturers early in 1942 had been mainly concerned with spares and plant of British manufacture, but not with those of foreign make. By the late summer of 1943 stocks of tractor spares, the greater part of which came from the United States, had run very low. To remedy this shortage a committee called the Crawler Tractor Spares Committee was set up by the Ministry of Supply (in conjunction with the Ministry of Works, the Ministry of Agriculture, the Service Ministries and the distributive trades) and first met on 7th September 1943. The recommendations of the committee, embodied in a report dated 22nd December 1943, were adopted, and the manufacture of tractor spares on a large scale was undertaken for the first time in the United Kingdom.

Before the war in Europe ended the Ministry of Works was able to obtain the spares called for by plant owners in more than eighty per cent. of the breakdowns reported to them.

(iii)
The Allocation of New Plant

The decision to set up an allocation committee, to which reference has already been made, had far-reaching effects on the control of plant. Its chairman was the Director of Labour Requirements and Plant at the Ministry of Works. The Contractors' Plant Requirements and Allocation Committee, as it was named, had the following terms of reference:

1. To co-ordinate the forecast requirements of all Government departments from the point of view of production programmes and allocations of production, based upon details of such forecast requirements to be submitted by departments to the Ministry of Supply.

2. To receive reports from the Ministry of Supply as to available production against these demands.

3. To allocate available production to Government departments.

4. To advise the Ministry of Supply of the types of plant most suitable for general departmental use.

The Ministry of Works represented all the civil departments on this committee. This arrangement, though consistent with the machinery that made the Ministry of Works responsible for issuing permits for the purchase of new plant for civilian use, was none the less unpopular with other departments.

The committee met for the first time on 11th March 1942, and held fifteen more meetings; its last meeting was in August 1943. The types of plant covered by the committee were in the first instance the nineteen types that formed the original list of items for which permits were required for purchase by civilians.

In order to be able to follow the ramifications of the allocation of plant from mid-1942 onwards, it must be noted that when, in January 1942, Mr. Churchill and Mr. Roosevelt agreed to pool the munition resources of the United Kingdom and the United States, a Combined Munitions Assignment Board was set up in Washington as well as a London Munitions Assignment Board. In July 1942 assignment machinery in Washington was applied to tractors and certain other engineers' stores, in which both civil and Service departments were interested. Certain classes of engineers' stores became 'munitions'. This had a direct result in London in the formation of the Engineers' Stores Assignment Sub-Committee of the London Munitions Assignment Board. Sir Nigel Campbell, head of the non-munitions section of the Ministry of Production, was appointed first chairman of this committee. On 26th August 1942 a draft paper on the functions of the Contractors' Plant Requirements and Allocation Committee for submission to Sir Nigel Campbell's Committee appears in the files. At its first meeting the Engineers' Stores Assignment Sub-Committee decided that the Contractors' Plant Requirements and Allocation Committee should continue to function as before except in respect of crawler tractors, and from time to time in respect of other items of engineers' stores.

The Engineers' Stores Assignment Sub-Committee of the London Munitions Assignment Board next turned its attention to mobile cranes (road and crawler), and at a meeting of the Principal Administrative Officers' Committee on 28th September 1942 agreed that mobile cranes should be made subject to assignment. It should here be noted that mobile cranes had been considered outside the scope of the Contractors' Plant Requirements and Allocation Committee, since there were many classes of users other than contractors. A separate committee was therefore formed which became known as the Engineers' Stores Assignment Working Committee, Cranes (Mobile and Crawler). This committee as first constituted was too unwieldy to manage the business in hand, and on 10th May 1943 an executive committee of its members was formed.

The Working Committee held nine meetings and the Executive

Committee four meetings, the last of which took place in August 1943. As a result of conclusions reached at the meeting of the Engineers' Stores Assignment Sub-Committee of the London Munitions Assignment Board on 5th August 1943, the Engineers' Stores Assignment Working Committee, Cranes (Mobile and Crawler) and its Executive Committee and the Contractors' Plant Requirements and Allocation Committee were combined into one committee which was from 1st September 1943 known as the Engineers' Stores Assignment (Special Plant) Sub-Committee, with Mr. R. M. Wynne-Edwards as chairman. This committee met at regular intervals up to and including 23rd August 1945 and ceased to function at 1st November 1945. The London Munitions Assignment Board and its sub-committees were dissolved by the Prime Minister and the President of the United States with effect from 16th November 1945.

The work which fell on the secretariat of the committee was extremely heavy and complicated. In order to understand its responsibilities it is necessary to define certain terms, and it is important to note that the term 'special plant' was coined in England and referred to mobile cranes, crawler excavators, compressors, concrete mixers, asphalt mixers, portable bitumen mixers, tar-spraying machines, portable crushing and screening plant, ditchers, finishers, pavers, spreaders and steel forms.

These items of plant formed part of a long list of items of 'assignable stores'. Assignable stores were divided into what were known in the United States as 'non-stockpile' and 'stockpile' items. There was 'special plant' in both 'stockpile' and 'non-stockpile' categories. The major portion of 'special plant' fell into the 'non-stockpile' category. Furthermore, where 'special plant' was referred to it meant special plant used by both Service and civilian departments. Availability of non-stockpile items was cabled by the British Army Staff in Washington to the Secretariat, and the availability of stockpile items submitted to the Secretariat in what was called the American Stockpile Status Report. The Secretariat obtained and compiled the requirements of Service and civilian departments for 'special plant' on the non-stockpile and stockpile lists and the requirements of civilian departments for stockpile items, a 'bidding directive' covering these requirements was cabled to Washington, and the British Army Staff bid on behalf of the Secretariat. The assignments made against these bids were cabled back and the Secretariat made allocations for confirmation by the committee, and then issued delivery instructions to Washington. At the same time, and in much the same manner, the Secretariat dealt with 'special plant' manufactured in the United Kingdom.

In effect, the Engineers' Stores Assignment Sub-Committee of the London Munitions Assignment Board was responsible for all assignable stores. It dealt with some of these itself, notably tractors and rollers, and delegated the executive responsibility for the others to its various sub-committees, of which the Engineers' Stores Assignment (Special Plant) Sub-Committee was one.

(iv)

Indirect Control by Departments

Indirect control over heavy plant came about whenever departments acquired on their own behalf, and for the benefit of contractors and others carrying out work for them, a number of items of plant. The Air Ministry, the Ministry of War Transport, the Ministry of Agriculture and Fisheries and the Ministry of Home Security were all parties to this form of control. But on 5th August 1943 the Ministry of Works established a pool of contractors' plant. Pumps, mixers, dumpers, excavators, tractors and a number of miscellaneous items, acquired by various divisions of the Ministry for works in progress or completed under their direction, formed the nucleus of the Ministry of Works pool. Certain crawler tractors acquired by the department on lend-lease terms were included. The allocation of plant in this pool to works in progress was undertaken by the Directorate of Plant, and its operation and maintenance by the Controller of Transport (Works), who was already controlling a vehicle pool and was better equipped to supervise the servicing of the machines.[1]

The pooling of plant by departments was an effective means of concentrating extra plant on priority works at vital stages of the rearmament programme. In many instances the machines were lent to firms who put their own operators on them. The firms preferred to do this, but the practice had the drawback that the upkeep of the plant was neglected. If a department decided to hold plant and lend it to private firms, it should surely have organised the business of hire in the way in which hire was organised in the industry; it should have had its own operators (working to the hirers' instructions) and its own maintenance and repair organisation.

It has already been noted that the Ministry of Works represented all civilian departments on the Contractors' Plant Requirements and Allocation Committee. This had been agreed to by departments, after discussion at a meeting of the Industrial Capacity Committee,[2] on how to define 'Government plant'. The point at issue was whether

---

[1] This pool should not be confused with a pool of light handling appliances under the Engineers' Maintenance Mechanical and Electrical Division of the Directorate of Works, for the primary benefit of food stores and the Ministry of Food.

[2] On 13th October 1941.

plant required by firms working for departments other than the Ministry of Works should be treated as Government plant or non-Government plant. Had it been included as Government plant, there would have been no need for firms or authorities to apply to the Ministry of Works for permits to purchase. It was agreed that plant required by firms or authorities working for departments should invariably be subject to the sanction of the Ministry of Works. Protests were lodged by the Ministry of Health on behalf of local authorities, by the Ministry of Agriculture on behalf of drainage authorities (catchment boards), by the Ministry of War Transport on behalf of railways and other public utilities, and by the Mines Department on behalf of mines and quarries.

On the Engineers' Stores Assignment Working Committee, Cranes (Mobile and Crawler) and its executive committee and on the Engineers' Stores Assignment (Special Plant) Sub-Committee the Ministry of War Transport were directly represented; they were users of cranes and of excavators for quarries, and allocations were made to satisfy their bids. In the issue of permits, the Ministry of Works acted as 'post office' for permits to firms nominated by the Ministry of War Transport, and as 'post office' for permits for excavators to catchment boards nominated by the Ministry of Agriculture and Fisheries. That Ministry made its own arrangements direct with the Ministry of Supply for crawler tractors, because these formed part of a larger requirement which included many types of wheeled tractors. The Ministry of Agriculture also had its own schedule of plant hire rates. All other applications for permits to purchase plant came direct to the Ministry of Works.

Relations with departments were cordial, but the procedure was complicated and the responsibility placed on the Ministry of Works never had the whole-hearted approval of other departments. There was considerable merit in the flexible nature of the arrangements, and it is doubtful whether any more efficient means of distribution of plant could have been found. Large committees are difficult to work with, and the Engineers' Stores Assignment Working Committee, Cranes (Mobile and Crawler) was no exception; nevertheless, interested departments undoubtedly felt the need for representation on the sub-committees of the London Munitions Assignment Board. Perhaps an alternative solution might have been found in a larger number of specialised sub-committees with fuller representation or in larger secretariats in all departments organising the distribution of permits of the plant allocated to them.

(v)
The Distribution of Contractors' Plant

A census of plant was begun by the Ministry of Works in 1942. This provided the only comprehensive information of plant in England, Scotland and Wales. The War Office and other departments had hitherto compiled lists on a voluntary basis which did not, however, cover the whole field. The following table gives comparisons of returns received at the beginning and end of the census period for excavators and tractors, and totals of items for which only occasional returns were asked.

Description	31/12/42	CP	31/12/44	CP
Compressors—portable . .	4,392	1		
Concrete mixers . . .	27,094	1		
Cranes—road and crawler mobile	1,627	7		
Cranes—steam and rail . .	100	7		
Dumpers	3,778	1		
Excavators—oil . . .	4,055	3	4,798	30
Excavators—steam and electric .	300	1		
Excavators—multi-bucket . .	58	12		
Loading shovels . . .	374	Pre		
Pile frames steel + wood .	231	5		
Tractors	1,679	7	2,750	30
Tractors—agricultural . .	450	12		
Trenchers	199	12		
Rollers—oil + steam . .	6,061	1		

The distribution of excavators and tractors at 31st December 1942 was as follows:

Trade groups	Excavators	Tractors
	%	%
Civil engineering including builders	52·2	68·5
Plant hirers	4·4	8·2
Local authorities . . .	3·0	1·4
Public utilities	0·8	—
Gravel pits	2·3	1·3
Quarries	22·7	0·9
Brickfields	1·3	0·3
Miscellaneous	13·3	19·4
	100·0	100·0

The trade groups owning plant were made up of about 9,000 individual firms or authorities, of which under 100 were plant hire firms, about 3,000 general builders, 2,500 civil engineering firms, about 1,500 pit owners and about 1,000 local authorities. Plant hire firms tended to increase in number throughout the period, and there were well over 100 firms engaged in plant hire by the end of the war. Most civil engineers, however, preferred to own their plant. This was natural, for while the plant hire firm was of use to the builders, the small civil engineering firm could keep plant on the move in times of shortages. At all times, however, the plant hire firms played a useful role, since they had every reason not to hold plant back in depots between the close of one job and the start of another. Nevertheless, better results were produced by firms which did not have to depend on the aid of plant hirers.

(vi)

Conclusion

To sum up, the compilation of a register of important plant was undertaken by the Ministry of Works under Defence Regulation 55. The Ministry was empowered to call upon owners of contractors' plant (including local authorities and public utility undertakings) to make a return from time to time of certain types of plant in their possession, showing where all important plant was situated. In this way a census of the more important types of plant was obtained.

In providing against scarcity of plant, no change was made in the existing arrangements by which plant was kept fluid through the plant hire trade and by the transfer of plant owned by contractors from one job to another. Maximum rates of hire, however, for specified items of contractors' plant for basic periods, and conditions controlling such hire, were laid down. These applied both to Government and private work in Great Britain and Northern Ireland,[1] and it was made illegal to exceed the hiring charges or modify the conditions in any circumstances.[2]

---

[1] Northern Ireland was subject to a Plant Control, but modifications in procedure were made to suit the special conditions prevailing there. In June 1942 a directive was issued empowering the Supplies Control of the Ministry of Commerce of the Government of Northern Ireland to forecast the contractors' plant requirements for all works in progress and contemplated in that part of the country, whether undertaken by the Government or by contractors working for the Government. The total demands were sent from time to time to the various committees in England charged with the co-ordination of demands. Plant allocated to Northern Ireland was then distributed by the Supplies Control there, operating its own system of licensing. It was not until April 1943 that the Ministry of Commerce was permitted to control prices of plant, either new or secondhand. It made the following Orders: S.R. & O. (Northern Ireland) 1943, No. 124, cited as the Contractors Plant (Control) (Northern Ireland) Order 1943; S.R. & O. (Northern Ireland) 1943, No. 37, cited as the Contractors Plant (Northern Ireland) Order 1943. The first gave the Ministry of Commerce power to give directions to owners of plant and powers to make inspections of books and to ask for information. It did not apply to plant owned by Government departments or to contractors taking plant into the country from elsewhere. The second gave the Ministry of Commerce power to prohibit plant being taken out of Northern Ireland.

[2] S.R. & O. 1941, No. 1277.

O

Maximum prices for second-hand contractors' plant and agricultural implements of certain types were also fixed by an Order which came into force in June of the following year.[1]

The provision of new plant, whether manufactured at home or imported, and of spare parts was primarily the province of the Ministry of Supply, but was carried out in close liaison with the Ministry of Works, which submitted periodically to the Ministry of Supply a programme of requirements of new plant. Modifications of the responsibility of the Ministry of Supply for sanctioning the purchase of some types of contractors' plant, and of the Board of Trade and other departments for giving steel authorisations for other types, were made in March 1942 when much of the responsibility for purchase and steel authorisation was transferred to the Ministry of Works.

Purchasers of new plant of certain types[2] other than Government departments (but including contractors engaged wholly or partly on Government contract and all local authorities, public utility companies and other civil users) had to apply to the Ministry of Works for permits to purchase. For steel replacements for new plant, however, and for spare and repair parts, manufacturers of these types of plant had to apply to the Ministry of Supply. For non-permit plant,[3] manufacturers had to apply for steel replacements to the Ministry of Works, though purchasers could obtain such plant and also spare parts for plant listed as permit plant direct from the manufacturers without a steel authorisation. Certain other types of plant could only be bought on a steel authorisation from the Ministry of Works.[4]

Not included in any of the above categories were mobile cranes, both on road wheels or vehicles, and on crawler tracks. These could be purchased only on authorisation of the Ministry of Works.

To organise the work of inspection and see that effect was given to the regulations six Regional Plant Advisers were appointed by the Ministry of Works with the following duties:

1. To advise on general problems relating to care and maintenance.

2. To assist in obtaining plant when this was needed for important work.

3. To ensure that all existing plant was fully employed, if necessary by the exercise of compulsory powers.

---

[1] S.R. & O. 1942, No. 1163. This did not apply to Northern Ireland.

[2] These categories included concrete and bitumen mixers; contractors' types of locomotives; mechanical excavators and trenchers; road rollers; tar-spraying machinery; and track-laying tractors and ancillary equipment.

[3] Wheelbarrows and navvy barrows; steel shuttering; tipping wagons, including railway wagons of contractors' type; and contractors' tipping wagons on road wheels (but not tipping lorries on road-wheels).

[4] These categories were: wire rope for replacement of contractors' plant; steel scaffolding and fillings; steel piling, to be used for temporary purposes only; steel for repair and maintenance of contractors' plant to be carried out in contractors' own workshops; railway track, contractors' type, for temporary purposes only.

In the control of the administrative machinery of the Ministry of Works the Director of Labour Requirements and Plant held a key position, and he extended his province over the whole field of construction methods. He travelled from site to site, passing on useful information in a diplomatic way and promoting efficiency. He guided the technical control of payment by results, and under him a whole technique of standardised war-time power construction was worked out.

* *

*

Most of the controls, described at their maturity and in general terms in this survey of a wide field of regulation, were still in force when the war ended. Many were then continued during an indefinite period. Their character was not negative; on the contrary, their underlying purpose was to free the Government building programme from all extraneous impediment and competition. To harness all the resources of the building industry to a grand strategic plan was the common objective of so many varied measures.

Alongside these war-time objectives there emerged post-war objectives, such as housing, the recruitment of the industry, standardisation and so on. From 1940 onwards post-war planning tied up with war-time controls, and this aspect is discussed in a later chapter.[1] The measures so far described were taken under the stress of war for its successful prosecution.

---

[1] See Chapter XIX.

CHAPTER IX

THE WORKS AND BUILDINGS
EMERGENCY ORGANISATION

(i)

The Need for Emergency Mobilisation
by the Industry

WITHOUT the willing co-operation of the building industry effective control over the repair of air-raid damage would have been impossible. In any emergency organisation for dealing with the effects of bombing it was only within the industry itself, and only on a voluntary footing, that labour, materials and plant could be rapidly mobilised. It has already been told how, in the early months of 1941, Lord Reith put before both sides of the building industry of England and Wales a plan to set up a series of regional groupings. Later in the year talks were begun with the industry in Scotland, where somewhat different conditions applied; but it was not until the end of the year that agreement was reached, and not until 1942 that Scottish resistance to the proposals was overcome or that the place of the civil engineering industry in the emergency organisation was defined.

Protracted and difficult negotiations preceded the setting up of the Builders' Emergency Organisations, later renamed the Works and Buildings Emergency Organisation. Since these exchanges throw light on the relations between the Ministry of Works and the industry, and are in themselves of importance, they should be examined more closely.

The first proposals of the Minister of Works for regional groupings were received with suspicion and reserve. The fear in the industry was that unfederated firms[1] might be given advantage over federated firms, nor was it clear what was to be the role of civil engineering firms in a scheme that appeared only to concern the building side of the in-

---

[1] The results of registration of building and civil engineering contractors showed that 104,000 individual firms had registered, but this figure included specialist firms or firms which were otherwise ineligible as not being builders or contractors in any recognised sense. That left some 80,000 registered firms, of which only ten per cent. were federated; that is, were members of one or other of the numerous federations of employers. See Chapter I.

dustry. Despite rumours and recrimination, by October 1941 the lines which the builders' emergency organisations should follow were agreed within the Ministry by the Central Council for Works and Building, on which nominated members of both sides of the industry were serving. The original premise that these groups formed a Ministry organisation, but were to be managed by the industry itself under the direction of the Minister, did little to reassure the employers' federations. Their doubts and objections are discussed later in this chapter; meanwhile let us look at the Ministry's objects and the means by which it was proposed to attain them.

As defined by the Central Council these objects were:

1. To secure that (while the demand for construction persisted) every efficient contractor should, so far as possible, be continuously employed on the right kind of work and in the right district, with the minimum transport of men and plant.

2. To help the smaller contractors to maintain their independence by making sure they obtained a fair share of the essential work.

3. To ensure that in case of emergency adequate management and labour could be made rapidly available to deal with first-aid repairs in all areas, and especially in target areas.

4. To secure accurate information of the capacity of all the contractors in the region, both for the purpose of the better selection of contractors and sub-contractors, and for the use of the Regional Commissioners and of the fighting services in the event of invasion or other emergency.

Towards the attainment of these objects the first steps had already been taken. Voluntary organisations covering the whole country had begun to appear and were in varying stages of development.[1] A typical organisation comprised a management committee and an executive board, 'county controllers' and 'group leaders', with the Assistant Director of Emergency Works,[2] an official of the Ministry of Works, as adviser. In the Southern Region, to take an example, the management committee comprised three federated builders, one unfederated builder, two operatives, and the late director and secretary of the Southern Counties Federation of Building Trades Employers. The executive board, which carried out the instructions of the management committee, was composed of two of the builders in that committee who had retired from their businesses and were giving their whole time voluntarily to the organisation, the late director and secretary already mentioned and a clerical staff. The county controllers were each in charge of one of fifteen areas covering the whole

---

[1] They operated in the following regions: No. 1 London; No. 2 Southern; No. 3 Eastern Counties; No. 4 South Western; No. 5 Midlands; No. 6 Yorkshire; No. 7 Northern; No. 8 North Western; No. 9 South Wales; No. 10 North Wales; No. 11 Scotland.

[2] See Chapter X.

region, and controlled builders carrying on business within their area. The process of decentralisation was taken a step further by the nomination of group leaders, one under each county controller. They were, generally speaking, efficient medium-sized contractors whose duty it was to organise groups of small contractors within their area to form larger cohesive labour forces.

The role of the Assistant Director of Emergency Works was an important one. As the senior officer of the Emergency Works Directorate in the region he was in close contact with the Emergency Committee;[1] he sat with the committee at their meetings and the organisation was carried on under his direction. His duties were to ensure that there was fair play within the industry as between federated and unfederated firms, that there was no favouritism to any firms or sections of the industry, that the regional organisation functioned in accordance with the conditions laid down by the Ministry, and that firms were grouped together in the most efficient and satisfactory manner.

In fulfilment of the fourth object of the builders' emergency organisations as set out above, each regional office was provided with an intelligence room in which an up-to-date census of the building industry within the region was maintained. The census was collated and tabulated in such a way as to give a complete and detailed up-to-date picture. Ancillary records enabled any question concerning the building industry within the region to be answered immediately and accurately. Thus, all movements of labour and plant were traced and recorded, and where possible were adjusted to fit in with new works in order to prevent needless travelling, and so reduce billeting and subsistence allowances to a minimum. This work, though carried on as part of the invasion intelligence system of the Emergency Works Directorate,[2] was available for use by the emergency builders' organisations.

For the census very detailed forms were sent out to obtain the information, which included the number of various types of tradesmen in the employ of the contractors on the last pay-day in July 1941; the contracts they were employed on; the Ministry or employer for whom the work was being carried out; the head office staff of the firm; the date on which the firm would be capable of dealing with fresh work, and the number of men available on that date; and a schedule of plant held by each firm.

By means of the decentralised machinery operating through the county controllers and group leaders it was found possible to include in the census practically every contractor in the region.

---

[1] For a description of the character and constitution of the Emergency Committees of the local authority, see Chapter X.

[2] See Chapter X.

The builders' emergency organisations, though put out as a means of mobilising the industry's resources to meet post-blitz and invasion conditions, were more than an *ad hoc* scheme: they were integrated in the wider policy of deploying the industry over the whole of the building programme. With that object, the plan for the registration of contracting undertakings had been under way in the summer of 1941 and in due course had taken its place under Defence Regulations. Prominent in the minds of the Minister and his advisers was their duty to safeguard the industry's future, and especially that of the smaller firms, whose survival and future existence were being jeopardised by war conditions. In seeking the guidance and approval of the Production Executive in February 1941, Lord Reith had written:

I ask approval to the principle of control and direction of the building industry. The method would be on general lines. . . . The country would be divided up into zones which might be the regional areas. Contractors for the most part will be allocated to zones. Specialist contractors will be kept on special classes of work. Contractors will be graded according to capacity. Work will be allocated according to conditions existing to the contractor best able to carry it out. Departments would be guided by the Ministry of Works. But there are many problems of administration.

Later Lord Reith, in outlining a scheme for the building industry, stated:

It is not intended to suggest either strict specialisation or actual regionalisation by zones; but it is intended to aim at the following:
  (a) that so far as possible the activities of individual contracting firms shall be kept within such bounds as will ensure the maximum efficiency of supervision;
  (b) the avoidance of dispersal of contractors' efforts all over the country, with the incidental unnecessary movement of contractors' plant;
  (c) the concentration of individual firms' efforts as far as possible on the types of work for which they are best fitted, and so that they work with the departments to which they have in the past given most satisfaction;
  (d) reasonable and more economic distribution of work over the whole building and contracting industry, compatible with securing the maximum use of the most efficient units.

In his submissions to the Production Executive, Lord Reith had consistently emphasised the need for rationalisation and regionalisation, for grading and specialisation. On various occasions, too, he had announced that it was the policy of his department to see that the smaller and medium-sized builders were brought as far as possible into the war effort; it was indeed one of the main reasons for registration. On 13th June 1941, he wrote:

> It is now desired to register builders and contractors and take power to obtain returns from all building employers including local authorities, public utility undertakings, companies, corporations, etc.
>
> This is the only way to get full information of the labour force and how employed, in order to concentrate builders, particularly smaller ones who belong to no federation, on essential work. Action is already being taken in certain areas to co-ordinate builders and contractors; but registration is necessary to enable the work to be done adequately.

By the autumn of 1941, there could be no question of what policy the Ministry of Works should follow on regionalisation. The Government were faced with a crisis in the building industry. Of the 80,000 or more registered building firms less than 8,000, as we have seen, were federated.[1] The Ministry had just obtained powers under the Defence Regulations to secure the drastic curtailment of unessential building work, and unless there was extensive air-raid damage (which no one could then predict) most of the work that occupied the small and local builders would be cut off. The Government, at that stage of the war, faced a continuous reduction of building work and building labour. Summarising the position, the Director-General wrote:

> However one looks at it, the industry has to suffer and to 'concentrate'. Unless we direct things at this stage with great skill, we shall kill the industry; and leave nothing but the big contractors at one extreme and the jobbing builders with one or two men each (that nothing will move) at the other. I do not know how far the experiences at the end of the last war were due to something of the same kind having happened. But with a far greater problem before us after this war, we cannot meet it with an impoverished and emasculated industry.
>
> I think, therefore, that Government must take the responsibility for stating now openly that its policy is to see that a balanced industry is preserved in all its grades and divisions as far as possible. Many firms must inevitably close down, permanently or temporarily, but we must keep as many of the efficient alive as possible. The large contractors that have grown to many times their pre-war size will have to contract in another sense.

One obvious difficulty was that the large contractors tended to be the most efficient; and certainly it was much easier for departments to pile work on to them. But the Ministry of Works set itself to secure the collaboration of other departments so as to achieve a fair division of work between large and medium firms (leaving the very small firms to rely on jobbing, decorating, minor repairs and so forth). Towards that end the Director-General enunciated tentatively the following principles of policy for the builders' emergency organisations:

---

[1] See footnote on page 196.

1. The builders' emergency organisations are primarily an emergency organisation and secondarily an instrument to secure that building contracts are placed, so far as possible, in such a way as to involve the minimum amount of transport, billeting, etc., and make the most efficient use of builders' and contractors' organisations and plant throughout the country.

2. No builder or contractor has any right to claim that any particular body of labour should be kept at his disposal. But the Government does recognise that most builders and contractors have a nucleus of key men and really permanent employees who normally would, and should, remain attached to the builder.

3. Where circumstances permit, and subject to reasonable safeguarding against the risk of improper combinations or 'ringing' of tenders, it is desirable to confine tenders for the smaller contracts largely to local firms competent, in terms of experience, capacity and resources, to carry out the work. The term 'local' may obviously vary from an individual town to a region.

4. In regard to contracts of a greater size, competent local builders should, as far as possible, be given reasonable opportunities to tender.

5. Tendering for large contracts must inevitably be confined to the most suitable contractors, irrespective of locality, but the principle of sub-contracting, where this is practicable and efficient, should be followed.

6. All contracts must be placed, wherever possible, as a result of competition on a lump sum or schedule basis.

7. Owing to the continuous and inevitable reduction in the building labour force, due to the demands for the armed forces and for munitions, and the fact that in any case the Government building programme must shortly begin to diminish, there is not, and still less will there be, sufficient work for all existing firms.

8. From first to last, what is in mind is efficiency and the prosecution of the war effort.

Of these plans and premises the building industry proper had been only in part apprised, and as late as September 1941 the civil engineering industry had not even been approached by the Ministry. This was a tactical error, inspired, no doubt, by the fear that by the premature disclosure of its intentions the Ministry might arouse intractable opposition in the industry. When later all the implications of emergency regionalisation became apparent, the whole idea was for a time suspect. After a brief initial period of approval, and even enthusiasm, at all events on the part of the smaller firms, alarm and resentment, fanned by exaggerated rumours, flared up in the industry. If, as now seemed to be admitted, the Ministry's intention was not merely to devise an emergency organisation for blitz and invasion conditions, but to set up a permanent system for the regionalisation of the industry, extending even to post-war conditions, then it was indefensible to present such far-reaching measures under cover of the

Directorate of Emergency Works. The federated building employers visualised a new and untried organisation cutting right across their existing machinery; while the federated civil engineering contractors resented bitterly, first, the fact that they had been excluded from the Government's counsels until brought into them at their own request, and even more the explanation offered that the civil engineering industry had been regarded by the Director of Emergency Works merely as a 'side' of the 'building industry' in its widest interpretation.

> 'The civil engineering industry is not . . . a "side" of the building industry', wrote the Secretary of the Federation, 'but is an industry which, though correlated in war-time to the former, is an essentially separate and independent one. The Director's misunderstanding of this fact may be responsible for the Federation not having been consulted in this matter *ab initio.*'

In the heat of their anger and resentment the civil engineers openly doubted whether the Minister was himself aware of the implications of the scheme of regional organisations and had personally approved of it. The Director of Emergency Works had indeed to expound the elementary truth that 'nothing of this kind could possibly be put in hand by a Ministry without the approval of the Minister'.

By mid-October feeling in the industry had reached a climax. Whatever goodwill there had been at first had broken down finally under misapprehensions and in an atmosphere charged with ill-feeling and suspicion. The Ministry's deficiency of tact and understanding in their launching of the scheme could only in part be made good by diplomacy on the part of the Director-General and the Minister himself. Some suspicions were quietened; but the co-operation secured from the industry was limited and cautious. The Director of Emergency Works had recently[1] received deputations from the Federation of Civil Engineering Contractors and had explained to them the scope and objects of the scheme, had even confidentially shown them the final report of the Central Council. The federation remained unconvinced. In seeking further assurances, they addressed themselves direct to the Minister. He could but suggest more talks, this time with the Director-General as well as with the Director of Emergency Works. 'After which', he added, 'I would gladly join in myself as I am very anxious to secure your federation's help.'

Meanwhile, Lord Reith and the Director-General attended a meeting[2] with chairmen of the builders' emergency organisations and officers of the Directorate of Emergency Works; it helped to clear the air for the more important negotiations that were to follow. In answer to the Minister's letter, the Federation of Civil Engineering Contrac-

---

[1] 23rd September and 9th October.
[2] 23rd October.

tors proposed that, as the principles at stake were of such importance, Lord Reith should himself receive a joint deputation from that federation and the National Federation of Building Trade Employers, who in turn assured Lord Reith that they shared the views expressed by the sister federation. A meeting was accordingly arranged for 26th November, but it was not until 26th December that the Minister was ready to make a statement on the Ministry's policy to which both federations, and the industry as a whole, were willing to subscribe.

Renamed the Works and Buildings Emergency Organisation, the scheme was declared to be an emergency creation for the period of war emergency. It was clear, too, that under pressure of the industry the Ministry's original design for 'the grouping of medium-sized and smaller builders into larger balanced forces' had gone, for the time being, by the board.[1] Yet fears and suspicion remained unallayed; they show through a memorandum prepared by the two federations for the Minister's meeting with the joint deputation.

After assuring the Minister of their fullest co-operation in all measures relating to post-blitz and invasion, the federations asked for clarification. How were 'medium and small' firms to be defined? Which of them could be called upon to participate in the war effort? What work would be found for them by the Ministry and how near to their homes? What limitations were placed by building emergency organisations on the choice of contractor by local authorities, or were the functions of building emergency organisations merely advisory *vis à vis* such authorities? What was the nature of the works which came within the ambit of the building emergency organisations other than first-aid repairs? What was the value of such works? Was it intended that contracts up to £150,000 should come within their competence? If so, would they include civil engineering as well as building work? Had the responsible Government departments agreed to consult the building emergency organisations as to suitable firms to tender for all such contracts?

Since it was understood within the industry that one of the objects of the building emergency organisations was to encourage sub-contracting, how would the Ministry act when 'smaller' firms could not take the work at the main contractor's price? Was it true that the Ministry would seek to compel Government departments to insist on a successful contractor sub-letting a named proportion—say twenty-five per cent.—of the work? If, as appeared, it was the main function of the building emergency organisations to keep labour available in any region to meet calls for first-aid and other emergency work, did that mean that work would be *created* for such labour? Or would

---

[1] As already recorded in Chapter VI, the grouping of firms in the Central and Regional Contractors' Records was later introduced, with the co-operation of the industry, to help speed up the Bolero programme.

labour remain immobilised at a time when the Ministry was insisting that labour did not 'belong' to individual contractors but was a general pool on which employment exchanges could draw in accordance with their needs?

And how were the building emergency organisations to be financed?

(ii)

Functions of the Works and Buildings Emergency Organisation Affirmed

In defining afresh the functions of the Works and Buildings Emergency Organisation the Minister reaffirmed that the regional organisations had been originally established to secure rapid mobilisation of local builders for urgent first-aid repairs to houses and buildings.

This work affected only builders—mostly the smaller ones; so that the organisation was at first limited to them. For public services and civil engineering works in post-blitz conditions and for anti-invasion purposes civil engineering contractors are also concerned. It was originally thought they could be on different lines, but in accordance with the wishes of the national federations they will now be included in the scheme.

The position of the civil engineering industry having thus been unequivocally stated and the emergency functions of the organisations further described, the Minister defined the policy of his department towards the smaller and medium-sized builders and contractors. The Ministry of Works, he stated, had two definite objectives:

In the first place to bring all possible assistance to the Government building and constructional programme; in the second, to do what is possible by greater local distribution of work to the extent that it is suitable for the medium-sized and smaller builders and contractors, to preserve as much as is practicable of the building and civil engineering industries, which otherwise would, in the rapid reduction before us both of the labour force and of the programme of new works, be more seriously or unequally affected.

But it should be emphasised that in this there obviously could not be intended to be any permanent reorganisation of the industries, or that the emergency organisations would compete or interfere with the industries' own recognised organisations. The ultimate structure of the building industry, both in the later stages of the war period and in post-war conditions, is a matter that will require and will receive the closest study by this Ministry—in conjunction with the two national federations and with other interests in the industry.

To ensure the fullest practicable use of local resources—remembering, however, that speed was paramount—implied the wider use of sub-contracting where that did not seriously threaten the success of the war effort. The Minister admitted, was indeed bound to recognise, that the building and civil engineering resources of the country had to be considered nationally as well as regionally and locally. He wanted to see local experience and information, and *esprit de corps*, used to the greatest advantage. For all these reasons he proposed to maintain the works and buildings emergency organisations and to make them more efficient. He added, however, that it was quite obvious that they could not be fully effective unless they had the universal approval and real support of the national federations.

On the definitions of 'medium' and 'small' firms the national federations had pointed out that, on the basis of the figures obtained by the Ministry, there was an enormous preponderance of small firms employing two or three persons. Clearly, these could not be brought into the picture of new building and works construction. They were part of the maintenance force of the country and it was the Minister's expressed intention to deal with them mainly, if not wholly, as such.

Far from there being any guarantee of work for everyone, there must be during the period of the war inevitably a growing reduction of work for all in the building and civil engineering industries.

On the selection of tenderers the Minister was explicit. He made it clear that the placing of contracts must obviously rest with the various Government departments:

It has never been otherwise; and there could be no question of delegating to the industries or to any section of the industries, or to the local committees of the works and buildings emergency organisations, decisions for which the departments and their Ministers are responsible to the Treasury, to the Public Accounts Committee and to Parliament. The same applies to local authorities. There is no obligation upon or suggestion to them in any way to restrict the selection of their tenderers or the placing of their contracts.

Nevertheless, the national federations were invited to express their view on how far the works and buildings emergency organisations could advise on the procedure for the selection of tenderers for contracts to be placed by the Ministry of Works.

Responsibility for finance had already been put upon the Government. The Central Council for Works and Building had recommended that the building emergency organisations should be self-supporting and that the money should come not from the Treasury, but from the industry, possibly by way of a levy on all building contracts, on Government contracts or on wage bills. The Minister of

Works, however, took a contrary view, and the money was found by Government. Any charges hitherto borne by the industry were adjusted, and at the same time the Ministry tightened up the regional arrangements. In each region, under the Assistant Director of Emergency Works, a full-time paid official of the Ministry was specially appointed to be in charge of the intelligence arrangements and to be the executive officer of the Works and Buildings Emergency Organisation. In addition to the authority with which the Ministry's executive representatives were invested by virtue of the office, they could look for support from the regional industrial organisations with which their duties were integrated. The Minister appointed regional advisory committees, under the direction of the Assistant Director of Emergency Works, whose members were drawn from firms of civil engineering contractors as well as builders. These committees were already in being, for the most part, and were earmarked for anti-invasion and post-blitz work. For such new works as were considered to be suitable and within their capacity, the committees acted as advisers on such matters as the capabilities and suitability of tenderers, and anything else within their province that might be referred to them. These regional and local committees were associated with the regional and local organisations of the national federations—but they were at pains to safeguard the interests of non-federated firms, and to reinforce the absolute authority of the Ministry's officers in taking action under conditions of heavy bombardment or the threat of invasion.

In notifying departments of the new arrangements the Ministry of Works described the procedure drawn up for the placing of its medium-sized contracts, which applied normally to to all new works up to an estimated cost of £25,000, and suggested what were to be the safeguards against 'rings'. The regional committees were to be enjoined, for example, to keep in strict confidence all matters discussed in committee, and in particular those which concerned the nomination of contractors to tender. No member of a regional committee might disclose to anybody outside the committee the names of the firms that had been suggested as tenderers for any particular work. They were under obligation not to countenance any suggestion of forming a ring to put in agreed tenders, nor were they to permit collusion of any kind between tendering firms. Evidence of such collusion would at once invalidate the tenders, while erring members of the committee would be instantly removed.

A committee was not in fact to be informed of the names on the list as finally submitted by the Regional Allocation Officer; nor was there any need for the amounts of tender to be disclosed to the Works and Buildings Emergency Organisation; but whether a firm was successful or unsuccessful had to be stated at once, since the names of firms would not ordinarily be put forward if they were already tendering for two jobs.

> The Works and Buildings Emergency Organisation accepts the responsibility for judging the capacity and position of every firm put forward, with specific relation to the particular job in question; and it is fundamental to the machinery that their advice be correct and be accepted.

(iii)
Opposition from the Industry in Scotland

While discussions with the two federations were going on in London the Ministry of Works, as has already been noted, had not brought into the negotiations the representatives of the industry in Scotland.[1] It is true that a Scottish builders' emergency organisation had been established in the summer of 1941, but the scope of its duties and functions had not yet been clearly defined; and its ultimate objectives remained vague and nebulous. In Scotland, too, alarm and suspicion, fed by rumour, were widespread; and with brusque frankness the Scottish employers upbraided the Minister of Works for the manner in which the new organisation was being imposed on the industry. They protested there was no truth in a statement attributed to Lord Reith (and subsequently denied by him) that the Scottish industry was in a state of chaos and confusion. It was of the nature of the building industry, and claimed as an asset, to be dispersed in countless small units throughout the rural areas of Scotland. So long as these small units provided the fibre of craftsmanship on which the industry depended they did not much care how it was organised. At the same time employers of eighty per cent. of the Scottish building labour force *were* organised, and employers engaged on contracting work, at least in the industrial areas, were practically 100 per cent. organised. The efficacy of its conciliating machinery, too, was such that for twenty years past there had been no major disputes in the building industry in Scotland.

> My Board (wrote Mr. McCowan Hill, the Federation's Secretary and Treasurer, on 16th December 1941), composed of practical men of the industry, whose 'niche' in life is bound up with the permanent well-being of the industry, are rightly jealous of the organisation which they themselves have created. It is their considered view that the present organisation is the one which is best adapted to meet the

---

[1] The Scottish National Building Trades' Federation (Employers) was the counterpart of the N.F.B.T.E.; the Federation of Civil Engineering Contractors included Scotland.

requirements of the industry, and that it should not be interfered with by any competing organisation constituted by alien sources. It is for this reason that my Board are concerned at the trend of the development of the builders' emergency organisation.

It was postulated that the emergency organisations were to be created by builders for builders. It would now appear that their sphere of activity is intended to be quite different from what was originally portrayed. . . . Created for an emergency purpose, doubt is now even expressed whether they are intended to be of temporary or permanent duration, or as to the extent of control which it is intended they may ultimately exercise over the industry. There is an entire lack of direction of administration, and the manner in which the organisation is being imposed on the industry is alien to the best traditions associated with the civil service.

My Board are gravely perturbed at the possible repercussions to the permanent organisation of the industry in Scotland, and are determined to oppose any attempt to usurp their own organisation.

During the early months of 1942 the storm, for a time, abated. On 26th January the Director-General travelled to Scotland to smooth out the difficulties, met the representatives of the federation, and succeeded in bringing the Scottish organisation into line with the plan for the country as a whole. But while the details of representation were being worked out with officials of the Ministry of Works, Lord Reith resigned and was succeeded by Lord Portal as Minister. This change was the occasion for a renewed offensive by the Scottish Federation, not only about the emergency organisations, but about other matters in which the federation thought it had been cavalierly brushed aside. The federation wrote of its grave concern at the trend of the Ministry's policy 'on the quick-changing constitutions and functions of the emergency organisations' as constituted by the Ministry of Works. These 'improvised organisations' had proved to be entirely at variance with Lord Reith's assurances, which had thus proved to be 'worthless'. Their feelings of anxiety had been further aggravated by references to the 'garrison scheme for building labour'[1] on which they had no clear information. If certain firms were to be subsidised and thus enabled to survive, to the exclusion of other firms, that had 'a foreign taint of regimentation which is alien to the instinct and sense of fair play of the people' and would be combated by the federation.

For a man to be deprived of his means of livelihood through force of circumstances in these abnormal times is a misfortune which must necessarily be faced. But for a Government department to provide for the selection of firms who are to be denied the opportunity of earning their livelihood is foreign to the principles upon which the free insti-

---

[1] See Notes and Appendices: Note XI. 'The "Garrison" Labour Force'.

tutions of this country repose, and this federation are not disposed passively to acquiesce. . . .

The effect of the 'garrison scheme' will disintegrate the industry and will deprive it of the means of quick recuperation to enable it to meet the demands with which it will be confronted when normal times again prevail.[1]

At the request of the federation, and because of the feeling now seen to be running high in Scotland, Lord Portal, on 23rd April 1942, received a deputation and was able to give the needed assurances. To meet the federation's general complaint that new measures had been imposed on Scotland without prior consultation, provision was made for consultation through the setting up of a Joint Advisory Panel, a Payment by Results Sub-Panel and a Registration Panel. On the constitution of the emergency works organisations, one disagreement remained outstanding—the percentage of civil engineers as against builders appointed to the committee. The civil engineers, who had asked for and been conceded fifty per cent. of the builders' representation, now claimed equal representation. But the civil engineering industry in Scotland was not large and the federation would not accept this claim. No similar claim for equal representation had been made by the Civil Engineering Contractors' Federations for England and Wales, and in the Minister's view no case had been made out for equal representation in Scotland. As had been pointed out earlier by the Director-General, there had never been any question of proportional representation. What was desired was that the various interests and sections should be able to voice their views. 'If you selected a representative of personality and accepted influence in the region', the Director-General had stated, 'you would, I suggest, be really adequately represented by only one such person on the committee in the region'. The disagreement was accordingly disposed of by this means.

---

[1] Letter from Scottish National Building Trades Federation (Employers) to Lord Portal, 3rd April 1942.

CHAPTER X

CONTROL OVER THE REPAIR OF AIR-RAID DAMAGE

(i)

Responsibility for Emergency Repairs

RESPONSIBILITY for the various works needed to make good the damage caused by air attack was shared by several departments. In the execution of these works, as in every other phase of the building programme, the basic problem was the shortage of labour. How to deploy a shrinking labour force effectively to meet sudden emergencies was, from the earliest days of war, a major concern of the War Cabinet, but it fell to the newly established Ministry of Works, with its tightening control over building labour, to provide the framework of an efficient emergency organisation.

At the request of the War Cabinet, and in consultation with the Ministers concerned, the Lord President of the Council[1] in February 1941 suggested means by which the supply of labour for emergency repair work could be ensured in districts that had come under heavy air attack. These arrangements provided the basis for a nation-wide organisation. On the executive side the Ministry of Works, through the regional mobilisation of the contracting industries, held a key position; on the administrative side the chief responsibility rested on the Ministry of Home Security, but was shared with the central government, the local authorities and the managements of public utility and commercial undertakings.

It had already been accepted in practice that for the repair of roads and dwelling-houses responsibility lay first of all with the local authority, for public utility services with the undertaking (very often the local authority) and for industrial and commercial firms with the management of each firm. On the local authority devolved certain specific duties, notably the repair of damage to buildings and services for which it was directly responsible and, as part of its civil defence functions, the more general duty of seeing that progress was made with the repair of air-raid damage of all kinds (other than damage to Government property) within its area. Experience had shown, how-

---

[1] Sir John Anderson.

ever, that when heavy attack was concentrated on a limited area, the scale of damage was likely to be beyond the immediate resources of the local authority. Under such conditions it was for the central government to back up local effort by securing help from the army as well as by arranging for additional civilian labour and, where needed, for technical assistance.

In framing the procedure to be followed in the repair both of 'normal' air-raid damage—in which it was enough to organise local resources—and of major air-raid damage (for which outside help had to be sought) the Government's aim was to keep the division of responsibility as clear-cut as possible. The help of the central Government would be ineffectual unless it were given promptly. Not only, therefore, was a pre-arranged scheme essential; it was also important that local authorities, public utility undertakings and private firms should carry out as much of the emergency repair work as they could. Self-reliance and mutual help up to the limit of their resources was expected of them.

'NORMAL' AIR-RAID DAMAGE

In the division of departmental responsibility for the organisation of local resources to meet what could be regarded as 'normal' air-raid damage, the role of the Ministry of Works was a prominent one. The Ministry already had a provincial organisation which comprised:

1. District officers concerned with the provision and maintenance of Government accommodation.

2. Licensing officers.

3. Liaison officers with the Regional Commissioners.

Of these representatives only the liaison officers had from the first been assigned to emergency repair work. In February 1941 their functions in this sphere were absorbed in the newly created Directorate of Emergency Repairs, which later became the Directorate of Emergency Works and Recovery.[1]

From its inception it was the policy of the Directorate to decentralise its functions as widely as was practicable. In each Civil Defence Region an Assistant Director of Emergency Repairs was appointed, and in each target town an Emergency Works Officer. The first duty of these officers was to help in procuring materials and labour for emergency repairs. Among their other duties was that of giving technical advice to the Emergency Services Organisation of the Ministry of Aircraft Production[2] and to the Regional Commissioners or their representatives; but their chief concern was to track down every source of supply of materials in the district and every Government

---

[1] See Section (ii) of this chapter.
[2] See Chapter XIV.

contract from which labour might be borrowed in emergency. They had to be familiar with the lay-out of local services. They had to keep an up-to-date list of essential war factories in the area, and to be in touch with the Local Reconstruction Panels (or War Factories Joint Committees) and the Area Boards of the Production Council. Together with the appropriate railway authorities, they had to plan well in advance railheads or dumps for the collection and distribution of materials where direct rail delivery seemed likely to become impracticable after an exceptionally heavy raid.

In giving their help with the supply of materials, the Emergency Works Officers could draw upon a reserve stock, known as the Emergency Materials Reserve, which had been accumulated by the Ministry of Works at convenient depots throughout the country. This was at the disposal of local authorities and others for materials which could not otherwise be obtained. The intervention of the Emergency Works Officers was also helpful in getting prompt delivery of controlled materials, under arrangements with the several controls which ensured the immediate release in emergency of such materials as, for example, steel, timber, and building boards.

Although it was for the local officers of the Ministry of Works to track down potential sources of building labour on the spot, it remained the duty of the Ministry of Labour to fulfil its normal role. Additional labour for emergency works continued to be found through the local labour employment exchange managers. Men could also be brought in under certain mutual aid arrangements. Public utility undertakings for such services as water, gas, electricity and sewage, whether they were direct employers of labour or worked through contractors, could use for emergency repair work not only the men ordinarily employed on the normal work of the undertaking, but where there had been heavy damage could look to neighbouring undertakings for labour reinforcements. Mutual aid arrangements of a similar kind governed the pooling of materials. All the most important undertakings had built up, with the aid of Government grant under the Civil Defence Act, reserves of materials for emergency repairs and could also draw, in case of need, upon other undertakings in the area.

To help public utility undertakings in making the best use of local resources, Government departments (through the appointment of special officers and otherwise) supervised and co-operated with these bodies. Thus, in the maintenance of water supply, each Regional Commissioner in England and Wales had the assistance of at least two Engineering Inspectors of the Ministry of Health with special experience of water supply problems and a wide knowledge of all the water undertakings in the region. These officers had the general oversight of the condition of water undertakings throughout the region, and ensured that each undertaking was able to maintain its services under war conditions. Where mutual aid arrangements had not been made or had broken down, they helped undertakings which had suffered heavy damage to get labour or materials from other undertakings within the region or, if necessary, from another region by invoking the regional organisation. In Scotland similar arrangements were made by the Department of Health for Scotland.

An analogous system applied to gas, under the direction of the Board of Trade; to electricity, under that of the Electricity Commissioners and the Central Electricity Board; and to sewers, under the respective Health Departments.

For the emergency repair of blitzed industrial or commercial buildings, managements were themselves responsible. The Ministry of Aircraft Production had, however, set up in all industrial centres throughout the country its own local reconstruction panels as part of its emergency services organisation.[1] At first the function of the panels had been to advise the managements of aircraft factories on the repair of air-raid damage and to help them to get labour and materials with which to resume production. Later, by arrangement with the other supply departments, similar help was given to all war production factories. In addition, owners of industrial and commercial buildings, not necessarily concerned with war production, could ask the local authority for help in getting materials for first-aid repairs.

Except where owners of dwelling-houses were able and willing to do their own repairs, emergency housing repairs were the responsibility of the local authority. For this work local authorities relied in the first instance on such labour and materials as could be found locally, but also looked to the central government, which could help partly through the emergency materials reserve already referred to, and partly through the regional architects of the Ministry of Health, who were authorised to advise on and direct emergency work. Mutual aid arrangements for labour supply were made by many local authorities with neighbouring authorities, and in case of need the regional architects, who were in close touch with the local representatives of the Ministry of Labour and the Ministry of Works, could bring in more men as well as materials from outside the region. Similar arrangements applied to Scotland.

HEAVY DAMAGE THROUGH INTENSIVE AIR ATTACK

The arrangements just described were designed to apply to the ordinary run of air-raid damage, not to intensive attacks, such as that on Coventry, for which they were quite inadequate. After any major attack from the air, responsibility for action lay with the Emergency

---

[1] Each panel consisted of a small number of the leading industrial representatives in the district who gave their services voluntarily. By the end of 1940 over a hundred such panels had been set up.

Committee of the local authority, assisted by representatives of the industrial and other interests primarily concerned. But where there was widespread damage a specially constituted executive body usually took the immediate initiative for every kind of emergency repair work and was competent to relieve the Emergency Committee, particularly on questions of priority. The authority of these executive bodies derived from a War Cabinet ruling that in every area which might become the target of a heavy attack such a committee, under a suitable chairman chosen in consultation with the local authority, should be set up in advance, and should meet to work out its plans and define the functions of each of its members. The normal composition of this body, known as the Emergency Repairs Committee, included representatives of the local authority (houses, sewers, roads); local public services (gas, water and electricity); the Ministry of Labour; the Ministry of Works; the Ministry of Health (or Department of Health for Scotland); the Local Reconstruction Panel (or War Factories Joint Committee); the Board of Trade; and the military commander wherever troops had to be called in.

After heavy raids the Emergency Repairs Committee, through the employment exchange manager, could look to several sources of supply for additional labour. Among them were unemployed men in the area; unemployed men from other areas recruited through the Ministry of Labour's national clearing machinery; men from the emergency repair squads; and men in employment who could be diverted temporarily to emergency repair work. (Of course, as the war proceeded the numbers of the first two classes became negligible and reliance was placed almost completely on men in the second two classes.)

Emergency repair squads in factories in the industrial areas were made up of men borrowed from local factories who were prepared to help with emergency repair work. They were needed especially for repairs to public utility services during the first three or four days after heavy air attack when, in the general dislocation, factory production was likely to be at a standstill. Lists of the firms which had formed such squads, and the number of men in each, were kept by the local employment exchange manager and could be used according to the discretion of the Emergency Repairs Committee. Employers whose factories were still in production were not asked to release their men except in circumstances of extreme necessity and when no other labour was available.

When large numbers of skilled men were urgently wanted for emergency repairs the Ministry of Works was given power to transfer complete contractors' organisations (skilled men, supervisory staff and equipment) from Government jobs within fifteen miles of the blitzed area. These transfers had to be made in agreement with the employing departments and according to the priority of the various contracts in the area; and the contractors' gangs were assigned to particular repair jobs, as described later, under the Defence Regulations.

To help in the emergency repair of houses the Ministry of Works established a special corps of building labour, composed of skilled men released from the Army. This Special Repair Service, formed originally for working in London, could be rushed to any part of the country.[1] It rested with the Emergency Works Officer to decide, in consultation with the employment exchange manager and the local representative of the Ministry of Health (or the Department of Health for Scotland) when to call on the corps for help in any particular area, and to apply to the Ministry of Works accordingly.

The Emergency Repairs Committee could, at its discretion, invite the Regional Commissioner to call in help from the Army (for example, for skilled men of the Construction Companies of the Royal Engineers in the repair of public utility services, and for unskilled men of the Royal Pioneer Corps in the clearance of debris). In special cases (for example, to rehouse employees at munition factories so that they could continue at work) troops could be detailed for some parts of the work on emergency repair of damaged houses.

PRIORITIES IN EMERGENCY REPAIRS

Where the amount of damage was 'normal', the determination of priorities in carrying out emergency repairs presented no problem: the various bodies or firms could be trusted to carry out their repair work with the labour they had at call, and with each deciding for itself which of its own repair jobs should be tackled first. On the repair of war factories, the Local Reconstruction Panels, together with the representatives of the supply departments in the region, could give advice and help. But where there was major damage and the demand for labour and materials was greater than could be met, some system of priority was needed to resolve competing claims. The War Cabinet accordingly defined the principle on which this should be done. The formula was that the Emergency Repairs Committee would deal with questions of priority in repair work as between factories and other buildings and services in the area, and in any dispute which the committee could not settle the Regional Commissioner would in the last resort determine the issue.

The allocation of any supplementary labour brought into a blitzed area devolved naturally on the Ministry of Works. Together with the employment exchange manager, the Emergency Works Officer assigned such labour among the various repair jobs in accordance with any priorities determined by the Emergency Repairs Committee. The Emergency Works Officer was concerned with the allocation of

---

[1] See Section (ii) of this chapter.

the labour in the transferred contractors' organisations, in the Special Repair Service and in any detachments of troops called in. It was his special duty to keep in close touch with the officer commanding such troops. Through the Regional Transport Commissioner, he was responsible for arranging for the transport of imported workers, and through the representative of the Ministry of Health (or the Department of Health for Scotland) for their accommodation: he could, if necessary, have camps constructed for their use.

(ii)

The Directorate of Emergency Works and Recovery

In the restoration of the life of bombed areas the Directorate of Works and Recovery played an ever-increasing role. At the time when the Directorate was set up (February 1941) heavy air attacks were frequent, but no urgent work of repair was stopped for lack of labour or materials. Between February and May there was intensive co-operation with Ministries: arrangements were made with the Ministry of Health in helping local authorities on home repairs and public utilities; with the Board of Trade for repair of general factories, shops and public utilities; with the Ministry of Food for repair of food factories; with the Admiralty for repair of works and dockyards; with the Ministry of Supply for repair of Royal Ordnance factories; with the War Office for repair of depots and works; with the Ministry of War Transport for repair of railway and other transport undertakings; and with Trinity House for repair of lighthouses. Stocks of Government emergency building materials were taken over in May 1941, augmented, and moved out of target towns to safer areas. Strategic dumps, each designed to serve two or more of the great industrial areas of the country, were planned; and methods of determining the amounts of stocks to be held for each town were worked out so that each target town should have at its disposal, apart from stocks in merchants' hands. enough material to carry on for seven days after a heavy attack. Provision was also made to supply during those seven days as much material as might be needed after that period. There were before 1941 some ninety-nine 'stockists'[1] and the value of materials in emergency stocks was approximately £1½ millions. In one way or another during that year help was given to

---

[1] This deplorable addition to the English language is used for convenience, but with apology and regret. 'Stockist' now carries the authority of the Oxford English Dictionary, though hardly, one must suppose, the blessing of its compilers.

some hundreds of factories, and local authorities were enabled to repair approximately 900,000 houses.

After the heavy raids at Liverpool at the end of April and beginning of May some 6,000 men were put in in four days; after the two heavy raids on London in the same month 16,000 men in a little over a week. In Plymouth the direction of all first-aid repairs was taken over with the agreement of the local authority.

In the bombed cities, notably London and Bristol, exceptional provision was made for static water supplies. In the London region alone some 400 tanks were constructed, of approximately 35 million gallons capacity.

The Special Repair Service of the Works and Buildings Emergency Organisations, and a similar organisation of roofing contractors, dispatched its 'flying squads' as needed all over the country to attacked areas. A fleet of 150 vehicles, consisting of sleeping vans and kitchen units, ensured complete mobility and overcame the difficulties of billeting. Nor were the flying squads available only for the post-blitz service to dwelling-houses, for which they had been created. They were soon extended to assist Government works of high priority, and in the construction of new camps and airfields their new role was to put up temporary camps for the building operatives before the major works were commenced.[1]

ANTI-INVASION PLANS

In addition to its responsibility in the repair of air-raid damage and the restoration of conditions after heavy air attack, the Directorate of Emergency Works was prepared to meet whatever circumstances might arise in the event of invasion, which for a time seemed imminent. A fully detailed plan of action was worked out and communicated as a secret document to all officers of the Ministry of Works on whom specific duties would devolve should the enemy invade. The first task of the officers of the Directorate in that event was to 'direct' building and civil engineering contractors to meet the authorised demands of the three fighting services, the Ministry of War Transport, the Regional Commissioner and other competent national and local authorities for labour, plant and materials for essential work.

All that was necessary and possible for the Directorate to do in repairing normal 'blitz' damage was to go ahead subject to one overriding rule—that works required for military reasons took first priority. Delegated powers under Defence Regulations were to be given to certain officers enabling them to 'direct' firms, to impress labour and to requisition chattels.

In the delegation of these and similar powers the aim was to ensure

---

[1] At the peak of its work the force numbered 12,300 (Summary Report of the Ministry of Works for the period 9th May 1945 to 31st December 1946. Cmd.7279).

the greatest possible degree of decentralisation. Emergency Works Officers, together with County Surveyors and other officers of the local authority, were to keep a check on the resources of builders and civil engineers in their immediate district and make use of them (if they were not already allotted to large Government new works) before asking for further help.

Where communications did not exist, or time did not permit, it was for the local officer to put through really essential work without reference to his superior at corps or district headquarters. In cases of extreme necessity, even reserve squads might be taken and used, provided they were taken as complete squads, after consultation with the Air Raid Precautions Controller, and returned as soon as possible.

Conditions where the maintenance of communications was more important than rescue work were seldom likely to arise, and only a very grave position would have justified interference with rescue work actually being carried on.

Provision was made to meet a variety of probable contingencies. If, for example, local resources for maintaining roads and bridges should fail, the first reserve was that of the Ministry of War Transport Repair Organisations, whose assistance was to be secured under specified conditions. Contractors, again, might be directed from work on airfields belonging to the Air Ministry or an air-raid precautions works, provided it was recognised that such work was of high priority and was not to be interfered with save in urgent and important circumstances.

It was expected that a difficult question of priority would arise if and when the sum total of current requirements of the various authorities should exceed the available resources, and a specific authority should nevertheless insist that its own requirement was one of overriding importance. It was laid down, therefore, that in an 'operational' area (that is, one which after invasion was so declared by a Regional Commissioner on the advice of an army commander) the competent military authority (that is, a corps commander, district, area, brigade or sub-area commander) would be responsible for settling priorities on conflicting demands for assistance between the three fighting services and on all other conflicting demands. Outside an 'operational' area the Regional Commissioner was responsible for settling all priorities as between competing military and civil requirements or between competing civil requirements. Where there were disagreements or uncertainty as to priorities, it was for the Emergency Works Officer himself to bring the matter to the immediate notice of the competent authority.

The compulsory powers thus delegated to the officers of the Directorate of Emergency Works fell under three main categories governed by Defence Regulations as follows:

1. The direction of contractors (under Defence Regulation 55).

2. The impressment of labour (under Defence Regulation 84AA).

3. The requisitioning of chattels (under Defence Regulation 53).

The direction of contractors. Since, under conditions of invasion, it would be impracticable to negotiate contracts with firms in the normal way where work was to be carried out, the powers of direction held by the Ministry of Works under Defence Regulation 55 could be delegated to Assistant Directors of Emergency Works and to the Senior Emergency Works Officer or the Emergency Works Liaison Officer at each invasion post. These officers were to be supplied with a warrant of authority which, on request, had to be shown to a firm to whom 'direction' was given. Under heavy penalties, direction was to be immediately obeyed by the firm to whom it was addressed. A responsible representative of a firm on a site was also bound to obey direction under the same penalties. There was no question of persuading or asking a firm to do work. In the event of refusal, wilful delay or obstruction, full information was to be recorded at once (and the names of witnesses taken) and the matter reported to the Assistant Director of Emergency Works and/or the Emergency Works Officer with the nearest military commander at the earliest practicable moment.

The impressment of labour. Unlike powers under Regulation 55, which could be exercised in any area at any time during the war, compulsory powers under Regulation 84AA could only be exercised by duly authorised officers if two conditions were fulfilled: first, that the area in which it was proposed to exercise them had been declared by the Regional Commissioner to be an 'operational' area; and, secondly, that the emergency work which the impressed labour was to be ordered to do was declared by a competent military authority to be necessary for meeting enemy action.

It was expected that Emergency Works Liaison Officers stationed at posts below county level or corps headquarters level would be able to carry out their invasion duties by directing contractors under Regulation 55 and that there would be no need to impress labour on a job in its own neighbourhood. If, however, circumstances arose where an officer without powers under Regulation 84AA found that impressment of labour was necessary, his duty was to apply to the nearest Operational Area Defence Officer of the Ministry of Labour—usually the local employment exchange manager. Delegated authority from the Ministry of Labour for the exercise of these drastic powers (including powers of arrest without warrant and over building and civil engineering labour only) was restricted to Assistant Directors of Emergency Works and certain officers of the Emergency Works Department who were full-time civil servants at county, corps or district and regional level. The powers were intended to be used by the authorised officer whenever a firm was directed under Regulation 55 and any of its workmen refused to obey the firm's orders, such orders being necessary to enable it to comply with the direction. It was also foreseen that an authorised officer might have to impress labour only, for example, unemployed building and civil engineering labour; or that in case of dire necessity (where a Ministry of Labour Operational Area Defence Officer could not be consulted) he might have to impress other than building labour, for example, factory workers.

The requisitioning of chattels. At action stations all officers of the Directorate of Emergency Works who were given delegated powers under Regulation 55 were also to be furnished with a warrant giving them powers on behalf of the Minister of Works to requisition plant, materials, tools, and articles of a building or civil engineering character. The purpose was to prevent a directed firm which could not obtain such articles in the normal way from being held up on urgent work through lack of them. The power thus given was naturally to be exercised with discretion, care being taken to avoid requisitioning anything owned or earmarked by military authorities in readiness for invasion. If, for example, a merchant or wholesaler were, under pretext of the 'emergency', to demand a price that the Emergency Works Officer and the directed firm considered exorbitant, thereby delaying vital work while the parties were bargaining, requisitioning would be justified.

Working arrangements with the War Department and the Ministry of War Transport were defined for the guidance of the Directorate's officers, who were instructed that, in all areas where fighting was actually going on, the military authority was paramount and controlled the civil population under its common law rights. The Emergency Works Department's organisation did not function in such areas. Where, on the advice of the military authority, a Regional Commissioner declared an area to be an 'operational' area, a definition that might cover adjacent parts of other regions, the military authority was the final arbiter as to the priorities of work to be carried out.

As already stated, the Ministry of War Transport was responsible, outside the fighting area, for the maintenance of roads and bridges. Liaison officers from the Emergency Works Department were to be attached to the Divisional Road Engineers, who were the Ministry of War Transport's responsible officers for this work and operated the Ministry's Road Repair Organisation as follows:

1. With certain bodies of direct labour known as agency service men. These were mobile and were to be mustered in action stations, with transport, rations, etc., under the control of the Divisional Road Engineers of the Ministry.

2. Through County Surveyors, who in their turn had District Surveyors.

3. Through City Engineers, Borough Engineers and Urban District Council Surveyors.

If the normal labour employed by these local authorities was inadequate it rested with the Local Emergency Works Officer to take the initiative to direct a firm to remove labour and other resources from an important Government new works job in the neighbourhood or, when all local resources were exhausted, to seek assistance at a higher level.

RECOVERY OF SALVAGE

A notable part of the work of the Directorate of Emergency Works from 1942 onwards was its share in the recovery of salvage. Imports of scrap metal from America had begun to fade out towards the end of 1941, nor was there any source of supply to replace this metal other than a possible increase in the amount recovered in the United Kingdom. The Ministry of Works, with its regional organisation for emergency works, was chosen as the appropriate department to undertake a scheme for the recovery of scrap metal from unusual sources. As the volume of steel scrap recovery increased, a separate Directorate of Demolition and Recovery was formed in January 1942. In March 1943 it was amalgamated with the Directorate of Emergency Works to form the Directorate of Emergency Works and Recovery.

The scrap recovered under contract included steel and timber from premises damaged by enemy action; iron railings, gates, chains and bollards, non-ferrous metal; tram rails (arranged with local authorities); scrap metal from the National Survey (Recovery); scrap metal from the National Survey (Dumps); and rubber.

The National Survey, begun in April 1942, followed on the Scrap Metal Orders Nos. 1 and 2, which required that all persons who had in their possession amounts of three tons or more of non-ferrous or ferrous scrap metal or both must disclose such metal to the department. The Orders gave the department power to requisition such scrap if the owners were not prepared to dispose of the metal to scrap merchants. The National Survey also covered a similar tonnage of disused or redundant plant and machinery which the owners were prepared to dispose of as scrap. If the plant or machinery so discovered was in such a condition that a useful purpose could be found for employing it, the appropriate Government departments were notified. If there were no inquiries from departments, particulars were circulated throughout the country on a national stock list which was issued by the Ministry of Supply. Three months after the issue of the stock list, if no applications were received, the breaking up of the plant or machinery was ordered, with the consent of the owner, and the materials disposed of as scrap metal.

Certain industries were given special treatment. These included the mining, cement and shipbuilding industries. Imperial Chemical Industries and certain public utility companies. Specialists in these industries were appointed by the Ministry to deal with scrap metal from them.

Arrangements for the collection of scrap metal from village dumps, farms and municipal depots were made by the Directorate of Emergency Works and Recovery. Such scrap was acquired by free gift or by purchase. All Government-owned motor vehicles which had been declared unusable were collected for breaking up in depots set up throughout the country and manned by direct labour. Metals, usable spare parts, leather, rubber and other materials were recovered.

(iii)

Damage by Flying Bombs and Rockets

Bombing attacks on London were renewed in the early months of 1944, and after a lull were followed by flying bomb (V1) and rocket (V2) attacks on south-eastern England. The first flying bomb fell on 14th June, and twelve weeks later the first rocket. The severity of the flying-bomb attacks, the havoc they caused, and the as yet unpredictable effects of the rocket attacks which were known to be impending, overshadowed the summer of 1944 and created a new series of problems. The urgent need to provide shelter for the bombed-out (whose plight had been aggravated by the untimely return to London during the previous months of many families evacuated earlier in the war) as well as the programme for the erection of permanent and temporary houses already announced by the Government, made severe demands on the resources of the industry and brought all long-term housing plans to a standstill.[1]

From 1940 onwards half the air raids on Britain had been concentrated on the London region. Here, even before the flying-bomb attacks, some 84,000 houses had been completely destroyed or damaged beyond repair, besides about one and a quarter million damaged in varying degrees not incompatible with repair.[2] It was soon apparent

---

[1] The number of males insured in the building and civil engineering industries as at July 1944 was 496,000 as against 1,362,000 in 1939 (see table Appendix 1). The gross output of the industry was now £290 millions as against £442 millions in 1939. For the number of houses actually built in 1944 and 1945 see *Statistical Digest of the War* in this series, Table 45.

[2] See p. 225.

that, in order to continue to make good that damage and the havoc caused by flying bombs and rockets, the existing emergency repair organisation would have to be strengthened and made to fit the new conditions. Towards the end of September the Minister of Reconstruction, Lord Woolton,[1] launched a campaign to bring London back to at least the condition it was in before the flying-bomb attacks began in June. The first aim of the campaign was that, if possible, every person who was suffering the results of the damage 'should with all speed be enabled to live under tolerable conditions in which the weather is kept out and the warmth kept in'.[2] While the Minister of Reconstruction remained in a general sense responsible for this aspect of physical reconstruction, most of the actual planning and the execution of the repair works had already fallen upon the Ministry of Health and the Ministry of Works. From the very outset of the flying-bomb attacks, it was clear to those in charge, at both these Ministries, that nothing would be achieved without the closest possible collaboration in every detail of the organisation of repair work and the supply of labour and materials. A Principal Architect from the Manchester Regional Office of the Ministry of Health was sent to work with the Assistant Director of Emergency Works in London[3] and these two officers with their staffs functioned as one unit. One side of their work was to keep in touch with local authorities, to find out their needs, and to advise and help them in making the best use of the technical staff lent by other local authorities both in meeting the special flying-bomb emergency and in solving day-to-day problems that would normally have been dealt with by the Ministry of Health alone. Equally important was the duty of making detailed arrangements to enable contractors to use their own labour and plant, and to allocate the limited quantities of materials to the places where they were most required and could be used to the best advantage. The enormous damage inflicted from day to day called for prompt action to maintain morale as well as to limit the material losses in buildings and their contents. An Intelligence Section, manned by the Ministry of Works and working twenty-four hours a day, was set up to keep a check and issue information on the almost hour-to-hour situation both of 'incidents' as they occurred and the forces at the command of Drake House. Often Emergency Works Officers would remain on duty long after their normal rotas to cope with whatever emergency might occur in their own particular districts.

Co-operation at the official level between other departments affected by flying-bomb damage was effectively maintained during this

---

[1] In this campaign Sir Malcolm Trustram Eve, K.C., chairman of the War Damage Commission, acted as Lord Woolton's 'chief of staff'.

[2] *The Builder*, Vol. 167, p. 273. Report on Press Conference.

[3] These officers had their headquarters at Drake House, Dolphin Square, and their activities became known under the designation 'Drake House' organisation.

period by a series of informal conferences. On 14th June 1944 senior officers concerned with repair work met the Principal Assistant Secretary (Mr. S. F. S. Hearder) and the Assistant Secretary of the Housing Division of the Ministry of Health. They discussed arrangements for ensuring complete collaboration during the attack which was about to develop. From that day what came to be known as the 'Hearder' meetings took place regularly and were attended by representatives of all interested departments when points had to be discussed. The meetings were informal, no minutes were kept, but the chairman summed up each day, and made it clear whose responsibility it was to implement decisions taken during the meeting. The next morning the action taken was reported before new problems were discussed. Local authorities were informed of the discussions through Serial Notes. During, and for several weeks after, the flying-bomb attack these meetings were held daily, including Sundays. Later it was possible to reduce them to three per week, and later still, when Mr. Hearder left the Civil Service, the body became the London Housing Committee.

When the first urgency of the flying-bomb attack had passed, an action committee, designated the London Repairs Executive, was formed. Its chairman was the Minister of Works, Sir Malcolm Trustram Eve was vice-chairman, and there were representatives of the War Damage Commission, as well as of the Ministry of Health, the Ministry of Labour and the Ministry of Works.[1] In January 1945 local committees, designated Joint Repair Committees, drawn from both sides of the industry, were set up in each borough in the London region,[2] and on 29th January a Central Progress Committee met for the first time to study and guide the work of the local committees. Meanwhile, at ministerial level, the War Cabinet Rocket Consequences Committee kept under review the wider aspects of the situation.[3]

On 11th December Sir Malcolm Trustram Eve reported to the Advisory Council of the Building and Civil Engineering Industries.[4] The

---

[1] The first meeting of the London Repairs Executive was held on 1st December 1944. Mr. Duncan Sandys, who had succeeded Lord Portal as Minister of Works in the latter part of November, presided. Weekly meetings were held.

[2] M.O.H. Serial No. 77. Official representatives from the local authority, the Ministry of Works and the Ministry of Labour were co-opted as members without power to vote. The local organiser of the Works and Buildings Emergency Organisation was also entitled to attend meetings.

[3] The Rocket Consequences Committee was appointed by the War Cabinet on 28th July 1944, 'to concert action and plans to meet the contingency of rocket attack on the scale anticipated'. The Home Secretary and Minister of Home Security was chairman. Other members were the Minister of Labour and National Service, the Minister of Production, the Minister of Health and the Minister of War Transport, and the Committee was given power to consult other Ministers as necessary.

[4] The Council was set up by Lord Portal in September 1942 as a fully representative body through which the Government consulted the building and civil engineering industries. At the suggestion of Mr. Duncan Sandys, his successor as Minister of Works, it was renamed in February 1945 the National Consultative Council of the Building and Civil Engineering Industries. See Chapter XVIII.

report summarised the position at the end of September as follows:

Category of damage	Up to 31st May 1944	Fly-bomb attacks 15th June to the end of September 1944
A. Completely destroyed ⎫ B. Damaged beyond repair ⎭	84,611	25,511
C. (a) Seriously damaged but habitable ⎫ C. (b) Seriously damaged but not habitable ⎭	155,258	129,307
D. Slightly damaged	1,194,218	873,177

Since an unknown number of buildings included in the figures of damage before 31st May were again damaged by flying bombs, the total number of damaged properties was something less than the aggregate of the figures in the two columns of the above table.

The first-aid repairs which were put in hand immediately after damage were likened to a temporary 'field dressing' and were intended to make the property weather-tight. The repair figures mentioned later in the text refer to 'second stage' repairs, and the target set by the London Repairs Executive for the winter was to make by these means 719,300 houses tolerably comfortable by 31st March.[1] To reach that figure by that date the building labour force would have to be swiftly expanded and effectively reorganised; at the same time a watchful eye would have to be kept on the economical use and fair distribution of building materials.

REGROUPING AND BALANCING OF THE LABOUR FORCE

Let us look first at the labour problem. When the flying-bomb attack began the labour force on the extended repair of war damage to houses in the London Civil Defence Region numbered 21,000: by December 1944 (after allowing for absenteeism and sickness) the number was just under 129,000, and made up for the greater part (96,297) of contractors' labour employed by local authorities and direct labour of local authorities. The balance was made up as follows:

Contractors' labour employed by the Ministry of Works	19,806
Working parties employed by the Ministry of Works and not included in above	4,775
Special Repair Service	3,025
Labour from the forces and the National Fire Service	4,874
	32,480

Between 16th June 1944 and December 1944 some 44,500 men were brought in from the provinces: 27,100 by the Ministry of Labour,[2] 14,300 by the Ministry of Works, with provincial contractors, and 3,100 civil engineering workers to carry out demolition.

---

[1] *The London Repairs Bulletin*, 21st February 1945. This was a broadsheet issued by the London Repairs Executive and circulated among contractors, clerks of works, chargehands and all others concerned with the repair of bomb damage in the London region.

[2] This figure includes 4,000 volunteers who had responded to an appeal by the Minister of Labour.

Labour was allotted in the first place to the various boroughs in proportion to the damage to be repaired. In some areas the work was exceptionally difficult and complicated, in others it was interrupted by new damage. At first the London Repairs Executive was determined to avoid the substantial movement of labour from one London area to another, but encouraged the transfer of small numbers of repair workers from some of the boroughs where the programme was far advanced to other boroughs where the work was going more slowly. At the end of 1944, however, when the labour forces in the different areas were reviewed, it became clear that if houses were to be repaired in the right order, and if the second-stage repairs were to be completed everywhere before the third-stage repairs were begun anywhere, there must be movement of labour on a considerable scale. Contractors, clerks of works and charge-hands were asked to explain to the men that although this regrouping of the labour forces would cause them considerable inconvenience, any other course would cause a degree of hardship to large numbers of householders which was indefensible.[1]

The more mobile contractors were moved first, the local firms last. Among the firms to be moved immediately were some of the provincial contractors who had settled their men in hostels or lodgings. These men had become accustomed to the district in which they were working, and although in some cases regrouping might cause hardship, in others it meant merely a change of quarters or more travelling. But the regrouping was a potential cause of complaint not only in the provincial firms who had been specially brought in. London firms, too, had got used to the districts in which they were working, and some of the small firms, employing only a few men, had for years been established in particular districts and had never moved outside them for their work. While the grievances of the men were sometimes exploited for political ends, it is nevertheless true that the inconveniences of regrouping were on the whole cheerfully endured by management and workers alike.

For the rapid progress of the work, the balancing of the contractor's gangs was as essential as their regrouping. Occasionally the 'teamwork value' of men used to working together might perhaps outweigh the disadvantages of a slight lack of balance, and the local war damage officer, who was responsible for initiating transfers, had to move with caution.[2] Sometimes labour was balanced by voluntary transfer between employers, and the changes were later approved by the issue of formal directions by the Ministry of Labour. A correct balance of

---

[1] *London Repairs Bulletin*, 21st February 1945. Report of speech by Mr. Duncan Sandys at meeting of Federation Shop Stewards.

[2] M.O.H. Serial Note No. 62, 20th December 1944. The proposal of the local war damage officer had to be approved by the emergency works officer.

trades changed with the varying nature of the work, but as a general guide for a typical gang on second-stage repairs up to the existing standards[1] the ratio officially suggested was carpenters thirty per cent, plumbers (exclusive of mates) two per cent., plasterers ten per cent., labourers thirty per cent., bricklayers fourteen per cent., slaters nine per cent., and painters and glaziers five per cent.[2] The war damage officers were instructed not to intervene except where there was serious lack of balance, to do so in agreement with contractors, and in any case to limit their activities to local authority contractors, leaving Ministry of Health contractors to the care of the Ministry of Works.

Reports from the Ministry of Health regional architects and the emergency works officers of the Ministry of Works in each of the five districts in the London region showed that on the whole, by January 1945, labour had been effectually balanced, as a rule, by the short-term loan of tradesmen from one contractor to another. Such difficulties as arose concerned workmen's compensation and general insurance.

ACCOMMODATION AND WELFARE OF PROVINCIAL WORKERS IN LONDON

If repairs were to be speeded up it was important that building workers from the provinces should be well housed and fed. As from 20th September 1944 arrangements for their accommodation and welfare were taken up by the Ministry of Labour. By January 1945, out of a total of some 130,000 workers, approximately 25,000 were put up in hostels and camps, and during the period of expansion about 20,000 additional hostel places were found.

Altogether 240 hostels and camps were now in use or preparation.[3] To help the Ministry of Labour an informal inter-departmental committee was set up, while the Ministry's regional welfare staff was reinforced with experienced welfare officers brought in from the provinces to co-operate with the welfare staff of the Ministry of Works.

Welfare amenities were primarily the affair of the employers: they comprised mainly mid-day meals, hot drinks on the site, and lavatory, washing and drying facilities and first aid.

From the outset the Ministry of Labour offered to help the employers' associations and the trade unions to overcome any difficulties, and in this work the department's welfare staff had the close support

---

[1] See p. 225.

[2] *Ibid.*

[3] These hostels were managed by the National Service Hostels Corporation, the Ministry of Supply and their associated voluntary bodies (including Y.M.C.A. Joint Committee, the Workers' Travel Association and the Co-operative Holidays Association), local authorities, Ministry of Works contractors and S.R.S. camps. In addition a number of L.C.C. rest centres were still occupied.

of the Ministry's Factory Inspectorate and its Building Labour Supply Inspectorate, as well as of the Ministry of Works, the Ministry of Health and the War Damage Commission group officers, the trade union site officers and the local authorities.

First-hand information from a large number of sites in eighty-five local authority areas at the end of February 1945 showed that sometimes men brought packed lunches and were given hot drinks on the site; others used the communal British Restaurants, to which they were carried in contractors' lorries if the distance was too great. There were also sites on which local cafés provided meals and gave priority to a certain period of the lunch-hour, and others with semi-mobile canteens and mess huts. Altogether, about two-thirds of the men took hot meals. On at least three-quarters of the sites contractors provided a service of tea at the mid-morning and mid-afternoon breaks; on over a hundred a service was provided by mobile canteens.

On Sundays mobile canteens were often used as a temporary expedient, with the promise of some more permanent arrangement; or it might be that British Restaurants gave a meals service, or local food officers used their influence to get cafés opened. Yet, after suitable arrangements had been made, it was not uncommon that workmen should fail to make use of them.

It was not always easy to feed the large bodies of workmen who were moved from site to site in order to deal with new 'incidents'; and only after discussions between the Ministries of Labour, Food, Health and Home Security were the emergency arrangements made by local authorities for dealing with the homeless supplemented so as to include, during the first few days, the influx of workmen. The Ministry of Health asked local authorities to use their mobile canteens and, where their own resources were inadequate, to call on group headquarters for help.

There was no serious difficulty about washing, lavatory and drying facilities. Such amenities were generally to be found on the sites in houses in which the men were working or were provided by householders; and the readiness with which contractors and local authorities accepted proposals for improvements suggests that the absence of statutory powers for enforcement was not a serious handicap.

Looking at the welfare arrangements as a whole, the surveys made by visiting welfare officers of the Ministry of Labour showed that over eighty-three per cent. of the facilities offered for meals were considered satisfactory, while the general welfare provisions were considered over eighty per cent. satisfactory.

THE LOCAL PROGRESS COMMITTEES

The local progress committees played a notable part both in keeping up the pace of the repair work and in sustaining the morale of the public and the workers. In spite of general criticism of bomb damage repair in the press and elsewhere, the people of Greater London were on the whole greatly cheered by the energy and success with which large-scale first-aid repairs were carried out, and they were gratified to see their local representatives joining with those of both sides of the industry in the control of the work.

The local progress committees were made up as a rule of equal numbers of employers and workmen. Four to eight representatives from each side, according to the size of the borough, were nominated by the National Federation of Building Trades Employers and the National Federation of Building Trades Operatives. Nor was representation of the employers' side restricted to members of the federation if in any particular area firms not in the federation but of suitable position and influence were engaged on the work.

Wherever provincial firms were taking part, at least one provincial builder was usually included among the employers' representatives, and one London builder from outside the borough; the remainder were from local firms.[1] The London builder from outside the borough was appointed by the London Master Builders' Association and was charged with maintaining direct contact with that association and thus with the National Employers' Federation. Parallel arrangements were made on the workmen's side, with one of their representatives maintaining direct contact with the regional and national headquarters of the federation.

The progress committees were called upon to give general advice to the local authority and the Ministry representatives on the progress of repair work in the borough—for example, when materials had to be ordered ahead or there was need for better balancing of the labour gangs—but not to intervene in the domestic organisation and arrangements of individual firms. It was enjoined also on the committees that any advice given was not to be in conflict with, or in extension of, joint industrial agreements. Wherever there was any doubt reference was to be made to the appropriate joint industrial machinery.

The inclusion of trade union site officers in the various progress committees helped them to forestall and smooth out many labour troubles and complaints.

ABSENTEEISM

It came within the scope of the London Repairs Executive to suggest measures for checking absenteeism. Recent official figures showed the need for intervention. In an inquiry carried out by the Ministry of Labour,[2] the figures of absenteeism (days lost) during two weeks

---

[1] *London Repairs Bulletin*, first issue (undated).

[2] The inquiry involved fifty-six firms selected at random in the London region employing a total of 3,043 workers.

ended 2nd December 1944 were as follows:

Total labour force	3,043
Total days which could have been worked .	42,602
Total days lost	2,577
with valid reason . . .	1,322
without valid reason . . .	1,255

The sample showed an average daily absenteeism of about six per cent. of which rather more than half consisted of justifiable absence, for example, through sickness. Separate figures were not available for each day of the week, but it was known that about thirty per cent. of unjustifiable absence occurred on Sundays.

At the ninth meeting of the London Repairs Executive on 2nd February 1945, it was agreed that in order to check unjustified absenteeism the central progress committee should support the local committees in forming absence committees for dealing with absenteeism and persistent lateness under Article 6 (3) of the Essential Work (Building and Civil Engineering) Order. These committees were accordingly set up. The local committees were told that the decision had the backing of both sides of the industry and the Ministry of Labour, and that though there might be no immediate need for an absentee committee, it was best to be prepared.

The absentee committees were not sub-committees of the local progress committees; they were independent bodies with specific functions under the Essential Work Order. But the initiative for setting up an absentee committee in any particular area nevertheless lay with the local progress committee of that area. After that, it was for the absentee committee and not for the progress committee to take up individual instances of absenteeism. It was appropriate, on the other hand, for a progress committee to consider such general factors as made for absenteeism, to urge employers to keep proper records of absence, and to refer specific lapses to the absentee committee.

The authority of an absentee committee was limited to finding whether the employee had in fact absented himself from work; whether he had in fact been persistently late in presenting himself for work; and whether, in either case, he had reasonable excuse: and the committee had the additional duty of reporting its findings to the appropriate National Service Officer. Such reports did not need to be unanimous.

It was for the National Service Officer to determine what action, if any, should be taken against an offender. A warning on future conduct might be thought enough, or criminal proceedings could be instituted. Absenteeism was defined as absence without the consent of the employer and for reasons that were inadequate. It was not practicable to lay down definite rules as to what excuses might be found adequate, either for absenteeism or for persistent lateness. Each charge was taken on its merits, and regard was given to medical evidence, domestic circumstances or other evidence of hardship, such as travelling conditions, and the past record of the worker. The local knowledge of an absentee committee was particularly valuable in determining culpability.

Experience showed that most workers who absented themselves from work, or who were persistently late, were confident that they had an acceptable excuse, or that they were merely careless or indifferent. It was preferable—and was recommended by the Central Progress Committee—that absentee committees should aim at improvement rather than resort to penal action, particularly where the past record of a worker was good. By the beginning of March 1945 not more than twenty-eight absentee committees had been set up in the sixty-two boroughs where local progress committees had been established.

USE AND DISTRIBUTION OF BUILDING MATERIALS

To promote the most economical use of materials and their fair distribution, the chief measures adopted were, first, the definition of a general standard of repairs, and secondly, a voluntary organisation of builders' merchants for regulating the distribution of materials.

For the definition of standards of repair, directions were issued to local authorities by the Ministry of Health, after consultation with the Ministry of Works. It was provided, in particular, that no un-essential rooms should be repaired; that the minimum painting needed to make the property weatherproof should be allowed; that satisfactory substitute materials were to be used wherever possible;[1] that as the supply of clear glass was insufficient, half the total glazing area was to be covered by obscure glass. Standard doors and emergency windows were to be used when existing frames could not be quickly repaired. Provided these instructions were followed, it was estimated, there were enough materials for the whole labour force engaged. Later in the year the standard of repairs agreed for the London Civil Defence was extended to districts in the Home Counties.[2]

In defining a suitable standard of repairs on licensed factories and similar buildings, the Ministry of Works laid down that satisfactory working conditions could be provided at a stage not very much above first-aid repairs; for example, by repairing roofs with curved asbestos sheeting, the substitution of glass with curved asbestos or, where brick gables or panels were blown out, their replacement with curved asbestos or corrugated black iron sheeting.

Generally the standard allowed was not higher than that permitted for second-stage repairs for housing. But there were exceptions:

---

[1] e.g. fifty per cent. of the slates could be of smaller size than standard; concrete tiles, which were available in large quantities, were to be used instead of clay tiles; and plaster-board was to be used only for ceilings and not for walls.

[2] M.O.H. Circular 60/45, 29th March 1945.

as when fine workmanship and delicate materials called for even temperatures and protection from atmospheric damp; when fine workmanship demanded exceptional lighting conditions and lack of daylight would necessitate augmented electrical services; when the production caused fumes and vapours deleterious in an active form to the structure; and when, in 'dirty trades', the factory inspector called for (and the conditions justified) a higher standard for hygienic reasons.

Where the buildings were not needed for production no repairs of any sort were carried out.

THE VOLUNTARY ORGANISATION OF BUILDERS' MERCHANTS

Reference has already been made to the voluntary organisation of builders' merchants in a scheme for regulating the distribution of materials. Under the designation Materials Distributors' Emergency Organisation, these arrangements followed the general pattern on which the Works and Buildings Emergency Organisation had mobilised contractors and their labour.[1] A Regional Committee reporting to the Assistant Director of Emergency Works was responsible for the behaviour and operations of their representatives at group level and in each local authority area. One merchant was chosen by the merchants for each local authority, and was free to help the war damage officer and his materials officer, at borough level, on the supply of any commodity. Nominations made by the merchants' meetings were submitted by the emergency works officer to the local authority, to ensure that the merchant chosen should be *persona grata* with the authority's officials.

The work of the merchants' local organisers was then co-ordinated at group level by materials group organisers and deputy group organisers appointed for each Civil Defence group or sub-group in the London region. To make certain that both the 'heavy 'and the 'light' spheres of the trade were amply covered, the group organisers represented the 'heavy' and the deputy group organisers the 'light' sections respectively, and both worked in the closest manner with the representatives of the departments at group level as well as with group liaison officers and area leaders of the Works and Buildings Emergency Organisation.

At regional level the London regional organisation was administered by an advisory committee whose chairman[2] worked with the Assistant Director of Emergency Works (London), with the Works and Buildings Emergency Organisation, and with the manufacturers' organisations to ensure satisfactory distribution.

Control of distribution of articles in short supply became the re-

[1] See Chapter IX.
[2] Sir Dudley Pryke.

sponsibility of the Assistant Director of Emergency Works (London) through whom they were allocated to all local authorities. They comprised plasterboard, hard wall plaster, slates and glass. Each authority was informed of the weekly amount allocated to it, given the names of the merchants by whom stocks of the materials were held, and made responsible for sub-allocation to its contractors. Other materials continued to be purchased through normal channels (with the help of the materials local organiser in cases of difficulty), but were liable to be similarly allocated if they fell into short supply.

'WINTER' AND 'SUMMER' DAMAGE AREAS

In the autumn of 1944 the people of London had been promised that 719,000 houses would be repaired up to a tolerable emergency standard by 31st March: by that date nearly 800,000 were in fact repaired.[1] A great many other houses were, however, damaged by the bombardment throughout the winter, and it was clear that a large labour force would have to be maintained in London on repair work at least until the end of June. Local authorities' areas were now defined in two categories—those which had, and those which had not, suffered serious damage since September. These were known as 'winter damage' areas and 'summer damage' areas respectively.[2] From now onwards overriding priority was given to winter damage areas, labour was drafted into them up to the maximum they could absorb, and withdrawn from the summer damage areas as soon as contractors had either completed or substantially completed repairs up to the emergency standard laid down by the Ministry of Health.[3] The labour in the summer damage areas eventually consisted of immobile labour and such mobile labour as could not be absorbed by the winter damage areas.

When mobile labour was available, it was reallocated among the summer damage areas according to their needs, and the work was brought nearer to the permanent housing standard;[4] but in the winter damage areas repairs continued to be limited to the emergency standard until all or nearly all of the houses in those areas had been treated. The full permanent repairs in the summer damage areas were up to, but did not include, the decoration stage. Distempering might be done, however, by labour which could not otherwise be used; and in carrying out these repairs, materials which were acceptable as final reinstatement (for example, clear instead of opaque glass, plaster and plasterboard instead of laminated board) were used to the utmost practicable extent.

---

[1] *London Repairs Bulletin*, 13th April 1945. Statement by Mr. Duncan Sandys.
[2] M.O.H. Circular 54/45, 15th March 1945
[3] M.O.H. Serial No. 56.
[4] As laid down in M.O.H. Serial No. 25.

In guiding local authorities the Ministry of Health suggested that when selecting houses for repair the emphasis should be on increasing the total number of dwellings rather than on giving greater comfort in houses already repaired up to the emergency standard.[1] That object, it was urged, could be best secured in three ways, that is:

1. By the further repair of empty houses which had been slightly damaged and which were likely to be occupied when repaired.
2. By the further repair of slightly damaged small houses in localities where it was the custom for small houses to be occupied by more than one family.
3. By the repair of seriously damaged large houses which could be let for occupation by a number of families.[2]

In order to make the best use of the limited labour force, the aim was to repair all such C(*b*) houses[3] as used no more man-hours for each house than the building of a new house; and those which could be repaired at a cost of not more than £500 were to be tackled first.

ACCOMMODATION IN HUTS

To provide additional accommodation for bombed-out families 6,569 huts had been allocated by May 1945 to thirty-four local authorities of which 2,000 were uni-seco[4] and 4,569 curved asbestos. Of the total allocation 4,823 (2,000 uni-seco and 2,823 curved asbestos) were ordered by the local authorities, and by 15th May out of 2,378 huts erected 2,194 were occupied. Local authorities readily found tenants for these hutments; and the only substantial lag between completion and occupation was because of delay in providing gas fittings.

The view of the London Repairs Executive was that where the erection of huts had not yet been begun, it was preferable to concentrate labour on the repair of houses. For this reason local authorities had earlier tended to reduce their demands, sometimes to much less than half. Most authorities were indeed agreed that, although the erection of huts met a public demand, it would be a mistake to place too much reliance on sub-standard accommodation of this character. Another restraining factor was the difficulty of finding sites for temporary houses as well as for the permanent housing programme of local authorities.[5]

---

[1] M.O.H. Circular 54/45, 15th March 1945.

[2] The adaptation of large houses was discussed with five central authorities and it was agreed that 1,600 dwellings should be completed by 31st March. By the end of January 170 dwellings were ready, of which 125 were occupied. Frost delayed the plumbing work and slowed down progress.

[3] See p. 225.

[4] Uni-Seco was made up of timber framing, asbestos cement sheathing and wood wool insulation. See M.O.W. Directorate of Post-War Building, 'A Survey of Prefabrication'.

[5] M.O.H. Circular 134/44.

Of 2,660 men employed on the erection of huts (in May 1945) 693 were Italian prisoners of war, 1,532 were brought in by ordinary contractors, and 169 by Ministry of Works contractors. The balance was made up of local authority direct labour, debris clearance parties, Ministry of War Transport road gangs and civil defence volunteers. In Lambeth, Lewisham, Croydon, Wandsworth and West Ham, United States troops erected 601 huts.

A 'SELF-HELP' SCHEME FOR HOUSEHOLDERS

As a contribution towards easing the repair position, a 'self-help' scheme, propounded by the Minister of Works in the House of Commons, was considered by the London Repairs Executive. Paint, distemper and brushes were to be made available for London householders to carry out their own decoration. There was strong criticism of the proposal by borough engineers and others who thought the scheme would create difficulties rather than give satisfaction. The main objection was that such a scheme would create ill-feeling among the workmen engaged on bomb damage repair, since a high proportion of them were painters who would prefer to be employed on their own trades rather than in the variety of ways in which they were being used. There was a shortage of paint and brushes of the kind likely to be wanted. Even borough engineers could not get for their own use the distemper brushes they needed. It was feared, too, that many old and infirm householders would be unable to do their own work, and that in the end public clamour would arise, as it had done over the Anderson shelters,[1] for the works to be carried out by the local authority. Once that happened, it was argued, it would often be difficult to resist the clamour, and the effect on the labour position would be very bad.

After considering these and other objections, the London Repairs Executive decided that the scheme should apply to paint and paint brushes only; that the distribution should be through the normal channels; that reserves of paint should be maintained in a few of the larger shops in each area; and that the scheme should apply first to occupants of houses which had just been repaired.

___
See Chapter XVII.

PART IV

Building Programmes of
Departments

PART IV

FOREWORD

In the preceding chapters of this volume the building programmes of the several departments have appeared from time to time in relation to the general survey of the co-ordination and control of the whole programme. In the seven chapters that now follow we turn to consider some of the building activities of individual Ministries. It is not, nor could it be, even if space permitted, an exhaustive survey, since much of this activity was directed to the solution of technical questions which have no place in this volume and are the subject of other studies in this series. What has been attempted here is to pick out some of the more stubborn administrative problems as they occurred in one or other department, and to look at them individually.

In peace-time it is natural enough that the aims and interests of departments should tend to diverge from the set administrative pattern envisaged by the central authority. In time of war, on the other hand, convergence towards a common aim, though it is equally natural and to be expected, does not by itself bring about uniformity of method or avoid a clash of departmental interests. In such circumstances the only relevant test is the strategic one: was this or that measure, this or that department's insistence on a right or a privilege under such and such conditions, the best contribution it could make towards the winning of the war?

Self-abnegation is not the spontaneous role of Service Ministries in war, nor does a wise administration encourage it as a virtue. In war —even in peace-time rearmament—speed and efficiency may be paramount, and departmental altruism has no place. If at times the War Office or the Air Ministry, for example, in their building policies are seen to stand stubbornly by their demands, that is not necessarily a matter for censure, provided the programme as a whole is not put in jeopardy.

The work of the department of the Civil Engineer-in-Chief at the Admiralty was often highly specialised in character or executed overseas, and a substantial part of it therefore falls outside the scope of this volume. Reference is made to many of its undertakings at home, and to the kind of administrative problems it was called upon to solve. What occurred in the councils of the War Office, the Air Ministry and the Ministry of Aircraft Production fills much of the immediate foreground of Part IV. As to other topics of the first rank, no attempt is made here to describe in detail the planning and building of the Royal Ordnance factories or of war factories in general, since these topics belong to the volumes on war production; but the growth of these factories is sketched in outline, and something is written of the division of responsibility in planning and construction between the Ministry of Works and the Ministry of Supply. The concluding pages of Part IV concern the building work of the civil departments, with particular emphasis on that of the Ministry of Home Security for Civil Defence.

CHAPTER XI

THE BUILDING AND CIVIL ENGINEERING WORK OF THE ADMIRALTY

(i)

Introductory

THE Admiralty's constructional work at home and abroad fell to the Department of the Civil Engineer-in-Chief.[1] Much of it was highly specialised: some of the undertakings were of great strategic importance and were conceived and executed on a massive scale. It is indeed claimed on behalf of the Admiralty that the Civil Engineer-in-Chief's Department was, at least during the rearmament and war years, the largest civil engineering body in existence. Although the Admiralty's peace-time constructional work was of impressive volume, it was but a fraction of that undertaken in war. The type of work, too, was often different; for while pre-war building, with few exceptions, was permanent in character, much of the war-time building was temporary.

Since the overseas work of the Admiralty—in Singapore, for example, or in Gibraltar or Malta, in Ceylon or Bermuda or in Hong Kong—falls outside the scope of this narrative, only a part of the general picture of the Admiralty's constructional effort can here be outlined. The distribution of the work between home undertakings and those overseas, as well as its volume, may be seen, however, in terms of cost, in the table on p. 242.

During the rearmament years the practical work of the Civil Engineer-in-Chief's Department was roughly divided, like that of corresponding departments in other Ministries, into two main classes —that is, new works in one category, and repairs and maintenance services in the other. New works would comprise, say, a small building costing a few pounds, a new workshop block costing some thousands, or a new naval base, such as Rosyth or Singapore, involving the expenditure of millions of pounds. Repairs and main-

---

[1] Much of the material on which this chapter is based was provided by the Department of the Civil Engineer-in-Chief, Admiralty.

Expenditure on Vote 10 Works Subheads B, C, D and E 1935-45

Year		B Major works £	C Minor works £	D Foundations of machinery £	E Repairs and maintenance £	Total £
1935	Home Abroad	365,432 813,524	65,755 46,326	27,753 6,714	333,357 85,751	792,297 952,315
		1,178,956	112,081	34,467	419,108	1,744,612
1936	Home Abroad	838,532 1,294,327	85,967 39,704	32,435 9,608	355,559 90,900	1,312,493 1,434,539
		2,132,859	125,671	42,043	446,459	2,747,032
1937	Home Abroad	1,091,128 1,625,874	117,702 33,606	36,823 6,311	367,706 109,152	1,613,359 1,774,943
		2,717,002	151,308	43,134	476,858	3,388,302
1938	Home Abroad	2,106,104 1,592,493	154,203 42,616	50,531 7,712	405,487 121,486	2,716,325 1,764,307
		3,698,597	196,819	58,243	526,973	4,480,632
1939	Home Abroad	6,531,464 1,843,478	192,111 58,880	48,358 9,020	436,457 110,065	7,208,390 2,021,443
		8,374,942	250,991	57,378	546,522	9,229,833
1940	Home Abroad	16,015,992 2,147,241	332,799 51,447	63,851 11,256	438,350 99,137	16,850,992 2,309,081
		18,163,233	384,246	75,107	537,487	19,160,073
1941	Home Abroad	17,697,917 2,639,396	580,261 73,127	77,490 8,875	591,762 94,381	18,947,430 2,815,779
		20,337,313	653,388	86,365	686,143	21,763,209
1942	Home Abroad	13,160,796 5,954,231	799,551 168,754	100,377 13,441	943,708 116,579	15,004,432 6,253,005
		19,115,027	968,305	113,818	1,060,287	21,257,437
1943	Home Abroad	15,928,872 10,932,910	950,000 244,992	108,000 17,919	1,337,000 235,623	18,323,872 11,431,444
		26,861,782	1,194,992	125,919	1,572,623	29,755,316
1944	Home Abroad	11,526,082 9,350,754	833,000 179,081	123,000 16,337	1,789,000 233,941	14,271,082 9,780,113
		20,876,836	1,012,081	139,337	2,022,941	24,051,195
1945	Home Abroad	6,767,246 14,707,819	435,000 218,205	104,000 19,910	1,674,000 620,649	8,980,246 15,566,583
		21,475,065	653,205	123,910	2,294,649	24,546,829

Source: Civil Engineer-in-Chief, Admiralty.

NOTE: Subheads B, C, D and E of Vote 10 indicate direct expenditure upon works. The remaining subheads are ancillary to cover various factors such as the acquisition of land, rents and compensations, miscellaneous expenses, etc. Expenditure on rents and compensation or the acquisition of land during the eleven years amounted to some £13½ millions.

tenance would cover anything from the renewal of water or other fittings to repairs to a large graving dock.

Works of all these kinds were carried out both at home dockyards and at naval bases all over the world. As in other branches of naval work, considerations of economy and quality were inexorable masters; and it is to the credit of the civil engineers in charge of so many, and such multifarious and widespread, undertakings that, despite what might be regarded as a relatively small allocation of funds at their disposal, they had everywhere maintained the traditional high standard enjoined by the senior Service.

The department, in addition, undertook its design work, the preparation, letting and settlement of contracts and, through the Lands Branch, the management of Admiralty property, the requisitioning of accommodation for naval needs and the settlement of claims arising therefrom.

Among the major tasks in home as well as foreign ports, during the rearmament years, were schemes for the underground storage of explosives and oil fuel, for the widening of existing docks[1] and the replacement of obsolete buildings for new accommodation for training in anti-aircraft gunnery and other forms of attack, for the installation of generating plants, and for the continuing development of the use of electrical power for all purposes.

At the outbreak of war the normal activities of the Civil Engineer-in-Chief's Department were switched over to a war footing and the labour force engaged on maintenance work at Admiralty establishments was pared down to a bare minimum. Greatly expanded staffs, on the other hand, were engaged on major and minor new works to meet the expanding needs of the Fleet. The records of the department, even when seen in meagre outline, tell an impressive story of concentrated effort, whether on defensive works or works of immediate importance for the Navy's offensive operations up and down the country and abroad.

(ii)

Defensive Measures

Let us look first at the defence programme—against submarines, against aircraft, against invasion. Against submarines, the largest single item of defence undertaken by the Civil Engineer-in-Chiefs' Department was probably the construction of causeways across the four eastern entrances to Scapa Flow in the Orkneys. Here a million tons of material had to be placed in swiftly flowing currents in what is

---

[1] To permit the docking of the more modern type of warships, the relative beam of warships having increased since most of the Admiralty dockyards were built.

perhaps one of the stormiest localities in Britain. As a defence against aircraft, novel types of reinforced concrete and steel forts had to be constructed and floated out from their building berths many miles away to strategic points in the Thames and Mersey estuaries and there sunk in position.[1] Against the chance of invasion, concealed flame-thrower defences operated by remote control were installed at harbour entrances in thirty-seven minor ports of the north-eastern, eastern and south coasts. There were, besides, piled, steel-framed or concrete maritime works in connection with the boom defences across the Thames, Spithead and other entrances. In addition, torpedo tubes, naval guns, mine-watching and other posts had to be mounted at many ports, and about 120 bomb-proof reinforced concrete observation minefield control towers built around the coast to protect the entrances to ports and harbours.

Much constructional labour and material went into works in various parts of the country for the protection of vital personnel against the enemy's bomb attacks. In London, the large new bomb-proof structure known as the 'citadel' was built at the Admiralty for the accommodation of the essential naval and Admiralty operational staffs. Similar headquarters, though on a smaller scale, were prepared at naval ports; all were complete with offices and operations rooms, and were fitted with air-conditioning plant and special lighting. Underground protected accommodation, similarly equipped, was provided in both newly constructed and disused tunnels at naval stations. Protected accommodation of another kind was built on Dover harbour in the form of reinforced concrete bomb-proof pens for the protection from air attack of motor torpedo-boats. This work, carried out by the Royal Marine engineers,[2] was designed to accommodate fourteen motor torpedo-boats, and included living quarters and shops.

Another task was the safeguarding of the steel tanks in which much of the Fleet's fuel oil was stored. This was done by building bunds and splinter-proof walls around the hundreds of tanks in use, and by the installation of fire-fighting facilities. At Rosyth, the large-capacity concrete oil-storage reservoir was made bomb-proof by concrete protection to its sides and the building of a concrete roof which in strength and

---

[1] They were equipped with guns, searchlights, radar, accommodation for crews and so forth, and they proved highly successful.

[2] Shortly after the outbreak of war, arrangements were made to resuscitate the Royal Marine engineers, as approved by an Order in Council in March 1940, to carry out for the Navy civil engineering and building works in certain areas. Recruiting continued from the initial level of 1,000, and the force increased in strength until it reached the peak figure of 8,000 in 1945. Contingents of the Royal Marine engineers served in all theatres of war—in North Africa and Sicily; from Arromanches to Hamburg; in Australia and in the Burma and Malaya campaigns—building camps and accommodation, repairing roads, docks and jetties.

thickness was comparable to the roof of the German submarine pens.[1]

In general, personnel were protected by extensive passive defence works throughout the country (air-raid shelters, decontamination centres, static water tanks, and so forth). Camouflage played a valuable role in concealing vital targets; major schemes were prepared and executed for thirty-one Fleet Air Arm stations, twenty-three oil installations, forty-nine ammunition and store depots and forty-five Royal Naval and thirty United States camps and stores. There were, moreover, some eighty minor camouflage schemes, and an elaborate programme was carried out for the preparation of the assault on Europe. Eighty-four decoy sites, ranging in area from one acre to two square miles, were constructed on suitable sites and drew to themselves many thousands of bombs which might otherwise have damaged vital works at ports and inland establishments.

(iii)
The Main Offensive Works

Extensive shore works costing several millions of pounds, designed for the combined operations in the assault on Europe, were carried out during the two years that preceded D-day. These works consisted mainly of a very large number of concrete 'hards' at various points on the coast as far apart as Dover and Inverary for the embarkation into landing craft of tanks, armoured fighting vehicles and motor transport. Some of the hards were constructed to take not only landing craft; railway tracks were laid from the main lines to carry large numbers of locomotives and wagons for shipment to the Continent.

Each hard was equipped with dolphins for mooring the landing and other craft during loading; and on most of them oil-fuel installations (sometimes for several grades of oil according to the type of craft using the hard) and fresh water were laid on. About eighty watering and fuelling installations were built complete with storage tanks, pipe-lines, and so on. At each hard there was accommodation[2] for the hardmaster and his staff, and for the ratings on embarkation duty. Suspense stations in the back areas, and assault stations nearer the embarkation hards, housed in hutted camps, requisitioned and other premises the personnel of the naval forces (about 50,000 men) before the operation. There were, too, maintenance bases and repair yards with slipways for the repair and maintenance of the enormous number of landing craft of all kinds used in the assault and build-up;

---

[1] This work was designed and begun some time before the outbreak of war.
[2] The accommodation included sleeping-galley and facilities for washing.

bases and areas for training and rehearsal; operational headquarters; and miscellaneous accommodation such as the covered storage of large numbers of reserve landing craft, dredging plant, emergency dumps for ammunition, balloon storage, and so on. Furthermore, a large amount of work was carried out for the American naval forces in their zones of operation.

In the planning of the Mulberry harbours a leading part was taken by the department of the Civil Engineer-in-Chief; and the layout and alignment of the Phoenix unit[1] was determined by the department on the information obtained from the naval survey parties. An officer of the department was appointed to the staff of the naval officer in command of the Mulberry operations to advise on the planting of the units as they arrived off Arromanches. The ballasting of the old merchant ships sunk to form the Gooseberries[2] was similarly dealt with by the department of the Civil Engineer-in-Chief. In addition, an extensive organisation, manned by Royal Marine engineers and civilian workmen, was set up for the repair of damage to the shore installation during the assault and build-up period.

The whole of this vast programme of works requiring months of planning and construction was commenced in April 1942 and completed by D-day.

In support of the Navy's offensive operations, schemes for the underground storage of oil fuel—the construction of which was commenced before the war—were completed, and long pipe-lines were laid to connect the tanks with the several naval harbours they supplied. Apart from these major oil installations, many smaller oil-fuel installations were erected in various places in the United Kingdom. An eight-inch pipe-line from the Clyde to the Forth, laid in the First World War, was duplicated by a much larger pipe in order to speed up transfer of oil from the west to the east coasts over a distance of some forty miles.

An important side of the Civil Engineer-in-Chief's Department lay in the Royal Dockyards. It was imperative that the yards should function effectively throughout the war, for the building, repair and maintenance of warships was vital. The provision in some dockyards of large new permanent buildings and jetties, and in others of many smaller buildings to give increased facilities, together with measures to counteract the effects of enemy bombing, were a heavy charge on the department. Among major tasks was the constructional work for the reopening of Rosyth dockyard: this was speeded up because of the dockyard's relative immunity from air attack. Here some three million cubic yards of accumulated silt in the harbour and approaches

---

[1] See Chapter XV.

[2] One of these craft shelters, or Gooseberries, was provided for each of the six assault beaches.

had to be removed by dredging to restore the minimum acceptable depth. In other dockyards, such as Portsmouth and Chatham, substantial permanent works (for example, electrical workshops) were constructed; and in Portsmouth, too, the work of extending one basin was carried out continuously throughout the war years. At Sheerness, a new timber-piled jetty, approximately 2,000 feet long, for berthing minesweepers and other small craft for the Thames area defences, was completed. Generally, in spite of all the difficulties brought about by war-time conditions, the Royal Dockyards were kept in a fit state to meet the demand upon them; but wherever it was practicable, minor dockyard activities were dispersed to the surrounding countryside, and although such dispersal meant more building and adaptations, it helped to maintain the efficiency of the Royal Dockyards.

It would be tedious to enumerate the dredging and other operations for which the Civil Engineer-in-Chief was responsible or to list the reconstituted or new bases, depots, and so on, concerned. It was, however, public knowledge that Scapa Flow once again became a Fleet base, with many shore establishments on all the surrounding islands, and it is noteworthy that two important destroyer repair bases were built by Royal Marine engineers in Scotland, with piers, workshops, floating docks, stores and housing accommodation for married dockyard men and single quarters for others. Arrangements had to be made at these places for shops, a post office, schools, a cinema, and other recreation facilities, since the bases were far from any large towns providing such amenities. Similarly, self-contained bases were prepared in Northern Ireland and Scotland for the assembly and escort of the Atlantic convoys.

As the Navy's manpower grew, so more and more accommodation had to be found, mainly in the form of temporary construction, but sometimes by requisition and adaptation; more than the bare necessities of living and training had to be provided in these camps.

The expansion of the Fleet Air Arm and miscellaneous special works are mentioned later. New naval armament depots were constructed, invariably in areas remote from townships, for the storage, servicing, examination and issue of all types of ammunition, depth charges, torpedo warheads, bombs, mines, and so forth. Other miscellaneous but extensive work comprised such items as a large propellant factory costing nearly £5 millions, new depots for naval and victualling stores, experimental establishments to deal with the development of ordinary and aerial torpedoes, wireless and radar stations.

For the repair of merchant shipping a new wharf was constructed at Greenock and a new destroyer depot was also built in the same harbour, with piers and jetties and a large shore establishment, for various classes of naval training. The Admiralty, acting as its own

Supply Department (similarly to the Ministry of Supply for the Army and the Ministry of Aircraft Production for the Air Force) dealt with a very large programme of commercial development and expansion of shipyards and factories. Some 200 private shipyards were adapted to deal with repairs to all Fleet units and the construction and fitting out of new types of vessels, such as corvettes and frigates, and about 700 factories were extended to give the increased capacity needed for the manufacture and supply of armaments and other equipment for both the Royal Navy and ships in the Merchant Service.

(iv)

Special Works

In addition to all the above, innumerable major works of special, unusual and naval character were carried out by the Civil Engineer-in-Chief's Department.

A large floating dock of reinforced concrete construction was built and launched from a south-coast site, and many small prefabricated floating docks were built in this country and towed overseas, while others were built abroad to the same design; and a reinforced concrete ship-type caisson, complete with all necessary penstocks, etc., was constructed in a dry basin and floated out on completion.

For the accommodation of large numbers of naval personnel, to be used in operations against Japan, reinforced concrete 'arks' provided with sleeping quarters, galleys, washing facilities, messing, stores and other services, were designed and put under construction in this country. This project was abandoned on the cessation of hostilities on VJ-day.

A reinforced-concrete craft of very unusual type, consisting of two cigar-shaped hulls in parallel, connected together by a steel lattice superstructure which contained full navigational equipment and a gun platform mounting two Army field-pattern 6-inch howitzers on deck mountings, was built in Great Britain for use in cross-Channel operations. This craft was self-propelled and installed with electric light, and was ingeniously provided with the means of allowing it to be partially sunk in position on a flat and suitable sea-bed before going into action. If too hotly engaged by enemy counter-battery fire the craft, by using compressors installed on board, could blow its ballast tanks in the hulls, rise to the surface and make off. This craft was completed and passed its acceptance trials; but it was never, in fact, used in action.

(v)
Airfield Construction

In the preceding pages some examples have been given of the wide range of constructional work carried out by the department of the Civil Engineer-in-Chief at the Admiralty. These tasks were not accomplished without much manœuvre of men and materials: it became intensified at the climax of the war when, in the winter months of 1942, the Admiralty were about to embark on an extensive programme of airfield construction for the Fleet Air Arm.

An air station, so far from being merely a flat area of grassland with a few sheds and huts, became, during the war, a small township of some 2,000 inhabitants, both men and women, with all that was needed to make the station self-contained, and the welfare and housing of these isolated communities was no light undertaking. Living quarters were complete and self-contained, with dormitories, baths, showers, wash-hand basins, lavatories, galleys, dining halls, rest rooms, recreation rooms, canteens, sick bays, cinemas, chapels, barber's, shoemaker's and tailor's shops and, for exercise and recreation, football, hockey and cricket pitches.

The main functions of a naval air station were the training of flying personnel for aircraft carriers, and the preparation of aircraft for service at sea. Apart from hangars (on an average about thirty-five for each large air station) some 170 separate buildings, large and small, were needed to house workshops, stores, offices, training devices, class-rooms, and so on. Many of these buildings, particularly the workshops and special technical and synthetic training buildings, were extensive and complex, and called for much skilled work in the fittings and finishings.

Training for service aircraft included the use of bombing and firing ranges at a considerable distance from the main stations. Such ranges had to have rest rooms and services for both the men and the women who operated them from the ground; and, in association with the stations, there were radio and radar installations in remote spots and at a distance from the road. These installations, too, needed water supplies and electric services, all of which had to be carried to the site.

During the war the Admiralty constructed twenty-seven air stations in the United Kingdom on new or partially developed sites, while eleven air stations were expanded from small to full-scale stations.[1] An airfield has to be used by modern aircraft weighing many tons, and surfaced runways had to be provided for landing and take-off, tracks

---

[1] See Chapter XIII. A number of airfields were constructed for the Admiralty by the Air Ministry. Broadly the requirements of a modern airfield are common to both the Fleet Air Arm and the Royal Air Force.

for the circulation of aircraft from and to the runway ends, and large areas of hardstandings for aircraft to remain on when parked, or when being refuelled or overhauled. The runways, taxi-tracks and pavings were in themselves a major problem in supply and transport, and might call for the use of some 200,000 tons of material—enough to construct thirty miles of road fifteen feet wide.

Five of the above stations had the special function of repairing aircraft—which meant more or bigger workshops—and, in addition, two large depots were built. Altogether 1,100,000 square feet of covered space were provided for the storage of aircraft parts and spares. The large new permanent naval aircraft repair yard at Fleetlands, Portsmouth, for the repair and maintenance of the aircraft of the Fleet Air Arm, comprising workshops, stores, sheds, hangars, engine-testing facilities, machine-gun butts and all ancillary services, was completed.

(vi)

Administrative Problems

In earlier chapters we have seen what were some of the factors affecting the supply of men and materials to carry out the building and civil engineering work of the Admiralty. The inclusion in the Admiralty's programme for 1943 of extensive projects for Fleet Air Arm expansion may be taken as a fair sample of administrative problems involved when the control of Government building was based, as it necessarily was, on estimates of the probable labour requirements of departments up to twelve or fifteen months ahead.

Such a forecast was given by the Admiralty—at short notice by telephone on 18th December 1942 after a Cabinet meeting the previous day—for the twelve months ending December 1943. It showed the approximate requirements month by month; and in particular a substantial increase in its labour force to a possible peak of 49,610 men by June 1943 if the naval programme was to be met, but dropping again to 27,910 in mid-winter. At the time this programme was submitted, the total labour actually employed was about 28,000, but there were unsatisfied demands for a further 3,000 or 4,000 men on work already in hand.

The programme included a peak requirement of 24,200 men during the summer of 1943 to introduce twenty or so projected works items for the Fleet Air Arm. When submitting this programme, the Admiralty were challenged by the Ministry of Works on the proposed use, for a large air station, of a peak labour force of some 2,000 men, with an output of about £50 per man-month, as compared with an

Air Ministry demand for a little over 1,000 men for one of their air-fields with an output of from £80 to £90 per man-month. What was further in question was whether, in view of the heavy forward de-mands for labour from all departments which it was impossible to meet, the actual programme of work for the Fleet Air Arm could be reduced.

Upon the last point, the Admiralty put forward a revised forecast for Fleet Air Arm works alone, reducing the total demand for such work to 156,800 man-months of labour during 1943, with a spread of the work into 1944, and a June demand of 15,750 men. At a meeting held by the Minister of Production on 23rd December 1942, and attended by the First Lord of the Admiralty, the Minister of Works, the Civil Lord of the Admiralty and others, it was decided to ask the Admiralty and the Ministry of Works to look into the apparent dif-ference in productivity and to invite the Admiralty to prepare, for the Minister of Production, a note setting out the proposed completion dates of the projected airfields in relation to the planned intake of men for training into the Fleet Air Arm, the anticipated production of aircraft and aircraft carriers, the anticipated strength of the Fleet Air Arm at the relevant dates, and the volume of special Fleet Air Arm training which that would necessitate. An alternative pro-gramme of construction based on a maximum figure of 25,000 for constructional labour was called for, and the possibility of siting air-fields in Northern Ireland was to be considered. It was left to the Minister of Production to consider further, in the light of the informa-tion to be made available, whether he could recommend that Royal Air Force airfields should be used by the Admiralty in order to reduce the construction programme of the Fleet Air Arm.

In the course of the investigation, the Admiralty were able to show the charge of under-production by their labour to be unfounded, since the high output figures for the Air Ministry were obtained on concrete runways laid during the summer months of 1942 at *bomber* stations—a type of construction lending itself to high mechanisation. The type of runway used by Admiralty for naval aircraft, however, was tarmacadam, on hardcore foundation; while the Fleet Air Arm stations included a considerable number of buildings for training duties which could not reach the high output figures of the mechanised runway job. Moreover, generally speaking, the site conditions for Fleet Air Arm stations—situated mainly in Scotland or north-west England—were not so favourable for high output as those which ob-tained for Royal Air Force bomber stations concentrated in East Anglia and the South of England.

The Minister of Production was given the information asked for about the proposed completion dates of the various proposed airfields and other factors, but the Admiralty could not state the volume of special Fleet Air Arm training which would be needed for that programme. The special training of the numbers shown could not be related directly to the number of airfields allowed in the programme, because air stations were wanted not only for training but also for forming and working up new squadrons, for accommodating squadrons disembarked from aircraft carriers, for accommodating alternative armament and so forth. But the Admiralty made it quite clear that the programme of air stations aimed at would permit of nothing like the complete training of all Fleet Air Arm personnel in Admiralty-owned airfields and establishments. The Fleet Air Arm would still have to rely largely on training facilities at Royal Air Force stations and at bases abroad. One reason why the Admiralty willingly continued its dependence for much of the training on the Royal Air Force was that, even when the airfields they had asked for were ready, they had to face the consequences of having cut out of the 1942 works programme three air stations so that other essential work could be completed within the limited Admiralty labour allocation they then had. The evil results of this cut were now appearing, and it seemed probable that they would be still more evident in 1943, so that a further cut would have been disastrous to naval interests. Requirements had been restricted to an absolute minimum, and had been based upon the expected first-line strength in aircraft rather than on the first-line strength which would be needed to man the carriers already arranged for. Had 2,500 aircraft recently asked for from America been forthcoming, considerably more shore accommodation than had been proposed would have been wanted in 1943 and part of 1944.

To the suggestion that the Admiralty should work out an alternative programme of construction based on a maximum labour figure of 25,000 for *all* new work, including air stations, the Admiralty's answer was that such an alternative programme would need a cut of something over twenty per cent. in the peak labour months in the revised programme put forward[1] and that such a cut would have adverse repercussions on operational schemes. In the first place, a twenty per cent. cut would have meant the omission of two new airfields from the programme. To omit only one would have had some or all of the following effects: a proportionate and permanent reduction in the training of one or other of the various categories (that is pilot, observer, gunner, and so forth); the dis-servicing of at least seven escort carriers; certain effects on disembarked squadrons in respect of operational technique and maintenance which could not have been stated in precise terms but would have been very serious.

---

[1] It was assumed that the Admiralty would still be allowed, in addition to the 25,000 men for construction work, a labour force of 3,500 men for maintenance, a figure which was not disputed.

Then, again, in equipment and repair facilities, the loss of a receipt and dispatch unit or a minor repair yard would have directly affected first-line strength; and, among other arguments put forward against the restriction of the programme, the point was made that it would have interfered with the rate of shipbuilding, with supplies and storage, and with the provision of training establishments and other accommodation for personnel.

The investigations carried out proved that there was no further scope for the introduction of economies in the construction of Fleet Air Arm stations. The Admiralty found it impossible to alter, to any appreciable or practical extent, the monthly labour requirements up to June 1943; a slight reduction was, however, made and a revised labour forecast was put forward showing a total of 138,250 man-months for the year 1943, the bulk of the saving being forecast in the later, and winter, months of that year.

The Bolero programme, as it applied to the Navy and was regarded by the Admiralty, did not allow of any cuts at all. Most of it was for embarkation hards for tanks, armoured fighting vehicles and road transport of all kinds, fuelling points and craft maintenance facilities right round the south and east coasts. None of it could be slowed down, even on the terms suggested by the Prime Minister for the War Office Bolero programme at a War Cabinet meeting on 17th December. But combined operations and defensive raids did not wholly depend upon the number of troops in the country at any particular moment. For example, a raid on Cherbourg, which was imminent at any time, would have required the whole of the Navy Bolero preparations in, say, the Portsmouth area to be fully deployed; and since it could not be foreseen from which coastal area any single operation might be conducted, it was obviously essential to bring the naval preparation up to 100 per cent. completion at the earliest possible moment. If any other view had been accepted it would follow logically that the building of offensive craft should also have been slowed down.

The Admiralty brought it home that the programme of works already placed before the Minister of Production made no allowance whatever by way of margin for unpredictable contingencies such as new works not already approved in principle. Any new works not so allowed for, which it might have become essential to execute, would have had to be carried out by diverting labour from the existing approved programme, and the effect of doing so might in itself have been serious.

The attempt to make substantial reductions in Fleet Air Arm projects, and particularly to curtail the Admiralty works programme as a whole to a requirement of 25,000 men, thus proved abortive; the necessity for a substantial increase in the labour force on Admiralty works was accepted and a labour ceiling of 31,000 was allotted for March 1943—a further review to be made before fixing the ceiling for June.

By the middle of March, however, it was clear that the labour ceiling was inadequate for the economical progression of essential naval works, and the Minister of Production was again told that a substantial increase would be needed—rising to 41,600 men for June and July 1943.

CHAPTER XII

THE WAR OFFICE PROGRAMME

(i)

The War Office and the Militia Camps

THE decision to raise the militia was taken in April 1939. The Military Training Bill was introduced in May of that year and received the Royal Assent on the 26th of that month. Accommodation had to be built at a cost then estimated at £21 millions, a sum which was to include the cost of extra works staff, training facilities and other special charges.

The new Act came into force at a time when vast programmes of work had already been undertaken by the War Office.[1] There had been no War Office building on any scale, whether for personnel or for stores, until 1937–38; and the War Office now stood upon the threshold of a period of heavy responsibility and of immense difficulties to be overcome. The militia camp problem was but one of many pressing War Office building tasks at the outbreak of war; its character, however, made it a subject of some public comment, much of it misinformed.

Since it was considered essential that militia men should not be in tents after September 1939, speed was demanded in the construction of the camps. The War Office accordingly engaged firms of contractors with experience of War Office work on the unusual basis of a 'cost plus fee' contract—a potentially wasteful and extravagant form of contract which (since it provides no direct incentive to efficiency) can be justified only by exceptional circumstances and calls for the very strictest control. In considering the militia camps the Select Committee on National Expenditure later found[2] that supervision had been lax and that, while the War Office had adopted the system with the knowledge of all its attendant disadvantages in order to achieve speed in construction, the end had not in fact been justified by the means.

---

[1] In part on a prime cost basis, but also on target basis, on measurement basis, fixed price basis and on maximum price subject to costings. The bulk of these contracts went through without any untoward consequences.

[2] S.O. Fifth Report from the Select Committee on National Expenditure, Session 1940–41. The Select Committee adopted with amendments a report from their Sub-Committee on Army Services which forms the substance of the Fifth Report.

Figures had been put to the Sub-Committee on Army Services[1] of the actual cost, so far as it was known, of the contracts for the militia camps. Almost invariably the final cost had exceeded the original estimate by a very large sum, sometimes by as much as four times.[2] Although the general localities were fixed, the actual sites where the camps were to be built were as a rule unknown, and in consequence it became impossible to estimate even an approximately accurate figure for the camps or the externals on the site. Nor was the definite establishment known of the units to be provided for: often there was a great increase over those originally covered by the estimate. Moreover, many alterations and additions to the estimates were made in order to provide greater comfort and amenities for the men.

In an earlier report of the Select Committee dated April 1940[3] it was shown that maximum economy could have been achieved only if reasonable time had been given to carry out the work, and that

> the term reasonable should be taken to mean a period that does not mean employing an excessive number of men for the size of the site, nor the purchase of material in such haste as to exhaust stocks and cause manufacturers to make special arrangements at high cost for intensive production.

One result of the need for speed in the completion of the militia camps was that, when contractors arrived at their destinations in May 1939 to start work, they found that some sites had not been finally selected and that others had not been wholly acquired. There were, moreover, no plans of buildings to be placed there, the sites had not been surveyed or contoured for levelling, nor had the existing roads or drainage been plotted.[4]

> Contractors were expected to commence work on virgin ground, make surveys and contour plans, and finally lay out the buildings. In one case it was stated that the contractor's sketch plans for the lay-out were not approved till 8th June 1939, more than five weeks after arriving on the site. A fixed series of buildings or standard drawings had to be adapted to an irregular and often unsuitable site, which in several instances necessitated a complete change of lay-out. One camp, for instance, which the sub-committee[5] visited was built on a slope of 1 in 16, so that each hut had to be built up considerably on the lower side in order to be above ground on the upper side. The whole of such work was additional to the estimates and was carried out at considerable cost.

Delay and increased expense were sometimes caused by difficulties

---

[1] *Ibid.*

[2] The War Office argument in reply to this and other criticisms is given on p. 259 *et seq.*

[3] S.O. Third Report from the Select Committee on National Expenditure, Session 1939–40.

[4] S.O. Fifth Report from the Select Committee on National Expenditure, Session 1940–41.

[5] The Sub-Committee on Army Services.

in obtaining water which in turn might well have been caused by the hasty choice of unsuitable sites. For these and other reasons, the original estimates for the militia camps were generally looked upon as bearing no relation to the fixed cost.

In the committee's view the great increases in cost flowed from three main causes: the failure to include certain essential works[1] in the original estimates; policy changes affecting the number of men and the type of equipment to be accommodated; and the failure to survey the sites before the estimates were prepared.

These and other points made by the committee in various reports were taken up by the War Office in a memorandum.[2] In this document it was objected that the only figure for militia accommodation given by the committee was the figure of £21 millions already referred to[3] and a percentage comparison of the final cost of five camps with the estimate. Now the committee had stated that the cost of the five camps (which might be taken as typical examples) varied from about two and a half times to nearly five times the estimate; and by an inference which connected the figure of £21 millions with the percentage estimate, the public press had arrived at the conclusion that the militia camps cost £80 millions. This, the War Office pointed out, was far from being the truth, and it was indeed unfortunate that the committee's report had been so interpreted.

The estimate of £21 millions for works construction,[4] it was explained, covered, in addition to self-contained militia camps to be built for militia in 1939, extensions to barracks and ancillary accommodation of various types, as well as some provision for additional intake in 1940. The actual original estimate of the cost of camps for 35,000 militia was some £5¼ millions. Later it was found that 50,000 militia had to be accommodated in camps in 1939 and the corresponding estimate for this number was £7½ millions. The actual final cost of the militia camps was some £16 millions, and the difference between the original estimate and outcome was attributed to:

1. An underestimate by the War Office of the cost on the date available at the time.[5]

---

[1] Including such items as additional camp buildings; contractors' buildings taken over by the military authorities; extra foundations and levelling, etc.; internal work; garages and petrol tanks; sewage works; main roads and bridges; water storage tanks and mains; passive air defence works; other camp services (incinerators, street lighting, police and fire services, etc.); and the preparation of plans.

[2] The War Office prepared the memorandum, which is quoted in its Eighteenth Report, Session 1940–41, on the invitation of the committee.

[3] Page 255. The figure of £21 millions was the cost of militia accommodation given in the Supplementary Estimates of July 1939—£20 millions in Vote 10 C, Works Construction; £1 million in Vote 10 A, Pay, etc., of Staff for Works.

[4] *Ibid.*

[5] Excesses were caused by (i) loss through exceptionally bad weather; (ii) overtime and increase in wage-rates; (iii) use of unusual number of workmen to ensure speed; (iv) rise in price of materials; (v) premature occupation of the camps by troops, which interfered with completion.

S

2. The cost of erection of temporary camps in addition to hutting construction.
3. Expenditure on additional building of which the requirements were not known at the outset.

As to the general underestimation of costs, it was argued that the factors named by the committee as having been left out were almost entirely those which were unknown or had not been encountered when the estimates had been framed. Thus, because of labour shortages, it was inevitable that workmen should be brought in from a distance—from Eire, for example—with all the extra cost of overtime and travelling and subsistence allowance. Since the actual sites were not known, nor the establishment of the units to be provided for, costs again outstripped original estimates. Equally impossible to forecast were the alterations and additions later made for the greater comfort of the men, and the scale of transport, which had not been fixed. But even if estimates had been fixed with the full knowledge available after the event, the War Office memorandum added, it would nevertheless have been necessary to carry out the service.

In April 1941 the War Office submitted a full report to the Treasury in which it was pointed out that if the various suggestions on procedure made by the Select Committee had in fact been applied to the militia camp contracts, construction could not have been started until after the date on which completed camps were needed for occupation.

The Public Accounts Committee later examined the militia camp programme in some detail, and in its report suggested that an excess on a conjectural estimate did not necessarily imply wasteful expenditure, but might merely indicate an underestimate, and they recognised that under prevailing conditions no form of contract other than the one used had been possible.[1]

---

[1] Report from the Committee of Public Accounts, 1941, paragraphs 29–35. The Report concludes:

'34. Your Committee have given careful consideration to the facts recorded above and the following points appear to them to emerge:

'(i) The fact that a conjectural estimate is exceeded does not necessarily mean that expenditure is wasteful. An alternative explanation may be that there has been an underestimate of the cost.

'(ii) It is recognised that under the conditions of urgency prevailing in 1939 there was no time available to place the contracts on any other than a cost plus fixed fee basis. No useful purpose can therefore be served by a discussion of alternative forms of contract.

'(iii) As regards the system of control, the Comptroller and Auditor-General has drawn attention to similar excesses on works services for which other methods of control were adopted, including certain important works in which the supervision, and in some cases the planning and design also, were entrusted by the Departments concerned to business agents of wide experience.

'(iv) There seems little doubt that part of the variations between the costs of different camps was due to variations in the general efficiency of the contractors. As to this it must be borne in mind that the employment of a number of contractors was necessary in order to cope with the volume of the work. As an example of the varying efficiency of building contractors generally, Your Committee note that during a short period in 1940 when the War Office found it possible to let a number of contracts on lump sum com-

In May 1941 the Secretary of State for War (Mr. Margesson) made a general statement in the House of Commons regarding the camps and assured the House that the defects in organisation which existed in 1939 were due to exceptional conditions and would not recur.[1]

(ii)

Reorganisation of the Army Works Services

At a meeting of the Army Council on 1st May 1941, Major-General C. J. S. King (at that time Chief Engineer, Home Forces) was appointed Controller-General of Military Works Services. In his first report on 28th May he pointed out that there was no existing organisation to collect, collate and disseminate civil and military engineer intelligence. Moreover, he could find no trace of any engineer appreciation having been prepared for any projected operation. In 1919 the appointment of an Engineer-in-Chief at the War Office had been recommended,[2] but the suggestion had been turned down. In 1939 an Engineer-in-Chief was, however, provided at the General Headquarters of the British Expeditionary Force,[3] but, General King maintained, that officer should have been able to deal with one man at the War Office. This position was reached when, on 4th September 1941, General King was appointed Engineer-in-Chief there.[4]

The appointment of an Engineer-in-Chief was followed by other changes (almost completely carried out between 1942 and 1944),

---

petitive tenders and obtained very good prices, these prices showed variations which ranged from $1\frac{3}{4}$ per cent. to $25\frac{3}{4}$ per cent. below their estimates.

'(v) Generally, it seems clear that costs were higher than normal owing to the necessity for speedy construction, but this necessity was accepted by the Treasury.

'35. Having regard to these considerations Your Committee are of opinion that the expenditure on militia camps was not exceptional when compared with other cases they have reviewed of works services where urgency was the dominant factor. They recognise that such occasions must occur and that the consequences must be accepted. But they are anxious that the occasions shall be as few as possible, and that the unfortunate results shall be reduced to a minimum. The Treasury have directed, following the recommendation of the Public Accounts Committee of 1940, that Departments should draw specific attention to cases where in their opinion urgent public requirements make it necessary to embark on works services on the basis of a conjectural estimate only. Your Committee trust that in all such cases careful consideration will be given before the need for speedy construction is also accepted. Haste is almost certain to involve extravagance. Where haste must be accepted as an overriding factor, supervision becomes an especially important element in the avoidance of waste. Your Committee are glad to learn that, in the light of the experience of the militia camps, the War Office recognised the need for improved supervision, and so far as in present circumstances the necessary technical staffs can be secured, have adopted various recommendations made by an advisory committee set up by them to consider that aspect of the question.'

[1] H. of C. Deb., 6th May 1941, Vol. 371, Col. 673.
[2] By the Rawlinson Committee.
[3] On the recommendation of the Finlayson Committee.
[4] Notified in War Office memoranda of 1st October 1941.

both at the War Office and in the Army Commands, the details of which do not fall within the province of this narrative. The underlying purpose was to give the Army Works Services a staff equal to its task and to restore order. While it would not be true to say that the Works Services Department had broken down (since it had not failed in its primary duty of providing works), its accounting machinery was badly in need of overhaul, and, when in the summer of 1940 defence measures had to be made effective over the whole country in a matter of weeks, the threat of invasion had led to a strong tendency in both staffs and executives to take short cuts, and thus overstep their powers.

Such conduct was excusable when the safety of the country was in question, but could not be permitted to continue. The measures taken achieved their purpose, but produced a less flexible, more cumbersome machine.

The essence of the new scheme was the setting up, in September 1942, of a central Engineer Accounts Office, and in succession corresponding offices at the various Commands—South-Eastern, Western, Scottish, Northern, London District and Southern. Under the Chief Engineer at each Command headquarters both construction and stores accounts came progressively to be maintained by experienced accountants using modern mechanical methods. Royal Engineer commanders were relieved of all accounting and were furnished with regular statements showing how their accounts stood. Stores provision was similarly centralised in the Command headquarters Stores Section, and the control of all storehouses passed from Royal Engineer commanders to the Chief Engineer.

(iii)

The Bolero Programme

While the complete reorganisation of the Army Works Services was being begun in the summer of 1941, the impending co-operation of the United States with Great Britain was becoming apparent. As far back as June 1941 American troops had begun to relieve British forces in Iceland, and a substantial American force had begun to assemble in Northern Ireland.[1] At about the same time officers of an American Special Observer Group, in plain clothes, were engaged on special reconnaissances in Great Britain.

---

[1] By March 1942 the strength of the American forces in Northern Ireland was 11,740; by July it had risen to 42,000. Plans made in March allowed for a total strength of 148,000 Americans and 14,000 British in Northern Ireland. This called for extra accommodation for 26,150 men, i.e. 367,000 square feet of new covered storage and a considerable increase in hospital beds.

With the entry of the United States into the war in December 1941, and the assignment of first place to Europe in the combined British-American strategy, vast accommodation and building tasks had to be undertaken in the face of severe handicaps. In Britain the manpower shortage was acute, and both the Ministry of Works, with responsibility for the allocation of labour, and the War Office, with the duty of accommodating the ever-growing influx of American personnel and equipment, were in process of carrying through schemes of reorganisation. The special building programme for the American forces carried out between 1942 and 1944, to which the code name Bolero was given, was the particular province of the War Office. It was a separate building undertaking on a massive scale.

Not only was the Bolero programme an Army works undertaking of unprecedented magnitude; it was launched at a time which, for the Engineer-in-Chief's department at the War Office, could not have been less propitious, since the labour problem, as earlier chapters have shown, was acutely critical, materials were in short supply, and within the War Office the most drastic reorganisation of works services was afoot. In fact, as a War Office report states, the Quartermaster-General felt that this reorganisation might have to be postponed or modified, and it was only after strong representations by the Engineer-in-Chief that he agreed to let it go forward as planned provided no delay to the programme was caused. This was without doubt a happy decision, for without the strengthening of the service by the district organisation it is probable that the programme would have broken down.

Early plans for the reception and accommodation of the American troops and stores were nebulous. Discussions went on at top level under conditions of extreme secrecy. Not until 23rd June 1942 was the secrecy embargo raised, at least in part, and for the first time discussions with subordinates were permitted. Meanwhile, the Bolero Combined Committee[1] had been formed in London, under the chairmanship of Sir Findlater Stewart, to work in close touch with the Bolero Committee in Washington in solving many and varied problems. Its terms of reference, as finally revised by the Chiefs of Staff in March 1943, made provision for co-ordinating plans and administrative preparation

for the reception, accommodation and maintenance of United States forces in the United Kingdom and for the development of the United

---

[1] The principal committees and sub-committees concerned, apart from the main committee, were the Principal Administrative Officers Committee, with the Quartermaster-General as chairman, the Joint Administrative Planning Committee, the Bolero Accommodation Sub-Committee, the Bolero Provision of Medical Services Sub-Committee, the Bolero Transport Sub-Committee, the Bolero Labour Sub-Committee, and the Bolero Supply Sub-Committee. Sir Findlater Stewart was chairman of the last two sub-committees, as well as of the main committee.

Kingdom in accordance with the requirements of plans for the invasion of Europe.

The committee acted under the general authority of the Principal Administrative Officers Committee, to whom disputed matters of policy requiring decision or arbitration were to be referred; and it was required to maintain close touch with the corresponding committee in Washington. Direct contact between particular Government departments and the United States forces was not discouraged, so long as the committee's secretariat was kept informed of policy discussions which might require to be co-ordinated with the policies of other interested parties.

The committee, in addition to the chairman and the United States representatives, comprised representatives of the three fighting Services, of Combined Operations Headquarters, of the Ministry of War Transport, and of the Ministry of Home Security. Representatives of other Government departments were called in from time to time as required, and each department nominated a senior official to serve as and when required on the committee.

In the War Office a deputy to the Quartermaster-General was appointed[1] to receive American demands and produce plans in consultation with the various Directors.

The perfecting of this elaborate administrative machine was a slow process: not until 1943 did the system of co-ordination become firmly established. In the early months of 1942, however, some indication of the scale of the Bolero programme began to leak out from the War Office to other departments. The Ministry of Works, with its direct responsibility for the allocation of building labour and materials, had every cause for concern, and on 24th April its Director-General wrote to Major-General King:

> I am alarmed by a report that you are contemplating accommodation for one million American troops in this country in the next six months, partly in billets or requisitioned houses and partly in camps. Even if only a small part is to go into hutted camps, of however rough a description, the demand for labour and materials would be enormous, and I know no means of meeting it from civilian labour. Can you let me know what truth there is in the story and what immediate action is necessary?

In his reply, Major-General King said that there was a lot of planning going on at high level in great secrecy, 'so the less said about it the better. Numbers are nebulous like many other things'. He emphasised that any Americans that did come must be prepared to do

---

[1] With the designation D.Q.M.G.(L). He sat as chairman of the Bolero Accommodation Sub-Committee.

their own work; that is, provide labour and most material. For the moment no action was called for.

After protracted discussions the main decisions taken by the Bolero Combined Committee were:

1. The implementation of Bolero would be a British responsibility.
2. Because of shortages of manpower and materials, especially steel, the Americans were to be called on to make a large contribution of assistance in both directions.
3. All necessary funds would be provided by the Treasury, and the amounts recorded for use in the final settlement between the two Governments after the war.

The most important of these decisions was the first, since it disposed of the danger of two agencies competing for the same labour and supplies. The United States did not have to set up a duplicate contracting agency.

In all, four Bolero 'Key Plans' were issued by the Deputy Quartermaster-General (L), the first not until 31st May 1942 and the last on 12th July 1943. Because of the distance between London and Washington, the differences in organisation, training and equipment of the British and American armies and vital accommodation commitments at home, it would indeed have been surprising if a detailed plan had been arrived at earlier. The numbers for whom accommodation was to be provided under the first Bolero Key Plan were:

			Men
Air Component[1]	.	.	240,000
Headquarters	.	.	2,900
Supporting troops	.	.	294,050
Divisions	.	.	235,050
S.O.S. (Service of Supply)	.	277,000
			1,049,000

By 25th July 1942, when the second Bolero Key Plan was issued, the total number of Americans had been brought up to 1,147,000. It was planned that 904,600 should arrive by 9th April 1943, with the balance at the rate of 120,000 per month. This plan, however, was upset by the course of events. In mid-August planning began for the North African campaign[2] mounted in November, and on the 11th of that month the third Bolero Key Plan was issued. By that time only one and a half American divisions and 100,000 Air Force and S.O.S. troops remained in Great Britain, and the Key Plan showed the following numbers as assumed to arrive by May 1943:

---

[1] Accommodation for the air component in the United Kingdom was the responsibility of the Air Ministry (see Chapter XIII). It should be noted, however, that in the United States forces the air component was reckoned as part of the Army.

[2] Operation 'Torch'.

				Men
Air Force .	.	.	.	172,000
Ground Force	.	.	.	150,000
S.O.S.	.	.	.	105,000
				427,000

The North African campaign was successfully concluded by mid-May 1943, but the supreme effort of the war—the invasion of Europe—was now at hand. On 12th July the full Bolero Plan was reinstated in the fourth Bolero Key Plan issued. The numbers were:

				Men
Air Force .	.	.	.	448,000
Ground Force	.	.	.	567,000
S.O.S.	.	.	.	325,000
				1,340,000

A still further increase a little later brought the figures to 1,446,000. All work was to be completed by 30th April 1944.

The distribution of work under the Bolero programme is described in later sections of this chapter. The inevitable checks and setbacks in so considerable an undertaking will be better appreciated if some of its inherent difficulties are first set down. In the early stages both the British and the Americans, in spite of much goodwill, found it by no means easy to adapt themselves to each other's ways. The Americans did not always give due weight to the fact that, quite apart from the Bolero commitment, the United Kingdom's own accommodation problem was on the widest scale and of much complexity. Not only were there two million troops in the United Kingdom in the early part of 1942, but the bulk of military labour was locked up in Army projects at Bicester and Kineton;[1] and before the American troops could be accommodated most of the Southern and Western Commands had to be evacuated and accommodation provided elsewhere.[2]

A range of difficult administrative and technical problems confronted the American Staff. First, there was the question of scales of accommodation. Since, on the whole, American approved scales were in excess of the British, and neither army could agree to better treatment for the American than for the British soldier, a complete new set of accommodation standards for the United States forces in the United Kingdom had to be worked out and agreed between the War Office and headquarters of the European Theatre of Operations, United States Army.[3] Quartering, works, and hygiene were all

---

[1] Page 272.
[2] Under the designation 'Bolero Repercussion'.
[3] E.T.O.U.S.A.

affected, and it was only after much negotiation and many conferences that complete agreement was reached.[1]

Again, the British system of works administration greatly vexed and irritated the American troops. As has been noted, the reorganisation of the Army Works Services was being hammered out when the Americans arrived, and neither the Quartermaster-General's nor the Works staffs had had time to appreciate their powers and limitations. The constantly recurring delays, the apparent absence of initiative, the lack of bustle, exasperated the more impatient Americans. Particularly did they find it hard to understand why so many services were referred to the War Office which could have been dealt with at a lower level; and although they were bound to recognise that the British system was a matter solely for the War Office, they could justly demand that their work should not be hampered or wasted by the slow working of the British administrative machine.

When the American troops arrived and began working on the Bolero programme, it was at once apparent that there were considerable variations between British and American standards of construction. The British were used to work with brick, tile, plasterboard, and corrugated iron, the Americans with wood. Before they could make good use of British materials they had to accept the delay and annoyance of being put through training schools specially set up for them. Again, in the United Kingdom voltages differed from those in the United States, and for the use of mixed British and American equipment additional transformers and circuits had to be found. Plumbing standards, too, were different, and early arrivals from America had to be supplied with British tools to which they were unaccustomed.

It took the Americans a long time to accustom themselves to the effects of British weather and soil, and more especially to working on clay soil. This was most noticeable in road-making. Here the British had found by experience the necessity for hand-packed soling, but this procedure was strange to many of the Americans, who must have rolled thousands of tons of granite into bottomless mud in their efforts to provide a road foundation.

The acquisition of sites for new construction, especially of depots, was a source of much delay because of the claims of other Ministries, notably those of the Ministry of Agriculture. Sites were often on low-lying land and on unsuitable soil, and much work might be needed to make them usable; nor was it uncommon for hospitals to be set up in private parks, miles from a railway, where complete water, power, and sewage disposal systems had to be installed.

Another embarrassment was that British store nomenclature was

---

[1] The final scale of accommodation in camps agreed upon was 72 square feet per officer and 36 square feet per man. See p. 269.

entirely strange to the American troops. To become familiar with it was a slow, sometimes a painful, experience; and such was the confusion caused by the difference in names, that British non-commissioned officers were detailed to help in American store depots.

The Americans had been told that, because of the shortage of labour, the early convoys of troops across the Atlantic should contain a large proportion of engineers. For various reasons the results of this recommendation, which had the support of the American staff in the United Kingdom, were disappointing; and the summer of 1942 was well advanced before American engineers began to make a useful contribution to the Bolero programme. This was the more unfortunate since the summer weather could not be wasted and many big jobs, for which American engineers would have been best suited, fell perforce to other agencies.

The United States engineer troops, who were organised in regiments, had to be dispersed over large numbers of minor jobs, such as camp expansions, for which neither they nor their organisation were suited. It was not until the large depots at Honeybourne, Boughton, Histon, and Lockerley[1] were authorised that the American engineer troops came into their own, with the use of the earth-moving machinery and the mass concreting for which they were trained and equipped.

As if the special problems which faced both the British and the Americans were not enough, handicaps of language and orientation made up an appreciable total of delays and waste, both of time and effort. We quote from a War Office report:

> While it was tolerably easy to cope with cases where two absolutely different words represented the same object (e.g. lift and elevator, tap and faucet), it was very difficult not to be caught out by a word which represented two entirely different things (e.g. track, road). Country dialects, too, were in many cases almost incomprehensible to the Americans. After the lapse of some time glossaries were prepared, but they were not available at an early stage.

To add to their difficulties in settling down in a strange land, the Americans found that in the course of preparation for invasion most of the road direction signs had been removed. It was hard enough for United Kingdom troops to find the way from a small-scale map; for the Americans it was even more baffling, and wasteful of time and petrol.

The Bolero programme comprised not only accommodation for the American troops, but also comprised hospitals and storage depots.[2] The rough estimated cost of the whole War Office programme was

---

[1] See p. 274.

[2] An item for workshops is included under storage depots.

£50 millions and, although many factors changed—numbers, scales and types of accommodation—the final figure of cost worked out, perhaps as much by chance as through superhuman foresight, at £49·9 millions. The cost of each of the three main items was approximately the same.[1]

In 1942, for the first time, the volume of work to be attempted during the year was carefully planned by the planning branch in the War Office under the direct supervision of the Engineer-in-Chief. Calculations were based on the labour which it was estimated would be available for new work, and the figure of £50 per man-month was used. Thus, an average labour force of 50,000 men would produce £50 millions worth of work.[2] But whereas in peace-time cost imposed a limitation of the works programme, this was not always so under war conditions; and, as had been seen in earlier chapters, there was a tendency to approve services without taking into account how much labour would probably be available to carry them out. In the War Office this tendency was now corrected. The Engineer-in-Chief could tell the Quartermaster-General that labour would only admit of so many million pounds' worth of work being attempted during the year.

The planning of work for a depot estimated to cost £500,000 may be taken as an example. Here it is considered that the maximum labour force which can be accommodated and work on the site is 2,000. This force will produce £100,000 of work per month on the average. But *at least* a month must be allowed at the start for the gradual build-up of the labour and correspondingly at the end of the work another month for its reduction.

The labour curve in its simplest form would therefore be:

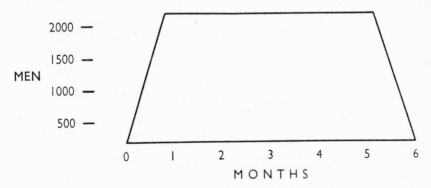

This equals 2,000 men for five months, that is £500,000 worth of work. Although such a calculation might appear somewhat theoreti-

---

[1] Accommodation for personnel £14·8 millions; hospitals £14·3 millions; depots and workshops £12·7 millions; miscellaneous and minor items £8·2 millions.

[2] For large works valued at, say, one million pounds, this figure was very nearly correct. It cannot be applied to small works or to maintenance.

cal, it was, nevertheless, based on practical experience; and, in fact, depots costing about £450,000 were constructed in 1943–44 in approximately six months with labour forces averaging a little under 2,000.

Civilian labour was substantially reinforced with military labour, mostly for projects where civil labour was in short supply. The troops thus used were drawn as a rule from Artisan Works Companies and General Construction Companies of the Royal Engineers, and from Pioneer Companies. Where it became necessary to reinforce contractors' labour with military labour, the contractor paid the War Office the normal civil rates for the men supplied. The soldiers, however, received their normal Army pay. As might be expected, this arrangement often gave rise to no little trouble. The contractors contended that the soldiers had not the skill of the tradesmen alongside whom they were working, and the soldiers felt that the Government were making a profit out of them; but it is difficult to see what other equitable arrangement could have been made in the circumstances which prevailed.

No trustworthy figures are available of civil labour used for military works in the first two years of the war. It was not until after 1941 that proper records were kept, and these are summarised below:

Civil Building Labour employed on Army Works

1942	Jan.	52,800		*1944*	Jan.	34,500
	Feb.	50,200			Feb.	33,100
	Mar.	52,400			Mar.	31,000
	Apr.	50,800			Apr.	30,100
	May	48,100			May	29,600
	June	44,000			June	29,000
	July	45,000			July	26,000
	Aug.	52,600			Aug.	24,300
	Sept.	62,100			Sept.	22,800
	Oct.	70,800	These high figures		Oct.	21,800
	Nov.	72,600	showed the effort		Nov.	20,800
	Dec.	76,100	required for the		Dec.	18,800
			start of the			
1943	Jan.	77,800	Bolero programme	*1945*	Jan.	17,400
	Feb.	75,400	for U.S. forces		Feb.	17,400
	Mar.	71,600			Mar.	16,800
	Apr.	71,500			Apr.	15,500
	May	50,250*			May	15,700
	June	44,000			June	14,900
	July	37,000				
	Aug.	36,100				
	Sept.	35,300				
	Oct.	33,700				
	Nov.	32,700				
	Dec.	33,700				

* This sudden drop had to be offset by the employment of more military labour.

CAMPS

Nearly all the new camps were built in standard sizes for 250, 500, 700, 1,000, 1,250 or 1,500 men. This work was mainly arranged for by the War Office, with the use of military labour, both British and American, as well as civil labour under various contracts. The camps were normally hutted and hutted expansions, but a large number of tents, some 'winterised' and others of summer type, were also used.

In the camp programme there was at no time an actual shortage of housing, but the original plan of providing hutted camps for all had to be modified. Effort was concentrated on winter tented camps to provide for the troops expected to arrive by the winter of 1943–44. It was also clear that many of the men would have to go into billets, and arrangements were made for a minimum of 100,000 men. For these special cooking, dining and sanitary accommodation had to be provided.

In the winter of 1943–44 sites were selected for summer tented camps to receive the troops expected in the spring of 1944, and work began for the accommodation of nearly 200,000 men in this way. On 1st June 1944, the total accommodation was made up as shown below:

Existing camps	650,034
Tented expansions on austerity scale	59,687
Hutted camps	162,004
Winter tented camps . .	30,470
Summer tented camps . .	192,564
Billets	111,590
	1,206,349

Troop strength on that date was 1,098,146, and when a ten per cent. figure for wastage is added it will be seen that practically all the demand for accommodation had been met. In addition there were bivouac sites for 171,250 used for training exercises, and for the invasion of Europe 201,618 troops were marshalled in Overlord camps.

The final scale of accommodation in camps was 72 square feet per officer and 36 square feet per man. Figures for construction were:

New hutted camps . .	1·07 man-months per man
Summer tented camps .	0·25 man-months per man
Winter tented camps .	0·50 man-months per man

Thus, with a labour force of 500, a hutted camp for 1,000 men could be completed in a little over two months.

HOSPITAL ACCOMMODATION

Included in the camp programme were a number of dual-purpose or convertible camps as part of the plan for hospital accommodation. Almost all the new hospitals for the American forces in the United Kingdom (built by contractors for the Ministry of Works as agents for the War Office) were of two types: the station hospital of 834 beds and the general hospital of 1,084 beds. On the original estimates the first type was to cost roughly £187,000, the second £250,000.

The construction, though hutted, was essentially of a semi-perman-
ent type and hardly that of a theatre of war. The standard adopted
was lavish and, as compared with British hospitals, the staff accommodation was on a generous scale. Covered ways with smooth paving
without steps connected the surgical wards with the operating block,
and the theatre appointments were of the costliest and most modern
types.

The original programme was for about 94,000 beds. It was recognised later that the build-up could be gradual, and that the last few
thousand beds would not be needed until the projected invasion of
the Continent had begun. Accordingly dual-purpose and convertible
camps were built, capable of being converted as needed into hospitals.
The build-up of the accommodation required was as follows:

Existing beds	11,746
Expansions	5,597
New	
35 Station hospitals . .	29,106
17 General hospitals . .	18,402
Conversions	
Militia camps . . .	14,929
Convertible camps: 10 at 750 .	7,500
Dual-purpose camps: 6 at 1,000 .	6,000
	93,280

By the end of March 1943, only eight new station hospitals had
been completed. Civil labour, which reached a peak of nearly 78,000
in January, fell off rapidly after April, and by July was as low as
36,000. Lack of labour in the good building weather of the summer of
1943 thus had a most distressing effect on the hospital programme.

Towards the end of 1943 it was becoming apparent that the total
of 94,000 beds would not be reached by the due date.[1] A proposal to
supplement contractors' labour with United States troops was considered and rejected. It had been difficult enough to make arrangements for mixing British troops with civil labour; how, then, would
it be possible to devise equitable arrangements when American troops
formed part of the labour? The answer was to provide, by the use of
American troops, 30,000 beds[2] in tented expansions adjacent to hospital wards. Standard ward tents were used. No expansion of water-
borne sewage was attempted, nor could bathing, ablution, or sanitary
facilities be installed. The expanded wards had to make shift with
latrine tents and bucket latrines.

Although this tented expansion was not part of the planned Bolero

---

[1] 30th April 1944.
[2] Included in the figure of 30,000 beds were three fully-tented hospitals of 750 beds
sited in areas not served by hutted hospitals.

programme, it later proved a vital factor in the handling of casualties. The following figures, from American sources, show this:

BEDS

	Requisi-tioned hospitals	Hutted	Militia camp conversions	Convertible and dual-purpose huts	Total	Patients
30th August 1944 .	9,164	50,939	6,329	13,500	79,932	82,526

Clearly, the tented expansions were justified.

By 30th April 1944 the total number of beds available was 61,805, over 32,000 short of the target figure of 90,000.

A reasonably accurate computation for the erection of the new hutted hospitals gives about four man-months per bed. For all practical purposes the programme was completed by the end of September 1944.

Some retarding factors should be noted. The conversion of militia camps, for example, had fallen seriously behind the time-table, partly because the camps had to be occupied while the work was in progress. Again, the type of flooring to be provided in hospital wards and operating theatres was the subject of much experiment and alteration. The original designs had been for steel-trowelled concrete, but this had proved to be too dusty in spite of wax treatment, and a grano-lithic finish or linoleum was next authorised. Even this did not prove satisfactory, and litch mastic was ordered for all new construction. In the operating theatres, because of the danger from explosions caused by static electricity produced by the litch mastic, another type of close-grained floor was put down; and wooden floors already laid in militia barracks and convertible camps were covered with a ruberoid preparation.

Another source of trouble was the large amount of fat contained in American tinned foods. This proved too much for grease traps of British design; filter beds in sewage disposal systems became clogged, and sometimes the media had to be removed and replaced with others of larger size.

STORAGE DEPOTS

The congestion of constructional work which fell to the War Office in the first two years of war had brought about, as we have seen, a drastic reorganisation of the Works Services. Meanwhile, the collapse of France and the return of nearly 350,000 men, for the most part without arms and equipment, had created an acute accommodation problem at home. To add to the confusion, invasion had become a real and imminent threat. In consequence the effort of the Royal Engineers had largely swung over to the construction of anti-invasion defences. At the same time the Dunkirk troops had had to be housed in any way possible—in billets, requisitioned buildings and tents—while they were being sorted out and restored to their formations.

During this period the Works Services could do little to help except by issuing, and where possible erecting, camp structures to supplement such resources as existed. Radical changes had to be made in the works programme. With but few exceptions, work had to cease on training camps, and all efforts concentrated on providing the accommodation needed to supplement the billets and requisitioned buildings in which men were housed. Hutting was still desperately short, and it was estimated that 30,000 huts would have to be produced and erected by 1st October if the troops were to be under proper cover before the winter.

The difficulties of the labour situation were appalling. Much of the civil labour, which up to then had been used on camp construction, was hurriedly withdrawn to help in building defences. The returned troops had to be organised, re-equipped, and trained for their new role, and could not for many weeks give any help to the hard-pressed Works. When, in the autumn, the 'blitz' attack on London and many of the chief cities followed, yet more men had to be diverted for rescue and hasty repair work.[1] Then, too, came shortages of material. Cement, timber, steel, asbestos sheets were all at one time or other scarce, and every kind of substitute had to be pressed into service Bearing all these adverse factors in mind, the measure of success achieved in getting the troops under cover for the winter was a notable achievement.

The passage of the summer and autumn without any attempt at invasion made it possible to return civil labour from defence works to camp and depot building. At the end of January 1941 there were approximately 1,900,000 troops in the country, and in addition 42,000 women in the Auxiliary Training Service. A new programme of hutting on an austerity scale was launched, much of it with double-bunking, and the congestion was to some extent eased. At the same time the large-scale work on depots could be resumed. The Royal Engineer Stores Depot at Long Marston, the Ordnance Service Depots at Chilwell, Kineton and Nesscliffe[2], and the great Ordnance Depot at Bicester (the most ambitious single project ever attempted for military purposes in the United Kingdom) were among the important undertakings for which the War Office was responsible. Quite apart from the Bolero programme, it is clear that in 1942 the Works Service was fully employed in dealing with its own considerable

---

[1] See Chapter X.
[2] Built by M.O.W. as an agency service.

long-term projects. There was, in addition, the Bolero Repercussion programme.

In September 1942 it was decided that for the supply and movement of stores for a Continental landing an additional Royal Engineers store depot was needed north of the Thames. There were two possible alternatives: either to take over ground in the Chelmsford area, or to take over some portion of London docks on the north side of the Thames.

The suitability of Victoria Docks, almost unused at the time, was recognised, and with the concurrence of Port of London Authority its use was sanctioned. One great advantage was that all capital expenditure was thus avoided at a time when labour was hard pressed. By the end of the year the docks were in full use.

It is against the background sketched in the preceding pages that the construction of storage depots for the United States forces must be viewed. In the early stages no definite proposals could be obtained from the Americans of the amount of depot accommodation they would need. Certain British depots, such as Ashchurch, near Cheltenham, were handed over, but the only large depot built for the Americans in 1942 was at Sudbury-Egginton, near Burton-on-Trent. This proved to be the largest of the specially built depots. Constructed entirely by British civil and military labour, it had well over a million square feet of covered storage and $9\frac{1}{2}$ million square feet of open storage. The cost was £1,650,000.

The construction of storage accommodation was not a task to be accomplished quickly, and since it was certain that before the Operation Overlord for the liberation of the Continent could be mounted, the American forces would need far more storage accommodation in the United Kingdom, a pilot model was built at Wem, in Shropshire, and plans were prepared for four to six similar depots in different parts of the country. The Wem depot was put in hand on 14th December 1942. It consisted of 450,240 square feet of covered storage, 1,375,000 square feet of open storage, and a camp for 1,250 men. It was served by both road and rail (eleven miles of rail and five miles of road), and was completed on 30th June 1943.

As early as August 1942, the construction by United States troops of a new depot at Moreton-on-Lugg, near Leominster, had been approved. It was unfortunate that because of the North African Operation Torch, the Americans were withdrawn before the work had really started. It was then decided to carry out the project by civil contract and, should the Americans after all not need it, to use the place as a British depot. The first contractor defaulted, and completion of the undertaking was much retarded. Ultimately the Americans took over the depot when it was about two-thirds complete,[1] and

---

[1] The building of the depot was not completed until 1943.

T

operated it. The size was the same as Wem, and the cost £533,000.

There was continuing uncertainty about the scope of the American plan, and it was not until 17th May 1943 that it could be stated at the Quartermaster-General's conference that four Wem pattern depots would probably be wanted by the Americans. Within a month the sites had been cleared. The places chosen were: Boughton, near Ollerton, in Nottinghamshire; Histon, near Cambridge; Honeybourne, near Evesham; and Lockerley, between Salisbury and Winchester.

Histon and Lockerley were built entirely by American troop labour, while Boughton and Honeybourne were planned and the work supervised by the British. At both the last-named places a proportion of American troop labour was used.

The amount of covered storage was the same at all four depots—450,240 square feet as at Wem. The open storage space varied with the site and averaged 1,450,000 square feet, while rail and road lengths worked out at an average of 11·80 and 4·70 miles respectively.

The building of these depots was marked by a friendly rivalry which provided an effective incentive and made for early completion. There was much good teamwork. Royal Engineers, Pioneers, civil labour, and American coloured troops could all be seen working together in complete harmony.

In round figures the total depot programme comprised 18 million square feet of covered storage and shops, 45 million square feet of open storage and hardstandings, as well as the corresponding accommodation for personnel (32,130). Of the covered storage a total of six million square feet was of new construction, and of the open storage 35 million square feet. The installations, either acquired or constructed, were:

> 20 General depots
> 12 Q.M. Service depots
> 14 Q.M. P.O.L. depots
> 12 Ordnance Service depots
> 7 Ordnance ammunition depots
> 19 Ordnance vehicle depots
> 3 Transportation Corps depots
> 1 Chemical warfare depot
> 2 Engineer depots
> 4 Medical depots
> ——
> 94

That the United States authorities appreciated the good work carried out in the construction of the depots is evident in their official reports. One report[1] states:

The outstanding problem on depots was the great difficulty in properly stabilising the open storage and road areas. The ground water

---

[1] Quoted in War Office records.

table was generally very close to the surface and heavy American equipment required more foundations than did the lighter British trucks and tractors. It was necessary in several locations to raise the entire open storage area as much as two feet.

The same report concludes:

Although the depot programme required the most time, energy and material of all the ground projects, it was the best organised and the most effectively executed. The British Ministries exerted every effort possible to provide the labour and material. Of those depots constructed, the construction records of Wem depot, which was done by a British contractor, should show it as being the outstanding project completed by British labour. The Lockerly depot, accomplished by United States engineer troops, is an outstanding example of good troop construction.

As a part of the depot programme 210 miles of road were made and 176 miles of rail laid, water supply and sewage disposal systems were provided, and several types of accommodation, such as offices, recreational centres, medical dispensaries and Red Cross huts, were built. The programme, of which the total cost worked out at about £12·7 millions, was completed in the early spring of 1944.

One important task in the preparations for a Continental invasion was the construction of 'hards'.[1] A scheme began to be worked out early in 1942. After a good deal of reconnaissance, the decision was taken in June of that year to build seventy-four hards. This meant not only the construction of the embarkation points themselves, but also new road communications to link up the hards with existing highways.[2] The Admiralty took over the responsibility for the building of the hards proper, while the War Office provided the access roads. Although a few of the hards were in Eastern, Western and Scottish Commands, most of them were in Southern and South-Eastern Commands.

It was not until the late autumn of 1943 that precise details of the hards needed for the projected operation were agreed. An extensive programme of road and bridge widening and improvement had now to be carried out in order to make approach roads fit to carry the immense volume of invasion traffic. The total mileage of these operational routes, some for two-way traffic, others for only one-way, was 1,550. In order to accommodate safely the largest military vehicles, the minimum carriage-way on two-way routes was twenty-two feet, and on one-way sixteen feet, with lay-byes at quarter-mile intervals. All bridges had to conform to these standards and to be appropriately strengthened. Several new bridges were also built.

---

[1] See also Chapters XI and XVI.

[2] Where entirely new roads had to be built they were generally constructed of concrete either six or eight inches thick and reinforced as necessary according to the bearing properties of the subsoil.

The roadwork included the construction of concrete or asphalt slewing points at junctions and sharp bends, and turning circles beside one-way roads.

The extent of this work is summarised below:

Length of new roads . .	16·61 miles
Existing roads reconstructed and widened	231 miles
Number of slewing points and turning circles . . .	409
Number of lay-byes . .	737
Area of hardstandings . .	144,888 square yards
New bridges	5
Existing bridges widened and strengthened . . .	56

The total cost was met from the Road Fund and amounted to approximately £1¾ millions Work was carried out by the Roads Department of the Ministry of War Transport and, apart from civil labour recruited from various sources, seven Road Construction Companies of the Royal Engineers and six Pioneer Companies were employed. The work was completed by the target date.

Among the special installations which formed part of the Bolero programme, and for which the War Office was responsible, were tunnelled headquarters, vehicle parks, post offices, special schools, parachute packing plants, salvage plants and tyre repair shops. The special preparations for the invasion of the Continent (Operation Overlord) included the building of a large number of additional camps sited conveniently for embarkation points and wired in to prevent communication between the troops and the civilian population.

Next came special depots for the storage and issue of the enormous quantity of stores and materials (including tar, cement and surfacing for airfields and roads) and technical equipment needed for the invasion. On the engineer side the technical equipment included bulldozers, cranes, earth-moving machinery, rollers, storage tanks, bridging and stone crushers. Altogether there were some 70,000 tons of engineer stores in this category, while the value of the work on the special camps and depots was £4½ millions. In addition, water supply, lighting, and hardstandings for vehicles had to be supplied, and all these undertakings hidden as far as possible from enemy reconnaissance aircraft.

On the part played by the War Office in the Bolero achievement, it was not unjustly claimed in an official report that

the completion of the programme (with the exception of the hospitals) within the allotted time and at a figure of cost comparing closely with the original rough estimate was a great achievement of which British and Americans may well be proud. Though shortages of labour, materials, and constructional plant were much in evidence during the entire programme, they were surmounted by good team-work on the part of all concerned.

The Americans were aware that the civil labour provided was not representative of British peace-time labour, and were consequently not disposed to be unduly critical. In general they considered that the work turned out was of high quality, but the practices employed on construction were not conducive to speedy progress. American equipment was new and produced quick results.

In all, the number of man-months spent on the Bolero programme was estimated at 1,010,000. The maximum effective labour force produced by United States troops was about 25,000.

CHAPTER XIII

THE BUILDING PROGRAMME
OF THE AIR MINISTRY

(i)

Expansion of the Royal Air Force, 1935

FOR the Directorate of Works of the Air Ministry the war might be said to have begun with the period of expansion of the Royal Air Force in 1935. This was a phase of rising tempo of demand and activity, and of planning and preparation for war;[1] and if these essential services were not always spectacular, they nevertheless made their own vital contribution to the war effort and to final victory. Before the expansion of the Royal Air Force in 1935, the few existing airfields were grass landing-grounds which for the greater part had remained unaltered since the First World War: thereafter extensions and improvements were carried out to meet the needs of the new types of aircraft. The construction of the first hard-surface runways was undertaken in 1937; but at the outbreak of war hard runways had been constructed at only nine existing airfields, and in none of them were there runways for landing and take-off in all directions of wind. In the pre-1935 period services had consisted in the main of reconstruction work on existing stations, usually carried out piece-meal and over a number of years. There had been no effective long-term planning; while design had tended to vary with the needs of individual stations, although for new buildings there was a measure of standardisation. The planning of buildings had, however, fallen short of the progressive technical development and domestic requirements of the Service. Now the expanding Air Force called for new methods and a greater application of standardised type design, so that buildings of the same planning and design could be erected at many stations and need only be modified to meet local conditions, e.g. at the Flying Training School at Hullavington where stone-facing work was used to conform to the traditions of the Cotswold country.

During this period, not only had accommodation at training and operational stations for the regular Air Force to be provided in per-

---

[1] The expenditure on major new works alone for the financial years 1934, 1936 and 1938 was: 1934, £909,346; 1936, £7,981,429; 1938, £20,576,030. The expenditure for 1938 was of unprecedented magnitude for a single department in peace-time.

manent construction, but schemes were also undertaken for non-regular units, generally in more or less temporary buildings. At the same time accommodation had to be provided for equipment units; for the storage of reserves of aircraft, bombs and other ammunition; for aviation fuel; and for bombing ranges, radar stations and a multitude of other ancillary requirements. Reserves had to be dispersed, protected and hidden from observation in suitable localities up and down the country; and these important schemes often called for major engineering works on a costly scale.

(ii)

Growth of the Royal Air Force Building Programme, 1939–45

The design, construction and lay-out of buildings for operational training and other establishments undertaken under war conditions differed from those provided in peace. The buildings were naturally of a more temporary kind, and the need for the greatest economy in the use of materials was accentuated by growing shortages. These in turn called for the substitution of new types of construction, for which materials were available in place of the older types affected by shortages. The need for widely dispersed living accommodation greatly affected the lay-out of stations. It was, however, in the planning and construction of the airfield that by far the greatest change took place. In the pre-war period (except in the few instances to which reference has been made) the airfields were surfaced with grass. But the growth of strong turf is a matter of years. Since there was no time, in any case, to grow the right kind of grass surface, it is clear that hard runways would have to be made.

Apart, therefore, from the fact that the time was in any case approaching when the provision of hard runways would be required to carry the greater loads of the new aircraft and to cope with more intensive use, suitable grass surfaces could not be provided in the time available and the construction of hard runways on all new airfields became inevitable.

In the pre-war period grass airfields had been divided into four intersecting strips in the line of which the approaches had the required flying clearance, but with the general adoption of hard runways, involving the heavy use of materials, labour and plant, it was decided that, in general, requirements would be met by the construction of three runways of suitable length and 50 yards in width at an angle of about 60 degrees to one another, the triangular lay-out being surrounded by a perimeter track, 50 feet wide, connecting the ends of the runways. While the length of runways increased as the war progressed, their width of 50 yards for runways and of 50 feet for perimeter tracks was retained, except in certain specified cases, and the lay-out pattern remained unaltered.

The runways and paved surfaces introduced new problems of design, both of the runway structure and its ancillary drainage. With the outbreak of war there was no longer time for long experiments and trials. The runways had to be designed and built quickly, and the materials available in the quantities required had to be used. The majority of runways were constructed of concrete, but tarmacadam was also extensively used; and in certain localities, including the islands of Benbecula and Tiree in the Hebrides, where other materials were not readily obtainable, the pavement was constructed of sand mixed with bitumen by what was known as the wet sand process. Always the insistent demand was for speed in execution, in order to achieve the earliest completion, and the standards of construction, which would have been obligatory under peace conditions, had to be relaxed. As the war continued and aircraft loads and intensities of user increased, the need for strengthening many runways became apparent and an extensive scheme of surfacing with tarmac and asphalt carpets was undertaken with most successful results.

The new problem relating to drainage arose from the fact that whereas on the grass airfields much of the rainwater was absorbed by the herbage and the soil, the rainfall on the impervious surfaces of hard runways had to be disposed of immediately by means of a complicated and extensive drainage system. And not only that, but steps had to be taken to ensure that the water-courses into which the drains discharged were capable of taking the increased flow without flooding or, if not so capable, were suitably enlarged.[1]

While the selection of airfield sites was the responsibility of the Airfield Board, it was for the Air Ministry Directorate of Works to determine how far such sites were suitable from the civil engineering aspect. The next step was for the Directorate to make surveys and detailed investigations, and to complete all the preliminary organisation up to the time of the letting of contracts for the actual construction of the airfields. With mounting demands on the Royal Air Force, it was an arduous and exacting duty for the Directorate to keep in step with the changes of policy, alterations to foundations and establishments and technical developments that accompanied the planned service expansion. Adroitness in technical and administrative manœuvre and good liaison between the technical branches of the Ministry, surveyors, contracts branches and contractors did much to smooth the way.

To give effect to the changed conception of a Royal Air Force

---

[1] Air Ministry Note.

airfield (that is, from a grass landing-ground to hard-surfaced, all-weather runways capable of standing up to vastly increased loads)was a costly as well as an intricate undertaking. By 1942 the average cost of one heavy-bomber airfield, exclusive of any building or services, was over £500,000; and during the years 1939 to 1945 some 444 Royal Air Force airfields were constructed in this country alone, with paved runways, perimeter tracks and hardstandings at a cost of over £200 millions, excluding any building construction.[1] During the peak constructional year of 1942, in addition to some sixty-three major extensions to existing stations, new airfields were being turned out at an average rate of one every three days.

In estimating, in greater detail, the growth of constructional work in the war years, one might begin by comparing the number of Royal Air Force stations for October 1939 and December 1944. Excluding such units as recruiting centres, embarkation units and similar small detachments, the respective numbers are 190 for October 1939 and 1,093 for December 1944. Taking airfield stations alone (that is, excluding the various depots, training establishments, Air Ministry experimental stations and so forth) the development can be summarised by tracing the growth in numbers and total acreage by stages during the war period.[2]

Summary of Airfield Stations in use by the Royal Air Force and United States Army Air Force in United Kingdom, 1939-45

Year	R.A.F. number of airfields	U.S.A.A.F. number of airfields	Total number of airfields
1939	158		
1940	229		
1941	353		
1942	421	75	496
1943	476	119	595
1944	490	133	623

March 1945: Total number of airfields (R.A.F. and U.S.A.A.F.), 590.
(No split between R.A.F. and U.S.A.A.F. available.)

Another, and perhaps more positive, picture (since it is world-wide) of the growth of constructional works at home and abroad in the war years is seen in a survey of the works expenditure and costs (excluding

---

[1] The overseas constructional work of the Royal Air Force falls outside the scope of this narrative. It was on a considerable scale and included works in Mediterranean islands and territories, throughout the Middle East, in East and West Africa and in the Far East.

[2] The information in this and the following sections is based on data furnished by the Air Ministry Directorate-General of Works.

maintenance) from the year preceding the outbreak of war to 1944.

1938	. . .	£25,000,000
1939	. . .	£50,000,000
1940	. . .	£75,000,000
1941	. . .	£125,000,000
1942	. . .	£145,000,000
1943	. . .	£126,000,000
1944	. . .	£40,000,000

Before the expansion programme (that is, before 1935) a year's normal expenditure on Air Ministry works was between about £750,000 and £1,250,000.

A comparison, perhaps even more illuminating, can be drawn between the works expenditure for the peak year 1942 of £145 millions and a typical total peace-time national budget of about £900 millions.

£145 millions in a year represents approximately £400,000 a day. In 1942 the country's expenditure on the war was stated to be round about £12 millions to £14 millions a day. Thus the Air Ministry works expenditure during the peak period represented about one-thirty-second of the total daily expenditure.

Quite apart from the number of new station airfields, impressive though they are in themselves, it must be remembered that because of changes in function, increases in establishment (sometimes to as much as three times the original figures) and the construction of runways and dispersal points on airfields previously grass, every existing pre-war station was increased and altered. Often, too, increases and alterations on stations were but partially completed when some change in policy or requirements created new demands: stations were changed from bomber to fighter, coastal to bomber, satellites became parent stations, and so on.

What is more, even new stations, as has already been observed, were hardly ever completed to original policy or plan. Changes in establishment both of personnel and aircraft, technical improvements and similar factors brought about endless alterations and changes in constructional work. These ever-changing demands added a vast load to the already formidable engineering task. And with each change in requirements, design, the supply of materials, and all the executive train of construction were affected in innumerable ways. Among the changes built up progressively during the war were these:

1. In 1940 the average establishment figure for a parent bomber station was 1,134 and for a satellite 586.

    By the end of 1944 a standard bomber station establishment was 2,500, and all operational ex-satellites had been up-graded to standard bomber.

2. In 1940 the standard dimensions for the runways for a bomber station were three runways of 1,000 yards by 50 yards.

Several stages in later development led up to the 1944 standard dimensions:

| Main runway | 2,000 yards by 50 yards |
| Subsidiaries | 1,400 yards by 50 yards |

3. In 1939 aircraft were dispersed at a considerable distance from the airfield. Access roads to dispersal points were merely prepared tracks. Under war conditions these dispersal points and tracks were found to be inadequate, and early in the war were replaced by standings and tracks of more permanent construction. As the size and numbers of aircraft increased, these were in their turn replaced by standings of substantial concrete construction which from 1942 onwards became the standard dispersal and marshalling provision at bomber stations.

In May 1941 the average cost of a complete bomber parent station was about £500,000.

By 1944 the average cost was £1 million.

In May 1941, the average cost of a typical fighter station was £500,000; in 1944 the cost was £900,000.

5. In 1939 the all-up weight of the heaviest bomber in service, the Wellington, was 30,000 lb., with a wing-span of 86 feet.

In 1944 the Lancaster had an all-up weight of 68,000 lb., with a wing-span of 102 feet.

The tyre pressures of these bombers were approximately the same at 45 and 43 lb. per square inch respectively, but, on the other hand, the United States Army Air Force Fortress, with a weight of 67,000 lb., had a tyre pressure of 85 lb. per square inch, imposing a greatly increased intensity on the runways and tracks on the airfield from which these aircraft operated.

Apart, therefore, from change of operational requirements in runway lengths, dispersal areas and so on, the effect on engineering design of runways, hangars, handling facilities, and so forth, had been considerable.

In 1943, in addition to contracts in hand for new stations, major extensions, between £20,000 and £500,000 in value, were in hand on 443 existing stations; all this construction, too, including new stations, depots and extensions to stations, was carried on to a strictly defined programme of completion dates. It was an essential and vital factor in the operational planning of the Royal Air Force. In spite of all the difficulties of labour, supply of materials, transport, staffing and other innumerable war-time factors, the Royal Air Force was given its stations by the times planned.

RUNWAYS, PERIMETER TRACKS AND HARDSTANDINGS

The making of runways and tracks on an airfield station was a considerable engineering work. It became almost impossible to select a site, in the large area contained by a modern airfield, which would allow for the construction of runways of suitable grade and orientation without extensive earthworks and preparation. Problems of drainage and topography could be overcome only by careful planning and design. It was not merely the formidable task of laying the pavement which in the case of the longest airfield required some hundreds of thousands of cubic yards of concrete; the preparatory work of excavation and drainage made up much of the whole effort, and on the many clay sites where the work had to proceed throughout the winter, the difficulties were particularly great. On some sites as much as a million cubic yards of earth had to be excavated and transported to spoil or used for fill.

On existing stations almost invariably the work of constructing or extending runways had to be carried out while the station remained operational for flying, thus adding yet another difficulty to the more normal engineering task.

The following data are illustrative:

1. Up to 1945 a total of 444 airfields (including airfields constructed for the Americans) were provided with paved runways.

2. The bulk of the runway programme was carried out during the years 1940 to 1943. The following summary illustrates the annual effort:[1]

Year	Airfields provided with runways	Airfields on which major extensions to existing runways were carried out
1939	9	—
1940	40	14
1941	143	49
1942	136	63
1943	78	31
1944	38	16

3. The total area of paved runways, perimeter tracks and hardstandings was approximately 175 million square yards. 175 million square yards of concrete or tarmac equals 36,000 acres. This acreage was greater than the area of land (not merely roads and so on, but all the land) within the boundary of the city of Edinburgh (32,000 acres) and nearly equalled the area for Birmingham (39,000 acres). It was also the equivalent of a 30-foot-wide road stretching for nearly 10,000 miles.

4. The emergency runways at Carnaby, Woodbridge and Manston were 3,000 yards in length and 250 yards wide. Each runway was equivalent to 40 miles of main road.

5. In the spring of 1945 further development of the runways at two bomber airfields was undertaken to cater for very heavy aircraft. The existing runways were increased in length to one of 3,000 yards

---

[1] Airfields shown as provided in any one year refer to those completed during that year; on many work was in hand in the previous year. Extensions have only been counted where they involved major contracts after initial completion—that is, extensions approved during initial construction have not been included.

and two of 2,000 yards and the widths increased from 50 yards to 100 yards. The thickness of concrete needed to support the aircraft loads was 12 inches, on top of a specially prepared and consolidated foundation. Perimeter tracks were widened to 100 feet and hard-standings increased in size. The cost of the work at each station (classed as 'extensions' to existing stations) was estimated at £1¾ millions. An identical scheme was carried out simultaneously at a third bomber airfield at which runways had not previously been constructed, as the grass surface on a pervious subsoil had successfully borne the traffic to which it had been subjected up to that time.

6. The construction of runways, perimeter tracks and hardstandings for a standard bomber station used about 90,000 cubic yards of ballast and 18,000 tons of cement—a total of approximately 130,000 tons of these materials alone. An additional item was some 50 miles of drainage pipes and cable conduits. Up to March 1945 the airfield programme (excluding building construction) involved the carriage and use of some 57 million tons of the basic materials, ballast and cement. This represents 14,250,000 lorry loads at an average of 4 tons a load. Hundreds of new ballast pits had to be opened and material had to be hauled as much as 50 miles to the site.

7. The Air Ministry Works Directorate was concerned not merely with paved runways, but also developed, or worked in close collaboration with other services which had developed, other forms of runways and tracks to suit special operational requirements. Among these were various methods of soil stabilisation: Sommerfield tract, bar and rod; pierced steel plant (American); metal grillage, etc.

8. Several outstanding performances in speed and effort are specially to be noted:

Station A   180,000 square yards of concrete laid in one month. This equals 10 miles of a 30-foot-wide road.

Station B   170,000 square yards of concrete laid in one month.

Station C   18,000 square yards of concrete laid in one day—equivalent to one mile of main road.

Station D   108,000 square yards of concrete laid in a fortnight.

NON-AIRFIELD STATIONS

In the emergency period immediately preceding the war, and in the war period, over 300 major non-airfield stations were constructed. They included large and often unique constructional undertakings, among them large reserve bomb and incendiary storage depots; reserve and distribution depots for aviation fuel and lubricating oil; equipment depots and storage units; experimental stations; schools for technical training, miscellaneous instructional centres and kindred establishments;[1] Royal Air Force hospitals; and Command and group headquarters.

---

[1] The larger of these schools were built for a personnel of 6,000, with instructional and lecture accommodation, at a cost of about £1½ millions each.

The reserve bomb and incendiary storage depots and advanced ammunition parks provided storage for 450,000 tons of explosive and incendiary bombs. Some forty-one depots in all were built. The main reserve stores were in special underground installations for the construction of which excavation and mining problems of unusual character had to be overcome. The total cost was approximately £6 millions.

The total storage capacity of reserve and distribution depots for aviation fuel and lubricating oil at March 1945 was 2,090,700 tons distributed in thirty-six main reserve and forty-two distribution depots. Several of the largest main reserve depots were in specially constructed and completely protected installations, while all the distribution depots were in underground protected installations of lesser protective value. The total cost was approximately £12 millions.

At March 1945 equipment depots and storage units comprised covered storage in several main aircraft equipment depots, six main ground equipment depots and fifteen equipment parks, with a total area of 12 million feet super. For aircraft storage there were hangars of various types in twenty-two maintenance units to a total capacity of 14 million feet super.

Works services for radar stations were first undertaken some time before the war. Afterwards the demands included the provision of high steel and timber towers from 500 feet to 105 feet in height,[1] special protected operations rooms, power houses and equipment, technical buildings, special gear for totalling aerials and much other specialised work. In addition, accommodation had to be provided for some 77,460 personnel at 280 sites—generally in remote and almost inaccessible places in coastal areas stretching from the Shetlands and Hebrides to the Isle of Wight. The total cost of works services for these installations during the war amounted to some £10 millions.

STATIONS FOR THE UNITED STATES ARMY AIR FORCE

Thirty-six new airfield stations were built for the United States Army Air Force at a cost of £34 millions. This did not include Royal Air Force stations reallocated to the Americans, and on which work of varying magnitude had been carried out to meet particular and varying demands. The total cost of meeting the American works programme carried out by the Air Ministry Works Directorate was £99 millions, and the task used 245,658,480 man-hours.

The Americans themselves constructed fourteen airfield stations. In these the labour and equipment were provided by United States Army engineers, and all materials, together with expert engineer staff, by the Works Directorate.

---

[1] Some 560 masts in all were supplied and erected at home stations.

MISCELLANEOUS BUILDINGS

In the building of an airfield, in addition to the civil engineering problem of providing runways and landing areas—considerable as was this task alone—a number of diverse building demands had to be met. Personnel had to be housed, technical buildings and facilities built, and all the multitudinous fixed ground requirements and installations constructed. Barracks, communal buildings, institutes, hangars, workshops, stores, ground staff facilities, administrative buildings, sick-quarters, mechanical and electrical installations, airfield lighting and control systems, wireless stations, drainage, water supply, roads and other services—all of these were part and parcel of Royal Air Force establishment, whether it were an operational airfield station, a training school or a maintenance unit.

In terms of personnel housed, one need merely compare the pre-war strength of the Royal Air Force with its strength in 1945 to appreciate the magnitude of the problem, which was further complicated by war-time factors of dispersal and camouflage, the shortage of materials and labour, and the urgency of demands.

In the very early stages of the war, as has been noted, in order to meet the rapidly growing establishments, the demand was for a quickly produced prefabricated type of hutting. Various timber and composite types were designed and produced, and because of shortage of steel and timber the fullest possible use was made of half brick construction. By the autumn of 1940 speed was all-important and many alternative types of hut were developed—all based on the most economical use of scarce materials.

Between 1939 and 1945 some 110 million square feet super of prefabricated hutting was constructed on Royal Air Force sites apart from other building *in situ*. Ancillary to this work was the provision of drainage and water supply, roads and other services. Covered storage for Maintenance Command reached a total of 26 million feet.

Early in the war, light, easily erected steel hangars had to be provided. The pre-war type of permanent shed was unsuitable for rapid war-time use, and because of steel restrictions economy of structure was essential. A light type of hangar, economical in steel and capable of mass production, was now taken into use.

THE AIRFIELD CONSTRUCTION SERVICE

The Airfield Construction Service was at first intended to carry out the emergency repair of airfields damaged by enemy action. Gradually that function was overtaken by another role—the carrying out of new airfield construction work in theatres of war, and in other theatres, as the need arose.

Between March 1941 and December 1943 more than thirty squadrons and other units were formed. At times the Airfield Construction Service expanded so rapidly as to embarrass the organisation as a whole. As the number of squadrons increased they were organised under a wing normally consisting of three airfield construction squadrons and one plant squadron. These squadrons held a wide range of plant and motor transport for the airfield construction squadrons.

As the number of plant squadrons rose, a Royal Air Force plant depot to receive and distribute the vast quantities of equipment and spares called for was gradually built up by the home and overseas units.

By the beginning of 1944 the Airfield Construction Service not only included construction and plant squadrons, but M. and E. squadrons and specialist units such as quarrying and well-boring flights. It spread over a large number of countries, including the Middle East, West Africa, Gibraltar, Iceland and the Azores. It had thus become a considerable construction force of nearly 29,000, trained and equipped to carry out works services for the Royal Air Force in any theatre.

In the spring of 1944 it was obvious that the Airfield Construction Service would have to play an important part in the construction and work of the Royal Air Force during the invasion of Europe. The airfield construction squadrons were reorganised to fit them better for this task. A total force of 11,000 was eventually phased into the Western European operation during the summer and autumn of 1944, and a new type of unit, a repair unit (plant), now undertook large plant repairs beyond the capacity of the wings.

(iii)

The Strategic Urgency of the Air Ministry's Building Programme

Merely to outline some of the main features of the Air Ministry's building programme is to paint a picture of unremitting, intensifying effort. It was maintained at that high pitch by a complex and efficient technical organisation ready to give effect to whatever new tasks and developments might be dictated by the changing strategy of war. Often enough, at the executive levels, abrupt changes and modifications had to be accepted blindly, since in time of war considerations of policy and strategy tend to mould action for reasons that remain obscure to those who have to implement them. This is well brought out in the Works History of the Air Ministry from which we quote:

The history of the Directorate for the period 1939–45 is essentially a record of continuous and high-pressure effort to meet demands which were not only formidable enough in original scope and programme but which in most cases, owing to constantly changing requirements dictated by the war situation and major policy, became in difficulty and intensity aggravated many times over. It is not a history of a period of outstanding developments in design or methods of construction. It records a period in which the romance of building was lacking, when for the science of building there was substituted the organisation necessary to produce drawings in their daily thousands, for procuring the corresponding quantities of material and huts and for erecting them where they were wanted. The creative interest of buildings existed only in the constant endeavour to provide great areas of accommodation in all its varying forms by the dates on which it was required.

Design branches, in their methods, became planning factories in which the members of the professional staffs became individual designing machines for the production of drawings, but it was rare for the machine to run uninterrupted through any one job, as changes of function, new requirements, alterations in establishment and methods of construction repeatedly upset the flow of production and intensified the effort to complete in time.

In retrospect, reason and justification can be seen, within the overall plan, in all the imperative demands for more and more accommodation and in all the many alterations made in respect of it, but, at the time of production, they represented to the staff in the drawing offices and on the sites, almost a nightmare of ever-increasing effort in which, in the absence of knowledge of purpose and strategy and controlled by the overriding factor of time, stations and persons lost all individuality in the one enveloping service.

In the pages that follow it will be seen that the main administrative problems of the building programme tend to group themselves around the struggle for manpower; and it is appropriate that we should see how that struggle presented itself, at the highest level and in terms of the first strategic urgency, at the height of the war.

In the troubled summer of 1941 the Secretary of State for Air, Sir Archibald Sinclair, had warned the Production Executive that unless in the near future his department's building labour quotas were substantially increased, airfield defence works would fall short of the scale recommended by the Chiefs of Staff. It followed that they would not get the urgently needed extensions to runways to enable heavy bombers to operate against Germany, that difficulties in operating night fighters would be increased, that training would be retarded —in short, that the operational efficiency of the Royal Air Force during the coming winter would be dangerously reduced. At that time, according to the Ministry of Labour's allocation figure, the Air Ministry's quota had already been increased from 87,000 to 92,000, and the number of men actually at the Ministry's disposal

U

was about 99,000, but there was disagreement with the Ministry of Labour and the Ministry of Works as to whether all those should count against the quota. For all their urgent works, the Air Ministry claimed, including the defence works specially recommended by the Chiefs of Staff, they really needed 129,000 men; and they asked that their labour quota should be increased from 87,000 to 110,000, with an additional special force of at least 4,500 men for the preparation of defences on high-priority airfields.[1]

The Ministry of Labour and the Ministry of Works, on the other hand, took the view that, since the Air Ministry's allocation had been fixed before the Essential Work Order and Payment by Results had been introduced, the allocation should be equivalent in output to a much greater allocation if works were scheduled and the system of payment by results rigorously applied. The Production Executive were reminded that the allocations had in fact only been agreed to on the understanding that payment by results would be introduced on all scheduled works. But Air Ministry contractors, it was reported, were not applying this system as freely as was desired, while many who held contracts on a 'time and line' basis were not releasing men as jobs neared completion but were holding them in the hope of carrying them on to other jobs.[2] More labour could only be allocated at the expense of other departments, some of which had not yet got their allocations.[3] If contractors did not retain their men unjustifiably, it was argued, the Air Ministry should be able to achieve a turnover of perhaps as much as 10,000, and by that means most of the important works could be brought up to schedule in two months' time. The 4,500 men specially asked for were already within the Air Ministry quota.

In view of the Prime Minister's Personal Minute of 26th August,[4] which also came before the meeting of the Production Executive on 2nd September, the Air Ministry's claim for an increased allocation was referred back for review in a general examination of building-programme labour. It was now necessary to get a firm decision on a matter of highest policy touching the proposed programme not only of the Air Ministry but of the Ministry of Aircraft Production. In applying the allocation system the Ministry of Works could rightly insist that departments should recognise that, even within their allocation, they could not disregard the labour capacity of the different areas. That indeed was the final factor: it was not possible rapidly to

---

[1] Many airfields were at least twenty per cent. behind their time schedule. It took seven months from the beginning of construction, with 800 men continuously employed on the work, for an airfield to be brought into use.

[2] 'Actually no contracts were let by the Air Ministry on a pure "time and line" or "cost plus" basis. All such contracts were let on a "target cost" basis.' (Air Ministry Note.)

[3] Thus, the War Office at this time were twenty-five per cent. below their allocation.

[4] See Chapter IV.

build up a large labour force in any region which could not provide the bulk of the labour from within itself. The fact that labour was not fluid, and the difficulties inherent in billets, hostels and transport, all had a major influence. But in framing their programmes departments tended to forget or disregard these points.

The problem could be seen in its most acute form in two of the regions in the autumn of 1941—the North Midland and the Eastern.

NORTH MIDLAND REGION

The North Midland region[1] was on the whole not heavily populated. The estimated building and civil engineering labour force was 58,500 of which about 37,600 were engaged on new works at 1st October. A few more thousands could possibly have been secured from the maintenance balance of 20,900, and it was also assumed that there could be, over a few months, an increase by importation from neighbouring regions if the programme in those regions were restricted. These importations, allowing for all factors of mobility of labour, available billets, building of hostels and so forth, could hardly have been more than 2,000 or 3,000 a month. On the other hand, the reduction in the building labour force coming into effect from 1st January was to involve a cut of 8,500. The position then was that on or soon after 1st January there would be not more than 53,000 and that this force might build up 3,000 a month.

In October 1941 the Ministry of Aircraft Production's labour force in the North Midland region was 615 and their immediate outstanding demand appeared to be about thirty. Their projected programme showed a peak demand of 23,500.[2] In no possible way short of complete conscription and universal evacuation to provide billets, or the total stoppage of all other work, could such a force be provided.

But, in addition, the Air Ministry's programme in the same region in April would have needed about 28,000 men for new airfields, apart from those engaged on existing Air Ministry contracts at that time still to be finished (8,500). Thus the combined labour force needed by the Ministry of Aircraft Production and the Air Ministry in March 1942 would, according to their programmes, have been about 60,000. The total required at the same time to cover Ministry of Aircraft Production, Air Ministry, all other departments and maintenance would have been nearly 100,000; but the utmost that it would have been possible to secure, according to Ministry of Works estimates, was 65,000.

---

[1] Derby, Leicester, Lincolnshire, Northamptonshire, Nottinghamshire, Rutland.

[2] On paper, M.A.P. should have had a demand in October 1941 for about 8,000 labour, but in fact there was no real demand outstanding at all, since the new programme had not yet been sanctioned nor had it been decided where the numerous factory extensions and new factories would go. Moreover, the construction labour force could only have been built up over some months. See Chapter XIV.

EASTERN REGION

The broad picture in the Eastern Region[1] was much the same. The existing regional labour force was 53,000, of which about 22,000 were employed on Government new works. The labour cut was to reduce the total labour force to 35,000 by October 1942.

The existing Air Ministry labour force was	15,000
Labour on existing works should by March 1942 have fallen to	9,000
New programme indicated a further demand then of	11,500
Making a total demand in March of	20,500
and by June of	25,500

The new Ministry of Aircraft Production programme showed a peak of 10,500 in the summer of 1942 compared with the existing labour force of 1,450.

If the projected new building programmes of the two Ministries were beyond any possible labour capacity within the time schedules, where did the solution lie? When Mr. Churchill called on Lord Reith for a report on the situation in the North Midland and Eastern Regions, the Minister of Works stressed that departmental programmes must be framed regionally according to labour facts. A direction, he suggested, somewhat as follows was required:[2]

For the North Midland Region:

1. Super-priority to either the Ministry of Aircraft Production or the Air Ministry, since both could not build as proposed.

2. If the super-priority were given to the Ministry of Aircraft Production then its programme would have to be cut by one-third.

3. The building of eighteen airfields to be spread over a longer period and practically none to start until March.

4. A virtual embargo on the new works of other departments.

5. Deferment of calling-up, together with regularised transfer with the Region.

For the Eastern Region:

1. Super-priority for the Air Ministry and sixty per cent. of available labour.

2. The programme to be cut by one-third or spread over fifteen months.

3. An initial embargo on new works of other departments for four to six months.

---

[1] Bedfordshire, Cambridge, Essex, Hertfordshire, Huntingdonshire, Norfolk, Suffolk.

[2] This was by way of example only, as the strategic knowledge on which it must be based (affecting the departments) was not yet available.

(iv)
An Intractable Labour Situation

Despite these suggestions the labour situation continued during the succeeding months to be confused and intractable.[1] Tension between the respective Ministries increased, and with the increasing tension came a marked degree of bitterness. On 24th February 1942 the Secretary of State for Air (Sir Archibald Sinclair) restated his urgent needs in a minute to Mr. Bevin. He reminded Mr. Bevin that Lord Reith had recently informed the Minister of Production that in order to meet Air Ministry requirements in the eastern counties a labour force of between 15,000 and 20,000 would have to be transferred, since the labour force in that area was insufficient. He had added that the transfer could be carried out slowly—which meant, however, that the Air Ministry programme would be set back by two or three months and that the airfields would not be completed during the summer of 1942.

Sir Archibald Sinclair, while noting that the transfer of labour had been accepted as a necessity, declined to agree to a slow-working scheme which would delay progress on the airfields in question. In order to complete the new bomber airfields in the Eastern and North Midland Regions he needed an addition to the labour in each of those regions of 10,000 men by the end of March.[2] The requirements in bomber operational airfields (which comprised practically the whole of the requirements in those areas) could not be reduced if they were to have facilities for the expanding bomber force ready by the time new units were formed. The retardation of aircraft deliveries would not alter the ultimate requirements but, if it were on a large scale, would enable some delay to be accepted.[3] Sir Archibald referred also to the need of a 'mobile labour force'.

> The Air Ministry, together with other departments, accepted the labour allocation system on the understanding that a mobile labour force was an integral part of the system, which indeed is not workable without it. The aim was to have a mobile force of 100,000, but a force of even 50,000 was regarded in April last by the Ministry of Works as virtually a complete solution of all difficulties. Both the Ministry of Labour and the Ministry of Works have expressed themselves as being in favour of a mobile labour force, but we have never seen even its beginnings.

---

[1] In a letter to the Minister of Aircraft Production (Lieutenant-Colonel J. C. T. Moore-Brabazon) on 10th December, Lord Reith speaks of the insoluble problems of the programmes of the Ministry of Aircraft Production and the Air Ministry.

[2] These figures took into account 13,000 men who could be released progressively from works which were then nearing completion.

[3] There was, however, no evidence of retardation on such a scale at that time.

He demanded 'immediate steps to be taken for the provision of an effective mobile labour force without which the labour allocation system would never have been acceptable'.

The reply from Mr. Bevin was terse and discouraging.[1] The men required for the Eastern Counties programme[2] were included, he wrote, in the Air Ministry's total allocation and must therefore be got by means of the release of men then employed by the Air Ministry elsewhere and their transfer (or an equivalent number of others) to the Eastern Counties. Officers of their two departments had worked out a detailed plan for the necessary releases showing totals of 3,848 in March, 7,561 in April and 8,821 in May.

> This was supposed to represent the sort of balance which your department thought right as between the new requirements and those now existing. If this is not right it is for you to say so.
>
> I do not understand that the question of what you describe as an effective mobile force really arises here. No doubt transfers would be easier if such a force were effectively in existence, but even so the men would have had to come out of your total allocation.
>
> I should add that your total allocation is at present 92,000. I understand that this total is to be subject to progressive reduction.

No reduction in the existing allocation of 92,000, however, was contemplated by the Air Ministry before mid-way in 1943 at the earliest. Meanwhile the expected transfers to the Eastern and North Midland Regions were hanging fire. Writing again on 31st March, Mr. Bevin said that reports from his regional officers showed completed transfers to East Anglia of under 200 men, and transfers in the immediate future of about 600 more.

> This is the measure, so far, of releases from Air Ministry contracts elsewhere.
>
> Your programme, as conveyed to my department, indicated releases during March of 3,800 men. I draw your attention to the discrepancy.

But the Air Ministry could not indicate enough redundant labour In May they were still over their allocation; and they had a very large number of new works for the start of which the Ministry of Works had to refuse approval, and which on that showing they would not be able to start for four months at the earliest. Apart from its preoccupation with other problems of its own programme, the Air Ministry had to take into account that the first contingent of the United States Army Air Force was expected to leave the United States from the middle of March onwards and would have to be accommodated at various

---

[1] Minute from Minister of Labour to Secretary of State for Air, 2nd March 1942.

[2] Presumably Mr. Bevin refers to both the Eastern and North Midland Regions under the term 'Eastern Counties'.

Royal Air Force stations in Great Britain and Northern Ireland. The Minister of Production had laid down that fresh building labour demands caused by the presence of the American Army were to be assessed and considered independently of existing building labour allocations. Accordingly, in addition to the representations made by Sir Archibald Sinclair to Mr. Bevin on labour needs in the Eastern and North Midland Regions, he asked, in a separate minute, for 5,000 men to be made available at once to meet initial requirements of the first eight stations which were to be occupied by units of the United States Army Air Force.[1] But the labour available for the building programme was already allocated, similar demands were being made by the War Office, and despite the Minister of Production's earlier ruling it was inevitable that the allocation position, indeed the building programme itself, should be reconsidered as a whole. At a meeting of the Contracts Allocation Sub-Committee on 31st March 1942, the chairman, Mr. Beaver, produced advance copies of a statement prepared for circulation to the Works and Buildings Priority Committee. This had been prepared in two sections, April to June and July to September respectively. On the basis of the information available the figure of 820,000 had been assumed as the total labour force. The garrison labour force shown was smaller than the number at that time engaged on that class of work and was to be achieved by squeezing out all mobile labour under forty-one years of age for the Services, other industries or W.B.A. jobs. The allocations themselves were shown in two parts—the number which could be guaranteed without reservation and an amount which would probably be available through a lag in the call-up and the fresh intakes into the industry. The Air Ministry's position was meanwhile eased by giving its demands a blanket super-preference, and an extra 3,000 was allocated to cover the American requirements. This made the Air Ministry allocation 95,000 from 1st April.

By December 1942 the Air Ministry pre-Bolero programme (that is, started before 1st June 1942) was reported to be eighty-two per cent. complete.[2] This programme as a whole had 69,500 men on it, but the labour force it employed was rapidly becoming available for the new Bolero programme, which already had some 44,500 men on it.

The value of work started on 1st December 1942 by the Air Ministry, using contractors and civilian labour, was £71,433,000.[3] By that

---

[1] These were all extensions to existing stations at: Grafton Underwood, Northants; Chelveston, Northants; Polebrook, Northants; Molesworth, Hunts; Podington, Beds; Kimbolton, Hunts; Little Stoughton, Beds; and Thurleigh, Beds.

[2] Bomber and bomber training stations, eighty-seven per cent. complete; bomber hardstandings, ninety-two per cent.; fighter stations, eighty-seven per cent.; miscellaneous operational, ninety-four per cent.; storage and maintenance, etc. (on which 35,000 men were employed under Command direction), seventy per cent.

[3] Excluding Northern Ireland.

date its labour force had risen to 118,000 and its estimated requirements were put at 190,000.

This massive programme must be viewed in the larger setting of the manpower cuts demanded by the War Cabinet. By the beginning of February 1943, the Minister of Production stated, there would be a shortage of 115,000 men in the building and constructional industries, and by March that figure was expected to increase by 20,000 to 25,000 men, consisting of the young mobile men called up. In these circumstances the War Cabinet decided that all new constructional work should be held up until the Minister of Production had reported on the building programme. Nevertheless, the Secretary of State for Air felt constrained to ask that an exception be made in regard to two airfield projects in Cornwall. The reasons he gave aptly illustrate the type of constructional problem that faced the Air Ministry and what strategic considerations hardened that department's doggedness in its demands for labour.

The two airfield projects were at St. Mawgan and Predannack, in Cornwall. That county, Sir Archibald Sinclair reminded Mr. Lyttelton, was of the first importance as a base for air operations. It gave aircraft the tactical advantage of maximum penetration not only into the Atlantic but against objectives in western and southern France; for similar reasons the area proved an ideal base for the dispatch and reception of aircraft to and from North Africa, while its flanking position enabled fighters based there to intercept enemy raiders operating in the south-western approaches and the Irish Sea, and to support offensive operations in the western approaches to the English Channel and in Brittany.

Because of offensive operations against submarines in the Bay of Biscay and the Atlantic, and the protection of convoys, as many as twelve squadrons of Coastal Command had to be concentrated in Cornwall. In normal circumstances five airfields would have been needed to accommodate this force, but only two were available at that time. Moreover, since the fall of France, Cornish airfields had been used for the dispatch of aircraft of the Royal Air Force to Gibraltar, Malta and the Middle East: the advent of American air forces in the United Kingdom and the acquisition of French North and West Africa had not only increased the commitment, but were bringing new arrivals from North Africa and from the United States by way of the South Atlantic under conditions which called for the full use of three airfields.[1] Finally, a minimum of four day and two night fighter squadrons was needed to undertake defensive and offensive operations from Cornwall. These squadrons would have to be reinforced, more-

---

[1] The aggregate arrivals and departures were now estimated to average 1,100 per month (that is, a crew and passenger personnel of over 5,000) and seemed likely to increase during 1943.

over, in the event of increased enemy air activity against this concentrated and vulnerable area. A minimum of three airfields was needed to accommodate both the static and the reinforcing squadrons.

To meet such varied and numerous commitments, eleven airfields would have been needed, but not more than six were in fact envisaged by the Air Ministry, since there was little likelihood of finding additional sites. Because every airfield had to be used to its utmost capacity it was imperative to develop St. Mawgan and Predannack airfields. The first was a new airfield in course of construction, the second was a station already in use to which important additions had to be made. The approval of the Building Directorate had been given to the construction of the runways at St. Mawgan but not for the buildings and services, nor for the additions at Predannack.

The operational argument was overwhelming. The Air Ministry was left free to make an immediate beginning with these works. 'But', added Mr. Lyttelton,

> this will not affect in any way my recommendation as to your building programme as a whole, and your total labour strength, that I have put before the War Cabinet.
>
> If these two works are put in hand as urgently necessary, then with our existing limited resources, all the more other items in your programme will have to be stopped or slowed down to keep the programme as a whole within the necessary limits.

(v)

The Royal Air Force Expansion Programme for 1943

While these discussions had been going on, plans for a revised Royal Air Force expansion programme were being worked out. A new Ministry of Aircraft Production programme had long been awaited, and it was only when this was at last produced[1] that Sir Archibald Sinclair could put before the War Cabinet the details of the new programme. The constructional work needed to meet the expansion of the Royal Air Force in 1943 can be summarised in three classes:

1. New airfields.

2. Extensions of existing airfields.

3. Miscellaneous constructional work other than airfields.

Included in the above were various new projects for which approval had not yet been sought. The labour force asked for was:

---

[1] See Chapter XIV.

January to March	115,000
April	110,000
May to September	101,000
October to December	82,000

The reductions in April, May and October represented part of the labour which would become available from completed works, the remainder being transferred to other works.

New airfields. There were 106 airfields in various stages of construction and eight for which it was proposed to seek sanction of the Ministry of Works. Of the 106, twenty-four were being constructed by Royal Air Force, American and Irish labour, leaving a balance of eighty-two which were being constructed by civil labour, and on which 49,000 men were engaged.[1]

It was expected that there would be a paper surplus of six airfields in September 1943, twenty-two in December 1943, and two in March 1944. The surpluses accruing in September 1943 and March 1944 were regarded as too small to justify a reduction of the labour force, more especially since it was problematical whether the surpluses would in fact be realised. Nor was any allowance made in the calculation for unforeseen contingencies, set-backs in construction and unserviceableness through weather conditions.[2]

Extensions to existing airfields. The aggregate cost of this class of work was estimated at £36·6 millions and was allocated as follows:

	£
Extensions to C.C.R.C.s and O.T.U.s	27,000,000
	3,500,000
Fighter Command:	
Extensions mainly in respect of United States Army Air Force occupation	4,000,000
Coastal Command:	
Extensions mainly in connection with the provision of lengthened runways and the completion of accommodation up to two-squadron standard	2,000,000
Army Co-operation Command	50,000
Minor extensions	50,000

---

[1] Details of the eighty-two airfields were:

Category	Total number	More than 25 per cent. complete	Less than 25 per cent. complete
Bomber	57	28	29
Emergency runway . .	1	1	—
Fighter	5	3	2
Advanced landing grounds .	8	—	8
Coastal	5	5	—
Army Co-operation . .	1	1	—
Transport	2	2	—
Flying Training . . .	2	1	1
Ferry Command . .	1	—	1
	82	41	41

[2] In the early months of 1942, for example, the building programme was very seriously set back by weather conditions.

Miscellaneous requirements other than airfields. These works, on which 9,000 men were at that time employed, covered a variety of projects in non-operational commands. They comprised the provision of storage for bombs, petrol and equipment, and facilities for training and works. There were other miscellaneous services such as command, group and living headquarters and operation rooms; and, in addition, various new projects for which the approval of the Building Directorate had not yet been sought (such as additional storages needed by the expanding force) and others which arose out of special operational considerations (such as offensive operations against submarines, the protection of convoys, the dispatch of reinforcement aircraft to various theatres of war, and deliveries by air of aircraft from overseas). The cost of these projects was estimated at £12 millions.

In the view of the Air Ministry there was no doubt that, were the labour force to be reduced below Sir Archibald Sinclair's demands, the Ministry would fail to provide essential airfields, the extent of the failure being dependent on the extent of the cut made in the labour force. The Ministry's building programme in 1943, it was calculated, was to cost approximately £101 millions, and experience had shown that for a programme of £100 millions approximately 100,000 men had to be continuously employed for a period of one year. That figure represented the average labour force asked for during 1943. The Ministry of Production had however asked what would be the effect of a cut in the Ministry's labour force on the following lines:

January	110,000
February	100,000
March to August	90,000
September	85,000
October	80,000
November	75,000
December	70,000

The Air Ministry's reply was that, expressing the proposed reductions in terms of the reduced number of airfields that would be available, there would be in September a deficiency of eight airfields. Since it was imperative to provide for the expansion of the Royal Air Force squadrons the result would be that eight American groups —that is over 300 aircraft—due to arrive by that date, could not be accommodated.

The Minister of Production for his part was prepared to support the Air Ministry's programme of airfields and other works, but with a reservation as to the timing of the programme and provided the Minister of Defence was satisfied as to the need of the eight new airfields not yet begun.

The whole position had been discussed with the Minister of Works, Lord Portal, and Mr. Lyttelton had been advised that (*a*) if the Air Ministry's labour force were to be cut to 90,000 by the end of March, as already proposed, continued at that level to the end of August, falling to 70,000 at the end of the year, and maintained at 50,000 for the first three months of 1944; and (*b*) if the whole programme were to be undertaken, including the eight airfields not yet begun—then one could count on all the work being finished by the end of March 1944. On the other hand, if they did not have to provide the eight new airfields not yet begun, then such a reduced labour force should finish the bulk of the work by the end of December.

As to the bomber airfields—a very large part of the work in hand— the Air Ministry's own figures showed that if all were completed by the end of December 1943 there would still be a surplus of twenty-two airfields over requirements, a surplus for which, in the existing circumstances, the Minister of Production could hardly be expected to budget. Moreover, despite very bad weather in the first three months of 1942, the Air Ministry had carried out £14·7 millions worth of work with a labour force of about 94,000 men. On that reckoning it seemed reasonable to aim at getting the runways finished by the end of the year, but to leave some of the remaining work on some of the airfields to be completed in the following months.

The Air Ministry insisted, however, that there was no work which could be postponed or slowed down if the programme were to be completed by December. Although the shortage had previously been expressed for convenience in terms of bomber airfields, the other work was equally urgent—for example, to meet the requirements of Fighter and Coastal Commands. There was not enough labour to bridge the gap between what the Minister of Production offered and what the Air Ministry required; and, as Sir Archibald Sinclair put it, the issue was

> whether it is reasonable to gamble on the possibility of a substantial amount of work being completed in the first three months of 1944. In my view it is not and I am supported in this by the experience of last year.
>
> So far from our completing £14·7 millions worth of work in January to March 1942, the amount of work done was practically negligible. It appears that Portal is referring to the cash payments which were made in this period. These payments, however, afford no indication of the amount of work carried out as about two-thirds represent supplies, and the balance was for wages which had to be paid under the Essential Work Order whether work was done or not.

The Air Ministry's claims were indeed overwhelming. On 11th February Mr. Lyttelton, writing to the Minister of Labour, Mr. Bevin, admitted that on a most careful scrutiny of the Air Ministry's plans he could not maintain his criticisms of their programme and the consequent labour requirements for February and March. He had in particular been unable to press the suggestion that any work in hand should be stopped. Nor could he himself recommend any modification in other parts of the building programme. If the Air Ministry labour force were to remain at 115,000 until the end of March, then on the figure which he and Mr. Bevin had agreed for inclusion in Mr. Lyttelton's last report to the War Cabinet they would be overdrawn by the end of March by more than 20,000. It followed that the War Cabinet might have to consider some change in the call-up policy if it were to meet so large an overdraft on man-power and yet keep the Air Ministry labour force up to 115,000 men. These requirements included labour[1] for the eight new airfields not yet authorised. If these were found to be essential on operational grounds and were to be built by civilian labour, then some modification of the call-up would have to be made.

When, on 21st April, the Minister of Production was asked by the War Cabinet to make proposals for the allocation of building labour for the six months April to September 1943, the Air Ministry's requirements remained as given to him in January. These were apparently based on an estimate of normal progress to be made during the remaining winter months. In fact, owing to the exceptionally mild weather, there had been an increased output per man in the first three months of 1943 of at least twenty per cent. as compared with the corresponding period of 1942. Mr. Lyttelton could now suggest that if the equivalent of 80,000 to 100,000 man-months had been gained in the first three months of the year, that would be no more than offset by a reduction of 10,000 men in the labour force for the six months April to September, allowing for the difference in value between winter and summer man-months. His proposed reductions of the Air Ministry allocation were therefore:

	Requirement stated	*Pro-rata reduction*	Allocation proposed
	(A)	(B)	(C)
30th April . .	110	*104·8*	104·5
31st May . .	101	*90·9*	92
30th June . .	101	*83·7*	81
31st July . .	101	*81·8*	80
31st August . .	101	*85·1*	80
30th September .	101	*87·5*	80

Mr. Lyttelton once more insisted that, in existing circumstances, they could not afford to plan completion dates on the assumption

[1] April, 2,000; May, 5,000; June to October, 10,000; November, 8,000; December, 7,000.

that the following winter would be a thoroughly bad building season.

> I appreciate the need for providing airfields for British and United
> States squadrons as they become available, and understand that in
> some respects there is reason to state requirements at the relevant
> dates somewhat higher than they were but a short time ago; but if
> some risk must be run in this, as in other fields, it must be borne in
> mind that airfields can be used in an emergency when runways, etc.,
> have been constructed, even if all buildings, etc., are not complete.[1]

Actually the labour force on the Air Ministry programme for April
and May was maintained at, or slightly above, the figures proposed
by the Air Ministry—that is, 110,000 and 101,000 respectively; and
by the end of May it became clear that the proposed allocation for
the remaining months, as shown in column (C) above, would be inadequate for efficient working. The Minister of Production was prepared to agree to 95,000 for June and 85,000 for July, leaving the
allocation for August and September at 80,000.

The effect of this proposal, as stated by the Secretary of State for
Air, would be to delay the provision of accommodation for some fifty
Royal Air Force groups, together with essential projects in Fighter,
Coastal, Flying Training, Transport and Maintenance Commands
(all of which were to be ready during the month of September) by
three or four weeks as compared with two months under the previous
allocation (column (C) above). A large number of projects due for
completion after September could be similarly treated.[2] Although
the revised figures thus offered an improved prospect, the Secretary
of State for Air remained unable for his part to accept the grave
consequences, more especially to the Anglo-American bomber offensive, that he foresaw; and he feared that failure to provide accommodation for the American formations might well result in the
transfer of these forces to the Pacific. Alternatively, if the American
programme of arrivals were adhered to and accommodation provided
for them at the required dates, the expansion of the Royal Air Force
would be still further impeded.

> The result would be that the increased American day bombing effort
> would be achieved at the expense of our own British night bombing
> offensive, and an increased number of British aircraft with trained
> crews would remain idle and unused.

But even if the call-up were modified to the greatest possible extent, the Air Ministry labour force could not be maintained at more
than 95,000 from the end of June onwards (80,000 plus 15,000). The

---

[1] Runways, perimeter tracks and hardstandings represent a little over fifty per cent.
of the total cost of airfields.

[2] This calculation took no account of difficulties in moving labour to the required
places (which had already delayed the programme) nor of other set-backs in construction,
which experience had shown almost inevitably occurred.

question for the War Cabinet's decision was, therefore, whether the Air Ministry construction programme should be delayed for a few months or whether they were to mitigate this delay by deferring the call-up of 15,000 men to the forces.[1] They chose the second alternative.

(vi)

Effect of American Labour Demands

While Sir Archibald Sinclair, despite the concession already made, continued to press for additional labour, the Americans themselves had not been behindhand in asking for British personnel. At the end of April 1943 the United States forces in the United Kingdom were employing directly some 76,000 British personnel, composed as follows:

British military labour . .	4,000
British civilian labour:	
Construction . . .	59,500
Supply installations . .	4,500
Administrative and clerical .	8,000

In addition to the above, all United States cargo was unloaded from ships by British dock labour.

In order to accomplish the constructional programme needed for the support of air and ground operations in Western Europe, and also in order to receive the supplies for the American forces, the following additional labour was demanded:

		Cumulative total
15th May	10,000	10,000
1st June	15,000	25,000
15th June	20,000	45,000
1st July	20,000	65,000
15th July	6,400	71,400[2]

On 28th April 1943, Lieutenant-General F. M. Andrews, of the United States Army, addressing himself to Lieutenant-General Sir H. L. Ismay,[3] wrote:

---

[1] The greater part of the call-up from the building industry to the Services for the six months April to September was due to fall in the months of April, May and June, and the maximum number that could now be deferred for the benefit of the building industry was about 15,000 men, of whom 7,000 were due for call-up in the second half of June and the remainder in the following three months. If the labour force were to be left with some 15,000 additional men at the end of September, the Army and the Royal Air Force would have been short by substantially the whole of this amount.

[2] For Air Force construction, 35,000; for storage and ground force installations, 20,000; for supply handling, 16,400. In addition, dock workers were asked for to unload at least seventy ships in July and ninety-five in August.

[3] General Ismay was Deputy Secretary (Military) to the War Cabinet, but the matter was outside the province of the Chiefs of Staff and was referred to the Minister of Production.

I propose as a solution to this serious situation that the British Government adopt a policy by which no British personnel, military or civilian, will be withdrawn from present employment with the United States forces during this present emergency. Furthermore, I request that the necessary steps be taken to make available at the various construction projects, and at supply installations, the additional 71,400 labour required, in place of the United States administrative troops which otherwise would have to be brought from the United States between now and the middle of the summer.

During the succeeding months the American demands became a subject of disagreement. At the War Office the Quartermaster-General's view was that the American demand for 71,400 labour was based on a force of 885,000 (including 250,000 Air Force) by 31st December 1943. The Americans knew that the War Office were planning for 600,000 by the end of 1943, and the labour they now demanded was the number needed to accelerate from one programme to the other, more especially because they expected stores ships to arrive at the rate of over 100 a month as from the beginning of August. As to the 35,000 men needed for Air Force construction, it was clear that 17,000 were included in the labour requirements already submitted by the Air Ministry to the Minister of Production and it was urged that the remaining 18,000 should be found from American engineer units so as to 'ensure a proper proportion between their combat troops and those required to support and maintain them'.

The various conferences and discussions produced no real clarification of American needs. The Ministry of Works declined to receive second-hand information of United States Army demands from the War Office and the Air Ministry, and maintained that they would never be in a position to make a report to the Minister of Production unless it were agreed that they should themselves carry out an investigation of the Americans' true needs.

Meanwhile clarification was being sought by the Minister of Production in consultation with the Harriman Mission in London. Writing to Mr. Lyttelton on 2nd July 1943, Mr. Averell Harriman said the Americans were distressed at the unfavourable prospect of the allocation of additional British labour for construction projects of the American forces. A new and completely detailed memorandum accompanied his letter setting forth item by item the 'must' projects and required completion dates

which are additional to those your Government has already assumed responsibility for and which cannot be handled by United States troops labour now in this theatre or scheduled to arrive here in the near future. . . . I recognise fully the very difficult situation that confronts you, but I cannot express too strongly my feeling that there must be a solution which will provide for the completion of these projects which are so essential to our common interests.

Mr. Harriman added that he had advised Lord Portal that this memorandum was being sent to Mr. Lyttelton and that Lord Portal had agreed to undertake a prompt analysis of it. The American General Moore and his staff would be glad to sit down with representatives of the Ministry of Works to give them whatever detailed information they wished.

A week later the building programme came under discussion at a meeting of the War Cabinet. It was then asked whether the dilemma could be overcome by bringing over additional United States construction companies at an earlier date; but it was reported that the United States authorities doubted whether they could send over in the near future as many construction companies as they had originally undertaken to provide. Some members of the War Cabinet thought the United States demand unreasonable and urged that there was no obligation to comply with it.

The Prime Minister's view, however, was that they should at all events avoid taking away men from the airfields which were being constructed for the United States forces in East Anglia. To do so, he thought, would have an unfortunate effect. He asked that the Ministers concerned—the Minister of Production, the Minister of Labour and National Service, the Secretary of State for Air and the Minister of Works—should have an early meeting in order to determine how much labour was needed to meet the eventual American demand, and how the additional labour could best be found.

Mr. Churchill expected a final settlement to be reached on this matter, and on manpower allocation generally, at a meeting to be held early in the week following the War Cabinet meeting on 9th July. Five days later the Ministers named, as well as the Secretary of State for War, Sir James Grigg, met under the chairmanship of Mr. Lyttelton. It was then agreed that up to October the Air Ministry labour force was to be maintained at 100,000 in order to cover the additional United States requirements. The War Office were satisfied with a labour force of 35,000 if they had the use of whatever United States troop labour was at hand. After October, both Air Ministry and War Office would require troop labour.

The American authorities, now well aware how serious was the problem of British manpower, in July arranged for Colonel Roy Lord (Chief of Operations in the European Theatre of War, United States Army) to make a special journey to Washington. He was to see what could be done to increase the United States troop labour force in England and to speed up the arrival dates of those already earmarked. The visit had its effect. Three additional general service regiments,

W

each of 1,250 men, were to arrive in England in October, and it was arranged that four more general service regiments should be made ready during that month. Under these arrangements the total United States general service regiments to be used for work on ground force and storage construction projects in the United Kingdom was increased to eighteen.

Other increases in United States construction labour, arranged for by Colonel Lord or already at work in the United Kingdom, included twenty-four engineer aviation battalions, each of 800 men, to be ready by October. The net effect of the acceleration of these battalions was roughly the equivalent of an additional thirty days' work from approximately ten battalions.

Writing to Mr. Lyttelton on 20th September 1943, Mr. Philip Reed, Deputy Chief of the Harriman Mission in London, said that these increases were the best that could be done.

> I mention this so that you will understand that the Army fully appreciates the seriousness of the construction labour shortage in this country and has used its best endeavours to reduce its demands upon you.

In the meantime, however, the situation appeared to have grown worse rather than better. The United States Army had undertaken more work than had been contemplated in July. One urgent need was the expansion of the depot programme, which was badly behind schedule; another was 'winterised' tented accommodation for which the War Office could not accept responsibility. Moreover, new undertakings would soon be required in preparing for the invasion of Europe,[1] and the Eighth Air Force had recently put forward a greatly expanded programme, which was now before the Air Ministry and in the detailed planning stage. These expansions at practically all stations, including as they did both housing and storage, threatened to be a heavy burden to the Americans as much as to the Air Ministry.

In the view of the American authorities, the increased demands (largely the result of the Washington and Quebec Conferences) could not possibly be completed in the time given unless the existing labour force, both United States and British, were maintained through January 1944. It was even suggested that if the expanded Eighth Force programme were to be met, an increase rather than a decrease in the British civilian labour force would be needed.

> You will agree, wrote Mr. Reed, that this is not an encouraging outlook and I need not tell you that I appreciate the difficulties on your side. Assuming, however, as I think we must assume, that these projects are essential to mounting the military operations which the

---

[1] See Chapters XI and XII. These included assembly areas near the coast, access to embarkation points, advance depots and hards at embarkation points.

Chiefs of Staff of our respective Governments have decided upon, I am sure you will agree that a way must be found to get this work done. From the information before me I must conclude that if the British construction labour force is reduced in October, as planned, the programme cannot be completed on time.

More than a fortnight earlier, General Marshall, at that time United States Chief of Staff, had made a direct appeal to Mr. Churchill. In a memorandum, dated 4th September 1943, he had requested on behalf of Lieutenant-General Devers, the American Officer Commanding in the European Theatre of War, the deferment of the call-up of skilled and unskilled labour usefully engaged on United States projects for which troop labour would have to be substituted.

I know (wrote General Marshall) the labour situation is extremely difficult in England, but I hope that you will be able to continue your assistance until the mounting numbers of American Service troops will make it possible for us to replace the troops diverted to the Mediterranean and to fully discharge our responsibilities. To do otherwise might seriously affect the preparations for Overlord.

It was not until 14th October that it became possible to arrange for a special meeting of the Bolero Combined Committee to discuss the problems touched on in General Marshall's letter. At this meeting it was reported that, after examination by officers of the United States Services of Supply and the Air Ministry Works Directorate, the American figures put forward on behalf of Lieutenant-General Devers had been modified. Agreement was reached on the demand for civilian labour; it came within four per cent. of the total man-months in question. The demand was calculated on the basis of the latest American phased construction programme, dated 9th October, which interpreted month by month the labour needs of the programme originally supplied to the Air Ministry.[1]

The United States figures must be compared with the *gross* Air Ministry commitments which did not form part of the construction programme as submitted to the Minister of Production. These comprised maintenance; the surfacing of runways; specialist British labour on American-built stations;[2] Northern Ireland, which lay outside the scope of the labour allocation system; and troop carrier stations on temporary loan to the Americans from No. 7 Group.[3]

---

[1] See table on p. 310, 'Labour Interpretation of the United States Eighth Air Force Construction Programme of 1st August 1943'.

[2] Mechanical, electrical, heating and ventilating tradesmen not covered by the building and civil engineering industry and therefore not returnable against the Air Ministry labour quota.

[3] The labour employed on these stations was already charged against the Air Ministry 'ceiling' as a British requirement. Previously and eventually these stations were required for the British bomber force.

The figures given in the second line of the table for the Air Ministry programme were therefore the Air Ministry Bolero requirements already put forward to the Minister of Production. These were included in the total Air Ministry building labour demands—that is, 100,000 men for October, 90,000 men for November, and 80,000 men for December.

The Air Ministry pointed out that there was a difference in the phasing between the United States and Air Ministry programmes. That arose from the attempt under the Air Ministry programme to increase construction in the current quarter so as to allow for the adverse effects of the weather in the period January to March. If, however, the additional 5,000 men postulated for October were not forthcoming, the British programme would inevitably have more nearly resembled the United States phasing and the risk of delay in completion would have been increased.

With exceptions in individual cases, no labour difficulties now stood in the way of the timely completion of the Air Ministry programme for the American forces.

(vii)
Checking the Programme

Subsequent building programmes of the Air Ministry were more easily prepared as the 'ceiling allocation' system, recently introduced, came to be applied to the demands of all building departments. Labour became one of the conditioning factors in the planning of the Air Ministry's works programme, and indeed it can be said that henceforth labour dictated the Ministry's planning to no small extent. The preparation of the detailed programmes served another and important purpose—they could be used as a basis on which actual progress could be compared and plotted. The shortcomings of contractors, as well as serious deviations from planning through other causes, were now clearly shown, and it became possible to apply a rapid and over-all check on progress for each job, as well as to check actual with programmed labour for the programme as a whole.

An over-all picture of the financial and labour state of the programme was presented to the Director-General each month by means of a financial and labour statement. This was calculated on the financial side not from the normal records of money disbursed but from a computation based on physical progress and of the value of work executed to date. The labour employed was obtained from labour returns submitted in the normal way for labour progressing and recording. While a vast amount of calculation and preparation went into these monthly statements, they were invaluable in giving a complete progress picture of the programme as a whole, and the preparation readily revealed any particular anomaly in progress or labour usage which could immediately be followed up. A complete statistical history of the departments' work could be obtained by examining these monthly returns over any desired period.

Labour Interpretation of the U.S. Eighth Air Force Construction Programme of 1st August 1943

	1943					1944						Total man-months from Aug.	Total man-months from Oct.
	Aug.	Sept.	Oct.	Nov.	Dec.	Jan.	Feb.	March	April	May	June		
Labour force required U.S. Programme	36,578	40,490	41,948	46,343	44,144	35,910	28,678	23,407	18,651	14,001	10,822	340,972	263,904
Air Ministry Programme	33,492	34,401	39,234	38,110	35,163	27,859	15,076	-7,925	3,350	653	1,650	236,913	169,020
*Add:**													
Maintenance			375	675	1,800	3,000	4,725	6,300	7,525	7,875	8,475	40,750	40,750
Surfacing runways		463	463	800	800	800	137					3,463	3,000
Non-building and civil engineering on U.S.-built stations	500	655	655	655	700	500	300	300	200	100		4,565	3,410
Northern Ireland	1,622	2,177	2,177	2,466	2,731	2,341	1,858	1,400	1,400	1,000	490	19,662	15,863
Extension No. 7 Group stations (troop carriers)	1,659	2,185	3,385	3,714	3,822	3,179	2,237	1,934	1,400	700	329	24,544	20,700
TOTAL = Air Ministry gross	37,253	39,881	46,289	46,420	45,016	37,679	24,333	17,859	13,875	10,328	10,944	329,997	252,743

* These items are excluded from the Air Ministry figures for the reasons given on pp. 307, 308.

CHAPTER XIV

THE BUILDING PROGRAMME
OF THE MINISTRY
OF AIRCRAFT PRODUCTION

(i)

Introductory

EARLY in 1943 the functions of the Directorate-General of Air-craft Production Factories were transferred from the Ministry of Aircraft Production to the Ministry of Works. The change was made on the proposal of the Minister of Works, Lord Portal, who urged that it had been the Prime Minister's intention from the first that a single Ministry should be responsible for all building schemes and that it was desirable to bring the Ministry of Aircraft Production into this arrangement. Although the transfer of the Directorate to the Ministry of Works was an important step in implementing the principle of placing all responsibility for building work in the hands of a single department of State, it had little practical influence upon the construction of aircraft factories, since it came at a time when the Directorate was already solidly established. The effects of the transfer will be considered later.[1] Meanwhile we must examine the stages by which the construction of aircraft factories reached maturity and describe some of the main problems that had to be solved in the process.[2]

In view of political developments in Europe, the Government had decided in 1936 upon a scheme of expansion in the aircraft industry. In addition to underwriting extensions at the parent firms, it initiated a scheme for the construction of nine new factories for the manufacture and assembly of aero engines, aircraft and associated equipment. The shadow factory plan, as it was called, was assisted from Government funds. In the rearmament years, and up to May 1940, the plan was carried out by the Air Ministry, and a small department, then known as the Directorate of Air Ministry Factories,[3] was gradually built up to take charge of the construction of buildings and the

---

[1] Section (vii) of this chapter.

[2] This chapter is based chiefly on studies that have been prepared for the War Production Series of the Civil Histories.

[3] See Section (vi) of this chapter.

provision of plant. In practically all new building construction, however, the responsibility was placed with the prospective operations company as agent. The company were given authority to place contracts and proceed with work within an approved sum of money to cover the estimated cost.

(ii)

The Scope of the Building Programme

Under the original Air Ministry 'shadow' factory plan seven factories were to be built. Two, which were to be managed by Messrs. Austins and Messrs. Rootes, were designed to build airframes; the other five (Daimler, Humber, Standard, Rover and Bristol) were to produce aero engines. These factories were all under construction by the spring of 1937. Two other shadow factories—H. M. Hobsons for the production of aero-engine carburettors, and de Havillands for the production of airscrews—began building during the year. There was comparatively little difference between this first batch of shadow factories and other factories, whether shadow or otherwise, built at the expense of the Air Ministry; in both the contracts were let by the agent or managing company. The main difference lay in the general planning policy. In the words of one report, the first shadow factories were concerned in making a specific contribution to the output of aircraft; the later factories or extensions were considered and approved *ad hoc* as the aircraft production programme was framed and, from time to time, modified. As a generalisation it would be true to say that the early shadow factories were planned before the aircraft programme to which they were to contribute; later factories were planned in accordance with the needs of a programme already laid down.

The construction of factories begun in the winter of 1939–40 was not completed until well into 1941, but by that time the foundation of war-time aircraft production had been laid down. That is not to say that the amount of building work decreased during 1940 and 1941, but throughout the critical months of 1940 and well into 1941 immediate production was more important than future plans, and it was then that the forward planning of 1936, 1937 and 1938 bore fruit.

The classification of the Ministry of Aircraft Production's constructional work from 1941 onwards comprised *inter alia* agency schemes for engine and propeller factories, schemes for armaments and instruments factories, as well as schemes for airframes, assembly and repair plant. Other agency schemes concerned factory airfields and landing grounds, civil buildings and railways and many miscellaneous undertakings. Between 1941 and 1943 the total value of these agency schemes was some £48,800,000. Direct works during the same period show a total of £23 millions.[1]

(iii)

Problems of Factory Construction 1936-1940

The direct entry of the Government into the sphere of factory provision from 1936 onwards gave rise to many new problems for the Air Ministry. These were especially evident in the construction of the shadow factories. Since some firms were responsible for shadow factories manufacturing their normal product, while others were not in the professional aircraft or aero engine industry at all, but were entering an unaccustomed field of production, it was only natural that difficulties should crop up in the placing and construction of extensions or new premises. Broadly, where the parent firm was manufacturing its normal product in a shadow factory, as when Rolls-Royce were making aero engines, the difficulties were not great; but where firms like Morris, Rootes or Austin stepped out of their normal sphere their lack of specific experience was apt to be reflected in spasmodic and uneconomic planning.

In general, indeed, the first Air Ministry shadow factories were planned with a lavishness which contrasts with the stringency that was to be the rule later. The organisation for the technical examination of projects started to be formed in the late autumn of 1938, that is eighteen months before the Ministry of Aircraft Production was formed. The Air Ministry itself, with the advent of accelerated expansion in 1938, took steps to set its house in order. It created special Capital Finance Divisions to watch the finance of expansion, and it set up a Directorate of Air Ministry Factories. Both these organisations grew in size as the work proceeded, and eventually reached large dimensions under the Ministry of Aircraft Production. Because, as we have seen, factories were planned and built more or less in accordance with the normal peace-time standards and requirements of the managing firms, divergencies in method and result were inescapable. Two contrasting projects of the shadow factory programme—the Castle Bromwich aeroplane factory and the Rolls-Royce aero engine factory at Hillington, near Glasgow, may be taken by way of illustration of the manner in which differing types of organisation influenced the efficient execution of building projects at this period;

---

[1] It is important to note that in this context agency schemes mean arrangements for the erection of new capacity through the agency of aircraft or other firms and not necessarily the administration by such a firm of capacity when created. See also Chapter XV.

nor must it be forgotten that in regard to other factories different circumstances gave rise to different problems.

In May 1938 the Secretary of State for Air had seen Lord Nuffield and initiated discussions for a proposed aircraft factory. It was then agreed that the Nuffield Organisation should undertake the production of the Spitfire on the basis of an order for 1,000, and in a new factory to be erected and owned by the Government and operated by the company on an agency basis.

The site chosen was in an area where labour was readily available. The Air Ministry authority for the construction of the new factory was given with very few restrictions upon the absolute discretion of the Nuffield Organisation, and the work was left largely with Mr. Boden, acting for Lord Nuffield. The firm were allowed to use their own building contractors and architects subject to the Air Ministry's approval of the estimates. The question of going to tender was left to the company.

The situation was complicated by the death of Mr. Boden, but even before this event it was clear that all was not well. A report made in October 1940[1] pointed out that the factory had been started without Mr. Boden being given specific instructions as to the manner in which it was to be designed. Contracts were entered into, the report stated, before the factory had been properly planned and before drawings of the various buildings and works could be produced.

To meet these conditions a schedule of items had been prepared which was to have formed the basis of quantities when these were made available, and five contractors were invited to price the schedule. The work was divided among a number of contractors; the main building was in the hands of one contractor, and such items as flight sheds and similar buildings were spread over the other contractors. The work was measured and brought to account as it proceeded, and these computations formed the basis of the certificates of payment on account periodically. It was stated that no fault could be found with the method adopted by the architect for dealing with accounts, but without a complete check of measurements and payments no opinion could be expressed on the question of the equity of the amounts paid.

There was no complaint about the quality of the work; on the contrary, it could only be criticised as too high for an emergency war production factory. The order of erecting buildings, however, was somewhat haphazard. Buildings erected for one purpose were ultimately used for something else. There does not appear to have been general consultation all round nor was a clear policy defined. The result was that those who had to run the factory demanded

---

[1] The report was made by an independent architect in the employment of the London Passenger Transport Board.

alterations, and there was a general dissatisfaction with the architect.

The death of Mr. Boden left the control of the work and the intentions of those charged with it in considerable chaos. The building work gradually relapsed into semi-activity, and as the report points out, no fixed programme seemed to be available of what was wanted and when. In the words of an official report,

> even when allowance is made for the unfortunate effect of Mr. Boden's death, the history of the construction of Castle Bromwich must be considered as reflecting the least happy consequences of leaving control very largely in the hands of an agent firm.

No such unhappy consequences attended the application of the same policy at Hillington. If developments at Castle Bromwich were exceptional, and indeed untypical of most of the shadow factories, those at Hillington represented fairly well what might be taken as the normal procedure of the Air Ministry from mid-1938 onwards. On 16th May 1938 the firm first appeared before the Air Supply Committee, when the Air Ministry stated an additional requirement for 2,050 Merlin and 450 Vulture engines by the end of March 1940. The firm's existing orders in terms of Merlins were 2,185 by the end of 1939.

On 14th June 1938 the Air Ministry approved in principle the expenditure of £1 million on providing the nucleus of a shadow factory at Crewe. Later this figure was amended to £1,220,000 for extensions at Derby and Crewe.[1] By 9th August 1938 the Air Ministry agreed in principle to a further extension of the Crewe factory (second portion) within a maximum cost for building and plant of £732,500.

The speed with which the Rolls-Royce expansion at Crewe was carried out justified the confidence of the Air Ministry in the firm. Authority to proceed was given in June, building began on 4th July and production on 5th November 1938.

In the spring of 1939 it became clear that a further expansion would be needed to meet war potential requirements. It was proposed to increase the output of the Rolls-Royce aero engines by the erection of a factory in Glasgow. This proposal was referred to in a letter from the company dated 21st March 1939. The company reaffirmed that any further extension would have to be entirely financed by the Air Ministry.

Estimated requirements of war potential showed that as a first measure it would be necessary to provide another factory capable of producing 400 engines per month. It was proposed to erect this factory near Glasgow, at a probable cost of some £6 millions. After some hesitation, and proposals for meeting two-thirds of the full capa-

---

[1] Of this expenditure the civil engineering and building part was £372,000 at Crewe and £10,700 at Derby.

city which were later dropped, the firm were authorised in August 1939 to go ahead with the full scheme for providing 400 engines per month.

Descriptions of aircraft factory building schemes could be multiplied endlessly, but after allowing for exceptions and variations it can be said that factory construction broadly followed an approved pattern and sequence. That factories might have 'gone to ground' on any large scale was never seriously contemplated. In popular imagination the creation of underground factory capacity offered a radical and dramatic answer to the danger from air attack, but a general policy for underground factories would have been difficult to apply. To have placed any particular factory underground would almost certainly have brought claims from others for similar treatment; and, according to one estimate, to have moved all aircraft production underground would have cost some £250 millions, or one-twentieth of the national income. The diversion of national resources on such a scale was out of the question and, because of the potential effect which the adoption of only a very small number of such schemes might have had on general morale, approval could only be given on a highly selective basis.

The number of underground schemes remained small. In general, proposals originated with the firms themselves and were examined by the Ministry of Aircraft Production on their individual merits. The only exception to this otherwise haphazard state of affairs occurred after the severe enemy raiding which made dispersal from Coventry and special protection of certain plant a matter of extreme urgency. The Air Supply Board gave its approval to a suggestion that a tunnel should be built near Coventry to accommodate an aero-engine factory. This differed from all other proposals in that the site had not yet been found nor had it been decided to what firm the space should eventually be allocated.

The final total of underground schemes was only seven. Of this total, schemes adapted from existing underground structures amounted to approximately 2,862,600 square feet, while those of completely artificial construction amounted to 337,000 square feet. Apart from these schemes, some sites were used which were partly underground and gave lateral protection from blast splinters.

The outcome of four major schemes showed that in the main the Treasury's reluctance to proceed on a large scale with underground work was justified. All four took longer and cost considerably more than was at first estimated, and thus exceeded the cost of overhead factories of equal size. Nor did they justify the confident hopes of their promoters that the labour needed for their construction, which was of the unskilled or navvying type, would be easier to find than ordinary building labour. Labour supply remained throughout one of the chief stumbling blocks; but the four major schemes were diverse in scope, and each had also its own special difficulties. These cannot be examined here, but the experience of the largest scheme, described in the following paragraphs, will give a general indication of the problems to be solved.

Under the original plan the area to be used in this scheme was 2,200,000 square feet and the cost was estimated at £1,746,000 for the factory and £595,000 for the provision of hostels for 8,000 single workers (that is, at the rate of 15s. and £1 per square foot, which compared favourably with the cost of surface factories). It was thought that the work could be completed within nine months.

On 24th December 1940 the Air Supply Board approved the scheme in principle subject to Treasury sanction and to urgent investigation of priorities for labour and materials. Only the most vital Ministry of Aircraft Production work was to be placed there. Treasury approval was given on 6th January 1941 on the understanding that the work should be completed within the time stated. Responsibility for constructional work was to devolve on the Ministry of Works, and the Ministry of Aircraft Production was made responsible for finance. The main reason for this decision was that the Ministry of Aircraft Production had not the staff to carry out supervision, draw up plans, and so forth. Moreover, the Ministry of Works was already accustomed to this type of work, and already had similar schemes on hand in the neighbourhood for the Admiralty, the War Office and the Ministry of Supply. It was therefore in an admirable position for co-ordinating requirements, particularly of labour.

In the event both limits—of time and of expenditure—laid down by the Treasury had to be exceeded. Among the causes of delay were excavation difficulties, lack of vigour on the part of some departments or of co-ordination on the part of others, the shortage of labour, changes in production schemes, and the shifting war situation, which called for the frequent modification of the plans. Of these retarding influences, lack of co-ordination seems to have been one of the worst evils, at least in the early stages. There are recurring references in the records of failure on the part of the Ministry of Works, both to secure an adequate rate of progress and to keep the Ministry of Aircraft Production in touch with the position. There were even attempts by the Deputy Director of Aircraft Production Factories, who declared himself dissatisfied with the situation, to get responsibility for the building work transferred back to the Ministry of Aircraft Production, which was after all answerable to the Treasury for the cost and progress of the scheme.

The results of this divided responsibility are seen more clearly in its relation to finance. Whether blame could be attached to the management of the scheme or not, it is undoubtedly true that the shortage of labour remained at the root of the problem and, despite every effort by the Ministry of Aircraft Production to get additional labour in 1942, the labour force continued steadily to decrease.

One noteworthy factor in the cause of delay was change in user. Additional firms were brought in, and the use of the underground accommodation by four firms instead of one meant the need to provide more means of access, longer roads, bigger car parks, increased partitioning, and so forth. The additional numbers of workers meant more housing, more amenities, services, and special installations. Further, the increase in the number of users and the changes of authority unavoidably led to piecemeal and wasteful occupation. Such changes and the demand for additional services by firms continued well into 1944, and it seems impossible to say that, at any time in the war, work on the undertaking was completely finished.

All the factors that caused delay at the same time contributed to the steadily rising costs. These rose from an estimated £2,341,000 to some £11,800,000 by January 1944. Although some of this discrepancy can be traced to laxness of supervision, expenditure on hostels and married quarters (about £2,750,000), the provision of railways and services of all kinds, and adaptations of the structure which were never envisaged when the scheme was launched, all proved to be formidable items on the bill of costs. Development was finally estimated to have cost some £4½ millions; while labour costs, as a result of the Uniformity Agreement and Essential Work Orders, came to £1¾ millions more than had been allowed for.

(iv)

Dispersal of Aircraft Factories

During the early days of the Ministry of Aircraft Production one of the chief factors in slowing down the programme of new building work was the dispersal of aircraft factories as a means of security against German bombing.

The question of dispersal had been investigated in 1934 by an Air Ministry Committee, the Brigstocke Committee, which submitted a lengthy report in 1935. In effect the problem resolved itself first of all into finding ways for dispersing new factories, and secondly, for dispersing types of production as opposed to factories. These were really two aspects of one problem, since the dispersal of capacity generally involved the creation of new sources. But, although in the planning of new factories great weight was given to considerations of security, factories had obviously to be built in areas where suitable labour could be got. This meant in practice that large factories could be built only in or near large existing industrial centres. Shadow factories, moreover, had to be reasonably near their parent organisations so that senior members of the management could exercise a measure of supervision. In these circumstances it was not in general possible to do much more, in the preparations which were made in anticipation of German air attacks, than avoid the areas that seemed most dangerous.

The word 'dispersal', however, in the history of the Ministry of Aircraft Production took on a new meaning in the prodigious effort which the department put forward when the first attack was at its height. The early dispersals were *ad hoc* jobs handled by officers specially designated by Lord Beaverbrook in each particular instance. Shortly afterwards a special organisation was created to look after dispersals generally. The first head of this organisation, which came into being during the Battle of Britain, was Sir Charles Bruce-Gardner.

During the summer and autumn of 1940, a policy was formed of which the main feature was planned dispersal—that is to say, the dispersal of capacity made in anticipation of possible enemy action.[1] Underlying this policy was the decision that at every stage up to final assembly manufacture should proceed in at least three different places, so that no component would be entirely lacking if one or even two factories were knocked out. A review was made covering all the important Ministry of Aircraft Production contractors with a view to seeing where and how a suitable dispersal could be arranged. It was inevitable that any scheme, with its heavy drain on building labour and materials, to adapt existing premises should have had a profound effect upon the Ministry's policy for new building. The policy for extending capacity was in fact radically affected. Before 1940, the tendency had been to create new capacity in large units. This tendency was now changed, and policy swung in the direction of a large number of smaller units. The change had some advantages, even apart from providing security against bombing. The adaptation of existing premises was frequently more expedient, from the Ministry of Aircraft Production's point of view, than the building of wholly new premises, at least so far as concerned the use of building labour and materials. Much attention was given to the possibility of saving new building work by requisitioning and adapting existing scattered premises wherever these could be found. Very rarely was an existing building found to be suitable for the production for which it was now required without more or less extensive alterations.

Planned dispersals were not, of course, the only dispersals that took place. Each of the heavy enemy blows, when they succeeded, de-

---

[1] From May to October 1940 emergency dispersal was limited to the Five Types, that is, the aircraft that were most capable of averting defeat.

stroyed building work which had either to be made good on the same
site or replaced elsewhere.

While it is a difficult matter to form any exact idea of the effect
of German bombing upon the building programme of the Ministry
of Aircraft Production, undoubtedly heavy damage was done to
the main airframe and engine contractors during the late summer
and autumn of 1940. In October of that year, the Minister of Aircraft Production reported to the War Cabinet a number of 'major
disasters'. In this report Lord Beaverbrook, referring to the scheme
of dispersal, stated that it took the form of splitting up the
main factories in vulnerable areas into a number of separate
premises, geographically convenient to one another. He commented
that the system of dispersal damaged production, but improved the
prospect of security. By October, 364 new premises had been acquired
for airframe and engine production alone. In addition, instrument
production and radio manufacture had been partly dispersed. It was
not, Lord Beaverbrook said, intended to convey the impression that
the dispersal process had gone as far as might be necessary, although
the picture which he presented showed that a good deal had been
done. In fact many new schemes were in operation and others were
contemplated. The Minister warned the Cabinet that his department
was undertaking 'an immense expenditure' upon dispersal.

Lord Beaverbrook reported further on dispersal in December 1940,
when he said that the process was being conducted 'with energy and
on a very large scale'. One Vickers-Armstrong factory had been dispersed to twenty-four places, a Westland one to twenty-nine places,
a Supermarine to thirty-four places, and another Vickers-Armstrong
to thirty-seven places. Two-thirds of the Hurricane production was
moved out of its existing location into forty-eight separate factories.
Armstrong-Siddeley were to be dispersed to the extent of seventy-five
per cent. of the tools, from one to twelve centres. About half of
Rover's production was to be dispersed to six centres. The benefits of
distribution were very many; the danger of damage from bombs was
reduced and the working hours were increased.

Financial arrangements had been made to cover this policy. Compensation for premises that were requisitioned, and the cost of alterations to them, were paid for by the Treasury, subject to rental charges
against the firm. The removal cost was borne by the Ministry subject
to a contribution by the firm taking the form of paying for lifting and
setting down their own tools.

With the cessation of heavy air attacks in 1941, the dispersal policy
languished, and in the changed circumstances it was ruled by the
Prime Minister that no further voluntary dispersal should take place.
This ruling gave an impetus to a tendency, which had already become noticeable, whereby the dispersed factories were reoccupied

and the dispersal points often became invaluable additional accommodation.

The results of the dispersal policy were generally regarded with satisfaction by the department. It would, however, be impossible to make any clear or certain assessment of what these results were. It was noted that in the last heavy blitz on Birmingham the proportion of Ministry of Aircraft Production to Ministry of Supply damage was lower than it had been in the previous big raids on that city, and it was felt in the Ministry of Aircraft Production that this comparative immunity was due in part to the fact that Ministry of Aircraft Production had, in the interval between the raids, done a great deal of dispersal, while the Ministry of Supply in general had not. Moreover, once the dispersed factories had been filled up again, the department found itself with a considerable amount of new capacity which was by way of being a bonus.

(v)

The Problem of Priorities for Aircraft Factories

The creation of additional floor space for the aircraft industry was carried out for the most part on an *ad hoc* basis. For a time no other basis was practicable. From May to October 1940 there had been the emergency dispersal of capacity for the Five Types ; and then, until September 1941, the prolonged crisis of general dispersal. Thus, at the end of eighteen months of heroic effort the Ministry of Aircraft Production was presented with a picture bearing little relation to the kind of orderly and coherent programme of building that might have been devised in advance. A fresh effort was made, however, to see the picture broadly, and to allow for priorities as between building premises for the production of aircraft or premises for the production of light alloys for aircraft, and the demands of the United States Air Force. Moreover, as the overall planning of Britain's resources, especially in the period mid-1942 to mid-1943, began to reveal the limits of capacity, so more and more did these limiting factors compel the Ministry of Aircraft Production—as they did other departments—to weigh all their projects scrupulously one against the other.

Priority arrangements are described in other chapters of this volume.[1] In effect, as has been seen, competition of priority lists was in itself unsatisfactory. Efforts by the Ministry of Aircraft Production to meet the crisis were associated with a similar inter-departmental review. The Works and Buildings Priority Committee, as has already

---

[1] See especially Chapters IV, V and VI.

x

been noted,[1] had adopted three classifications: 'A' factories which were to have the highest priority and were to be accelerated by every means; 'Z' factories which could be slowed down and from which labour and materials could be diverted; and 'B' factories, that is all those between 'A' and 'Z' whose rate of construction would continue unchanged. Each Production Director in the Ministry of Aircraft Production was asked to submit lists of factories under those heads.

This attempt to work out a system of priorities proved unworkable, and in the Ministry of Aircraft Production, as in other departments, it was displaced by the introduction of the allocation system in the spring of 1941. Henceforward building programmes were to be controlled almost wholly by the one overriding factor—manpower.

For 1941 the Ministry of Aircraft Production was given eighty per cent. (45,000 men) of its demand. This was fifteen to sixteen per cent. of the total building labour of war production factories, and eight per cent. of the total building capacity of the country. Since the allocation, even if reasonable, fell short of requirements the problem was how to curtail the programme. It was done by arranging internal priority.[2] Yet the Ministry of Aircraft Production could not get even the allocation given it of 45,000 men. The figure for December dropped to 30,100 and the highest figures for any of the remaining months of the year was only 33,800 (for November). Since the Ministry of Aircraft Production was relatively much worse off for labour than some other departments, the allocation system, so far as the Ministry's own demands went, was never regarded as working satisfactorily.

By September 1941 the building situation in the country as a whole had become very serious, and although in 1942 the position of the Ministry of Aircraft Production appeared to improve (absolutely as well as relatively to other departments), it was really deteriorating in so far as the job to be done was increasing. In the troubled months of 1941–42 an additional problem was that of finding accommodation for building labour. The solution was to set up a special labour accommodation section in the Ministry—applying to housing, factory construction and similar contracts—to hold a pool of Nissen huts; and an initial expenditure of £135,000 for that purpose was approved by the Air Supply Board on 13th January. There were also welfare measures, such as special clothing, windscreens, the heating of camps and so

---

[1] Chapter IV.

[2] Priority I.   Factories of prime importance to be completed in the shortest possible time.

Priority II.   Factories which, though of great importance, must take second plate to I.

Priority III.   Schemes from which labour should not be drafted away.

Priority IV.   Schemes of lesser importance from which it might be necessary to draw labour to satisfy I and II.

Priority V.   Waiting list to be moved up into one of the higher priorities as vacancies occurred.

forth, which cost a further £117,000. It was laid down, as a measure of economy, that men who, under the Essential Work Orders, were guaranteed a minimum week's wage should not be laid off more frequently than was necessary. Of the total estimate of £6 millions, the buildings proper were to cost £1,365,000, light and power a further £270,000, while ancillary services, civil engineering works, etc., brought the estimates for buildings, apart from those for plant, to a total of £2 millions.

The general factors which in 1941 influenced the supply of labour continued to do so in 1942. The labour force rose from approximately 40,100 in January to a maximum of 54,400 in July.

In the late summer of 1942 the Ministry's efforts to obtain building labour reached a climax, with a concentration on the higher priority schemes at the expense of the smaller and lesser ones.

On 17th December 1942, as has already been related in an earlier chapter,[1] the War Cabinet asked the Minister of Production to arrange for an immediate review of all departmental building programmes. He was then to adjust the demand to the reduced labour force remaining after (as had already been decided) 225,000 men were withdrawn from the building industry during 1943.

The Minister of Aircraft Production met the Minister of Production and the Minister of Works on 22nd December. The Minister of Aircraft Production offered that, as urgent works were completed, the labour force at the disposal of his department should be progressively reduced, so that it should be twenty-five per cent. less by 1st July 1943 and fifty per cent. less by 3rd June 1944. The offer was accepted, and the reduction was carried out. As against 41,000 men in December 1942 the Ministry of Aircraft Production were employing 29,300 in July 1943 and 22,000 in January 1944. Thus, even if the reduction in a year was not a full fifty per cent., the reduction in six months had been greater than the planned twenty-five per cent.

(vi)

The Headquarter Organisation of the Ministry of Aircraft Production

When the Air Ministry embarked on the shadow factory programme, there was no special headquarter organisation to control this activity. The then existing Directorate of Works and Buildings was a technical directorate which employed architects, quantity surveyors and civil engineers. It was almost entirely concerned with

---

[1] Chapter V.

direct works, mostly airfields; that is, the directorate controlled building and civil engineering work by contractors directly employed without the intermediary of any agent company.

Between 1936 and 1938 an organisation developed gradually as requirements became evident. The scrutiny of an agent company's building proposals was undertaken jointly by the Production Directorate and the Directorates of Works and Buildings and of Finance. Control was very uneven. In some of the original shadow factories the process of technical examination was prompt and thorough; in others the company and its architects were given, more or less, a free hand—as, for example, in the Castle Bromwich factory. The machinery of control was certainly there, but its use was inadequate or faulty.

In November 1938 a Directorate of Air Ministry Factories was set up. The new directorate was responsible for the general supervision, without interference with management, of all Air Ministry factories and for the efficiency of their administration; it had, moreover, the duty of reporting on progress and on measures for improvement. The directorate's primary interest, however, was in existing factories, and the construction of new factories was only a secondary responsibility; yet it was with this secondary responsibility that, between 1938 and 1942, the directorate largely concerned itself. After hesitant beginnings the directorate had become, by the early months of 1939, the recognised adviser on the construction and equipment of factories. Building proposals—now rapidly increasing—were, as a matter of routine, referred for technical approval to the architects and quantity surveyors who formed its staff. The Directorate of Works, relieved of this function, was free to return to its own rapidly increasing duties. By the time war broke out the functions of the directorate foreshadowed its war-time role.

Between the outbreak of war and May 1940 the directorate consolidated its position. The supervision of existing factories was recognised to be a production function and remained with the Production Directorate; it dropped once for all out of the sphere of the Directorate of Air Ministry Factories even after its transfer to the Ministry of Aircraft Production in 1940. But the recognition of its growing responsibility was evident in the creation of a Directorate-General. In June 1940 Mr. Quartermaine, Chief Engineer of Great Western Railway, was appointed Director-General of Aircraft Production Factories—an appointment in which he was replaced, early in 1941, by Mr. Brian Colquhoun.[1] Further expansion and reorganisation now

---

[1] Mr. Colquhoun was a civil engineer of wide experience who had already acquired a knowledge of the Ministry's problems while on the Coventry Reconstruction Committee and in similar work in Birmingham, Southampton, Sheffield and Manchester. He had also been engaged on drawing up plans for the utilisation of Spring Quarry, Corsham, by the Bristol Aeroplane Company and had produced for Lord Beaverbrook a general report on the exploitation of underground production space.

took place. Lord Beaverbrook, the then Minister of Aircraft Production, realising that without factories there would be no aircraft, gave authority for the complete reorganisation of the Directorate-General. Apart from the examination and approval of agents' proposals in connection with new construction, which was increasingly required to be more detailed and also much more rapid, the work itself, it was realised, needed more active pressure and assistance from the Ministry. A special branch, known as the Directorate of Progressing, was accordingly set up to carry out this function. Developments in the war and the technique of air fighting threw upon the Ministry much work for which there was no agent company; and to manage that work a Directorate of Direct Works was formed.

The department maintained a fairly steady staff strength, but met sudden rushes of work by employing outside consultants; and since there was no design or drawing office staff on the engineering services side, it became the practice to employ consulting mechanical and electrical engineers for this work too. For greater speed it was customary to prepare in the Direct Works Branch the preliminary bills for the directly-handled work and to employ outside quantity surveyors for the site measurement and accounts.

From 1940 onwards the scrutiny of contractors' proposals became steadily closer, more detailed and more rigorous. The Director-General of Aircraft Production Factories kept closely in touch with the Ministry of Works and interpreted to the Ministry of Aircraft Production contractors the various rulings which were made in order to conserve materials as they became scarce from time to time.

The tendency for scrutiny to become more severe continued until the end of the war, but it may be taken that by the end of 1941 it had reached a point of severity beyond which it could only go very slowly.

(vii)

Transfer of the Directorate-General of Aircraft Production Factories to the Ministry of Works

It was first proposed by Lord Portal in December 1942 that the Directorate-General of Aircraft Production Factories should be transferred from the Ministry of Aircraft Production to the Ministry of Works, since that Ministry had been set up to be responsible for all Government building schemes. In the negotiations between the two departments the Ministry of Aircraft Production laid down certain conditions which they considered would have to be observed. The general effect of these was that the Directorate-General was to be transferred as a body and was to carry out exactly the same functions in the Ministry of Works as it had done in the Ministry of Aircraft Production. No delay in Ministry of Aircraft Production work was to be caused and the Director-General of Aircraft Production Factories was not to lose any of his discretionary powers or responsibilities.

To apply the new arrangements to agency schemes (that is, to the greater number of all schemes) was simple enough; the only doubt was when there was no agent or managing company. Then, as was generally agreed, it was right that the financial responsibility should be that of the Ministry of Aircraft Production, but not until the Ministry of Works had given an estimate for the work proposed, or for later substantial modifications. For action after the financial decision (including the letting of contracts, the settlement of prices and minor modifications) the Ministry of Works was to take responsibility. Further conditions of the transfer to the Ministry of Works were agreed in January 1943: for example, that the Ministry of Aircraft Production should retain responsibility for site searching and the purchase, leasing and requisitioning of land or buildings, and that it would not seek to interfere with the discretion of the Ministry of Works in the internal organisation of staff or departmental procedure in that Ministry provided that efficient and expeditious service was guaranteed.

The main heads of agreement were finally summarised for general information in the Ministry of Aircraft Production. It was made clear that the Ministry of Aircraft Production was to retain responsibility for final decisions on the nature and extent of schemes, whether these were for building and works services only, or for plant and equipment only, or for both buildings, plant and equipment. Guided by the advice received from the Ministry of Works, they could approve estimates of costs and of substantial variations.

The Ministry of Aircraft Production, moreover, was to continue to employ managing firms as agents on certain matters, and when doing so to look to the Ministry of Works for advice. These matters comprised:

1. The reasonableness of the estimates of cost of building work, services, plant or equipment, submitted to the Ministry of Aircraft Production by managing firms.

2. The suitability of sites from the building aspect.

3. The layout and design of buildings and works in terms of constructional design and economy in the use of labour and material.

4. The selection of architects and of contractors to be invited to tender (but with due regard to the wishes of the managing firms by whom the commissions or contracts were to be placed).

5. The terms and conditions of the contracts for works and services to be entered into by managing firms.
6. The relative merits of tenders received.
7. The progress of work both of building and services and of the construction and installation of plant and equipment.

Several points of some importance in interpreting the agreement between the two Ministries came up shortly after it had been entered into. One of these concerned priority. Major questions of building priority, such as came before the Building Directorates, were not at issue; but it had to be decided which department was to determine the priority of plant (such as extrusion presses, forging hammers, casting plants, and so on). The view of the Director of Aircraft Production Factories was that, as such plant was obtained on the orders of the Ministry of Aircraft Production—either direct or agency—and as the Ministry's priority department had experience of arranging priorities among the several items of plant, whereas the Ministry of Works priority department had not, it would be helpful if the Ministry of Aircraft Production continued to perform that work. This view was accepted by the Ministry of Works.

Although the transfer of the Directorate-General of Aircraft Production Factories to the Ministry of Works was an important move in applying the principle of placing all responsibility for building work in the hands of a single department, it had little practical influence on the construction of aircraft factories. The Directorate-General of Aircraft Production Factories had already been built into the structure of the Ministry of Aircraft Production, and the new arrangement did not alter the very close relationship which existed between the Production and Finance Divisions of the Ministry of Aircraft Production on the one side and the Directorate-General of Aircraft Production Factories on the other. No serious differences of policy came between the Ministry of Aircraft Production and the Ministry of Works, and higher authorities of that department presumably saw no reason to tamper with a machine which had functioned smoothly since long before the transfer took place.

CHAPTER XV

THE MINISTRY OF SUPPLY: ROYAL ORDNANCE FACTORIES AND OTHER BUILDING TASKS

(i)

The Royal Ordnance Factories in the Rearmament Years

T HE vast burden of responsibility carried by the Ministry of Supply included the construction of the Royal Ordnance factories and the provision of other factory space for the manufacture of munitions. Much of this constructional work was taken over from the War Office when the Ministry was set up in 1939; and it was within the War Office that the basic problems of a great building programme had first to be solved. For at least two centuries Royal Ordnance factories, and especially the Royal Arsenal at Woolwich, had been the centre of Government armament production; and in 1935 the three factories remaining in production after the First World War were within the administrative province of the War Office, but were available to meet requirements from the three Services.

In modern times the factories had been of three kinds: engineering factories, explosives factories and filling factories. The engineering factories produced guns and mountings of all sizes, small arms ammunition ranging from revolver cartridges to the largest types of bombs for the Royal Air Force, and an enormous variety of shells and fuses. The explosives factories produced cordite, T.N.T. and other explosives. The filling factories loaded shells, cartridges, fuses, bombs, mines, flares, etc., for Service use. Although during the First World War there had been a great expansion in the number of the Royal Ordnance factories, only three remained in operation when rearmament began—the Royal Arsenal at Woolwich, the Royal Small Arms factory at Enfield and the Royal Gunpowder factory at Waltham Abbey. These establishments had been retained in active being to meet peace-time needs and employed under 10,000 workpeople—a nucleus which under the stress of war rose to 350,000, while the three Royal Ordnance factories expanded to forty-four.

How these factories grew and the manner in which their organisation was developed by the War Office and the Ministry of Supply, during rearmament and in war, is described in detail elsewhere.[1] This chapter can but outline some of the chief problems inherent in their construction.

The Royal Ordnance factories building programme in the rearmament period grew from a project to replace Woolwich Arsenal, and later Waltham Abbey, because of their vulnerability. Later it became part of the Government's rearmament policy to supplement the existing ordnance factories on a massive scale. The first plan had been to replace the filling section at Woolwich Arsenal by ordnance factories at Chorley and Bridgend; but before long other counsels prevailed. It became clear that to meet the needs of the Services in war more filling factories would have to be added to those at Chorley and Bridgend. A subsequent decision of the Cabinet to postpone the re-equipment of the Territorial Army reduced the need from four filling factories to three, and eventually it was decided to go ahead only with Chorley, Bridgend and Glascoed. As the rearmament programme took shape the replacement of Woolwich Arsenal and Waltham Abbey became a factor of less moment than the urgent general need to increase production. Former Royal Ordnance factory sites were built upon; and factories which had lain derelict since the end of the First World War were brought to life. Of these new Royal Ordnance factories the first to begin production was that at Nottingham: it had been reconstructed within a year in 1937 for the production of guns and carriages. The factories at Birtley, Irvine and Hereford, which had been retained on 'care and maintenance' basis, were similarly reconditioned and expanded for rearmament requirements. By the outbreak of war, eighteen Royal Ordnance factories had been approved, and of that number six were in production.

Throughout the years before the war, and even in the early months of the war, the Royal Ordnance factory building programme went forward despite hesitation and uncertainty on what would be the ultimate needs of the Services. Some of these building projects were executed piecemeal, with the Treasury granting authority to proceed at each stage yet withholding sanction for the total scheme as such.

The results of this method of progression are exemplified in the development of the great filling factory at Chorley. This, it had been agreed, was to be constructed on a plan of duplicated buildings, so that buildings might be added to, and taken away from, the complete

---

[1] In the volume 'Factories and Plant' in the War Production series of this History. With the exception of Section (iv), this chapter is based mainly on material prepared for that volume. It should be recorded, however, that between 1937 and 1940 the building of some nineteen Royal Ordnance factories was not only initiated but carried through to completion by the War Office.

set without difficulty. Although the War Office protested to the Treasury Inter-Service Committee that it would be impossible to add to the services at Chorley in piecemeal fashion except at a wholly disproportionate cost, the committee preferred that the final decision on the limits of the Chorley factory should await a general decision on the capacity required by the Services. On behalf of the War Office it was urged that delays in granting authority for the completion of the factory would hold up the granting of tenders as well as increase the cost—a view reinforced by that of the Office of Works (which was responsible for the building work) with the plea there must be a decision on the total capacity required before they could invite separate tenders on the site. The delay, too, made it impossible to plan the provision of transport, water and other services on the site. The Treasury could not, however, give a clear authority. The committee, while agreeing that the building work at Chorley should go on as though the full Chorley scheme had been approved, in effect reserved the right to reduce it at will, since a final decision on Chorley had to await a general decision on the Government rearmament policy and the needs of the Services.

This cautious approach to the programme had its effect not only on progress at Chorley but at most of the other Royal Ordnance factories under construction before the war; but it would not be true to say that the mounting cost of Royal Ordnance factory construction was entirely attributable to the reasons put forward by the War Office in its discussions with the Treasury Inter-Service Committee. The War Office did not in fact dispute what was manifestly beyond dispute —that a proportion, at least, of the increased cost was because of the inevitable and natural growth in Service requirements, which again was inseparable from the development of new military technique. None the less, the discrepancies were enormous. In 1935, for example, the cost of construction at Chorley was estimated at £4½ millions and at Bridgend at £2½ millions. At the end of 1936, when construction was begun, the respective estimated cost was £7 millions and over £4½ millions.[1] The greater part of these increases followed the decision to build underground magazines so as to increase the load and do away with further building for storage, as well as in order to provide for more types of explosives; nor did the Treasury withhold its authority for additional expenditure which had such purposes in view.

THE EMPLOYMENT OF AGENTS

The use of agents for the design and supervision of the construction

---

[1] When Chorley was completed in October 1940 the estimated cost had risen to nearly £11 millions, and for Bridgend in June 1940 to nearly £7 millions. These figures exclude the Ministry of Works agency charge of five per cent.

of factories in the rearmament programme was a natural development in the conditions of the middle nineteen-thirties. The decision to employ an intermediary or agent was taken in 1936, when the Office of Works became the first agent. This appointment followed negotiations between the two departments in which it had been agreed that the Office of Works should be responsible for the building work and the provision of transport, drainage and the purchase and installation of plant in those projects for which the War Office would seek the services of the Office of Works. The War Office was to retain responsibility for the formulation of requirements and was also to inspect the plant both before and after installation. The staff at Woolwich was to continue to plan the general lay-out of the factories and was also to be entitled to comment upon the drawings of the Office of Works in order to secure their suitability for factory requirements. This agreement was amended from time to time. In the main the staff at Woolwich retained its responsibility for deciding upon the size and the position of the buildings. By 1939 they had reserved the right to make suggestions as to 'method of construction', yet at no time were they responsible for the detailed design of the building work; in that sphere the Office of Works remained autonomous. In actual practice its staff were prepared to submit to the staff of the Chief Mechanical Engineer at Woolwich any deviation in principle from the agreed drawings, since they had not had the experience of the staff at Woolwich in determining the correct relationship between the disposition of various components in a factory and the most efficient production upon completion of the factory.

With minor exceptions, the Office of Works (and until 1943 its successor the Ministry of Works) were only employed on filling and explosives factories. None the less, employment of the Office of Works as an agent in the execution of the War Office programme was but the beginning of an inevitable trend. Even before the war-time expansion of the building programme, which taxed the energies of the staff at Woolwich to the limit and made the employment of some agents on a large scale inevitable, agents were being employed other than, and in addition to, the Office of Works. In 1939 Sir Alexander Gibb & Partners were called in to act as agents for the construction of three Royal Filling factories. This firm was in complete charge of the building work, including the acceptance of tenders and the issuing of certificates for payment. The authority retained by the Chief Mechanical Engineer for design and layout was similar to that stipulated in the agreement between the War Office and the Office of Works. Yet although agents, usually the Ministry of Works, were employed for all new filling and explosives factories, they were rarely used for engineering factories. Agents were in fact used for only two of the twenty-two engineering Royal Ordnance factories.

While the employment of agents was not free from some serious objections, there was no real alternative to their employment in the construction of the Royal Filling and Explosives factories. By 1937 the burden being carried by the staff at Woolwich Arsenal was becoming insupportable; but for the services of agents, it would have been overwhelming by the time war broke out. Clearly, if agents were to be employed in war, it was desirable that they should begin to gain experience as early as possible in peace. The chief objection to their employment, even though the agents should be the Office of Works, was that they were unlikely to possess the specialised knowledge of the staff at Woolwich, and that they had no immediate experience in the type of building required. These disadvantages, it was contended, led to unnecessary delay. At the same time the War Office had cause to complain that the Office of Works rarely completed the work in the time the War Office considered appropriate. While, doubtless, there was often good reason for delay because of shortages of labour or materials or difficulties of transport or administration (such as have been described in other parts of this narrative), there was a natural tendency for the Office of Works to produce a more elaborate structure than the staff at Woolwich had envisaged. The War Office wanted the rapid construction of temporary buildings good enough to meet the needs of the rearmament programme; but the professional training of the architects and surveyors of the Office of Works enjoined on them more consideration, more caution, more thoroughness. To a lesser extent these objections applied also to the contracting firms who were brought in; but whoever they might be, the employment of agents made inevitable some dislocation of working organisation at Woolwich. There was a feeling that the construction of factories could have been equally well performed, without the services of agents, by the expansion of the engineering divisions at the Arsenal, and that after all the agents were in the position of middlemen between the Chief Mechanical Engineer and the many similar firms to whom contracts were normally let. Was it not true, too, it was urged, that time was lost in educating the civil and mechanical engineering staffs of the Office of Works and the other agents, and in the submission of drawings? And, especially, was it not difficult for the staff at Woolwich to exercise proper supervision, since the agents were unwilling to work away from their own offices?

In such an uneasy relationship liaison was hampered or became ineffectual. Responsibility remained divided, and many of the working arrangements which had been evolved at Woolwich for constructional work went by the board.

(ii)

Problems of Design and Construction

The design and lay-out of each factory was a task that primarily concerned the expert staff at Woolwich. For a factory of the size of Chorley at least twelve months would normally have been spent on working out contract details, but the urgency of need reduced this to four. The experience here gained made for greater care in designing the next factory; but design became progressively easier, since many plans for one factory could often be applied to another without alteration. As an example of the time schedule, Glascoed site was surveyed in October 1937; in January 1938 the Office of Works gave Woolwich Arsenal the details of levels and other site conditions; before March, when the general lay-out was finished, work had commenced on railway sidings and approach roads; and the detailed lay-out was completed in April. For later factories the dimensioned lay-outs were often handed over to the agents within two months.

Lay-out necessarily depended upon the size of factory; this in its turn depended variously on the quantity and type of requirements, the area of site available, the storage capacity which could be provided, the need to keep explosives buildings at a good distance from each other and from the factory limits, the labour available, maximum electrical loads and so forth. To some extent, at least in pre-war factories, room was left for considerable further growth.

When the various factors had been collated to fix the desired size and the load of requirements to be carried, the disposition of work over the factory area had to be considered.[1] Any bad arrangements at this stage might well affect adversely the speed and economy of production. Approach roads and railway connections were a prerequisite of all other work on site, and were accordingly planned first, in conjunction with the railway companies. Then came the general grouping of different classes of filling, arranged so that work flowed naturally through the factory and sections between which there was heavy traffic lay near each other; but also with an eye to levels, mounding, subsoil, so that civil engineering work was minimised and the maximum area taken into use.

While the main factory lay-out was being agreed, the detailed survey of site would be carried on by the agents. Upon a skeleton plan made up of internal roads and railways, together with the systems of

---

[1] It is noteworthy that, in general, the Royal Ordnance factories tended to be much larger than those of the First World War, a fact due only in part to the need for much greater dispersal of buildings; and although there was a marked decrease in the size of successive factories, yet the brunt of filling programmes was borne by factories which were very large indeed.

water, power, steam mains and so forth, the shops had to be disposed, in such a way as to reduce traffic and walking time, with a flow of work from the outside to the centre of each section, from empty component stores to transit sheds. The distance between shops had to take into account that each might contain explosives equivalent to so many hours' output. These safety distances were of the first importance. Any accumulation of explosives had to be kept out of working areas, and buildings dispersed as widely as might be consistent with compactness. Finally, the shops would be linked up by clean-ways, along which traffic would normally proceed in one direction only, taking empties, explosives or finished work from platform to platform.

The size of each individual shop was the next consideration. It had been a lesson of production in the First World War that filling factory buildings should, and could, be more standardised, and a committee had been set up in February 1936 to see the effect of new technical developments on this requirement. It was known that buildings should not be too wide, since light from side windows would not then suffice. Nor must they be too long, lest more explosives be concentrated than was safe. Account had to be taken of a possible switch in the type of store to be filled, and buildings might even have to be built before their actual task could be defined. Output capacities per hour all had to be carefully worked out for each class of ammunition.

Now came the task of designing standard units for carying out each kind of work. Four main types were devised, each of which was interchangeable for many stores. The 80 ft. by 30 ft. building would thus fit most types of fuse or gaine work; the 60 ft. by 30 ft. building became the standard workshop for cordite filling of any calibre; and a standard shifting house was also designed for all groups where more than 500 people were employed.[1] Canteen rooms, lavatories, expense magazines were treated in the same way, and the machine shop group of buildings needed only slight revision according to the size and type of factory. There was some criticism that agents would go to unnecessary trouble and expense to produce separate drawings for each factory. But even with such an early factory as Bridgend it was found that most buildings were identical with others already planned for Chorley, and at Glascoed there were very few that needed new drawings.

The planning of later factories may have been much easier in that so many drawings could be used wholly or in part for one after the other. But in some important respects the later factories were planned differently from their predecessors, the difference being due either to

---

[1] It could be easily reduced for smaller groups by deleting one or two of the standard bays.

the experience acquired through trial and error, or to the growing shortage of building materials and greater urgency of construction. Lessons had been learnt at Chorley which made possible greater simplifications in lay-out and greater speed in construction. Production buildings tended to become larger so that there should be more elbow room and less crossing of paths. Means of protection against explosion became less exacting, and questions of black-out ventilation were important. The outbreak of war made camouflage much more real a problem. The protection of buildings from air attack had naturally been an important consideration from the first, but decisions about it were made late, and numerous changes in policy were a continual impediment long after the war had begun. Finally, the later factories differed in that they were built hurriedly with fewer materials to choose from, without frills or refinements, and clearly as temporary constructions based on a useful life of two or three years. There was thus more timber work, walls reduced to $4\frac{1}{2}$ inches of brick and no steelwork inside buildings to carry shafting. Relaxations were made for floor coverings and clean-ways, and open ditches were used for drainage.

When enough information had been collected on lay-out and dimensions, tenders were invited by the agents and the various contracts signed. The question of timing was important; some contracts could be begun (sometimes they had to be begun) before requirements were exactly formulated, and that committed the builders to an undertaking of a size not yet approved. Design and lay-out often continued simultaneously with building operations. The case of Chorley may be taken to illustrate this aspect of the work and its peculiar difficulties.

The Chorley contractor could not be said to have had final instructions until two years of building had gone by. Plans for the main building contract were begun in August 1936 and tenders invited on 16th November. Apart from numerous inquiries from firms obviously too small, some thirty-one possible contractors were considered. These had been chosen after inquiries of the Service departments, local authorities, and large utility companies. Tenders were eventually received from five only. The lowest of these was accepted on 6th January 1937. In six months there had thus been done what in the original Woolwich plan had been estimated to take twice or thrice as long.

Thus began the troubles which later were seen to be the results of excessive haste in letting the contract, and the adoption of measures of acceleration giving savings in time at disproportionate expense. The contractor could claim almost at once that changes in requirements made the scheme no longer that for which he had originally tendered, and there was no choice but to amend the contract in his favour. Much the same situation was later to occur at Glascoed, where new work as it came in had likewise to go to firms which had labour and machinery already on site.

Confusion and disagreement on the Chorley contract were aggravated by the successive political crises and the acceleration in building they demanded. The unfortunate results of these accelerations were first the cost, secondly the fact that they undermined the contractor's responsibility for the job, and thirdly that the saving in time was largely illusory owing to the faulty workmanship which had to be made good. The amended Chorley contract was signed on 1st April 1937. Soon after this, unforeseen difficulties appeared which gave the contractor grounds to claim an extension of one year. He rejected the special methods needed for completion by March 1939 unless he could disregard economic considerations in organising the work; and in a supplementary agreement dated 18th August a minimum net profit had to be guaranteed, this time with no final date for completion exactly specified. Meanwhile the approved cost grew rapidly.

Not only because of changing Service requirements, but for many other reasons the actual work of building tended to fall behind schedule. Once possessed of their contract, contractors, especially when guaranteed a minimum profit, had less motive for pressing forward to complete. Besides, many incidents were bound to occur which gave excuse for extensions: shortage of building materials, for instance, or bad weather. Site conditions, too, had often been hurriedly or inadequately investigated, so that extra piling or foundation work had later to be put in, or part of the factory re-sited; and always there was the temptation to tackle easy jobs first, and not in such a sequence that the factory might begin production without disturbance from structural work still proceeding. Labour shortages were continuous, and their effects were felt to a greater or less degree in the building of all factories. With later factories another impediment was the lack of absolute priorities among so many claimants. In the face of all the delaying factors, many of which could not be foreseen by contractors when tendering, the difficulty of producing a realistic time-table is readily understood, as is shown in the fact that all contracts received for Chorley quoted the exact twenty-four months given by the agents as their minimum.

(iii)

From War Office to Ministry of Supply

When, in the summer of 1939, the Ministry of Supply was set up, the Royal Ordnance factory building programme was one of the major responsibilities transferred from the War Office to the new department. With the outbreak of war there was a large increase in building schemes for agency factories and for factory extensions. These schemes were, however, largely under the control of the firms who were to operate the factories; and in consequence up to 1941 only the construction of the new Royal Ordnance factories came under the direct control of the Ministry of Supply. In March 1941 a general organisation,[1] embracing all building construction schemes and serving all directorates of the Ministry, was set up.[2] A Controller of Building Construction was appointed with the special duty of co-ordinating the demand for labour and materials on building projects. This officer represented the Ministry on the Works and Buildings Priority Committee. The allocation system was then about to be introduced, and the Controller of Building Construction was made responsible for arranging the construction programme of the Ministry within its allocation.

In February 1942 an entirely new committee, which became known as the 'Building Executive', was set up in the Ministry of Supply, and it was now laid down that any new building scheme was not to be supported unless it fulfilled specified conditions. Was it required for the maintenance, improvement or expansion of essential Ministry production? Could building work not be avoided by the re-allocation of existing accommodation, the use of existing buildings or the fuller use of capacity existing at the firm or elsewhere? Were they assured of the operational labour, the machine tools, the plant for the work proposed? And was that work of an economical war-time standard of construction?

All schemes were referred to the Controller of Building Construction at an early stage. The committee considered each project in turn, calling on its sponsors for explanations. A statement of the projects. finally passed and placed on the approved list, was then sent to all concerned; and next the Building Executive looked into each project, taking as their criteria necessity, economy and relative urgency. In so doing, the Executive set a standard high enough to impel the Production Directorate—who sponsored the projects and attended the meetings to urge their claims—to be chary of putting before the committee any but fully justified schemes.

---

[1] It was not, however, until the autumn of that year that the new organisation began to take final shape.

[2] It should be noted that although the Royal Ordnance factory construction up to 1942 absorbed more than half of the resources employed on the Ministry of Supply building programme, the agency factories were more numerous, and the number of schemes for building work at firms' factories ran into thousands. Indeed, over the war period the financial commitment for agency factories and other building work was at least equal to the commitment for Royal Ordnance factories.

(iv)

Liaison with the Ministry of Works

Reference has already been made[1] to the divergence in outlook and method, during the rearmament years, between the department of the Chief Mechanical Engineer at Woolwich and the Office of Works in its capacity as agent. As the programme grew some of the causes of friction were removed; but with the transference of the Royal Ordnance factory building programme to the Ministry of Supply in 1939 there was again a marked malaise. This subsided, and by the time the Office of Works was absorbed in the newly created Ministry of Works, in the autumn of 1940, there was better liaison between the two departments. When the Controller of Building Construction was appointed in March 1941 the liaison began to be formally defined.[2]

During the preceding months there had been some concern in the Ministry of Works lest they should lose control over a substantial part of the Royal Ordnance factory programme. For this they had, during the past four years, made a special disposition of staff and resources, without, however, knowing the full scope of the programme. There was every desire that liaison with the Ministry of Supply should be more systematic; but there was also the fear that the technical officers of both Ministries might be arranging matters between them without proper reference to the administrative officers of the Ministry of Works. Although that view was not shared in the Ministry of Supply, awareness of it at least helped to clear the way for better relations between the two Ministries.

In the discussions that had preceded the setting up of the Ministry of Works there had been no detailed arrangement between the two Ministries; and after its creation the unsatisfactory situation is reflected in an official Ministry of Works minute, dated 5th December 1940. Here reference is made to a recent decision of the Ministry of Supply, under which the Ministry of Works were assigned three of ten factories comprised in a new programme, the remaining seven to be undertaken by outside agents. Objection was taken by the Ministry of Works to this decision because it ignored its responsibilities as recently defined in the House of Commons.

It is clearly laid down that this Ministry would take over, to begin with, the work of the Ministry of Supply, including the new buildings section of the ordnance factories and the approval of plans of new

---

[1] See p. 330 *et seq.*
[2] See p. 337.

private factories or extensions to the existing private factories, to the cost of which the Ministry of Supply is contributing. Having regard to this Cabinet decision it is for this Ministry to decide what work may reasonably be left to the Ministry of Supply to finish rather than for the Ministry of Supply to say what new work they will or will not hand over.

Mr. Gibson[1] proposes that this Ministry should handle an additional solventless cordite factory, but that the question of the agents to undertake the additional two filling factories which would be required to work in association therewith, should be left over for consideration at the time they are to be put in hand. I suggest that there should be no misunderstanding as to which department should be responsible for taking over the whole of this work, which clearly falls within the Ministry's[2] functions.

On 6th January 1941 the Ministry of Supply sent a full statement to the Ministry of Works giving particulars of contracts for construction of Royal Ordnance factories.[3] It was now made clear that the factories which the Ministry of Supply proposed that the Ministry of Works should take over were all those on the first page of the list, except the Swynnerton, Risley and Kirkby factories, and none of those on the second page, except Pembrey and Wrexham.[4]

Following upon this decision in the early months of 1941 a great deal of discussion had turned on the transfer of staff from the Ministry of Supply to the Ministry of Works; nevertheless, uncertainty continued about what kind of control and liaison was appropriate between the two Ministries. When, in March 1941, a Controller of Building Construction was appointed in the Ministry of Supply, that uncertainty was removed. In future all contacts of the Ministry of Works with the Ministry of Supply were to be made through him; at the same time the province of the Controller was defined. In general, his responsibility embraced the selection and approval of sites and the co-ordination of requirements of all constructional materials and labour; and he was to represent the Ministry of Supply on the Works and Building Priority Committee. It was for him to ensure that the Ministry's building programme complied with the allocation of construction capacity; and he was to negotiate with the Ministry of Works on technical matters connected with the building programme, with an eye especially to uniformity of practice, simplification of design, mutual assistance and the avoidance of any clash of interests.

That these arrangements had begun to clear the air is evident from

---

[1] Mr. J. W. Gibson, who in October 1939 was appointed Assistant Director of Ordnance Factories in the Ministry of Supply, to carry out special duties, had in March 1941 been appointed as the first Controller of Building Construction.

[2] That is, Ministry of Works.

[3] See Notes and Appendices: Appendix X, 'Statement Giving Particulars of Contracts for Construction of R.O.F.s'.

[4] *Ibid.*

a letter addressed by the Minister of Works, Lord Reith, to the Minister of Supply, Sir Andrew Duncan, on 9th April 1941.

> Thank you for your letter of 1st April, about the division of construction and building work between the two Ministries. What you say is not quite in line with my recollection of our talk, and on assisted schemes surely a departure from what was settled when this Ministry was formed? But my object is to get the work done in whatever way is quickest and best, and I will fall in with your desires as now expressed. I hope this will put a stop to criticisms and complaints and that we can go straight forward.
>
> My responsibility for the building programme is exercised in the interest of all departments and depends on their collaboration and goodwill. We look for it particularly from your Ministry which has such a large part in the unwieldy programme. Even more, we want your collaboration in the further task of helping the building industry into better order.

If the air was beginning to clear in 1941, it was not until the spring of the following year that the relationship of the two Ministries was firmly and formally settled. At a meeting held at the Ministry of Supply between the Minister of Supply, Sir Andrew Duncan, and the Minister of Works, Lord Portal,[1] agreement was reached and put on record.

These arrangements were designed to smooth the way for the supervision of the Ministry of Supply's building work by the Ministry of Works, and thus reduce to a minimum any delay in getting approval for, and progress in, the Ministry of Supply's building programme. The arrangement came under three main categories:

1. Responsibility for construction and design.
2. Control of design for economy of material and labour.
3. Liaison between the departments.

The general responsibility for construction and design was related, first, to projects under the direct control of the Ministry of Supply, such as the Royal Ordnance factories, storage depots and kindred installations. Then came the agency factories and assisted schemes; and finally houses and hostels for the accommodation of Ministry of Supply workers.

It was now clearly laid down that the Ministry of Works would be responsible for the construction of 'large new factories' and 'large new extensions' to existing factories.[2] Where the work was of a particularly technical nature calling for specialist knowledge and the closest

---

[1] Others present were: Sir William Douglas, Sir William Rootes, Mr. Oliver Franks, Mr. Ralph Assheton and Major Howard, representing the Ministry of Supply, and Mr. Hugh Beaver representing the Ministry of Works.

[2] A 'large' new project or extension was defined as a scheme to cost £50,000 or over. Schemes falling below that limit might be carried out by the Ministry of Supply. The limit could be reviewed after three months' experience of its operation.

co-operation of production departments, it was to be carried out by the Ministry of Supply. As to extensions, where the original buildings had been carried out by the Ministry of Supply it might often be advisable that the extension should be similarly treated.

Apart from these reservations, the Ministry of Works carried complete responsibility for major direct building schemes; but in respect of the agency factories[1] each building proposal was to be dealt with on its merits. If it was thought that the Ministry of Works could best carry out the work, they were to be asked to do so. In some instances, however, especially those where responsibility for the construction and design of the work rested upon the agents themselves, it was thought preferable that the Ministry of Supply should exercise control. So, too, with assisted schemes, where the work was to be handled by the firm itself, responsibility was to rest with the Ministry of Supply.

Ministry of Supply houses and hostels, with accommodation for more than fifty, were to be designed and built by the Ministry of Works; and it was also laid down that where accommodation for less than fifty could best be provided by a standard self-contained unit responsibility might still be allocated to the Ministry of Works.

The two Ministries were agreed that decisions on the allocation of responsibility for work under any of the above categories should be given where necessary by the Building Executive,[2] or in special circumstances by the Minister himself.

In the control of design, materials and labour, it was the right of the Ministry of Works to scrutinise any of the plans of work to be carried out by the Ministry of Supply, whatever their category, and to see that standards of economy were enforced. This duty was made easier as a result of new liaison arrangements under which a representative of the Ministry of Works was appointed to the Building Executive. A senior liaison officer from the Ministry of Works maintained close contact with the Controller of Building Construction and attended the meetings of the Building Executive. He was accommodated in the Ministry of Supply and was assisted by an Assistant Liaison Officer. Lastly, a representative of the Ministry of Works was specially nominated to maintain contact with the Iron and Steel Control.

The arrangements made in April 1942 were modified in March 1943. The limit of £50,000 was now reduced to £20,000; and in June 1943 a transfer of staff was made *en bloc* from the department of the

---

[1] 'When the construction of a new factory is involved, an "agency" factory may be defined as one which is 100 per cent. Government owned, which the Government builds and equips and then brings a firm in and pays it a management fee to operate. An "assisted" scheme is one where a firm is assisted to provide buildings or equipment, the building and equipment belonging to the Government or the firm, according to the financial arrangements agreed upon'. (Official Minute.)

[2] The Building Executive was to continue to review all projects estimated to cost more than £2,500.

Controller of Building Construction to the Ministry of Works. The effect of the transfer was that, except for certain works under £5,000 which the Ministry of Supply itself carried out at Royal Ordnance factories and other installations where they had a maintenance staff, the Ministry of Works took over all but certain highly specialised work of the Ministry of Supply.

*   *

*

Of the special projects in which the Ministry of Supply was vitally engaged, its share in the construction of the floating harbours ('Mulberry') for the invasion of north-western Europe was the most notable. Much of this achievement belongs to the story of the engineering rather than the building industry and so falls beyond the bounds of this narrative. But in the actual construction of the floating caissons that formed a portion of the harbours and were known as 'Phoenix', building workers (despite the dearth of skilled craftsmen and the pressure of an exigent time-table) made a positive, indeed a spectacular, contribution to victory. For the supply and organisation, under conditions of the most stringent secrecy, of all the skilled men who could be mustered for the undertaking—carpenters, steel-fixers, scaffolders and other tradesmen—the responsibility was that of the Ministry of Works and of the building industry, as well as of the Ministry of Labour and the Ministry of Supply.

A special branch of the Ministry of Supply, largely recruited from outside specialists experienced in kindred work, was formed on 27th September 1943 to carry out the Phoenix programme. This branch was responsible for the methods of construction, and for finding contractors to carry out the work and consulting engineers to supervise it in detail. The branch also arranged, in conjunction with the Ministry of Works and the other Ministries concerned, for the supply of materials and labour, the acquisition of sites, the transport both of material and of labour, and the billeting, welfare and supervision of the large number of workers engaged.

The first estimate was for a labour force of 16,000, but the number rose in fact to a peak of 20,000.[1]

To avoid the scramble for labour that would otherwise have occurred, a general embargo was put on the commencement of new works within thirty miles of a Phoenix site.[2] At the same time departments deferred or curtailed as many as possible of their building labour demands in the specified areas, and deferred as much as they could of their building programmes elsewhere.

---

[1] 3,500 carpenters, 1,500 steel-fixers, 1,200 scaffolders, 12,300 labourers, and 1,500 other trades. In the week ending 15th March 1944 the labour force on site actually reached 22,545.

[2] The whole of London came within the affected areas.

Despite these cuts, the overriding priority given to Phoenix meant that other works competed among themselves for the remaining supply of men. Reinforced-concrete workers, scaffolders and carpenters were hard to come by; and for steel-fixers and scaffolders the Phoenix demand was greater than the total supply. For steel-fixers, indeed, special training and dilution schemes were introduced on Phoenix sites, while scaffolders were released from the forces. But the training schemes seemed likely to break down because skilled workers held back from teaching the unskilled. When, by arrangement with the trade unions, designated craftsmen were substituted for training, the dilemma was overcome. The call for carpenters, too, was very heavy: in addition to other releases, some 2,000 men were lent by the Army and the naval dockyards, and some 250 from the maintenance staffs at Royal Ordnance factories.

For the required contractors' plant the Ministry of Supply looked to the Ministry of Works. But it was not always easy to meet demands, particularly for derricks, nor could the Ministry of Works avoid minor delays in the delivery of other items of plant. As to materials, the aggregates were formidable[1] and meant the provision of special transport. In the arrangement of transport by rail the Phoenix programme was given first priority. Where the use of railways seemed likely to be difficult, as much material as possible was sent by road with the help of Army vehicles. In the main, the effect of the rail priority was a small delay spread over a large volume of other traffic; but a special problem for both rail and road transport was to provide long trucks for the steel reinforcement.

Other problems, solved by the appropriate authorities, were how to light the sites so that work could go on night and day; how to give shelter from enemy air attack; how to guard against stoppage of concreting work by frost; and how to safeguard the living accommodation, transport and welfare of the thousands of workers brought together in the special areas from all over the country. In the welfare arrangements the Ministries of Labour, Health, Works and War Transport all had a share. Conferences were held in each area before work began there, and where necessary camps were put up to eke out inadequate billeting facilities.

---

[1] 400,000 tons of crushed stone or ballast; 200,000 tons of sand; 100,000 tons of cement; 30,000 tons of reinforcing steel bars; 6,000 standards (20,000 tons) of timber; 3,500 sluice valves and fittings; 250,000 tons of rubble for dock bottoms; 80,000 square yards of hollow tiles; 600 steel bollards; 5,000 fairleads; 150 sets of towing gear; and 50 miles of steel wire rope.

CHAPTER XVI

THE CONSTRUCTIONAL WORK
OF THE
MINISTRY OF WAR TRANSPORT

(i)

Railway Problems

THE constructional work of the Ministry of War Transport, so far as it concerned inland communications, was mainly on railways, roads, harbours, docks, and canals.[1] Although in terms of the value of work done and labour allocated the Ministry's building programme fell considerably below the programmes of the other Service and Supply Ministries,[2] its constructional tasks were no less vital to the war effort; and, as has already appeared in earlier chapters, were linked, particularly in the Bolero programme, with the civil engineering work of the Service Ministries.

Let us look first at the background against which the railways carried out their war-time programme. A review of vulnerable points was undertaken during the rearmament period by the railway companies. They were asked *inter alia* to consider the effects of the destruction of the main London bridges over the Thames, as well as of important bridges elsewhere in the country which, like the Thames bridges, might be targets of air attack. When, soon after the Munich crisis, war preparations were taken in hand, the Ministry of Transport suggested to the companies that they should consider—as an 'insurance' scheme—the replacement of certain junction lines, which had been constructed in the First World War and later removed, in order to provide alternative routes for freight traffic between North and South that normally passed through the London area.[3]

The question of financing such 'insurance schemes' does not appear to have been pursued. In the spring of 1939 the companies as a whole were apathetic about them, but their attitude changed with the outbreak of war. In September 1939 the Railway Executive Committee

---

[1] Inland Transport forms the subject of detailed study in another volume of this series.
[2] See Chapter XVII. Tables at pp. 352, 353, 396.
[3] Much of this traffic crossed the Thames at Blackfriars or Battersea.

submitted a programme of works to enable North to South freight traffic to be diverted away from the London area, or to pass through it if Blackfriars Bridge were damaged. These works covered a wide area.[1] At the same time smaller insurance schemes were carried out at the instance of the Ministry of Transport.

The strain imposed on the railways by war conditions manifested itself by degrees. The shoe began to pinch first in one place, then in another as fresh traffic developed, as new Government factories began production,[2] and as certain routes became far more intensively used than in peace-time. Among the war-time changes were the diversion of imports from east coast to west coast ports; the transfer to rail of freight formerly carried coastwise; the transfer of traffic from road to rail to save petrol, rubber and manpower; the growth in consumption of home-produced iron ore transported by railway from the Midlands to the north-east coast and to South Wales; the switch of Anglo-Scottish freight traffic to the east coast route in order to free the west coast route for the movement of United States troops disembarking in the Clyde; and, later still, the improvement of lines leading towards Southampton and the south-west in readiness for D-day.

The experience of the first year of war reversed over-optimistic assumptions made by the railways about the capacity of their lines to handle war-time traffic; and on 27th November the chairman of the Railway Executive Committee placed before the Ministry of Transport a comprehensive programme of new railway works, to cost approximately £10 millions and to be spread over a period of two years. He concluded that all the improvements previously submitted by the railway companies had been put forward on their individual merits without considering the problem of increased capacity as a whole. No new routes, however, were proposed: the £10 millions scheme or the 'Wedgwood' plan, as it was informally named, was aimed principally at the development of existing routes to meet the needs of war-time traffic.

The view taken by the Minister of Transport was that, although he favoured a comprehensive scheme for developing railway facilities, the programme should be regarded, in principle, as one of £5 millions covering a year rather than as a scheme to embark on heavy works needing £10 millions or more and taking two years or longer to complete. Since this view was taken largely because both labour and steel were expected to be scarce, the Railway Executive Committee modified their original proposals and in March 1941 submitted a revised

---

[1] They included making use of the London Midland and Scottish Railway line, Cambridge-Bedford-Bletchley-Oxford, and the provision of marshalling facilities well to the south of London for traffic approaching from that direction after diversion well to the west of that area.

[2] Operatives often travelled daily by train from considerable distances.

programme of works to cost £5 millions and to be carried out, at least for the greater part, within one year. The programme was designed to increase the capacity and fluidity of traffic over sixteen principal routes.

Not all the original proposals in the 'Wedgwood' programme were approved and carried out. But, since that programme was not exhaustive, other schemes of equal urgency were at the same time submitted by the Railway Executive Committee and were approved and executed.

> The Ministry of Transport in fact considered each scheme on its merits. No distinction was drawn between works which formed part of the 'Wedgwood' programme and other works which were equally necessary. Moreover, in approving the works, the Government had to take account of the supply of materials and labour, for which there were other competing demands.

The real value of the works begun in 1941 was not apparent until the later years of the war, but of the total sum of £11½ millions spent by the Government on railway work during the war, the bulk was approved between 1941 and 1943.[1]

(ii)

Inland Sorting Depots

A separate aspect of war-time constructional work by the Ministry of Transport was the provision of inland sorting depots. Even before the heavy bombing began the storage and sorting of large quantities of essential supplies at the ports was (for reasons which cannot be analysed here) causing vulnerable congestion. Inland sorting depots were proposed as a means of relieving the ports and carrying on at a safe distance from them the various sorting processes normally undertaken in the ports.[2] The Ministry of Transport decided in favour of the scheme, and the Lord President's Committee were asked for authority to construct six inland sorting depots. To this they agreed on 20th December 1940. Difficulties arose, however, about obtaining land, labour and materials, for which there were many competing demands. In the end the matter was settled, since the Prime Minister

---

[1] See Notes and Appendices: Appendix XII, 'Civil Engineering Works on Railways carried out on Ministry of War Transport Account'.

[2] The scheme was beset with difficulties. The arguments for and against the construction of inland sorting depots are reviewed in other volumes of this series. See especially Behrens, C. B. A., *The Battle of the United Kingdom Ports*.

strongly favoured the scheme, and work was started in the spring of 1941.

Six depots were constructed altogether—at a cost of between £2 millions and £3 millions[1]—two in the vicinity of the Clyde, a double depot at Liverpool, one near Avonmouth, and another near Cardiff. Early in 1941 the Clyde Navigation Trust produced proposals for the twin depots in the Glasgow area, and these were carried out by the Trust engineers, who conferred with the Ministry of War Transport on matters of general principle. The three remaining depots, started in the summer of 1941, were the responsibility of the Ministry of Works in consultation with the port authorities concerned and with the London Midland and Scottish and Great Western Railway Companies. Part occupation of the Liverpool scheme was given seven months later; Cardiff was completed in eight months (on previously piled foundations), Avonmouth in eleven months, and Liverpool in thirteen months.

The concentration of ships in convoy at the ports at that time demanded that cargoes should be rapidly discharged direct into waiting trains and transported to the inland sorting depots, where the goods could be sorted under cover and re-transported to their ultimate destinations. A duplication of the dock services[2] was required at the depots and, besides the sorting sheds and ancillaries, a system of railway communication and marshalling yards with equipment for on-and-off loading and handling. To provide against temporary disruption of the railways an alternative road transport system was devised, and the county authorities, in liaison with the Ministry of War Transport and the Ministry of Works, improved and widened all unclassified roads in the neighbourhood serving the depots as far as the nearest trunk roads, so that road transport could deal with the flow of goods in an emergency.[3]

Relatively level sites were selected of from 90 to 140 acres, with ready access from main lines and trunk roads. The lay-outs were designed to merge, so far as possible, with the pattern of the landscape, and by giving maximum dispersal to avoid more than two targets in one bombing run. The sorting sheds, together with the port authority's and railway company's administration offices, and canteens for staff and dockers, were the key units; and there were ancillary buildings for electrical charging, workshops, police guards, weighbridges and sanitation.[4]

---

[1] These depots were the largest single items of expenditure during the war on civil engineering and building works at ports. The total capacity was about 25 million cubic feet.

[2] See Section (iv) of this chapter.

[3] *Ibid.*

[4] The depots continued in operation after the end of the war for sea transport storage, food and raw material storage; and in the Clyde depots for normal port storage.

(iii)

The Work of the Highways Department

On the outbreak of war the numerous improvement works which were being carried out on highways for the needs of ordinary peace-time traffic were closed down. Only work essential to the war effort was now permitted; and throughout the war years the ordinary maintenance work was cut to the minimum needed to keep the roads going. All the effort of the Highways Department was transferred to war purposes in the categories shown below:

Direct labour works for other departments. Between the two wars a 'direct labour agency services' organisation had been set up to carry out work for other Government departments, mainly for the Air Ministry. The projects were of an experimental and special character.

On the outbreak of war this organisation was transferred to the various Divisional Road Engineers of the Ministry of Transport and considerably expanded. Among the works undertaken were the construction of roads in military establishments and the construction of runways and other works at airfields operated by the Royal Navy and the Royal Air Force. These included the construction of large underground bomb stores for the Air Ministry; surface bomb stores at Royal Air Force stations; the construction of hard runways at airfields; the development of the wet sand bitumen process for surfacing runways at airfields. This process was not only cheaper than the normal methods of runway construction, but could be completed in little more than half the time. It was used at Blackpool, Formby, Rhosneigr, Connel Ferry, Benbecula, Tiree and Islay. Other large schemes carried out by this organisation were single landing runways over a mile long and 400 yards wide at Sutton Heath, Suffolk, and Bridlington.

About 5,000 men were employed on works for other departments, and the cost of the works carried out during the war was approximately £20 millions.

Highway works. Not only were many new airfields under construction, but the construction of new military installations of all kinds and of the Royal Ordnance and other factories was bringing heavy traffic to roads which had previously been used for the most part by light traffic.

The roads giving access to these establishments were strengthened and widened, and this often meant, especially in airfield construction, the closing of existing roads and the improvement of other roads for use as alternative routes. Sometimes, too, new diversions had to be constructed.

The work on the highways was necessarily maintained throughout the war. It was often carried out in the face of a shortage of labour or of materials, and it was costly.[1] Entirely under the direction of the Ministry of War Transport, the works were carried out either by the Ministry's own direct labour or by a highway authority, or by contract. On roads that were seriously damaged by heavy military traffic, special maintenance work was carried out under the supervision of the Ministry.

Defence against invasion. Reference has been made in an earlier chapter[2] to the plan of action of the Ministry of Works under the threat of invasion, and to the methods of co-operation with the Ministry of War Transport on the building of road and other defence works. When, after the fall of France in 1940, the danger of invasion was imminent, the Ministry of War Transport was called upon by the War Office to help in the construction of defences such as road blocks and aircraft traps,[3] as well as to prepare bridges for demolition and roads for cratering at strategic points. The Ministry of War Transport carried out the preliminary work, leaving the site ready for the military to insert the explosive charges.

During the critical period of invasion risk, the Ministry of War Transport, like the Ministry of Works, set up a number of mobile labour gangs to deal with damage to roads under invasion. The gangs were kept ready at strategic points and were completely self-contained, with their own transport, food, plant and tools. Ministry of War Transport engineers were attached to military commanders as liaison officers, with the duty of ensuring the rapid repair of damaged roads. Separate gangs were organised for the repair of bridges.

Preparations for invasion of the Continent. In the preparation for the invasion of the Continent, the Ministry of War Transport's main role was to make new roads, or to improve existing ones, leading directly to the embarkation 'hards' on the south coast. It was a task that also took in the widening and strengthening of many miles of roads and bridges in the assembly areas behind the 'hards'; and it was carried out under conditions of urgency in the space of four or five months. Labour was assembled from several sources—the department's direct labour, that of the highways authorities, contract labour, and both British and American troops.[4] At the same time mobile gangs were held in readiness for immediate action in the repair of roads that might be damaged by enemy counter-bombing.

---

[1] The total cost was approximately £24 millions.
[2] See Chapter X.
[3] The traps consisted of high tensile steel wire stretched between posts on straight lengths of road.
[4] The cost was about £1½ million.

The repair and replacement of bridges. Both before and during the war, the Ministry of Transport were prepared to repair or replace bridges damaged in air raids or by invasion. A large reserve of unit construction bridge materials suitable for spans up to 200 feet, and of timber and pre-stressed beams for shorter spans, was assembled and stored in the dispersed depots. Engineers of the highway authorities and contractors were trained in the erection of these bridges, and certain firms were allocated to each area.[1]

It was important, if the bridges were to carry their load, that their strength should be correctly calculated. The strength of all bridges on classified roads in Great Britain was accordingly assessed; and in some parts, particularly east and south-east England, there was an assessment of strength of all bridges, including those on unclassified roads. Altogether nearly 100,000 bridges were assessed.

Many of the bridges were strengthened, and some temporary bridges were erected for use in emergency. In London, for example, three temporary bridges were built.[2] The old disused railway bridge over the Medway at Rochester was brought into service to carry emergency road and rail traffic, and Saltash Bridge was adapted to take emergency road traffic. Another important bridge, at Westgate, in Gloucestershire, on the road to South Wales, was removed and replaced by temporary bridges in order to give more head-room for petrol barges.

(iv)

Harbours, Docks, Canals and Inland Waterways

The restriction of works in this category to the essential war minimum meant that only such works were permissible as would enable the port authorities to function efficiently.

Some of the larger schemes which were in hand at the outbreak of war (for example, the works on the New River Entrance, West Waterloo Dock, Liverpool) were closed down until the end of hostilities. Works carried out during the war fell into four classes:

1. Essential maintenance which could not be deferred.
2. Works without which undertakings could not function.[3]

---

[1] The actual damage to bridges from enemy bombing fortunately proved to be very slight.

[2] These bridges spanned the Thames at Millbank, Chelsea Embankment and Victoria Embankment. A temporary bridge was also erected at Staines.

[3] These works were assisted by grants under Section 39 of the Civil Defence Act 1939.

3. Works in connection with the provision of additional facilities.[1]

4. Works authorised under Defence Regulations.[2]

In addition to ordinary repair and maintenance works, the types of works undertaken by the Ministry of War Transport under the Civil Defence Act during the war included the provision of first-aid posts, cleansing stations, underground cables for electric sub-stations, alternative road access, transit sheds, railway sidings, water mains, hydraulic power, telephone installations, police accommodation and canteen facilities. There was, too, the resurfacing of quays, the levelling of sites, the alteration of jetties, the extension of breakwaters, the adaptation of berths, the drainage and construction of tidal oil jetties and oil pipe-lines, the construction of quay walls and river widening.

Works authorised under Regulation 56A (1) of the Defence (General) Regulations 1939 included the reconditioning of quay walls, the provision of electrical switch houses, sidings, canteens, and shelters, the widening of bridges, the renewal of lock gates, the reconstruction of war damage to warehouses, the erection of air raid shelters, the provision of crane tracks, locomotive sheds and pumping stations, the reconstruction of wharves and the resurfacing of storage grounds.

Numerous small works, such as the provision of mess rooms, lavatories, and workshops, added a substantial load to this programme.

As in every other section of the building programme, in the harbours and docks, shortages of labour and materials hampered constructional work. The Ministry of War Transport had, however, this advantage that, with the exception of the Port of London Authority, practically all maintenance repair work, and a proportion of the smaller new works, were carried out by the undertakings' own staffs. On contract works, on the other hand, the skilled labour of platelayers, bricklayers, carpenters and painters often fell short of the Ministry's needs.

Because of the shortage of materials, particularly of timber and steel, demands for licences could not always be met, so that some were slowed down; but for essential works enough materials could generally be found to keep them in full progress.

During the war the more important independently owned canal undertakings were under the control of the Ministry of War Transport. No major improvements were carried out. Work was confined to such essential maintenance and repairs as would enable undertakings to operate efficiently.

---

[1] Aided by grants under Section 41 of the Civil Defence Act 1939.

[2] Regulation 56A (1) of the Defence (General) Regulations 1939.

CHAPTER XVII

BUILDING BY
OTHER DEPARTMENTS

(i)
The Volume of Work Done by Other Departments

ALTHOUGH the volume of building works for the Service and Supply departments was greatly in excess of essential work for the other departments, a hard-and-fast line cannot always be drawn dividing strategic from other types of war building. But, as earlier chapters have shown, Service and Supply and 'Civil' depart-

Government Building: Value of Work Approved by Departments
Three-Months Moving Average (1942–43)

The following figures are taken from the 'W.B.A.' lists of work approved by the Building Directorate. The figures exclude most works under £5,000* and all extensions of existing contracts not requiring approval. The monthly figures have been smoothed by a three-months moving average.

£ millions

	Admir-alty (1)	W.O. (2)	Air Min. (3)	M/S (4)	M.A.P. (5)	Other M.O.W.T. (6)	Depts. (7)	TOTAL (8)
1942								
Dec.	0·4	1·2	5·4	0·6	1·4	0·3	1·3	10·6
1943								
Jan.	1·1	0·8	2·6	0·5	1·3	0·3	1·2	7·8
Feb.	1·3	0·6	1·3	0·5	1·2	0·3	2·0	7·2
Mar.	1·8	0·6	1·8	0·6	1·7	0·5	2·6	9·6
Apr.	1·7	0·3	2·2	0·5	1·1	0·5	2·7	9·0
May	2·0	0·8	2·4	0·5	1·3	0·7	2·4	10·1
June	1·4	2·1	3·9	0·4	1·1	0·6	3·5	13·0
July	0·8	2·2	3·8	0·4	1·2	0·6	3·7	12·7
Aug.	0·3	1·9	4·1	0·4	1·1	0·5	3·9	12·2
Sept.	0·4	0·5	2·1	1·8	1·2	0·4	2·8	9·2
Oct.	0·5	0·6	1·7	1·8	1·1	0·3	2·4	8·4
Nov.	1·3	0·5	1·3	1·8	1·3	0·1	2·5	8·8
Dec.	1·2	0·7	1·7	1·0	1·0	0·1	3·8	9·5

Source: Ministry of Works Statistical Bulletin.

* *Small Works (under £5,000): Value of Work Approved by Service and Supply Departments—Three-Months Moving Average (1943)*

£ millions

Jan.	Feb.	Mar.	Apr.	May	June	July	Aug.	Sept.	Oct.	Nov.	Dec.
0·7	0·7	0·7	0·6	0·6	0·6	0·7	0·7	0·6	0·7	0·6	0·6

Source: Ministry of Works Building Programme Division.

ments fell respectively into two convenient groups. On the one side stood the Admiralty, War Office, Air Ministry, Ministry of Supply, Ministry of Aircraft Production and Ministry of War Transport; and on the other side the remaining departments for which an appropriation of building labour and materials had to be made.

The difference in volume at the height of the war between these two categories is illustrated in the table on previous page.

The totals of the twelve actual monthly figures of work done (excluding most jobs under £5,000 and all extensions of existing contracts not requiring approval) in the year January to December 1943 were:

£ millions

	Value of work done in the year (1)	Value of works approved in the year (2)
New Work		
Admiralty	17·3	14·5
War Office	23·2	11·3
Air Ministry	85·8	27·0
Ministry of Supply . . .	16·5	10·3
Ministry of Aircraft Production .	26·2	14·8
Ministry of War Transport .	6·9	4·7
Other departments . . .	50·5	32·7
	226·4	115·3

Sources: Ministry of Works Statistics. W.B.A. List of Work Approved

In the same annual period the monthly average of operatives employed was:

	January–December 1943 Operatives employed (a monthly average) ('000)
New Work	
Admiralty	27·5
War Office	34·8
Air Ministry	95·6
Ministry of Supply . . .	37·0
Ministry of Aircraft Production	30·8
Ministry of War Transport .	8·9
Other departments . . .	75·6
	310·2

Source: Ministry of Works Statistical Bulletin

The ratio between the volume of building work as between Service and Supply Ministries and the other departments was thus roughly three to one. The other departments, apart from the Ministry of

Works itself (either in its capacity as an independent Ministry of as agent for other Ministries) comprised the Ministry of Health, the General Post Office, the Ministry of Food, the Ministry of Fuel and Power, the Board of Trade, the Ministry of Information, the Ministry of Agriculture and Fisheries, the Home Office (Ministry of Home Security), the Ministry of Education, and the Scottish departments (Health, Home, Agriculture, Education).

(ii)

The Shelter Programme

Overshadowing in volume of building work of all the other departments in the first year of war was the vast inchoate air raid precautions programme of the Home Office and the local authorities.[1]

Out of an estimated expenditure of £337,659,000,[2] on the Government building programme in the four quarters ending 30th September 1940, £57,845,000 was earmarked for air raid precautions.[3] Although this estimate, like other departmental estimates at that period, proved to be much in excess of the true demand, it did foreshadow a vast deflection of men and materials from other war objects which were not purely defensive.

After the First World War the Office of Works had been charged with the task of producing a schedule of buildings according to the degree of partial protection they might afford in the event of another war. The task was found to be impracticable; and in October 1933 responsibility for making these surveys was transferred to the local authorities.

Plans for shelters must depend, however, on precise data about the practical effects of bombs. Experience gained in the First World War, and in trials undertaken by the Service departments for their own purposes, had proved an inadequate guide. Nor was there, until 1935, a clear definition of responsibility for experiments in air raid precautions and for the heavy expenditure such experiments entailed. In that year a more workable central administrative organisation was created, funds were made available for experiments (although not for the construction of shelters) and the ban hitherto imposed on publicity was lifted.

---

[1] This section is based largely on studies prepared for the history of civil defence. In the Civil Defence History shelter policy as a whole is more fully considered.

[2] See Notes and Appendices: Appendix V, 'Survey by Departments of Estimated Expenditure on Building Works by Government Departments in the four quarters ending 30th September 1940'.

[3] See Chapter II.

Nevertheless, the Munich crisis found both the Air Raid Precautions Department of the Home Office and the public largely unprepared. There had been no real progress in providing shelters either for the general public or for Government servants; and the Government could merely resort to encouraging local authorities to dig temporary trenches. On 21st September 1938 London local authorities were informed of arrangements under which the Federation of Civil Engineering Contractors were to put one contractor at the disposal of each local authority to assist in a preliminary survey of entrenching operations. Three days later local authorities in densely-populated areas throughout the country, many of whom had previously enquired whether they should begin digging trenches and had been dissuaded, were advised to do so forthwith. The aim was to provide within ten days from the start of work reasonable cover from blast and splinters for ten per cent. of the population of those areas. Either voluntary or paid labour could be employed, and shelters were to be constructed only in open spaces owned by local authorities, or elsewhere with the consent of the owner. Alternative systems of trenching were suggested. The public trench system would, it was hoped, be supplemented by simple garden trenches lined with wood for which a design had been produced in August 1938; and the Press were invited to publish advice on constructing these simple trenches and on the gas-proofing of rooms.

After the Munich crisis a more active approach to the shelter problem began to be made by the central Government; and on 21st December 1938 the Lord Privy Seal, Sir John Anderson,[1] was able to give the House of Commons details of the most comprehensive shelter policy so far announced.[2] For the protection of Government offices the central Government could not but accept full responsibility, and it was stated that a beginning had been made with at least strengthening the most vital points in London. For the protection of the public the 'Anderson' steel domestic shelter and steel basement fittings were now introduced. This advance was followed by the announcement in April 1939 of a new design for a domestic surface shelter,[3] to be made of brickwork, mass concrete or concrete block masonry, with a reinforced concrete roof and, where necessary, a concrete floor. The standard design gave shelter for six people, but the internal dimensions could be increased to provide for a maximum of twelve. The cost of the materials was to be borne by the Government,[4] and local

---

[1] The functions of the Home Secretary under the Air Raid Precautions Act had been informally transferred to the Lord Privy Seal during the Munich crisis.

[2] H. of C. Deb., Vol. 342, Cols. 2880–92.

[3] A.R.P. Department Circular 91/39, 25th April 1939.

[4] A substantial part of the other costs of erection was also borne by the Exchequer in the form of grants; and a year after the outbreak of war it was decided to reimburse the whole cost of shelters constructed by the local authorities.

authorities were to be responsible for erecting the shelters, which were to be supplied to householders on the same basis as the steel shelters.[1]

The Civil Defence Act, passed on 15th July 1939,[2] made industrial and commercial shelter obligatory in certain areas, and its effect on the development of both public shelters and shelters in industrial premises proved decisive.

The Act now made it possible for local authorities to designate buildings regarded as suitable for public shelters, enter and adapt them in peace-time for use in the event of war and take possession of them if hostilities broke out. They were empowered also to enter land to construct shelters or underground premises or to provide entrances, shafts, ventilation, drainage, lighting, and so on, for shelters. They were urged by the Air Raid Precautions Department to use their new powers with energy, but also with discretion.[3]

From the beginning the Air Raid Precautions Department had attempted to persuade individual employers to prepare schemes for protecting their employees. In November 1936 the Department had published in a handbook[4] general advice on various possible forms of shelters giving protection against blast splinters and gas. Employers were advised to begin selecting sites for shelters and to make a survey of such structural alterations as might be necessary. They had been, however, under no statutory obligation to do so and the Government had had no intention of giving them any financial assistance. In April 1938 the Air Raid Precautions Department had issued a provisional code showing the standard of shelter required; but it was only with the passing of the Civil Defence Act that the provision of shelters of this standard became a definite obligation on the occupiers of factories and the owners of mines and commercial buildings in which more than fifty persons were employed and which were situated in specified areas or specified individually. This meant that shelters would be provided for four million workpeople.

The statutory obligation was accompanied by the financial concession for which employers had been pressing.[5] The Act was a great step forward: nevertheless, it remained difficult to form a complete picture of the amount of shelter available in any area or to keep a check on progress.

After the outbreak of war the pattern of shelter construction was to

---

[1] These were provided free to persons with an income of less than £250 a year; others had to pay for them.

[2] 2 and 3 Geo. 6, Ch. 31.

[3] A.R.P. Department Circular 158/39, 3rd August 1939.

[4] A.R.P. Handbook No. 6 (Air Raid Precautions in Factories and Business Premises).

[5] Grants were given from the Exchequer towards capital expenditure at a rate corresponding to the standard rate of income tax for the year 1939–40 (7s. in the £) on condition that the shelter was completed before the end of September 1939 or there were good grounds for thinking it would be completed within a reasonable time afterwards.

a large extent shaped by scarcity of labour and materials—especially of steel and cement.[1] Because of the shortage of steel, modifications were made in the supply of Anderson shelters and steel basement fittings. By the spring of 1940 local authorities were driven to rely for domestic shelters chiefly on brick and concrete surface shelters which had been intended for use only where other forms of domestic shelters were unsuitable.[2]

Shortages of material and of labour brought about, at the same time, the use of a new communal type of domestic shelter and caused modifications in design of both individual and communal shelters.[3] The communal shelter, large enough for forty-eight people, consisted of four compartments (each for twelve people) which could be arranged in different ways according to the shape of the site available. They were cheaper and quicker to build and needed less labour and material than the individual type of shelter; but because they were larger they tended to be weaker.

Already, before communal shelters were introduced, the shortage of cement had made necessary certain modifications in the design of domestic surface shelters which were to have unfortunate consequences later. Soon after the outbreak of war the Research and Experiments Department and the Chief Engineers Branch[4] had begun to investigate the possibility of reducing the amount of cement in the mortar used for surface shelters. The first instructions about domestic surface shelters issued in May 1939 had specified a mortar consisting mainly of cement and sand with only a very small proportion of lime, but the technical experts later held that where bricks of only medium strength were used for the walls of surface shelters the strength of the brickwork would not be substantially reduced by increasing the amount of lime in the mortar, even to a proportion of two parts of lime to one part of cement.[5] Instructions were accordingly issued in September 1939 that lime, up to this proportion, should be used as much as possible in the mortar in the brickwork or concrete block masonry of surface shelters; and in October the British Standards Institution issued a specification for lime and cement mortar suitable

---

[1] See Chapters II and VII.

[2] H.S.C. Circular 68/40 of 17th April 1940 (which announced that production of Anderson shelters and basement fittings would be stopped) directed the attention of local authorities to precast concrete units which were now on the market and could be used in much the same way as the Anderson shelter.

[3] It should be noted that the original conception was for shelters which people would occupy, seated, for comparatively short periods in daylight, but that all-night bombing, a development that was not foreseen, made it necessary to provide sleeping accommodation, thus adding immensely to the volume of constructional work required.

[4] The Research and Experiments Department and the Chief Engineer's Branch were respectively a Department and a Branch of the Ministry of Home Security.

[5] The lime-producing firms were fairly widely distributed, and the substitution of lime for cement was not only to save cement but also to release the strain on transport facilities.

for the purpose, with particulars of alternative types of materials and methods of mixing.

At the end of April 1940, shortly after the decision to discontinue the production of Anderson shelters, the Air Raid Precautions Department issued a revised version of the memorandum giving directions for erecting domestic surface shelters. This unfortunately contained ambiguous wording[1] which some Borough Engineers and local builders interpreted as permission to use mortar consisting entirely of lime and sand, and containing no cement. This type of mortar, which was of a much lower standard than anything officially contemplated, was used in some places not only for domestic surface shelters, with which the memorandum was concerned, but also for communal and even public shelters.

The ambiguity was removed in July by an instruction prohibiting the use in future of mortar consisting of lime and sand only, and making it clear that mortar used for shelters should never contain more than the proportion of lime given in the British Standards Institution specification.[2] But this new instruction could apply only to shelters constructed in future, and although Regional Technical Advisers, Borough Engineers and many professional institutions received the instruction in July, it is conceivable that a small local builder might continue to work to an unamended copy of the memorandum for some time afterwards. There were, moreover, apart from the ambiguity of the official instructions, instances of faulty workmanship and the use of inferior materials by unscrupulous contractors. In fact, when some of the surface shelters had to be strengthened, and even rebuilt in 1941 after experience of bombing, it was found that in the London region alone, well over 5,000 had been constructed in lime mortar, ungauged with cement.[3]

The instruction issued in July coincided with the temporarily acute shortage of cement described in earlier chapters.[4] This was virtually a famine in some areas,[5] and one or two local authorities who protested that if they obeyed the new instructions they would have to suspend their shelter programme entirely had to be given permission to use hydraulic lime instead of cement for some of their shelters.

---

[1] *A.R.P. Memorandum No. 14, Domestic Surface Shelters,* 29th April 1940. See also Fourteenth Report (Session 1940–1941) of Select Committee on National Expenditure.

[2] Circular C.E./43, 17th July 1940. This did not, however, mention the previous ambiguity but gave the impression that it was a new instruction issued because certain limes were unsuitable for use in mortar for shelters which might have to withstand bombing almost immediately.

[3] A large number of these were communal domestic shelters divided into four compartments, each for twelve persons; in arriving at the estimate of the number of shelters the compartments were not counted separately.

[4] See Chapters II and VII.

[5] At the end of May the Production Council had decided that, for the time being, any urgent requirements of the Service departments for controlled materials should be given a clear priority over home and export needs.

The revised version of the memorandum on domestic shelters issued at the end of April 1940, which contained the ambiguous description of the mortar, gave details also of other modifications in the design of the shelters made necessary by the shortage of steel for reinforcing concrete and of timber. Four new types were described. One was similar to the original surface shelter, but on a smaller scale, although, it was claimed, still large enough for six people. The other three had different types of roofs which were made of concrete but had no steel reinforcement and, since they rested on pre-cast concrete units, did not need timber for shuttering. The walls of the shelters were of brick, mass concrete, solid pre-cast concrete block masonry, or hollow concrete block masonry filled with ballast or sand. It was intended that all domestic shelters constructed in future should conform to the new designs unless contracts had already been made or plans were far advanced for shelters of the old patterns.

Local authorities tended to favour the first of these designs. Like the original design, it had a reinforced concrete roof. By June 1940 it became clear, however, that there would have to be further economies in the use of steel rods for reinforcement. It was decided that reinforced concrete roofs should no longer be used for individual domestic shelters and that all those built in future should conform to the last three revised designs. With a few exceptions, the same ruling was applied to communal shelters. Revised designs for these (similar to the three surface shelter designs) which had already been issued informally were now officially sanctioned.[1] Similar designs were not adopted for public shelters, as it was obviously more difficult to use roofing without reinforcement for these because of the width of span.

Of the occupiers of the factories covered by the Civil Defence Act, some ninety per cent.—or twelve thousand in all—had, by the end of 1939, fulfilled their obligations under the Act and submitted shelter schemes. By the end of the year the percentage had risen to ninety-eight and a large proportion of the shelters had actually been completed;[2] and by the time heavy raiding began shelter was complete in almost all the factories that came within the provisions of the Act.

Shelter in commercial buildings produced greater difficulties and complications. Not only did they usually call for more timber and steel strutting than was needed in factories, but the responsibility for ensuring that occupiers carried out their obligations rested with the local authorities. These were often preoccupied with their domestic and public shelter work, and were reluctant as a rule to press occupiers of business premises at a time when materials were scarce and when some firms were moving to the country. Moreover, since local

---

[1] H.S.C. 137/40, 19th June 1940.

[2] Cmd. 6251 (1941). Annual Report of the Chief Inspector of Factories for the year 1939, pp. 40–41.

authorities were not required to prepare statistical reports on commercial shelters, comparable to those produced by the Factory Inspectorate for factory shelters, the central Government had no means of knowing precisely what progress was being made in the provision of shelter, or even how many commercial buildings were covered by the Act. Some partial surveys were attempted, but they were of little help.

(iii)

The Effects of Intensive Bombing

When the ordeal came the total weight of bombs was considerably less than had been expected. The practical experience of attack gave the Research and Experiments Department[1] the opportunity to collect information about the powers of resistance of the different types of shelters[2] which were designed in the absence of adequate data. The earliest scattered raids supplied information chiefly about the Anderson steel shelters. These appeared to be exceptionally effective when properly sited and covered, and indeed gave a higher standard of protection than they were designed to give. Their value was fully confirmed by the later raids on provincial towns and the mass attacks on London in September. (It was unfortunate, however, that the use of Anderson shelters was limited by the fact that they were subject to flooding; and that to render them proof against water entailed a great deal of building work and the substantial expenditure of labour and financial resources.) Brick and concrete surface shelters were, on the whole, less successful than the Anderson steel shelters, mainly because of the action of unexpected forces.[3] Nevertheless, many surface shelters stood up well, and gave a considerably higher standard of protection than had been expected. No doubt most of the shelters found to be unsatisfactory were those built during the cement shortage with mortar containing a high proportion of lime[4] or even consisting of lime and sand only. The use of other inferior materials,

---

[1] Of the Ministry of Home Security.

[2] The first appreciation of the results of air raids was prepared on 11th July 1940, and was based only on the experience of minor raids on coastal towns. The second was dated 26th September 1940, and was based on the medium scale raids on provincial cities and mass raids on London—though detailed reports of damage in London were not yet available. A third memorandum was produced 23rd January 1941; it gave a survey of shelter needs based on the experience of four months of intensive raids.

[3] Report by Sir Alexander Rouse and Sir Reginald Stradling, 18th October 1940. Memorandum by T. Hutson, 11th December 1940.

[4] But a report from the Eastern Region stated that even lime-cement shelters had set well and were not weak (letter dated 8th February 1941); and at a Regional Shelter Conference, held at the Ministry of Home Security on 25th February 1941, a representative from the Midland Region said that in Birmingham some of the barrel-type shelters constructed with cement mortar had proved unsatisfactory.

and faulty workmanship, may have caused some of the catastrophes. There was also a defect in the design of the surface shelters: the roof slab was not anchored to the walls and was therefore likely to be raised and to crash down again on to the shelter if the walls were shifted by surface earth-movement caused by bombs exploding near them. Yet in the height of the blitz, and with shortages of labour and materials, it was out of the question to abandon this form of shelter entirely, for surface shelters of various kinds had on the whole proved very popular with local authorities and formed a large proportion of the total shelter available in many areas.[1]

On the whole the surface shelters withstood the test of attack well and gave a much higher standard of protection than had been expected. The weaknesses were not all unforeseen, and because some of the brick and concrete surface shelters, basements and trenches had proved unsatisfactory, it was clear that although the total volume of shelter would have to be increased it would be advisable to strengthen or close some of the shelters already provided and to restrict the field of new construction to certain types that had proved particularly successful. Experience showed, too, that a much higher degree of protection seemed probable than had been expected in pre-war days without the very large increase in expenditure needed for complete protection.[2]

In December 1940, local authorities were asked to examine carefully all brick and concrete surface shelters constructed with mortar containing lime, and were given detailed instruction for strengthening or partially rebuilding them according to the degree and character of their deficiencies. They were also advised about methods of remedying various kinds of dampness in surface shelters—a further attempt to make these shelters more acceptable as dormitories.[3] Later, in March 1941, it was decided that communal domestic shelters built with mortar consisting of lime and sand only, with no gauging of cement, should, without exception, be put out of action, either by demolishing them (where they were visibly unstable or where the site or materials were needed for other purposes) or by obstructing the

---

[1] A number of disquieting incidents had, however, the effect in some areas of producing in the minds of the public doubts about the safety of surface shelters as a whole. Practical experience also cast some doubt on the value of two other forms of shelter widely used —trenches and basements.

[2] Buildings with steel frames, it was found, withstood the effects of bombing excellently, and gave good shelter not only in their basements but also in higher floors. In applying the experience gained in the first intensive bombing raids, an early decision was to prohibit the use of lime-cement mortar for surface shelters constructed during the winter months, since one great disadvantage of this type of mortar was the lapse of time before it set, which was likely to be prolonged in winter. Instructions were given that the cement mortar used should contain not more than four parts of sand to one part of cement. The prohibition was later extended indefinitely.

[3] In the London Region it was reported that very few shelters were bad enough to be demolished, but a certain amount of repointing was necessary in most areas.

entrancing and exhibiting 'closed' notices.[1] The cost of demolition was reimbursed by the Exchequer, regardless of the date of construction of the shelter, except where defects were clearly due to shortcomings on the part of the contractors. Shelters built in lime-cement mortar were to be examined on their merits, and if necessary closed or demolished also. These instructions did not apply to individual domestic shelters which, because of their small size, were stronger than communal and public shelters.

The defect in the original design of the surface shelter (which had become apparent because of the unexpected menace of earth shock and earth movement) was remedied in a new design prepared by the Research and Experiments Department.[2] This was intended to prevent the roof and walls from separating and the walls themselves from disintegrating when bombs exploded near them.[3] Local authorities were instructed to use the new design for all communal shelters built in future. For individual surface shelters, the earlier designs were permitted, but the shelters were to be constructed in reinforced brickwork (the reinforcement being carried into the covering roof concrete) and provided with a bituminous damp-proof course.

After the spring of 1942 shelter work throughout the country was severely cut down. This was done to conform with the Prime Minister's directive that the number of workers in the building industry must be drastically and progressively reduced by 1942. Although there was no immediate change in the labour allocation for civil defence works, Mr. Churchill's directive had an early effect on shelter policy. On 21st March 1942, local authorities were given a preliminary warning that the special allocation of building labour for shelters and civil defence works would cease at the end of June, and that it might not be possible to retain the whole of the existing labour force after 1st April. Early in April it was announced that the labour allocation would in fact be progressively reduced from its existing level of 40,000 to 30,000 by the middle of May and to 20,000 by the end of June, when it would be withdrawn completely. In practice, however, men employed on shelters were not dismissed until the Ministry of Labour could arrange for them to be transferred immediately to other essential work. The limited labour now available was

---

[1] The fact that all shelters constructed with lime-mortar, and even some of those constructed with lime-cement mortar, had to be demolished or closed provoked much adverse public criticism: e.g. H. of C. Deb., Vol. 370, Cols. 304–05, 20th March 1941.

[2] Of the Ministry of Home Security.

[3] The walls were constructed in brickwork (or hollow concrete blocks) reinforced with vertical steel rods, or in ferro-concrete. The vertical reinforcements were tied to the roof and, wherever possible, to the floor so that the shelter could be shifted bodily without breaking. In addition, a bituminous felt damp-proof course was provided at ground level to serve the dual purpose of helping to reduce dampness and to increase the shelter's resistance to surface earth-movements by allowing it to move slightly in a horizontal direction. In a further effort to reduce dampness the roof was designed to overhang the walls

devoted to strengthening and installing essential amenities in existing shelters rather than to constructing new ones.

It had been estimated at the end of 1941 that, with the existing labour force, it should be possible to complete, by the end of March 1942, about seventy per cent. of the shelter work which had been outstanding at the end of August 1941, and that if the labour allocation for the following three months were cut to 38,000 the work would be virtually complete by the end of June. But the estimate left out of account the extra shelters that had to be provided in certain important places.[1]

At the beginning of June, regions were warned that after the end of the month any work then outstanding would have to come within the 'garrison' scheme. Before the end of June, however, the system of allocating the country's mobile building labour had been completely reorganised. This was now almost entirely confined to work sponsored by the Service and Supply departments. Certain individual shelter works, however, were regarded as in a similar category: these included shelters with a claim for first priority (category A) at nodal points, four tunnels already in hand in Birkenhead, Newcastle and Plymouth, the new 'tube' shelters in London and new shelters in a small number of important and vulnerable areas. The work of strengthening and installing essential amenities in shelters of high priority (that is, those classified as coming within A and B areas) which were likely to be substantially used was also continued, but for this local authorities had to rely on what labour could be mustered locally (although it might at any time be transferred by the Ministry of Labour to work considered to be of greater importance). In those areas of lower priority (classified as C) which could not be regarded as 'quasi-B',[2] shelter work (including new construction, strengthening and the provision of amenities) was now barred entirely, with the exception of simple maintenance work such as could be undertaken by local authorities with their own staffs.

(iv)

Storage and Other Depots

In that borderland of the constructional programme which was common ground for many different kinds of building undertakings —whether military, quasi-military or civil—an important place was held by the great war-time depots—for the storage of munitions, of

---

[1] These were technically classified as 'nodal points'.

[2] The classification 'quasi-B' was applied to a number of areas whose claims were somewhat above the general requirements of C areas.

perishable foods, of grain and of the thousand-and-one material reserves of a nation at war. Among these installations were those already mentioned in earlier chapters[1] for the construction of which the Service and Supply Ministries were sometimes directly responsible: others were built by the Ministry of Works on an agency footing.[2] These included:[3]

1. Storage depots for ordnance.
2. Standard stores for general purposes.
3. Storage depots for special articles and materials.
4. Cold storage buildings.
5. Grain silos.
6. Inland sorting depots.

STORAGE DEPOTS FOR ORDNANCE

Before the Royal Ordnance factory programme had been completed a large number of storage depots were needed for the reception of bulk explosives from the new explosives plants being installed in the United Kingdom, as well as for those coming from the United States. Storage capacity had to be found, too, for filled ammunition from the new Royal Ordnance factories as they came into production on an immense scale, as well as from existing Government factories and from firms working for the Government. Added to these formidable demands was the demand for storage capacity for empty components from the many Government and privately-owned engineering factories engaged on ammunition parts of all types, sizes and metals as they poured into the filling factories. Most of these depots were sponsored by the Ministry of Supply, others by the Admiralty and the War Office. All were sited in relation to the particular factories or group of factories to or from which they were to issue or receive the bulk materials or filled ordnance. Over twenty were constructed at a total cost of more than £8½ millions.

The filled ammunition and bulk explosives depots consisted essentially of a number of storage buildings protected by earth and moundings and concrete traverses, and served by standard gauge railways (and narrow-gauge tracks) with marshalling sidings connected to the main line. Administration and ancillary buildings, and in some cases sleeping accommodation, had also to be provided. The empty component stores were standardised structures presenting no very unusual features. All had road access, and some had rail access also.

Among typical schemes were:

---

[1] See Chapters XI to XV.

[2] See Section (x) of this chapter.

[3] It is to be noted that for the storage of many goods, especially foodstuffs in 1943 and 1944, temporary steel houses proved a useful expedient in emergency.

Yardley Chase. This depot was constructed in two parts. There were twenty-nine storage buildings in the first part and twenty in the second. The ancillary group of buildings comprised offices, petrol stations, garage, workshop, canteen and kitchen, police hostel, locomotive shed and oil storage. The store sheds were each 100 feet long by 40 feet wide and had a loading platform on the long side for rail service. Reinforced concrete frame construction was used with $4\frac{1}{2}$-inch brick wall infilling and 5-inch precast solid roof units, felt-covered. Some of the sheds had asphalt floors and changing rooms.

Nesscliffe. At the beginning of the war, the War Office took over the old Shropshire and Montgomery railway running from Shrewsbury to Llanymynech, a distance of about eighteen miles. Sub-depots were constructed off this line at Ford, Shrawardine and Kinnerley, with sheds built in pairs, each served with a railway spur. Building work commenced in March 1941. The first store shed was taken over by the War Office in January 1942 and the last of the 144 store sheds were completed in December 1942; the total area for storage was well over one million square feet. A camp at Nesscliffe to serve the depot was also built, and there were many ancillary buildings.

In June 1943 building began on an additional sub-depot at Knockin. It comprised sixty-four sheds, giving a further storage of 632,000 square feet, and was completed in June 1944. The total cost of the completed scheme was over $£2\frac{1}{2}$ millions, excluding the railway work, which was mainly carried out by military labour.

Admiralty Ammunition Depot at Ditton Priors. This £600,000 scheme was begun in September 1940 and completed in December 1942. There was dispersed storage in thirty-six buildings of 4,000 square feet each and thirty-six buildings of 1,000 square feet each; thirty were earth-mounded. There were also five laboratory examination rooms, two railway trans-shipping sheds, general offices, police offices, a maintenance depot, canteens, shifting rooms, lavatories, general stores and tractor sheds. Alongside the depot were erected a hostel for Admiralty civil police and key workers, barracks for the military guard, hostel and recreation buildings for industrial workers, and the depot commandant's bungalow. In this isolated district, without public services of water, drainage or electricity, two bore holes about 300 feet deep were sunk, a sewage disposal works was constructed and electricity was brought ten miles across country to a transformer station.

The site consisted of 550 acres at the end of a practically disused branch of the Great Western Railway and was between 640 feet and 820 feet above sea level. It was undulating and in part heavily wooded. The subsoil was clay, and the many streams crossing the site were subject to sudden flood: this made excavation and permanent drainage a major problem, particularly during the two winters of construction. On one occasion, after a heavy fall of snow, fifty miles of public roads had to be cleared by the contractor's bull-dozers in a week in order to restore communications with the neighbourhood. Labour in this remote area was scarce. Men were recruited from all over the coun try, and from Ireland, and it took fourteen months to reach the peak of 1,000 men. Most of the workers were accommodated in a very fully-equipped camp on the site, and the rest were taken to their homes each day by a fleet of hired buses.

The constructional work included the tasks of enclosing the open site with nearly four miles of unclimbable iron fencing, of excavating 40,000 cubic yards of clay and rock, and of providing 42,000 tons of stone pitching for the ten miles of roads, and 22,000 tons of macadam. The roads were bounded by twenty-one miles of kerbing, and there were twenty-three miles of new drains and open ditches. In all, there were 220 buildings which used $4\frac{1}{4}$ million bricks, 670 tons of steel, 17,000 tons of hardcore, 28,000 tons of aggregate, 12,000 tons of sand, 4,000 tons of cement and 305,000 square feet of asbestos sheeting. Eleven miles of separate surface water and soil drains were laid, with a sewage disposal works taking 18,000 gallons per day, with effluent discharging to open streams.

For the fire-fighting system an emergency reservoir of 240,000 gallons was constructed at the highest part of the site with a full hydrant system, static fire pools and trailer pump houses, and dispersed dormitories with passive air defence protection for the firemen. The electrical work was carried out by the Admiralty.

STANDARD STORES FOR GENERAL PURPOSES

Storage capacity in widely-scattered areas was wanted for the Ministry of Food, the Ministry of Supply, the Stationery Office and the Controller of Supplies of the Ministry of Works. The standardised type of building evolved was a structure 214 feet in length and 120 feet in width, giving an area of approximately 25,000 square feet of storage space on one floor. Access was either along the length or the width of the store by means of large door openings, with enough head-room for lorries.

The sites chosen were as level as possible for quick development and were above flood level. Wherever practicable they had connection by road, rail and water for the transportation of stores, but where none of the three existed either road and rail facilities (or road and water) were provided. It was essential that there should be access to the sites at all times.

The buildings were light steel-framed structures in three spans of forty feet, designed to 'war-time economy stresses' with concrete floors, brick panel walls and corrugated asbestos roofs.

In the several stores special facilities were installed for the needs of the occupying department. Thus, for the Ministry of Food, wherever bulk grain was stored, grain handling plant was put in; for some of the Ministry of Supply buildings special lifting tackle was installed for the movement of machinery, and for the Ministry of Works there were fire-break walls and special stoves.

The work was carried out in two programmes. In the first, over 100 buildings were erected which gave over $2\frac{1}{2}$ million square feet of storage space at a cost of about £1,350,000. The erection of the first store was begun in April 1941 and the programme was completed in December 1941. In the second programme over sixty buildings were erected giving over $1\frac{1}{2}$ million square feet of storage space at a cost of about £900,000. That programme was begun in November 1941 and was complete by December 1942. Railway sidings were provided in the first programme, and rail and dock works in the second.

For salvage two depots were erected consisting of nine storage and transport sheds of steel-framed and sheeted construction. Railway sidings were made, and offices and ancillaries were constructed in brick and partly framed in steel.

STORAGE FOR SPECIAL ARTICLES AND MATERIALS

Several schemes were undertaken early in the war for the safe keeping of national art treasures. In one example, a large number of old masters (nominally valued at £10 millions, but in reality priceless) were stored in a slate quarry in North Wales. The quarry could only be reached along five miles of narrow mountain road which was liable to be snowbound for weeks at a time. The store was in five caves whose approaches had to be widened so as to take large pictures on special trucks running on narrow-gauge railways. The floors of the caves were levelled, the roofs propped to prevent falls of slate, and in each cave a store building was erected. A studio was built outside the caves for examining the pictures. In order to obviate any risk of damage to the ancient pigments on the canvases, the Ministry of Works designed plant to give controlled de-humidified air conditions with an even temperature never varying more than one degree. A generating plant was installed for electricity supply.

During the storage operations the mountain road had to be remade on two occasions, and a bridge over the road remodelled in order to allow space for the pictures to pass under.

Among the special items dealt with in this and other special storage schemes the following are typical examples:

> The Rubens ceiling at the Whitehall Banqueting Hall. This was carefully taken down in two days and removed to a safe place.

> The King Charles I statue in Whitehall and many other London statues of special interest.

The Van de Velde pictures from the Board Room at the Admiralty after the building had been bombed.

The bronze screen and stalls in the Henry VII Chapel at Westminster Abbey.

The Crown Jewels from the Tower of London.

COLD-STORAGE BUILDINGS

Early in the war the Ministry of Works was commissioned by the Ministry of Food to carry out a programme of cold-storage buildings with a total capacity of 5,000,000 cubic feet of refrigerated space. Eight buildings were planned, seven of them to be new structures and one an adaptation of an existing building. The two largest buildings, situated near large ports, were each capable of providing 1,000,000 cubic feet of cold store; five other stores provided between them 2,600,000 cubic feet; and the eighth—the adapted building[1]—made up the balance.

The programme was barely under way when a second commission for 5,000,000 cubic feet of cold-storage buildings was given, to be followed shortly after by a third for an equal quantity. The efficiency of the stores erected under the later programmes was enhanced by the experience gained in the first series. The German air raids had shown that reasonable immunity could be obtained only through dispersal, and the 10,000,000 cubic feet later commissioned was therefore divided among forty buildings each with a capacity of 250,000 cubic feet of cold-storage space. With buildings of this capacity it was possible to design a standard type. In each, requirements were almost identical, and comprised duplicate engine-house and machinery to avoid the disaster of a total breakdown; road and rail access with loading banks and wide canopied platforms outside the cold rooms; lifts to the three floors; a boiler-house; and staff accommodation.

These forty stores were widely scattered in rural and semi-rural areas chosen by the Ministry of Food and were near towns where services were available, and where labour for operating the stores could be recruited. Road access and rail facilities were major factors in deciding the sites of individual stores. Some were founded on rock and others had to have piled foundations.

The system of refrigeration adopted was cold air from coolers placed within the structure, and to minimise the risk of both being knocked out in a raid the duplicate engine-houses for operating the machinery were placed as far apart as possible. In the first programme two methods of insulation were used. One provided for the separate insulation of each floor within the main frame of the building; in the other the whole frame and floors were insulated in the form of a great box.

---

[1] This was later destroyed by enemy bombing.

The last method saved a considerable quantity of insulating material, and was adopted for the standard buildings of the second and third programmes. Cork was used throughout the first programme for insulating both floors and walls, but cork became scarce as the war went on, and in the later storage buildings the vertical insulation of the walls was carried out with slag wool.

The envelope method of insulation required a rather special type of construction. In a normal steel-frame building (and all the cold stores were steel-framed) the external stanchions are incorporated in the main walls, but in this type of building the steel framing was itself insulated to allow for contraction of the framing when cooling down, and a space of some $12\frac{1}{2}$ inches was left between the face of the stanchion and the inside of the main walling. At each floor level this space was filled in with carefully fitted cork slabs set in bitumen, and these points formed the flexible attachments which the external 14-inch and 18-inch brick walls had with the steel structure. A $4\frac{1}{2}$-inch brick skin was built on the edges of the floor slabs, and the space between the skin and the outer walls was filled in with slag wool which rested on the cork slabs fitted at each floor level and was tamped until it reached a density of 12 pounds per cubic foot. The walls of the storage rooms were protected with vertical concrete dunnage slats. These prevented goods from being packed close against the wall and thus allowed a good air circulation.

The average total cost of a standard storage building, including rail and road works, was £136,000. The cost of the total programme was nearly £7 millions (excluding the cost of adapting the store which was destroyed) for 200,000 tons of storage.

Storing was possible at zero Fahrenheit in the earlier schemes, since refrigeration was by cold-air circulation from air-cooler batteries operated in conjunction with high-speed ammonia refrigerating machines. In the later stores, the plant was designed to give additional freezing capacity to cool down and refreeze defrosted produce and to freeze home-killed meat.

GRAIN SILOS

The grain silos erected for the Ministry of Food embodied the novel principle of providing in one building a drying plant and storage space for the increased crop of home-grown wheat. Sixteen silos were built with a total storage space for a reserve of 80,000 tons, and each silo was capable of storing 5,000 tons.

The machinery and drying plants were housed in a brick-built steel-framed central working tower, eighty feet high and thirty feet square. This was flanked by two wings, each composed of six pairs of reinforced concrete storage bins sixty-two feet high, supported over a semi-basement; the whole was carried on raft, sometimes on piled, foundations. These wings were topped by a brick-built steel-framed pent-house carrying the conveyors which delivered the wheat from the intake elevators or the dryers to the storage bins. Rail sidings were brought in on one side of the building only, and included a separate fuel bay adjoining the boiler-house. On the opposite side of the silo, arrangements were made for the reception and despatch of grain by road transport.

Irrespective of widely varying site conditions standard plans and foundations were used, and two types of bins, circular and square, were employed to prevent a run on any one kind of formwork. The record time for the construction of a battery of twelve bins was seven days and nights of continuous working. In several schemes the bin roofs were precast and hoisted as monoliths into position sixty-seven feet up. Each silo absorbed in its construction about 750 tons of cement, 450 tons of steel and 130,000 bricks.

The approximate cost of a silo on a normal site was £54,000 plus site work and machinery costs, amounting to about £41,000, that is, £95,000 for each silo, exclusive of railway work.

(v)

Hospitals, Hostels and Houses

Problems of social policy form the subject of detailed study in other volumes of this series. In the present volume reference has been made, where relevant, to new construction of hospitals and hostels, as well as to the restrictions put upon the building of new dwelling-houses. The following pages revert to this topic and describe some aspects that were the particular concern of the Ministry of Works as agent for the Ministry of Health and the Department of Health for Scotland.

The Emergency Hospital Programme. In 1938 and 1939 the Ministry of Health and the Department of Health for Scotland went forward with plans to provide casualty beds in readiness for the expected effects of intensive enemy bombing on large cities. In certain existing public hospitals and institutions near large centres of population, and in some voluntary ones, the number of beds was to be increased; and additional accommodation was to be found for over 36,000 beds in hutted extensions. These plans comprised a hundred schemes at a total cost of some £4 millions. Building work was begun in March 1939 under the general direction of the Office of Works, but was controlled by private architects—selected from panels prepared by the Royal Institute of British Architects—who were experienced in hospital design and were in practice in the locality of the institutions to be extended.

The institutions undertook in general to provide accommodation for staffs, catering and administration, but it was often found necessary to build emergency operating theatres, kitchens, and sometimes staff quarters. The first of the contracts was completed and the hutted buildings were in occupation before the outbreak of war; and the whole programme was virtually complete by the end of 1939.

Rather less than half of this early programme was in timber construction; most of the rest was designed in brick or concrete blocks, frequently with steel stanchions and trusses. Occasionally both external and internal walls were built of three-inch and four-inch thick compressed wood-wool slabs which gave good thermal insulation. In the later stages of this first programme three complete hospitals were put in hand, each with a capacity of 600 beds and all the usual hospital services. Subsequently one of these schemes was doubled.

Early in 1940 a second programme was put in hand. Its purpose was to meet new assessments of needs arising from the evacuation of population from the larger centres, the growing military forces in the country and kindred factors, as well as to provide facilities for some of the hospitals partially evacuated from London. This programme was originally for a further 28,000 beds estimated to cost £8 millions. It included twelve fully-equipped hospitals (mostly of 600 beds) and also a number of major extensions to schemes constructed in the first programme.

The number of beds was reduced from time to time, and the programme as completed made provision for 8,600 additional beds at a cost of £4¼ millions. Because of developments in the Emergency Hospital Service and the range of patients for which it was provided, many special treatment facilities were introduced: for example, special buildings to give treatment for wounds caused by burns, and for physiotherapy and manipulative treatment. For the fully-equipped hospitals, sites of about thirty acres each were acquired in various parts of the country. This programme was partly the responsibility of the Office of Works and partly that of nominated architects; and the cost was higher than that of the first programme because of the added ancillaries.

The second programme was set going just at the time of the fall of France, and the shortage of materials added to the problems of construction. The use of timber for structural purposes was forbidden, and every economy was demanded in the use of steel and other scarce materials.[1]

To meet these shortages a flat roof of precast units was designed with a minimum use of steel-rod reinforcement, later increased to provide resistance to blast and ground shock. Except in special cases,

---

[1] See Chapter II.

the use of steel stanchions and beams was eliminated and precast reinforced concrete members were used. The first of the fully-equipped hospitals in this second programme, at Horley, was for 1,000 beds and cost £190,000. It was commenced in July 1940 and became the prototype for the remainder.[1]

One centre of a special type was that for communicable diseases. It was presented to the country jointly by the American Red Cross and Harvard University, and an American field hospital unit was sent over to operate it. The British Government were asked to acquire a site selected by representatives who came to England for the purpose, to construct foundations, drains and roads, and to arrange for the erection of the prefabricated structure which was brought from America complete from superstructure and plant down to balls of string and bottles of ink.

In Scotland the hospital building programme followed the same general lines but it included from the beginning six completely new hospitals, each of 640 beds—four were later extended to over 1,200 beds each—and one of 400 beds. In addition twenty-four hutted annexes, providing over 8,500 beds, were erected at existing hospitals. The first completed ward unit in the United Kingdom was opened by the Secretary of State for Scotland at an Edinburgh hospital in May 1939.

Together with this new construction over 1,100 beds were provided at three hotels which were requisitioned and which thereafter had a number of structural adaptations; while a further 3,500 beds were found by the adaptation of sixty-two large houses taken over by agreement with their owners and again adapted for hospital purposes. In all, 16,600 general hospital beds and over 3,800 convalescent hospital beds were added to the existing hospital resources of Scotland.

Industrial hostels and married quarters. When, in the spring of 1941, many of the Royal Ordnance factories and aircraft factories were coming into production or expanding production on a vast scale, factory workers in great numbers were being directed to them. To accommodate these workers over forty-five hostels, with a total capacity of 35,000, were erected by the Ministry of Works for the Ministry of Supply and the Ministry of Aircraft Production at a cost of some £7 millions. Each of these hostels housed from 500 to 1,000 workers, men or women, or both. Married quarters, too, were put up for trans-

---

[1] These war-time hospitals were all single-storey buildings. They usually had open-sided covered ways which formed connecting corridors. As a rule the wards were heated with slow-combustion stoves. Non-essential and expensive equipment—such as, for example, shadowless lamps in theatres—was eliminated, and the standard of staff accommodation was reduced. Generally these emergency buildings, although they had not the finish of peace-time construction, provided a very good standard of hospital service and were not in any way the improvised type of hut used in the First World War.

ferred key workers. By the end of 1941 over 7,000 men were at work, on building hostels and married quarters, for the Ministry of Supply alone; and the work was dovetailed, for the most part, into the Royal Ordnance factory programme.

Since the evidence of many industrial surveys has established the concept that the output of work is directly influenced by the comfort and contentment of the workers, the design of the hostels became not only a material but a psychological problem. In collaboration with the other interested departments, the Ministry of Works set itself to evolve the best type of hostel within the permissible expenditure of labour and materials. A standard hostel was thus designed, and on the experience gained in running hostels of that type revised standards were brought into use. The hostels already built were, for the most part, modified to bring them into line with the newer designs.

The essential hub of the hostel was the welfare centre. It made provision in one way or another for the leisure time of practically the whole population of the hostel. For a hostel of 1,000 capacity, there was an assembly hall for 500, a canteen for the whole number in two sittings on the cafeteria principle, a lounge and tea bar, games and reading rooms. Occasionally the welfare block on one site also served an adjacent hostel. Every care was taken to avoid an institutional atmosphere by using furnishings, textiles and decorations of a fresh contemporary character, with individual colour schemes chosen for their psychological influence on the residents.

Economy and speed of erection were achieved by using only single-storey buildings. The units were grouped to form a pleasant lay-out and comprised, besides the welfare block, sleeping blocks, staff quarters, laundry and hairdressing rooms,[1] a sick bay[2] and ancillary buildings such as garages, stores, workshops, boiler houses, and water towers. There were air raid shelters, too, in many of the earlier schemes, but not in the later ones.

Double-bunking was the general rule in the sleeping blocks of the very early types of hostel, which were capable of taking 2,000 on this basis. Soon, however, they were planned for single beds. Each standard block had twenty-eight double and six single bedrooms with wash-basins in each room, a small common-room, and sanitary accommodation, including shower-baths.

After the main programme of hostel building had been completed, a number of schemes of normal size, and some smaller schemes of 50

---

[1] One problem in factories was absenteeism through the girls taking time off to have their hair dressed. Hair-dressing units were accordingly included in the hostel plans, and also a laundry for 'home' washing.

[2] The size of the sick bay depended on the hospital facilities of the neighbourhood. Normally a two per cent. proportion of the normal number of residents had to be provided for.

to 200 capacity, were carried out. They were mostly for the private firms working for the Ministry of Supply.[1]

Most of the construction of the sleeping and other blocks was at first in hutting of the plasterboard, concrete and sawdust-concrete types; but brickwork was also used. Later came the Ministry of Works standard hut, with clayblock or other infilling, according to whatever materials were to be had; and for the assembly halls, three-pinned steel-welded open-webbed transverse frames of fifty feet span, designed by the structural engineers of the Ministry of Works. The engineering services included heating, hot water, ventilation and electrical schemes.

It was mainly for the ordnance and aircraft factories that married quarters were needed, but some were put in for the Admiralty, the Ministry of War Transport and other departments. Schemes varied in size from 20 to nearly 700, and about 6,500 were built in all. Quarters were semi-detached, with two or three bedrooms (usually half of each type) and were built of bricks or blocks, or in the various types of hutting available at the time—precast concrete, plasterboard, asbestos wood, sawdust-cement—to two standard plans, one of which had a single external entrance only. In addition to the bedrooms there was invariably a living-room, kitchen, bathroom, W.C., linen cupboard and larder. Hot water was provided by a back-to-back grate in the living-room and kitchen.

Accommodation for Land Army Volunteers.[2] In the second winter of war it had become an acute problem over most of Britain to find accommodation for Land Army volunteers. When, in the spring of 1941, the Agricultural Executive Committees were instructed to deploy men and women workers for land reclamation and drainage, and for contract work for farmers, the problem had to be tackled on a new scale. While the girls employed on farms could often be accommodated in the farm-house or sometimes in near-by lodgings, other arrangements were needed for the employees of the committees, of whom groups of ten or twenty might be required to live and work in a small area. For them hostels were provided either by taking over existing buildings, such as large country houses, or by building special hostels. A programme of 299 hutments, holding either thirty or fifty beds, was drawn up by the Ministry of Agriculture and the Ministry of Works and was to have been completed by the end of July; but because of the difficulty of finding sites, and the unexpectedly high cost per worker housed of these small hostels, the Ministry of Works was driven to press for a reduction in the standards proposed. As a

---

[1] Some of the hostels were later released for the use of American troops. Others were partially converted to married quarters, and one was converted for use by the Home Office as an approved school. The boys did much of the work of conversion.

[2] The following pages are based on studies that have been prepared for the history of agricultural policy and food production in war.

result, single cubicles for each occupant or double-tiered bunks in one long dormitory became the accepted system. On this basis, construction was speeded up and the greater part of the programme was completed by the end of the year.

The hutments were in fact ready before all the workers had been found to occupy them, so that the Ministry of Works, in discussing the labour allocation for 1942, could not but point out that only about 4,500 beds were occupied in March out of the 12,225 which had been provided under pressure, and with such speed, in the previous twelve months. This deficiency in manpower was made good in the course of 1942 by the employment of large numbers of the Women's Land Army for gang work. Between January and June 1942 nearly a hundred of these hutments were filled with girls, while others were used to house Italian prisoners of war; and when pressure on the building industry was greatly intensified during 1942 by the arrival in large numbers of the American units, it proved fortunate indeed that a temporary surplus of housing had accrued.

Great efforts had been made meanwhile to find buildings which could be used as hostels. Most of the premises so requisitioned had to be adapted considerably before they could accommodate far larger numbers of persons than they had been originally designed to house, but in spite of such difficulties, and the attendant delays, the Ministry of Works and the Agricultural Executive Committees were remarkably successful, as the following tables show:

Hostels for Agricultural Workers: England and Wales

	Requisitioned premises		M.O.W. hutments		Total Beds
	Hostels	Beds	Hutment	Beds	
1941	31	980	—	—	980
1942	265	6,320	302	11,080	17,400
1943	561	15,788	306	11,771	27,559
1944	772	22,000	312	12,344	34,344

Source: Ministry of Agriculture and Fisheries

In the two years from March 1941, more than 500 hostels had been established in England and Wales in requisitioned premises of every variety.

In Scotland, the greater part of the accommodation required for the Women's Land Army was obtained by the use of existing houses; new building was limited to nineteen hutments for the Land Army and four for men employed by the Executive Committee:

Hostels for Agricultural Workers: Scotland

March	W.L.A.	Men
1941 .	—	16
1942 .	46	25
1943 .	70	34
1944 .	116	39

It was found that the standard type of new hostel was generally too large for Scottish conditions, since ten to twenty workers were usually as many as could be continuously employed within reasonable travelling distance of one centre.

By the spring of 1943 nearly 970 agricultural hostels were in use in Great Britain. When, in January, recruitment to the Land Army was reopened, Ministers hoped to secure another 40,000 girls before the harvest (as well as 30,000 extra prisoners of war whose housing was primarily the responsibility of the Ministry of Works). A series of conferences, both in London and between regional officers in the counties, was hurriedly organised by the Ministries of Agriculture, Health and Works to discuss the very grave problem of housing these workers in England and Wales. The existing commitments of the Ministry of Works were on such a scale that it was agreed that new housing could be built only as a last resort. Billets were to be found by the Ministry of Health or the Land Army, or suitable houses were to be requisitioned and adapted.

A review of the 1943 housing programme in June and July cleared up a misunderstanding between the two Ministries as to the number of beds the Ministry of Works was to supply for the Ministry of Agriculture by means of new construction. Inquiries among the counties showed that progress had been generally satisfactory, and that in most areas accommodation had been found, or would be found before the harvest. In some ten counties a serious shortage of billets and hostels for the workers was still expected. While the authorities concerned were discussing how this shortage could be relieved, their difficulties were largely solved by the decision of the Cabinet to suspend, for the time being, all recruitment to the Land Army and to limit future recruitment to the level needed to keep the combined strength of the Land Army in Britain at 80,000. In some areas, where housing was being provided in advance for the expected flow of autumn recruits, this decision inevitably created a temporary surplus of accommodation, but this was, for the most part, only temporary. Some hostels, already equipped, were transferred to the War Office for the use of prisoners of war; houses requisitioned, but on which adaptations had not been begun, could be released or transferred to other Government departments.

Two other ventures in the housing of agricultural workers may here be noted. In 1942 the Ministry of Works possessed prefabricated concrete sections for some 1,500 emergency bungalows which had been designed for the housing of key industrial workers and their families; they were at this time lying unused, as it had recently been decided that no more separate bungalows were to be provided. The Ministry of Agriculture made the suggestion that these prefabricated bungalows would solve one peculiarly difficult problem—the provision of accommodation for key workers, stockmen or foremen, on farms in the possession of Executive Committees; many of these farms had been acquired because they were derelict and had no living accommodation of any kind. After much negotiation and delay, fifty pairs of such bungalows were authorised as a first instalment followed by authorisation of a further thirty-four pairs, sites were found and construction was begun in the summer of 1943. After a visit of inspection to one pair in Wales, Ministers were so dissatisfied with the limited space and inadequate amenities of these bungalows that all further building of this type was suspended. It was agreed that if accommodation had to be provided on isolated holdings for a key worker, the standard brick cottage, built to last, would have to be erected.

In 1943, on the joint initiative of the Minister of Agriculture and Mr. Ernest Brown, then Chancellor of the Duchy of Lancaster, a programme of 3,000 cottages for agricultural workers was undertaken by the Ministry of Health, despite the virtual ban on all house-building. In December of the following year it was stated that of the 2,844 cottages which had been put in hand, 2,528 had been completed.[1]

In Scotland assistance was given to the mobility of essential labour by some 2,000 houses built for war workers by Scottish local authorities and the Scottish Special Housing Association.[2] The main contribution was 1,500 houses built by Glasgow Corporation at Penilee from 1940 onwards under an arrangement whereby they would be let on completion to the Ministry of Aircraft Production for workers in the Rolls-Royce factory at Hillington and would revert to the Corporation for letting to ordinary tenants as soon as the Ministry could dispense with them after the war. (The Production departments received similar assistance from other local authorities in England and Wales and in Scotland.)

The programme of 1943 for 3,000 cottages for agricultural workers in England and Wales had its counterpart in Scotland, where there was a corresponding programme for 1,000 houses. Owing to the dif-

---

[1] H. of C. Deb., 12th December 1944, Vol. 406, Col. 1128 *et seq.*

[2] This was a Treasury-financed organisation which had been set up under Section 2 of the Housing (Financial Provisions) (Scotland) Act 1938.

ferent nature of the Scottish housing problem 800 of the houses were allocated to industrial areas in the west of Scotland; the remaining 200 houses were allocated among thirteen county councils for rural areas in which they were urgently required in the interests of food production.

Among the other hostel and kindred schemes which were undertaken by the Ministry of Works brief mention should be made of the 'intermediate' hostels, the miners' hostels, the American Red Cross hostels, the recreational and community centres and the rehabilitation centres. The 'intermediate' hostels were commissioned by the Ministry of Health in February 1943 to house essential workers bombed out from some of the larger seaport towns. Originally ten schemes had been planned, but the number was later reduced to six, with accommodation for about 7,500 persons, married and single, and staffs of 160 persons. The first contract was let in April 1942, but, because of the limited supply of labour allowed for this work, was not completed until June 1943. The hostels had the standard amenities, and the construction generally was eleven-inch brick cavity walls with light wood trusses and asbestos roofs; but the dormitory blocks—about a quarter of the total accommodation—were mostly of standard reinforced concrete, with flat roofs.[1]

In 1943 the Ministry of Labour directed to the mines certain groups of young men due to be called up for military service; and in December of that year the Ministry of Fuel and Power commissioned the Ministry of Works to carry out a programme of hostels to accommodate these 'Bevin boys', as they were popularly nicknamed. Schemes were planned to accommodate between 100 and 600 men each. The total programme provided for 21,350 miners[2] and was divided into three stages. Included in this total were 700 houses built in Scotland as married quarters. Nine of the hostel schemes, and 550 of the houses, were carried out by private nominated architects under the control of the Ministry of Works. On some sites, where there was a risk of subsidence because of underground mine workings, special foundations had to be built, and steel—instead of brick—chimney-stacks were put in.

The American Red Cross hostels were started in May 1943 to give accommodation for American troops on leave in the United Kingdom; a secondary aim was to provide club facilities for Americans stationed in the neighbourhood of the hostels or on the move from one station to another. Even before the programme was undertaken many existing buildings had been adapted, and it was to supplement these that sites were obtained for seventeen new hutted schemes in the

---

[1] The total cost of the six hostels was £680,000.
[2] At an estimated cost of £5½ millions.

provinces. In all there was sleeping accommodation for 2,400 men, at a cost of £300,000.

Recreational and community centres were built for the Ministry of Labour to provide club facilities in localities and towns which were short of them and to which non-Service war workers had been directed. The community centres were gifts of the British War Relief Society of the United States to severely bombed communities. Both the recreational and the community centres were similarly planned and were ultimately taken over by the local authorities concerned. The accommodation comprised the nucleus of an assembly hall with stage, changing rooms, canteen, kitchen and reading and writing, rooms. Sometimes there were additional facilities such as laundries, baths and a limited amount of sleeping accommodation. In all some twenty centres were built, mostly in the south of England, at an average cost of £6,600. In this connection mention must be made of the rehabilitation centres for the reception of industrial workers during and after the war. The first establishment of this kind was built at Egham in Surrey, in wooded country in the grounds of a large country house. The accommodation was for 250, extendable to 500, and contained the customary amenities in Ministry of Works standard hutting.

(vi)
War-Time Accommodation for Schools

A period of great activity in school building during the rearmament years was drastically curtailed on the outbreak of war.[1] In the financial year 1938–39 approximately £16½ millions of capital expenditure had been approved, and in the first five months of 1939—and up to the outbreak of war—approximately £8 millions. This large expenditure had been mainly brought about by the intensive building of new housing estates—an activity which in turn had meant providing or adapting schools. There had also been preparations to meet the raising of the school-leaving age under the 1936 Act. In effect, new sites and new buildings had had to be found for a considerable proportion of the school population.

When, immediately on the outbreak of war, the Treasury put severe restrictions on all borrowing, the Board of Education required that all building schemes on which work had not actually begun should now be referred back to the Board for a new consent to be given.[2] Directions were issued that where the work was well in hand

---

[1] This section is based chiefly on studies prepared for the history of education.

[2] Board of Education Circular No. 1477

every effort should be made to press on with it, but questions of priority were a source of great difficulty. Unless a new building was of great urgency, or was nearing completion, education authorities were required to seal it off—that is, to confine themselves to such work as was needed to protect from deterioration the work already done.

The effect of these measures was that only about £7¼ millions of work was allowed to be completed. In the year 1939–40, £14 millions of capital expenditure was approved in all, but of this nearly £6 millions was in respect of air raid precautions. At the end of July 1940 it could be said that no loan approval had been given for a new elementary or secondary school since the beginning of the war, with the exception of one in which the school buildings were collapsing. By that time all the schools being built, with a few belated exceptions, had either been finished or had been sealed off. That was also true of technical colleges, with the exception of a few workshops in process of being completed for the training of Service technical personnel or munition workers.

From 1941 onwards the Board had to agree from time to time to alterations and extensions of schools, either to provide for the return of children into a district where the schools had been blitzed or were being used for some essential purpose that prevented their return to their proper use, or to provide school accommodation on the emergency housing estates for the married workers at large new factories. In order to use the minimum amount of labour and material for these extensions the Board normally required that they should take the form of hutting. The Ministry of Works and other departments, with the guidance of the Building Research Station, applied themselves to the design and manufacture of mass-produced huts; and the Board's architect was brought into consultation to ensure that they could be adapted to serve as classrooms. After a period of experiment, a standard hut was introduced consisting of a reinforced cement framework with fillings of clay blocks, bricks, and so on, according to local convenience. These huts proved on the whole satisfactory. The earlier mass-produced huts were of a uniform width of 18 feet 6 inches and could be obtained in any multiple of 6-foot lengths. Those used by the Board were usually 72 feet long, forming a unit of two classrooms of about 550 square feet, with a space of 220 square feet between them for cloakrooms and lavatories. From 1942 onwards a hut of 24-foot width and 6-foot length also became standard, and although slightly heavier on cost and materials it gradually began to displace the 18-foot 6-inch hut. For most school purposes the new type of hut was admittedly better, and whenever the advantages it gave were appreciable, it was allowed.

To conform with the control over building programmes by the

Ministry of Works, a corresponding control had to be exercised by the Board over all proposals for school building work. Improvements to schools, even 'blacklisted' schools, were almost completely stopped. Only where existing arrangements were held to be endangering the children's health or safety were improvements sanctioned, and the work was in the main restricted to such alterations and extensions as were essential for full-time attendance. Sometimes, too, the use of hired buildings proved so detrimental that additional accommodation was allowed. Where other accommodation was unobtainable, sanction was given for huts, or small alterations and extensions were made to provide premises for school meals, for the Youth Service or for Junior Schools of Building. As a rule, the making good of war damage was permissible only in so far as accommodation was essential for immediate use.

Additions to premises could not be made in permanent construction unless the cost (that is, the amount of labour and materials to be used) did not appreciably exceed that of huts, or if conditions made it undesirable that huts should be erected. Normally huts were not designed with outside corridors, and until a late stage in the war they were heated by stoves so as to save the steel and case iron needed for central heating. In the later stages of the war, however, because of the shortage of caretakers able to do the heavy work of keeping a large number of stoves supplied with fuel, central heating was again allowed.

In the summer of 1943 plans were made for a rapid increase in the provision of school canteens to enable three-quarters of the children in average attendance to have dinner at school. Since 100 per cent. grant was offered on the construction of the canteens, there was a substantial extension of the Board's building programme. Where education authorities agreed, the construction of the canteens was carried out by the Ministry of Works. Over one-half of the new canteens and major extensions were built by the Ministry. All were accommodated in huts except when the work could be more economically done by adapting and extending an existing building. The plans of the Ministry of Works were based on a forecast by the Ministry of Education up to the end of 1944. Over 6,000 projects were to be carried out by the Ministry of Works and local authorities, at a cost of over £8 millions; one and a half million children were to be fed; and a labour force of nearly 14,000 men was to be engaged on the work of construction. But these plans had to be modified because of the shortage of labour and material caused by the flying-bomb attacks. Despite such setbacks, however, this building programme contributed substantially to the doubling of the Schools Meals Service in the course of three years.

When new buildings had to be erected for the provision of school meals, all but the very smallest canteen kitchens and sculleries were prefabricated; standard Ministry of Works huts[1] were used for quick and economical building. But, although standard plans were prepared, there were, of course, no standard sites, and each case had to be dealt with on its merits and negotiated with the several authorities concerned.

(vii)

Camp Construction

Most of the war-time camps were constructed by the Ministry of Works on agency terms. The camps were of many kinds: camps for prisoners of war; camps for the fire brigades and civil defence workers; camps for the building workers of Phoenix and Pluto;[2] camps for the Royal Air Force and the American forces and many others. Reference has already been made in earlier chapters to the militia camps built by the War Office before and after the outbreak of war[3] and to other camp undertakings such as those built for the United States Army under the code name Bolero.[4] The first prisoner-of-war camps undertaken by the Ministry of Works were built for the War Office, starting in the later summer of 1941. This relatively small programme was completed by the Ministry of Works about a year later at a cost of £650,000. The first main programme of nearly forty camps was carried out in 1941 for the Ministry of Agriculture and Fisheries, and cost nearly £2 millions. A further batch in 1943 consisted of nearly forty main camps and over 160 satellites in other camps and extensions, the cost of which was about £2½ millions. In 1944 a programme of tented camps was carried out. This comprised three large camps, eight hostels and over thirty extensions to existing camps and hostels.

Sometimes the prisoners themselves constructed parts of the camps under the supervision of contractors; sometimes hostels originally built for industrial workers were taken over and adapted for prisoners of war; but on the whole the accommodation for prisoners of war was similar to that of the American troops under the Bolero programme.

After the 'blitz' period of late 1940 and early 1941 it became the policy of the Ministry of Home Security to group fire-fighting personnel and equipment in camps. During enemy air raids the fire forces could operate radially from the camps, and so minimise the dislocation, through enemy action, of fire-fighting services in the towns. When the situation eased, the original camp programme was cut

---

[1] The span of these huts was 24 feet and 18 feet.

[2] Phoenix was the code name for the concrete floating caissons used in the invasion of Western Europe (see Chapter XV); Operation Pluto ('Pipe-Line under the Ocean') was the 1,000-mile oil pipe-line across the Channel stretching into Germany.

[3] See Chapter XII.

[4] *Ibid.*

down to a plan for five camps[1] which could also be used as training and rest centres for the regional fire forces. Some of the camps were on new sites and others on sites where existing buildings could be used, and adapted as part of the schemes. The lay-outs were planned to take the maximum advantage of natural cover and the buildings were grouped to minimise fire risks. Open and covered standing space for about sixty vehicles was a part of each camp and there were workshop buildings, repair shops, underground petrol stores and reserve water supplies. The huts were heated by slow-combustion stoves and hot water was supplied from independent boiler-houses. The roads and paths on the sites were surfaced with tarmacadam and were designed for the quick movement of traffic in and out of the camps. A parade ground and training area, which included a hose-drying tower,[2] created conditions approximating to those of an urban headquarters.

The programme of civil defence camps followed early in 1943. Its objects were similar to those of the fire-brigade camps programme. Services in the Civil Defence regions were to be centralised at a distance from the cities and larger towns so that, under enemy attack, ambulances, rescue squads and other equipment and personnel could be moved quickly from these centres to the scene of operations. Seven new camps were built by the Ministry of Works[3] for over 1,600 men in the Eastern, Midland and North-Western Regions, with accommodation for 250 to 300 men in each camp, and women's quarters for the canteen staffs. The buildings on the sites were constructed in Ministry of Works standard transverse-frame hutting, with dormitories accommodating forty men to each hut, administration, lecture rooms, kitchens and canteens, equipment stores, sick bays and recreation rooms. Garages and workshops were in brick buildings of 50-foot span and housed the ambulances, mobile canteens, rescue vehicles and other Civil Defence equipment.

In an earlier chapter[4] it has been noted that building labour was used on the concrete Phoenix monoliths of the Mulberry harbours. That unique task meant the drafting of thousands of building trade workers into various coastal areas and places on the Thames and other estuaries, and it brought upon them hardships and physical stress for which many who were past the prime of life were unfitted. For most of these workers no billets could be found, and they were housed in several large camps erected mostly in plasterboard hutting.

These workers came from all over the country and 'the hours they put in were limited only by their maximum powers of endurance.

---

[1] To cost £95,000.

[2] The hose towers were of braced tubular scaffolding or light structural steel.

[3] To cost £190,000. Some smaller additional camps were built by the Maintenance Division of the Ministry.

[4] See Chapter XV.

In many instances twenty-four hours' work was put in in a day for days in succession. Much of the work was done in failing light, and all was done under conditions of stringent secrecy. Operatives worked to the danger of their lives, and many of them did, in fact, lose their lives. Much of the task was performed under the nose of the German air force. Immediately there was an alert the lights went out, and men were left high and dry, many situated precariously on scaffolds, unable to continue work. Much of it was done without any kind of protection, and with no shelters. In point of fact, it was difficult to get to the shelter in time, having regard to the circumstances that the job was so comparatively close to the enemy shores'.[1]

Although the conditions of work were exacting and often dangerous, some redress was made by providing amenities in the camps which, though hurriedly erected, had dormitories, canteens, welfare and recreation rooms, sick bays and sanitary accommodation, water towers, sewage disposal arrangements, and so on. At a Fareham camp, which was an extension of an earlier blitz repair workers' camp, a hutted canteen to feed a thousand workers was built, and was in fact the largest of all the temporary canteens erected by the Ministry of Works.[2]

Among the other preparations for the invasion of Western Europe, in anticipation of enemy bombing before and after D-day advance plans were made for rapidly erecting twenty camps for a total of about 8,000 building workers to do emergency repairs in coastal towns if the need should arise. Shadow schemes were prepared, sites found in the coastal *hinterland*, drawings made ready, water and drainage arrangements worked out, supplies of hutting and equipment ear-marked. As D-day approached a nucleus of huts was erected on eighteen of the sites, and later sixteen of these schemes were taken as far as emergency occupation standard, but only four were finally completed and fully occupied. As the expected bombing did not materialise in those districts, the remaining sites were ultimately used for other purposes.[3]

Not to be confused with these emergency camps were the preliminary camps erected by the Ministry of Works on sites remote from large towns. Many jobs, especially in 1942, were carried out in isolated areas where no billets for workmen could be found, and accommodation on sites had therefore to be built before any real work could begin. To cut down delays on making a start with the undertaking itself, a scheme was devised under which a small preliminary contract

---

[1] Statement to the press by Mr. (later Sir) Richard Coppock, General Secretary of the National Federation of Building Trades Operatives.

[2] The total cost of the Phoenix camps was about £250,000 and was carried out with direct labour by the Directorate of Emergency Works of the Ministry of Works.

[3] The cost of these emergency camps was £280,000.

was let for the erection of a camp for fifty men. This usually took from two and a half to four weeks to put up, and was then handed over to the main contractor as the nucleus of his labour camp. Here he could house enough men to make a good start on his main job. But before such a position could be reached, accommodation had to be found for the first batch of operatives—a party, it may be, of sixteen to twenty-four men—who were to put up the preliminary camp. Sometimes the advance party could be billeted in a near by village; but more often there was no near by village, and so no billets even for this small number of men. A solution was found by borrowing from the Directorate of Emergency Works of the Ministry of Works a number of mobile units or 'flying squads', as they were called,[1] together with their specially-designed motor caravans, and using them to put up the preliminary camps. The building departments of the various Ministries, especially the Service and Supply, were thus able to make good use of these self-contained units of mobile labour.

(viii)
The Post Office: War-Time Building Tasks

At the outbreak of war the Office of Works had in hand a five-years' long-term site and building programme for the Post Office, involving an expenditure of some £16 millions on new buildings. The scheme included post offices, telephone exchanges, engineering depots, garages and workshops, stores and factories, as well as office accommodation for clerical and administrative staff. Much of the programme had to be postponed after war was declared, and where work was already in progress it was stopped, whenever possible, at a convenient stage.

The total expenditure on all services for the Post Office incurred by the Ministry of Works during the financial years covering the war period was as follows:

	Post Office Loan	Vote	Total
	£	£	£
1939–40	2,470,000	1,130,000	3,600,000
1940–41	1,190,000	1,400,000	2,590,000
1941–42	565,000	2,110,000	2,675,000
1942–43	340,000	1,600,000	1,940,000
1943–44	200,000	1,490,000	1,690,000
1944–45	105,000	1,380,000	1,485,000
TOTALS	£4,870,000	£9,110,000	£13,980,000

[1] See Chapter X.

2B

During the rearmament period various classes of protective works had been carried out for the safety of the staff, the buildings and their contents, and as the war progressed, air raid problems and war conditions called for more works. These included refuges for staff; the protection of buildings, telephone, telegraph and other equipment; the protection of basements for sorting work during danger periods; the provision of dormitories in refuges; protected accommodation for emergency defence, telecommunications and controls; the bricking-up of windows; the provision of decontamination centres; camouflage; the protection of Air Observer Corps posts and kindred work.

During the war years damage to about 1,500 Post Office buildings in England and Wales was reported. Some of these buildings were damaged more than once.[1] A total amount of about £850,000 was spent on repairs to war damage or reinstatement, but that amount covered only a proportion of the ultimate total cost.

The major items of war damage repairs and reinstatement (whole or partial) included the following:

	£
Metropolitan Telephone Exchange	50,000
Central Telegraph Office	150,000
South Eastern District Office	52,000
Mount Pleasant Parcels Office	130,000
Liverpool Head Post Office	54,000

New war-time buildings included:

	£
Faraday Building, N.E.	250,000
Criggion Wireless Station	163,000
Hendon Ring Main Exchange	90,000
Programme of emergency telephone exchanges and repeater station, wireless stations, etc.	70,000
M.S.S. Recording Factory, Wraysbury (extension) M.S.S. Recording Factory, Colnbrook (new factory)	36,000
Holborn Telephone Exchange (Tunnel Scheme)	15,000
Hawthorn (Corsham) Post Office and Telephone Exchange	14,000
Birmingham Factory Department Maycrete huts	15,000

(ix)

The Salvaging of Historic Buildings and Ancient Monuments

In the account already given of war-time building work carried out by the Ministry of Works for other departments there are necessarily many omissions. Space does not permit the inclusion of all the varied commissions carried out: of small standard factories, for example, built for the Board of Trade; of flax factories and retting tanks for the Ministry of Supply; of the miscellaneous factories and extensions for

---

[1] There were 140 items of damage each costing more than £500, and many below that figure.

that department other than Royal Ordnance factories; of the temporary office buildings erected for civil servants in many parts of the country; of all the heavily protected structures known as 'citadels'; and of the thousand and one technical installations urgently demanded by the Service and Supply departments. All that agency work formed a substantial part of the total Government building programme and was in itself a major contribution to the war effort.[1]

We now turn to another side of the Ministry which was autonomous, and carried over into the war years an important peace-time function of the Office of Works—the care of ancient monuments and historic buildings.[2]

On 18th November 1940, not long after the start of destructive air raids on London, the Royal Institute of British Architects, in collaboration with the Society for the Protection of Ancient Buildings, met to discuss what action should be taken to prevent damage to historic buildings. The meeting was a representative one, and was attended by Lord Reith, as Minister of Works. The chief result of the meeting was the establishment of the National Buildings Record, for which the Treasury, at the suggestion of the Ministry of Works, supplied the first financial support. The minority of those present at the meeting expressed, for the most part privately, their misgivings concerning the fate of damaged historic buildings at the hands of the normal demolition gangs which were being sent to tidy up the 'incidents'. Much unnecessary demolition had already been noticed, and there seemed to be no guarantee that the debris would be carefully searched for the remains of fittings or small objects which had escaped destruction.

Since the meeting had not concerned itself with this aspect of the situation it fell to the Ministry of Works, as the successor of the Office of Works,[3] to take the lead in ensuring the preservation of the remains of any historic building damaged by enemy action. The great difficulties of such an undertaking at once became apparent: there was no organisation for reporting damage to historic buildings, no comprehensive list of such buildings, nor in the Inspectorate of Ancient Monuments at the Ministry was there enough staff whether for the preparation of a list or the examination of damage.

Inquiry of the Ministry of Home Security showed that the plotting of individual 'incidents' was not normally reported higher in the scale of the air raid precautions organisation than to the office of the Air Raid Precautions Controller of the scheme-making authority; as a

---

[1] In 1942, for example, the Ministry of Works labour allocation for agency works was between one-fifth and one-sixth of the total allocation. See Section (x) of this chapter.

[2] The overseas work of the Office of Works (diplomatic and consular buildings, etc.) lies outside the scope of this volume, but it should be recorded here that wherever possible it was maintained throughout the war.

[3] The Office of Works had been charged by Act of Parliament with specific duties in the preservation of ancient monuments and historic buildings.

rule it was not known to Regional Headquarters. It was not feasible, therefore, for the Inspectorate to organise what soon came to be called its 'salvage scheme' entirely on a regional basis. Because of this, and because it was obvious that much, if not all, the success of the scheme would depend upon the thoughts and the actions of the men actually on the spot after a raid, it had to be organised according to the areas of scheme-making authorities.

To achieve that object negotiations were taken up with the Ministry of Home Security. One thing was certain: if the Inspectorate wished Air Raid Precautions Controllers to report damage to any historic building, they could not leave it to the discretion of the Controllers to decide which buildings should be classed as historic. Since no list of such buildings had so far been compiled for any part of the country, except for a few towns like Ipswich and Plymouth, the first need was to prepare one.

To compile the list entirely within the Ministry of Works from the information to be found in published sources would have been impossible. Similarly it would have been impracticable to supervise closely from the Ministry the attention given to all damaged historic buildings, even had the staff been available. In collaboration, therefore, with the Royal Institute of British Architects and other bodies, a panel of architects was formed of all those in the profession in various cities, towns and country districts, who were known to be in sympathy with the aims of the salvage scheme.

Over 300 architects were appointed either singly or in panels for specified areas. Their scale of remuneration was agreed with the Royal Institute of British Architects, and they were fully instructed by the Inspectorate. Their first task was to prepare lists of buildings in their districts which they considered to be historic. After being carefully checked in the Ministry, the lists were issued to the local authorities concerned without delay (in view of possible enemy action) and later revised. Uniformity in time and method was naturally not to be sought in so large a body of professional men, many of whom were exceedingly busy in other ways, but it was none the less true that, for the first time, there now existed a comprehensive list of the historic buildings of Great Britain.

The local lists were given out to the Air Raid Precautions Controllers of the various authorities,[1] and they were asked to send information of damage to any of the listed buildings to Regional Headquarters. Here the information was passed to the Ministry of Works representative (the Senior Regional Officer) whose duty it was to instruct the panel architect to act. Later the Ministry of Home Security issued another circular, substituting the engineer or surveyor

---

[1] Under Ministry of Home Security Circular No. 44/1941 of 15th February 1941.

of the local authority for the Air Raid Precautions Controller as the officer responsible for the initial report. The scheme did not apply to the London region, where special arrangements were made with the Corporation of the City of London and with the London County Council.

The circulars were issued in February 1941, and only a few of the lists had been compiled before the heavy raids of 1940–41 were over. One could not yet say whether the scheme was a practical one. The real test came with the later raids on historic towns—Exeter, Norwich, York, Bath, Canterbury. The arrangements for those cities, with perhaps one exception, were judged to have been made with every care; for that reason officers from headquarters were instructed not to visit them at once, but after a short interval. It was then found that the panel architects were alive to their responsibilities, and that the local authorities were collaborating with them to the best of their ability. In one place only had the scheme failed. Here the panel architect was precluded from acting for the Inspectorate because of his other, most urgent, duties: another architect was soon found to take his place. In a few buildings in some of the cities a little unnecessary demolition had taken place, usually through the employment on the initial work of clearance of soldiers whom the local authorities found it difficult to control. But such incidents were exceptional. The salvage scheme as a whole achieved its objects; and without it many buildings and fragments of historical or architectural value would have been lost.

The prime purpose of the scheme was to give proper guidance in the initial work on damaged historic buildings. This included such measures as the shoring up of dangerous portions of a structure or ensuring that parts were taken down carefully rather than felled with a rope. Fittings of value were noted, so that the local authority might store them, if and when they had to be removed from their setting. Often, however, it was not enough merely to stop demolition. Parts of a damaged building might still be dangerous, or be liable to become so because of the action of weather between the time of damage and the time when its future could be decided. One example was that of a row of seventeenth-century houses in Ipswich[1] with some good plaster ceilings. The roofing tiles had mostly been removed by blast, and the ceilings stood in danger of severe damage and probable collapse if the houses were not made watertight. The local authority had no intention of giving them first-aid repair, or of demolishing them as dangerous structures. As the owners were willing that the minimum of work should be done in order to save the buildings from deterioration, but were unwilling themselves to undertake the work, the Minis-

---

[1] Nos. 12 to 18 Church Street.

try of Works did it through a contractor, using the panel architect as its supervisor. The War Damage Commission agreed to reimburse the expenditure as a 'temporary works payment' without prejudice to the final settlement of the war damage claim submitted by the owner.

This procedure was later adopted elsewhere. In Plymouth, as in Southampton, before the salvage scheme had been devised, the Ministry of Works undertook a general survey of the damaged historic buildings. They were divided into three categories:

1. Total losses, that is, those which had nothing of value remaining or of which so little remained that the Ministry of Works did not need to take it into account, although there might still be valuable fittings to be recovered by the local authority during clearance.

2. Buildings, only slightly damaged, to which first-aid repairs had been done or were likely to be done by the local authority or by the owner.

3. 'Crippled' buildings which needed attention from the Ministry of Works, since no one else would attend to them adequately.

Of the last class in Plymouth there were only two individual houses and one terrace out of many dozens of buildings examined. Similar work was undertaken in London, Southampton, Bristol, Hastings, Canterbury, Norwich, Yarmouth and Exeter. In a few of these special cases the owners were keen enough to sponsor the work: the Ministry's only part was to encourage them, and to support their application for a civil building licence and for compensation by the War Damage Commission.

By such means not only were damaged buildings saved from demolition immediately after a raid, but all that could be done was done to prevent them from deteriorating so badly during the war that they would become a total loss by the time their future came to be discussed.

The salvaging of buildings of historical interest was one side of the work of the Inspectorate of Ancient Monuments. Another side was the discovery, excavation and safeguarding of archæological remains of earlier periods. Since in the course of rearmament the Service departments had to acquire large tracts of land for conversion to war-time uses—the construction of airfields and so forth—the Office of Works had a direct interest in being kept informed of such acquisitions.

On 21st January 1938 Sir Horace Wilson presided over a meeting of the permanent heads of those Departments of State which were then interested in the acquisition of land. A system of mutual consultation was then agreed, and each department subsequently appointed one representative, whose duty was to include the maintenance of liaison with all the other departments, so that each should be consulted whenever its interests seemed likely to be affected.

This meant in practice that in peace-time the Office of Works received notification, usually with a plan, of all the land which the Admiralty, the War Office or the Air Ministry proposed to acquire. Quite early in the war, however, the War Office was forced to fall out of line. Because of the vast amount of land which the Army required, often in small parcels, it was found best to deal with its acquisition or requisition locally. An effort was made, though without effect, to ensure even then that notification reached the Office of Works in London. Local liaison with War Department land agents in the various counties was not at that time feasible, but later it was found possible to arrange it. In effect, throughout the first two and a half years of war only the largest requisitions of land by the War Office became known to the Ministry of Works in London. On the other hand the Admiralty and the Air Ministry were able to adhere to the arrangement of 1938. In 1942 an all-embracing system of liaison between nine departments was worked out. Land acquired for the Services was now scrutinised on plan to ensure that no ancient monuments were affected; and the land used for the erection of Royal Ordnance factories, or for other purposes, by the Ministry of Works as agent, was similarly investigated.

It was indeed in respect of such a factory site that the principle was established of excavation of a site by the Ministry of Works before its destruction for defence works. That happened before the general arrangement already mentioned. Sir Cyril Fox, Director of the National Museum of Wales, undertook a survey of the area acquired for the erection of the Royal Ordnance factory at Bridgend, in Glamorgan. He found no buildings of interest, but there were two unrecorded round barrows on the land, one which at least was certain to be involved in the lay-out of the factory, and so sooner or later to be destroyed. The second barrow lay away from the main building, but there seemed every likelihood that it, too, would eventually be destroyed. Sir Cyril Fox excavated both barrows in 1937, with most satisfactory results.[1] At about the same time Sir Cyril Fox, with the collaboration of the Admiralty, had visited and recorded details of all the interesting primitive houses and cottages in the Trecwn valley near Fishguard, Pembrokeshire.[2]

During the remaining years of peace the expansion of the armed forces, particularly the Royal Air Force, took in areas which contained ancient monuments. Thus, at Crichel Down, Dorset, some fourteen barrows lay within such an area. They were excavated on behalf of the Office of Works by Mr. and Mrs. Stuart Piggot. The

---

[1] These were published in *Archæologia*, LXXXVII, 129–80.

[2] His account of them is in *Antiquity*, 1937, 427–40. Later he made similar regional surveys of old houses elsewhere in South Wales, including a detailed study of a very interesting Elizabethan house in Glamorgan.

results were of great value.[1] Similarly one round barrow on Admiralty land at Caerwent in Monmouthshire was excavated by Dr. H.N. Savory. Although not Roman, as its position beside a Roman road had suggested, it proved to be of great archæological interest.[2] At St. Eval, in Cornwall, too, Mr. C. K. C. Andrew excavated one round barrow on the airfield.

From the outbreak of war, as the needs of the Defence Ministries and of other departments engaged on the prosecution of the war vastly ncreased, even larger areas were needed for airfields and factories, and for the dispersal of sites as a precaution against air attack. It was often difficult for the Ministry of Works to discover just how many departments were interested parties. Whenever possible, liaison was established with them, in order to ensure respect for any ancient monuments on the land, or to arrange scientific examination before their removal. Of the various departments, the Air Ministry might well have been the greatest destroyer of ancient monuments, for the simple reason that all inequalities on a flying field must be flattened, whereas in factory building they could perhaps remain untouched. In spite of difficulties, the co-operation of the Air Ministry was whole-hearted. Nearly always the Inspectorate was permitted to complete its scientific examination, and if sometimes the archæologists had to step aside, it was because the needs of the Air Ministry were overwhelmingly urgent.

(x)

The Agency Work of the Ministry of Works

The agency functions of the Ministry of Works, under which a great proportion of the work described in this chapter was carried out, were defined in Parliament on the setting up of the Ministry of 1940.[3] Under the powers then bestowed, a wide constructional field was left open to the new Ministry. Not only was the department made responsible for all new civil works and buildings required by any other Government department, but by agreement it could carry out new programmes for the Service Ministries and the Ministry of Supply except when 'highly specialised' work was in question. Many instances have been given in this and earlier chapters of the extensive and varied constructional activity which was thus undertaken side by

---

[1] *Archæologia*, XC, 47–80.

[2] The results were published *Archæologia Cambrensis*, 1940, 169–91.

[3] H. of C. Deb., 24th October 1940, Vol. 365, Col. 1150 *et seq*. Statement by the Lord Privy Seal (Mr. Attlee).

side with the Ministry's new and complex administrative function of co-ordinating the whole of the Government building programme. The chart on page 394 illustrates the spread of new work over the rearmament and war years, and it will be seen that the bulk of it is work done on agency footing.

The distribution of the agency programme naturally varied according to the fluctuating demands of the departments, but the table on page 396, which shows the labour allocation made by the Ministry of Works for the period April to October 1942 and the Ministry's sub-allocation for agency works, may be taken as typical.

It was perhaps inevitable, for reasons already discussed in an earlier chapter,[1] that there should sometimes be difficulties and disagreements between the client department and the Ministry of Works in its capacity as agent. For the most part these checks were overcome by co-operation and goodwill on both sides, but it was not until the Ministry of Works had become fully established, and its administrative authority recognised, that its agency functions could be more firmly asserted. Since the divergencies of viewpoint were most marked as between the Ministry of Works and the Ministry of Supply in their earlier relations, the following extract from an official memorandum in the Ministry of Works may be taken as a fair sample of what really lay at the bottom of most disagreements between client and agent:

> The instructions of the Ministry of Supply come to us through the Secretariat and through the Controller of Building Construction.
> In neither case does the Ministry of Works have any direct contact with the ultimate user. The liaison with the Controller of Building Construction is working without any friction, but in our opinion, since he is not intended or organised to handle technical matters, he becomes, so far as we are concerned, purely a channel of communication and 'booster'.
> What we want is to know from the person ultimately concerned what he wants, and when he wants it; and then to be given a free hand to go ahead. All questions of detailed design, administration of the contract, control of the labour and materials, etc., are solely our concern. . . .
> We want to be able to discuss the all-important question of progressive completion of those large factories with the user department. It is solely a matter to be settled by the Superintendent, or someone who actually knows how the factory works. It is even more important to have the contact when the factories are being designed. Much good time has been saved in the past in this way.
> The selection of sites is the duty of this Ministry, the acquisition of the sites is done by the Ministry of Supply. In fact the Ministry of Works is a competent authority to acquire; and other Ministries leave

---

[1] See Chapter XV.

New Works 1936–45: Calendar of Principal Programmes

1936	1937	1938	1939	1940	1941	1942	1943	1944	1945
PEACE				WAR					

Public Buildings

Employment Exchanges

Post Offices, Telephone Exchanges, Repeater Stations, Wireless Stations, Experimental Establishments

Coronation

Royal Ordnance Factories for War Department and Ministry of Supply

Civilian Hospitals for Ministries of Health and Pensions

Ordnance and Explosive Depots, Hostels and Married Quarters

Bomb Damage Repairs to all kinds of Government Buildings

Temporary Office Buildings for evacuated Government Staffs

Cold Storage Buildings

Underground Storage Space

Inland Sorting Depots

Food and General Stores

Citadels, Flax Factories

Underground Factories

Fire Brigade Camps

War Office and P.O.W. Camps, Civil Defence Camps

Hostels and Married Quarters for Ministry of Aircraft Production

M/Agriculture Hostels

Preliminary Camps

Camps, Hospitals and Stores for D-Day Troops

Intermediate Hostels

Grain Silos, Miners' Camps

USAAF Deps.

Phœnix C'mps

School Kitchens and Canteens

Standard Factories

Training Centres

Disposal Depots

Demonstration Houses

Bomb Damage Repair

Workers' Camps

Temporary Houses

H.M. OFFICE OF WORKS   MINISTRY OF WORKS

it to us to do so. It is illogical and must add unnecessarily to the machine that the Ministry of Supply insists on acquiring.

There seems to be too much consultation with a large number of authorities and interests (including the Council for the Preservation of Rural England) before any site is taken. This is to avoid subsequent criticism—but I suggest that we should risk criticism in the interests of speed.

In practice, *vis-à-vis* the Ministry of Supply, the selection of sites was never admitted as the duty of the Ministry of Works;[1] but in principle the broad claims of the agent department were indisputable and were in accord not only with the functions carried over from the Office of Works but more expressly with the powers conferred on the Ministry at its inception.

---

[1] See Chapter XV.

Government Building Programme
Labour Allocation: April–October 1942
M.O.W. Agency Work

NOTE: M.O.W. Agency Works Allocation refers to Client Departments current proposals and is subject to adjustment should the programmes be varied.

Department	April–June		July–September	
	Total allocation	M.O.W. sub-allocation	Total allocation	M.O.W. sub-allocation
Admiralty	32,000	2,000	34,000	1,650
War Office	40,000	6,000	40,000	3,000
Air Ministry	95,000	150	92,000	60
Ministry of Aircraft Production .	59,500	16,250	69,500	10,000
Ministry of Supply . . .	78,000	31,500	65,000	17,500
Ministry of War Transport .	15,000	700	15,000	700
Ministry of Health:				
Housing and Water Sewage, etc. .	6,500	—	6,500	—
General Post Office . . .	4,500	840	4,500	420
Ministry of Food . . .	8,000	7,200	8,000	5,050
Electricity Commission . . .	13,000	—	13,000	—
Board of Trade:				
Gas	1,000	—	1,000	—
Mines Department . . .	2,000	—	2,000	—
Petroleum Department . .	3,000	—	2,000	—
Ministry of Agriculture:				
Drainage . . .	600	—	600	—
P.O.W. camps and hostels .	2,500	2,500	2,500	2,500
Ministry of Information . . .	1,500	—	1,500	—
Department of Agriculture for Scotland	550	240	550	240
Department of Health of Scotland:				
Housing and water sewage, etc. .	2,000	—	2,000	—
TOTAL A	364,650	65,380	359,150	41,120
Ministry of Health:				
Emergency hospitals ⎱				
Other hospitals ⎰ · . .	5,000	3,200	4,500	1,800
Intermediate hostels . .	3,500	3,500	2,500	2,500
Ministry of Works	4,500	4,500	4,500	4,500
Board of Trade:				
Civil licence ⎱				
I.C.I. ⎰ . .	1,000	—	1,000	—·—
Ministry of Home Security . .	30,000	—	—	—
Board of Education . . .	2,500	—	2,500	—
Static water	10,000	—	—	—
Fire Services . . .	3,000	—	3,000	—
Fire brigade camps, etc. . .	1,000	1,000	700	700
Home Office:				
Police	600	—	600	—
Camouflage	2,000	—	2,000	—
Approved schools . .	350	—	350	—
Scottish Home Department:				
Static water	1,000	—	—	—
Police, etc. . . .	500	65	500	200
Department of Health for Scotland .	3,300	730	3,100	730
Scottish Education Department .	550	—	550	—
Other Departments . . .	550	565	550	710
Steel Salvage	15,000	15,000	15,000	15,000
TOTAL B	84,350	28,560	41,350	26,140
TOTAL A AND B . .	449,000	93,940	400,500	67,260

NOTE: M.O.W. Agency Works: Allocation, October 1941–April 1942   93,300
Labour employed February 1942   79,150

PART V

Reflections

CHAPTER XVIII

RETROSPECT

(i)

The Human Aspect

WHEN the war in Europe came to an end the number of workers in the building and civil engineering industries had dropped to less than half of what it had been in July 1939. At that date the labour force had reached the total of 1,362,000 male workers; by the middle of 1945 it numbered less than 600,000.[1] It was inevitable that, under the mounting demands for more and more men on the part of the Services and the munition industries, the industry's resources of manpower should decline steeply both in numbers and quality. What was far from inevitable what indeed was unpredictable and unlikely, and therefore all the more a paradox, is that despite every retarding human factor—increasing years, diminishing skill, absenteeism through sickness or slackness, weariness and occasional weakening of morale—so great a volume of building should have been carried out by the shrinking labour force.[2]

Whatever might be the ultimate statistical assessment of the part played by the building industry in the war effort, in terms of endeavour the building workers' contribution to victory stands high in the record of achievement. Too little has perhaps yet been said of the vast enterprise of the rank and file of the building industry in the aid it gave to the armed forces. Not only in the direct contribution the workers made to such operational works as the construction of the Phoenix caissons,[3] but in their total contribution to operational obectives, the part they played was notable. Let us quote again from

---

[1] Thereafter the total rose rapidly to 963,660 in July 1946, and 1,101,560 in July 1947. See Working Party Report, *Building* (H.M.S.O. 1950).

[2] For the estimated value of work done by the industry see *Statistical Digest of the War* in this series, Table 46 (reproduced at end of this chapter). The totals there given are: for 1940, £425 millions; 1941, £470 millions; 1942, £425 millions; 1943, £350 millions; 1944, £290 millions; 1945, £290 millions. The total building output in 1938 has been estimated at £606 millions. This total includes the output of firms in other industries and of public authorities (I. Bowen and A. W. T. Ellis, 'The Building and Contracting Industry', *Oxford Economic Papers*, No. 7, March 1945). Against the war-time totals must be offset the decline in productivity and the rising cost of labour and materials. It is a fair estimate that between 1938 and 1947 the productive efficiency of the building industry generally declined to about two-thirds of its pre-war level. See Working Party Report *Building*, p. 11 and Chapter XIX.

[3] See Chapter XV.

one of the most prominent of their leaders. Writing in 1944 Mr. (later Sir) Richard Coppock states:

> Building workers have been recruited into the Services to a greater extent than any other skilled occupation. In spite of the reduced personnel our men have gone on with their work, putting their all into it. They continued steadily at work during the 'blitz'; they worked in London when the 'blitz' was at its worst under all sorts of conditions. Welfare arrangements have considerably improved, but are still by no means what they should be and what we would like them to be. There are occasional public expressions of dissatisfaction at the productivity of the building operative, but the public does not really understand what is happening. . . . No industry has ever been faced with such a variety of tasks as has the building industry during the war. Our men have responded to every change of practice within the industry.[1]

It was complained that the story of the building trade worker and his participation in the war was kept almost as great a secret as the movements of the Fleet. The building industry, after all, had gone into action much earlier than any other industrial organisation. It had had to build under pressure great munition factories and vast installations for the Services; and after the fall of France in 1940 it was to the building industry that the nation looked to prepare the beaches against invasion, to use hundreds of thousands of tons of concrete for fortifications, to prepare street blocks, and to cut trenches in fields and open pasture land. That task had been done within twenty days. But already it had been

> necessary to build camp accommodation for tens of thousands of soldiers and to make it ready for the vast number of persons being rapidly recruited into the Services. Thousands of building workers were employed in the erection of Royal Air Force camps, airfields, repair depots, hospitals, filling and shadow factories. Men moved in their thousands from place to place. Little preparation was made for their reception, and welfare arrangements were non-existent. The accommodation for receiving the men was totally inadequate; men tramped miles and miles hopelessly seeking accommodation. During the summer months in 1940 after Dunkirk men slept in the streets as accommodation was not available. Numerous instances arose of our men working under fire of hostile aircraft and bombs. It was not until the National Federation demanded better facilities that consideration was given to the question of welfare, and it proved necessary to establish a department for the purpose of examining this question. Thousands of our men were employed in the Orkneys and Shetland Isles, under almost intolerable conditions, but nevertheless making

---

[1] *The Builder*, 8th December 1944, p. 458. 'Statement by Mr. R. Coppock, General Secretary of the National Federation of Building Trades Operatives'.

this group of islands practically invulnerable, as far as it was possible for the building and civil engineering workers to do so. Men had to travel for three or four days in overcrowded trains both to and from the job, and had to remain on the job for three months at a stretch, unable during that period to see their wives and families because of their desire to complete what was then a massive task.

At a later period, with the entry of America into the war, it was necessary again to make rapid completion of airfields and camp accommodation. There was a complete reshuffling of men in the industry which, as a consequence of the unfortunate wholesale recruitment of labourers into the Services in the early days of the war, had become unbalanced. Thus, in order to assist in winning the war, we agreed to a scheme known as the 'designated' craftsmen. The industry decided that the rate for the job did not meet the particular circumstances, and the Government in its desire to protect key men failed to appreciate the significance of the labourers and that it would be practically impossible to get men back from the Army. We therefore insisted that any person 'designated' to perform the particular labouring work should, if a craftsman, receive the craft rate. Thousands of men were 'designated' to do all kinds of jobs during the period preparatory to D-Day, and as a consequence of the arrangement little or no demarcation trouble arose within the industry. Men did whatever was necessary to be done in the interest of victory.[1]

(ii)
Advisory Bodies

Of the approach to the Government building programme by the employers, the manufacturers of building materials, the distributing firms, the builders' merchants, and so forth, enough has been said in previous chapters to show that there was, in general, a resigned submission to voluntary Government controls, much goodwill and a genuine desire to co-operate. The urge towards co-operation had sprung from the side of industry rather than from that of Government —as well it might with all that was at stake for the industry's future.[2] But when the question came as to whose voice was to be heard on behalf of the industry, the answer was far from simple. In the first negotiations for the execution of the Government building programme the two main federations of both sides of the industry—the two employers' federations and the one operatives' federation—were the obvious spokesmen of the industry; and their representatives, too, were prominent in the deliberations of the Joint Consultative Committee

---

[1] *The Builder*, 8th December 1944. 'Statement by Mr. R. Coppock, General Secretary of the National Federation of Building Trades Operatives'

[2] See Chapter I.

and the other joint committees at official level. But, as has already been shown in the opening chapter, the building industry (including in that general description the civil engineering industry) was so vast, so varied and so loose an association of interests that no single body or group could be said to represent them. Still, on the creation of the Ministry of Works, one voluntary body, the Building Industries National Council, believed itself to possess the nucleus, at all events, of an organisation that could be expanded into a council fully representative of the whole industry; and thus able to advise the Minister of Works in his relations with every branch of it.

The Building Industries National Council, which had been created when the sudden financial collapse of 1931 threatened disaster in the building world, represented architects, surveyors and quantity surveyors, builders, operatives and materials manufacturers; and the volume of its work was reflected in its publications, particularly in 'The Building Industries Survey', issued by a special committee for public relations. Under its constitution the constituent interests retained authority over all internal and domestic matters. The Building Industries National Council, for example, did not discuss wages or conditions of contract. On 26th November 1940, the Minister of Works (Lord Reith) and members of his staff met informally representatives of the Council in order to discuss possible methods of co-operation. From this point negotiations went forward with the object of widening the basis and strengthening the personnel of the Council or creating some authoritative body available at all times to advise the Minister on matters of broad policy and developments.

During the succeeding few months no agreement was reached, and on 23rd April 1941 the Minister of Works invited a Judge of the High Court, Mr. Justice Lewis, to examine the question of the establishment of a body, fully representative of the building and civil engineering industries, to secure the closest possible co-operation between the Ministry and the building industry.[1] Mr. Justice Lewis, after sitting

---

[1] The terms of reference were as follows: In order that the best possible use may be made of the building and civil engineering industries in the Government's war building programme, and in post-war reconstruction, it is desirable that there should be a united body fully representative of the building and civil engineering industries supported by the various interests concerned, and communicating their views. Mr. Justice Lewis has therefore been requested to examine whether this could be achieved—

    (a) by extension of the present membership of the Building Industries National Council;

    (b) by the amendment of the Building Industries National Council's present constitution;

    (c) by the setting up of an entirely new body, bearing in mind that neither the professional nor the contracting side of the civil engineering industry as such is represented in the Building Industries National Council and that various other interests have either applied for membership of that body or may wish to be associated with a reorganised or new body.

Mr. Justice Lewis has also been asked to consider what would be the best machinery of contact between a reorganised Building Industries National Council or a new body and the Ministry of Works.

for twenty-three days and hearing the views of various interests in the industry, as well as considering much evidence in documentary form, reported on 24th July 1941. The report pointed out two things about the Building Industries National Council:

1. Apart from the fact that the Institution of Structural Engineers were members of the Council, there was upon it no representative whatever of the civil engineering side of the industry.

2. At its creation the Council did not include manufacturers or the 'materials' side of the industry, and was later only partially representative in that section.

Mr. Justice Lewis was satisfied that no council could be in a position to speak for the building industry unless on that council there were representatives of civil engineering; but there were difficulties which prevented the Institution of Civil Engineers and its associated professional bodies[1] from joining up with or becoming members of the Building Industries National Council, despite the willingness of the Council to amend its constitution to overcome them.

Because of this impasse, and because he did not think the introduction of the materials element in the Building Industries National Council had tended to improve its efficiency, Mr. Justice Lewis was unable to recommend that it was possible for the Council as then constituted to provide what was required.

On the basis of Mr. Justice Lewis's report, there appeared to be two alternatives in the creation of a body representative of the many interests in the industry and able to speak to one general policy. These alternatives were:

1. A close-knit and comparatively small body of interests wholly concerned with building and construction.

2. A more comprehensive but less homogeneous body whose fringes would mingle with almost every interest in the country.

Mr. Justice Lewis made suggestions which were a combination of these alternatives. He indicated a council of three parts—professional, employers, operatives—elected by institutions, federations and unions. Other interests were not to be included, but before advising the Minister on any matters affecting them the Council would discuss matters with them. At the same time the report recommended that the Building Industries National Council should continue to function and carry out its existing work.

Meanwhile, as far back as February 1941, in order to secure maximum efficiency in the building industry, Lord Reith had already decided in principle to create an *ad hoc* advisory council. The decision was discussed with the industry as an essential part of the plan for the

---

[1] Representing the several branches of civil engineering connected with works and buildings.

direction of the industry,[1] and on 26th April 1941 the new council, under the designation 'Central Council for Works and Building', held its first meeting. The Director-General, Sir Hugh Beaver, was appointed chairman. His functions, however, were limited to general oversight, and the main work was independently carried out by the deputy chairman, Sir Ernest Simon (later Lord Simon of Wythenshawe), who acted as chairman of all committees under the Council, and by the secretary to the Council, Mr. E. J. Rimmer. Membership of the Council was confined to those interests most directly or immediately concerned—employers and operatives, with a few professional and independent members. The Council had the help of higher officers of the Ministry, so that a close connection was maintained with the executive machinery; and since the chairman, Sir Hugh Beaver, was the technical administrative head of the Ministry, there was no cleavage between the Council and the Ministry. It must be stressed, however, that the members of the new Council were nominated by the Minister; they were not delegates of sectional interests appointed by those interests to represent them.

Arrangements to get the official views of organised industry on matters of broad policy remained in the 'industrial advisory panels';[2] but the Minister relied on the Council and its committees for guidance on his many problems and difficulties.

The constitution of the Central Council was unwelcome to the industry, whose spokesmen pressed on Lord Reith's successor, Lord Portal, the view that the industry should elect its own representatives. But the fact remained that an impartial survey of an industry was not possible by a body whose members were all bound to defend their own sectional interests: it was the very independence of thought and action that was the Council's real value.

When, in 1942, Lord Portal succeeded Lord Reith as Minister of Works the Central Council for Works and Building continued to function, but a new body was now set up under the title 'Advisory Committee[3] of the Building and Civil Engineering Industries', with Lord Portal as chairman and the Joint Parliamentary Secretary to the Ministry, Mr. George Hicks, as deputy chairman. Lord Portal accepted the industry's view that the existing organisation did not enable him to receive direct guidance from the industry. The new Council was to be the channel through which the views of the industry could be made known. In contrast to the Central Council, there was now for the first time an elected body representing the professional

---

[1] Mr. Justice Lewis was aware of this and had considered it in making his report.

[2] See Notes and Appendices: Note III, 'Inter-departmental Committees for the Supervision of the Building Programme, 1937–40'.

[3] The designation 'Committee' was at the second meeting (30th September 1942) changed to 'Council'.

and constructional sides of the industry;[1] but the Minister required that the new representative Council should have the opportunity of considering the recommendations of the Central Council. The Advisory Council's terms of reference were consequently framed in the widest and most general terms.[2] On 28th December 1942 Mr. G. J. Parker (National Federation of Building Trades Employers) was elected chairman, and Mr. J. W. Stephenson (National Federation of Building Trades Operatives) vice-chairman.[3]

During the two years following the creation of the Advisory Council many reports were submitted to the Minister on a variety of problems, most of which, however, concerned the post-war period. The Council had been appointed to give personal advice to Lord Portal, and in that sense its reports obviously had their value. The appointment in November 1944 of Mr. Duncan Sandys as Minister of Works in succession to Lord Portal gave the Council the opportunity of reconsidering, in conjunction with the new Minister, its methods and objectives. Following the pattern of his experience at the Ministry of Supply, and of the Ministry of Production's National Advisory Council, Mr. Sandys thought that much closer integration could be secured, not only between the Minister and officers of the department, but between the Minister and the Council, which at that time was 'an entirely independent body'. He thought it would help the Council if, as Lord Portal had done, he maintained constant personal contact with them; and proposed that he should act as President of the Council, while the Council retained its existing chairman and vice-chairman.

The designation of the Council was changed, as from 7th February 1945, to 'National Consultative Council of the Building and Civil Engineering Industries'. Its terms of reference were again of the widest: 'to consider problems affecting generally the building and civil engineering industries other than matters which are normally handled by joint organisations of trade unions and employers in connection with wages and conditions of employment'. The bodies nominating representatives remained the same, but the Minister could bring in representatives of such other organisations as he might from time to time decide.

The usefulness of the work of the Central Council for Works and

---

[1] The representatives came from the National Federation of Building Trades Employers, the Scottish National Building Trades Federation, the Federation of Civil Engineering Contractors, the National Federation of Building Trades Operatives, the Civil Engineering Conciliation Board, the Royal Institute of British Architects, the Institution of Civil Engineers and the Chartered Surveyors' Institution.

[2] The Committee was described as 'an advisory committee of the building and civil engineering industries for examination and mutual consideration of problems and policies affecting the present and future position of these industries in relation to the demands of the country's building and civil engineering requirements'.

[3] Mr. Parker died in March 1943. Mr. Stephenson succeeded him as chairman, and Mr. F. L. Wallis (National Federation of Building Trades Employers) became vice-chairman.

Building and its numerous committees was recognised on the creation both of the Advisory and the National Consultative Councils; but the Central Council was now out-dated. It was agreed accordingly that when remaining committees under past organisation had discharged their terms of reference there would only remain the National Consultative Council as the representative body to assist the Minister. There was now only one channel of approach by the Ministry to all the industrial interests.

Before its dissolution the Central Council for Works and Building played a notable role in the development of the Ministry's work. It considered the numerous problems arising out of the building programme referred to it, as well as others on its own initiative; and it produced a number of reports and recommendations, dealing *inter alia* with the standard schedule of prices, training for the building industry and the placing and management of building contracts, an especially valuable study of a very difficult problem.

The Building Apprenticeship and Training Council, which was set up in June 1943, was the child of the Central Council. Its Education Committee had put forward proposals for dealing with the expansion and maintenance of the personnel in the industry, some of which were short-term expedients and one—the setting up of an Apprenticeship and Training Council for the Building Industry—intended for permanent application. The Education Committee's recommendations were accepted, and the Minister of Labour and the Minister of Works jointly presented to Parliament in February 1943 a White Paper 'Training for the Building Industry'.[1] The Government announced their decision to take the initiative in establishing without delay a Council which would be primarily representative of the industry, but would include representatives of other important bodies, as well as of all the Government departments concerned.

(iii)

The Sixth Floor Organisation

We turn now from the relations of Government and industry to examine a little more closely the mechanism by which the Government building programme was administered within the Ministry of Works.

It was a mechanism that had its origin in the organisation of the Office of Works and had developed from a time when the Permanent Secretary himself made all major decisions and gave authority for even small purchases and works services. Since, with the growth of

---

[1] Cmd. 6428. See Chapter XIX.

work, it became impossible for the Secretary personally to carry out these functions, some of his duties devolved upon a secretariat which acted for him in authorising works and expenditure. The executive work of acquiring sites, providing buildings and purchasing supplies was carried out by various executive divisions. The services carried out by the department were thus the result of the work of various divisions acting as a team. This organisation was carried on into the new Ministry, in so far as it was possible to deal with new work and new problems in this way, and for the works and supplies services the organisational methods remained practically unchanged.

The problems arising from the new responsibilities which the Ministry assumed for the building and civil engineering industries and for the building materials industries, and of planning the use of labour and materials for the war-time building programme as a whole, were met, as we have seen, in various ways, and in this sphere the 'Sixth Floor Organisation,'[1] as it came to be called, played a large part. In the direction of the works and supplies services, on the other hand, the Ministry took over a tradition of Parliamentary and administrative responsibility from the old Office of Works. The First Commissioner of Works had been responsible for presenting to Parliament and for defending the estimates for most of the works and supplies services which were borne on the Votes of other departments. When the rearmament programme began and the Office of Works took responsibility for the erection of ordnance factories and other projects, these services were undertaken as agency services, that is, the cost was recovered from another department's Vote. The fact that for the majority of services the Commissioner of Works bore the cost on his own Vote, made it necessary and possible for the Office of Works to exercise control over expenditure and to query the demands of departments on its services. The demanding departments, although they were often called the client departments, were not so in fact because they did not themselves provide the money for the services they demanded. This tradition of financial responsibility was maintained by the administrative divisions through the war, even when the actual provision of the money was made from the Vote of Credit. The administrative divisions were not therefore merely the secretarial or accounting sections of the Ministry, but they played their part in control of policy and of expenditure.

We have already seen something of the working of the Sixth Floor Organisation, and it will be recalled that at its maturity the organisation comprised a series of directorates and divisions, each of which was responsible to the Director-General. It will be remembered, too, that on the creation of the Ministry of Works, the Minister was entrusted with responsibility for 'such control or central purchase of

---

[1] See Chapters III and IV and later portions of this chapter.

building materials not at present controlled as may be necessary'. Sir Hugh Beaver's first appointment in October 1940 had been as Controller of Building Materials as well as Priority Officer, and there were Directors of Bricks, Cement and Roofing Materials.[1] When, in April 1941, Sir Hugh Beaver became Director-General, with responsibility *inter alia* for the control of building materials, the post of Controller of Building Materials was not filled, but a Departmental Building Materials Board was set up under the chairmanship of the Director of Cement.[2]

Although, as we have seen,[3] each of the Directors of Building Materials was responsible to the Director-General, it was left to the Building Materials Board to bring about co-ordination. The Directors did not attempt to regulate prices, but by a 'gentleman's agreement' with the industries concerned prices were not increased without the consent of the Ministry. Proposals to increase prices, after preliminary investigation, were referred direct to the Director-General.[4]

The power of the Sixth Floor Organisation was derived not so much from the effective control of building materials as from the effective control of the building programme in its entirety. Its functions were vital to the main purpose for which the Ministry of Works had been set up, and although a Director of Building Programmes was appointed shortly after the appointment of a Priority Officer and Controller of Building Materials, it was inevitable that during the critical months of 1941 and 1942 the Director-General should himself remain in close control of the programme. The first Director of Building Programmes, Mr. Paul Gilbert, was given the duty of advising how the programme, whether for works in hand or for new works, could be kept within the known resources of labour and materials. When a Director-General was appointed, the method used for the control of materials was applied to building priorities. The post of Building Priority Officer was not filled, but as a counterpart to the Departmental Building Materials Board, a Departmental Building Programmes Board was set up under the chairmanship of the Director of Building Programmes.

Mr. Gilbert resigned in October 1941. During his term of office the initial surveys and investigations were carried out, the allocation system was set up, and the procedure for the adjudication of new pro-

---

[1] See Chapter IV.

[2] To make sure, in preparation for the introduction of payment by results, that there should be no shortage of materials on sites, the post of Controller of Building Materials was temporarily revived in June 1941, but only continued for a period of three months. The Controller's main task proved to be the organisation of transport, and at the end of three months, when it was clear that no serious risk of shortage of the principal materials existed, the post was discontinued.

[3] See Chapter VII.

[4] Proposals to increase the price of bricks, however, were dealt with on behalf of the Ministry by the Price Regulation Committee of the Board of Trade.

posals was worked out. On his resignation the post of Director of Building Programmes was left vacant for a time, and the Director-General resumed the chairmanship of the Contracts (Allocation) Sub-Committee, which Mr. Gilbert had taken for him, while the Building Programmes Board ceased to meet. The building programme work continued to be carried out by the Building Programmes Directorate under the direction of the Director-General. He was in effect, during this period, Building Priority Officer and Director of Building Programmes, as well as deputy chairman of the Works and Buildings Committee and chairman of the Contracts (Allocation) Sub-Committee.

Under the Director-General six officers were concerned with the building programme work, and were each directly responsible to him. They were the Deputy Director of Building Programmes, the Director of Allocation of Materials, the Chief Statistical Officer, the Secretary to the Works and Buildings Committee, the Director of Constructional Design, and the Director of Plant.[1] During the

---

[1] The duties of the six principal officers of the Sixth Floor Organisation were:

1. *The Deputy Director (later Director) of Building Programmes.* His principal duties were the examination of the building programmes of the different departments, the preparation of draft allocation proposals at quarterly intervals for the approval of the Director-General and submission, through the Minister, to the Minister of Production, and the scrutiny of individual projects. He also dealt with the scheduling of works under the Essential Work Orders. The scrutiny of the projects required technical qualifications, and he was in fact a civil engineer; he had a small staff of technical and clerical assistants.

2. *The Director of Allocation of Materials (later Chief Allocation Officer).* This officer (who also acted as Deputy Director of Building Programmes) was in the first instance responsible for devising the charting system on which all major jobs were recorded. Each job appeared first as a forecast of labour requirements month by month; then when the monthly returns were received the actual labour usage was entered and the forecasts for future months adjusted. The charts served to show the future labour requirements for each department, for each region and for the whole country. He advised on the probable availabilities of labour in the areas where new programmes of building were commencing. When the system of weekly returns on Form ED 622 came into operation he was in the position of being able to report the up-to-date state of progress for every important contract. The Chief Allocation Officer, an architect with special experience in progress planning, had a small staff of technical and clerical assistants at headquarters and regional allocation offices, similarly staffed, in all regions.

3. *The Chief Statistical Officer* maintained the returns of labour employed and materials used on the various works, building them up into totals for the respective departments for comparison with the authorised allocations. His principal function in the sphere of building programmes was the very important one of forecasting the total labour force likely to be available at the beginning and end of each allocation period.

4. *The Secretary to the Works and Buildings Sub-Committee and to the Contracts (Allocation) Sub-Committee* was an engineer who came to the Ministry as Chief Technical Assistant to the Director-General, but his duties were secretarial. He was responsible for promulgating decisions on policy and on individual cases. He was also secretary to the Joint Advisory Panel and various other committees, and represented the Works and Buildings Committee on the Materials Committee of the Production Executive.

5. *The Director of Constructional Design* was responsible for the examination of the design of all large projects. He had to ensure the maximum standardisation in construction, with a view to economy in the use of materials in short supply, particularly timber and steel. He evolved new standards of economy in materials and issued a number of brochures which were widely circulated.

6. *The Director of Plant* was responsible for the effective use of plant as well as that of labour on construction. He controlled the technical advisers on the working of payment by results and the fixing of schedules.

period of the Ministerial Directorates, from May 1941 until the end of the year, the functions of the building programmes organisation were largely confined to the routine work of according W.B.A., 'first urgency' and 'super-preference' to the works of the several departments in accordance with the instructions of the Ministerial Directorates. It was not until the reversion to the allocation system at the beginning of 1943 that the organisation began to work as had originally been intended. By that time the Deputy-Director of Building Programmes had become Director, and the Director of Allocation of Materials had become Chief Allocation Officer. From January 1943 until the end of the war the organisation fulfilled its functions as an inter-departmental organisation without any committees.

The six officers, although independent of each other, worked in close co-operation. The first three had a daily meeting. Their work fell under two main heads:

1. The quarterly preparation of draft allocations.

2. The routine handling of individual projects.

1. *Allocations.* Some six weeks before the commencement of each quarter the Director of Building Programmes asked the departments to outline their future programmes and labour requirements, firm for the next quarter, provisional for the succeeding quarter. The Chief Statistical Officer, in consultation with the Ministry of Labour and with the Director of Building Programmes and the Chief Allocation Officer, drew up a forecast of the total labour strength of the building industry at the end of each month for the ensuing half-year, with transfers to the forces and to munitions, and deductions for clericals, for men unemployed, in transit or sick, and for men required for essential maintenance and minor works, with the balance available for allocation to the departments.

The Director of Building Programmes and the Chief Allocation Officer interviewed representatives of each of the departments in turn and discussed details of their programmes, with particular reference to the urgency of the projects.

Tentative allocation sheets were then drawn up showing each department's demand and the allocation proposed. The proposed allocations were discussed with the Director-General, and in their final agreed form were submitted through the Minister to the Minister of Production.

On the basis of estimates of manpower available, the Director of Constructional Design made recommendations to the Ministry of

Supply on the requirements of the building programme in steel and timber.[1]

2. *Individual Projects*. For every new building project costing £5,000, or more, including buildings for which a civil licence was needed, an application for approval was made to the Building Programmes Directorate on Forms BP1 and BP2. The Secretary to the Committee registered it; the Chief Statistical Officer stated how the department stood in relation to the allocation; the Director of Constructional Design investigated the requirements of material to ensure that economy in design was being observed; and the Chief Allocation Officer checked the labour demands. He also advised whether they could be met within the departments' allocation, and whether particular difficulties were to be expected from the geographical situation of the project.

After the Director of Building Programmes had considered the application as a whole in the light of the advice of the other officials, and had made his recommendations, the Director-General gave his decision. Before the formation of the Ministerial Directorates, the project was then listed by the Secretary and brought before the Contracts (Allocation) Sub-Committee for confirmation; but after that committee had ceased to function the decision was promulgated without further formality.

If a department wished to contest an adverse decision it could appeal to the Minister of Production.

In a small proportion of the approved projects, the need for a higher priority might not become apparent until after the work had commenced. It was then for the Chief Allocation Officer to advise whether the local conditions made an upgrading necessary and desirable, and the Director of Building Programmes advised whether the urgency of the project justified it. The Director-General made the decision, and the Chief Allocation Officer implemented it through the Regional Allocation Officers.

The building allocation system was on the whole one of the more

---

[1] Both the Statistical Officer and the Director of Constructional Design also had duties not directly concerned with the building programme work. The first dealt with all the statistical requirements of the 'sixth floor'. He was called upon as might be required by the other directorates and by the Central Council for Works and Building. In connection with the registration of builders and civil engineering contractors, he translated the particulars into returns which gave pictures of various aspects of the industry. He created the first attempt to give statistics of the building and civil engineering industries, and of the value of building work carried out in the country. The Director of Constructional Design was one of three assessors representing the Ministry on such bodies as the Building Research Board, the Roads Research Board, and the Committee on the Design of Prefabricated Huts. He had three sections under Assistant Directors, dealing *inter alia* with timber economy and prefabricated hutting, each with a small number of technical assistants. This officer was an engineer, and his was a technical job in which he worked in close co-operation with all technical divisions of the department. His activities extended to the work of other building departments, for which reason he occupied a 'sixth floor' status rather than one in which he would be normally responsible to a departmental chief.

successful of the war-time controls. It was almost unknown to the general public because it was conducted entirely between departments. There had, from the start, been a very clear picture in the minds of the Director-General and the Building Programmes Directorate of the way in which the allocation system should operate, but to operate effectively certain powers of enforcement were needed which were not there at the outset. On the contrary, there was in the early stages a general lack of co-operation from the other departments and even active opposition; the old-established departments, as we have noted earlier,[1] resented the surrender of part of their liberty of action to a comparatively new department. They were sometimes apt to forget that a paper allocation meant nothing if there were not enough jobs to employ the numbers of men allocated, and sometimes they were inclined to ignore the physical difficulties in implementing an allocation when a proportion of their projects was sited in out-of-the-way places. Departments whose allocations were reduced were often slow to release the labour, with the consequence that other departments went short.

It must be remembered, too, that before the introduction of programming and progress-planning by the Ministry of Works some departments made no attempt to measure their programmes in terms of materials and labour. The need to 'phase' the works which made up a building programme so that as jobs neared completion others were begun had never been properly appreciated. Estimates were sometimes made of time and cost, but these were nearly always wide of the mark. In some of the departments contracts had been let by different branches without reference to each other, and there was in fact no single person who knew how much work the department had in hand.

It was not until Mr. Churchill issued his memorandum on 27th November 1941[2] that the principles put forward by the Lord President, on the recommendation of the Minister of Works, for the control of the building programme, were confirmed, and clear guidance given on the policy to be followed. The allocation system became fully effective from that date.

It is true that, on the part of some of the departments, there was still a certain lack of co-operation; and these difficulties might well have continued indefinitely if it had not been for the temporary reversion to a priority system in 1941.[3] After that experience all departments were glad to return to the allocation system; and, it might fairly be added, by this time it was realised that the Ministry of Works, through its Building Programmes Directorate, was genuinely striving to be impartial in its co-ordination of the programme. Nevertheless,

---

[1] See Chapter IV.
[2] *Ibid.*
[3] See Chapter V.

it is true that originally there had been great suspicion of the Ministry of Works as themselves claimants for a share of the inadequate labour force which they were to distribute. But after 1942, as will be recalled, there was no inter-departmental committee meeting of any kind on building programmes, nor was there ever any serious demand for a meeting. The allocations were settled at Ministerial level before the Minister of Production, and once they were fixed the departments were willing to leave the operation of the system to the officials of the Ministry of Works, to whom they could always bring special cases for exceptional treatment.

At no time, nor in any country, had there been a precedent for a planned control of the operations of the whole of the building industry, or for a central co-ordination of some thirty-five different Government building programmes. The system for carrying it out had to be devised *ab initio*; and it says much for the clarity of the original conception that there was never any need to modify it materially, although the system was suspended for a time, as we have seen, with disastrous consequences.

The labour graph for any building contract is not a straight line, or even a simple pyramid; it is parabolic in form, starting at zero, building up slowly at first, then accelerating rapidly until it nears the peak; after the peak is reached the process is reversed until there is only a handful of men left for tidying-up. To fit these parabolas together—dovetailing them in with one another so as to ensure that there was always a new job for every man when his work on a contract had finished and to ensure at the same time also that the minimum number of contracts were kept waiting for labour—called for very intricate planning by the Building Programmes Directorate, since not only the allocation of each of the departments, but the labour availabilities of every area, had to be taken into account.

By the end of 1942 the system was working so well that the future building labour position of the country as a whole, of each department, of each area and of every major contract, could be foretold several months ahead with a surprising degree of accuracy. Real flexibility in the operation of the system was brought about by the innovation of the weekly return on the Form ED 622. The monthly return on Form W.B.I. had proved cumbersome and slow; it was not until the 22nd of the month that the labour position at the end of the previous month was known. With the new ED 622 form the labour position at Friday of every important job in the country was known in London the following Tuesday, and with this information the trends of the different programmes could be estimated.

With this new flexibility the system was able to take in its stride sudden major changes in the programmes, such as the Phoenix operation and the repair work necessitated by the V1 and V2 attacks. It might even be said that the flexibility of the system of building control was a not unimportant factor in the success of the Mulberry harbours.

To deal with the administrative work of the Sixth Floor Organisation, on the appointment of the Director-General an administrative division was set up under a Principal Assistant Secretary. This was an experimental move, and the scope of the division was laid down by the Director-General.

The administrative division functioned in three ways. First, it assisted the Director-General in the formulation of policy; secondly, it acted as a secretariat to the Director-General, dealing with business of all kinds arising out of the Sixth Floor work; and, thirdly, it had a definite field of operations in connection with the Essential Work Orders, reservation from military service, the control of civil building, the registration of building and civil engineering contractors, the control of plant, and the authorisation of iron and steel for repair of essential plant and the building materials industries.

The main lines of policy were naturally determined by the Director-General, and in practice he also personally controlled the technical heads in the Ministry. The Principal Assistant Secretary was usually associated with the Director-General in the many conferences and committees which advised on policy. But below the Principal Assistant Secretary the administrative staff had no direct part in the formulation of policy and, in its application, were sometimes under a disability because they were not well informed of the underlying motives and intentions. This disability followed from the expansion of the Office of Works into the Ministry of Works. Since the small administrative staff of the Office of Works was quite inadequate to meet this expansion, important key positions had to be filled by appointments from other departments, by outsiders brought in, and by rapid promotions. Policy can only be made, however, by those with the right experience or background and can only be administered by those steeped in the method and the routine of a department. It was in helping this inevitable gap to be bridged that the Sixth Floor Organisation proved so valuable an expedient. At its best it had a spirit and an outlook that reflected the war spirit of the whole country: the temporary association of all sorts and kinds with only one objective—the war.

(iv)
Works and Supplies

In the execution of the Government building programme, the implementation of the war tasks of the Ministry of Works fell in full measure upon the Directorate of Works. The old organisation of the

Office of Works had been on wholly administrative lines, with several departments each headed by a technical officer, and all co-ordinated by the Permanent Secretary and his secretariat. The first Minister of Works (Lord Reith) decided to combine all the technical departments under a technical Director of Works. Under the Director-General, he was entirely responsible for the direction of all works, except that the Contracts Directorate did not come under him. The first Director of Works, Colonel Howard Humphreys, a civil engineer, was appointed in December 1940; he died in June 1941 after some months of illness, against which he struggled. His place was taken by Mr. (later Sir) T. P. Bennett, who resigned in 1944 and was succeeded by Mr. (later Sir) Charles J. Mole.

The Directorate of Works, as earlier chapters have shown,[1] bore a heavy burden of responsibility. It was by far the largest division in the Ministry and its functions reflected the executive side of the Ministry's dual character: to be the 'handmaid' of the departments, to supply them with new buildings and to adapt and maintain existing ones, and to render other services. With the other side of the Ministry's character—the administration of the Government building programme and the building industry, and everything related to them— the Directorate of Works was not directly concerned. The Ministry of Works in the one role was to the Ministry of Works in the other role just one of a number of departments. The first role called for the considerable expansion of an existing organisation; but the second role meant the creation of an entirely new machine. It was not until long after the setting up of the Ministry of Works that the distinction was fully grasped—not only by the departments, but within the Ministry itself.

Of the other divisions and directorates carrying over from the Office of Works, those dealing respectively with supplies, with lands and accommodation, and with contracts were predominant; and their expansion to meet the mounting demands of the war effort is the measure of their importance.

Up to about 1912, the Supplies Division of the Office of Works was responsible not only for the supply of furniture and fuel to some of the civil departments, but it also dealt with premises and land questions. There was much duplication of purchase, both within the Supplies Division itself and within the various divisions of the department, and no centralisation. About this time a central purchasing organisation was set up within the Supplies Division to take charge of its purchase work as well as some of the purchase work of the other sections of the department. During the First World War, when the department undertook many agency supply services, that work was greatly extended.

---

[1] See especially Chapter XVII.

In 1920 the premises side of the Supplies Division was formed into the Directorate of Lands and Accommodation, and the Supplies Division retained its functions in regard to supply, furniture and fuel, by this time on a nation-wide basis. The machinery of the Supplies Division had now a good general reputation, not only inside but outside the department, and Lord Weir's Committee recommended that consideration should be given to the possibility of centralising the whole of the supply of Government furniture in the hands of the Office of Works. Although this recommendation was not fully implemented, there was a general trend in that direction. By 1938 a very large part of the furniture needed for Government premises was centralised in the Supplies Division.[1]

When, towards the close of the rearmament period, the Auxiliary Fire Service was set up under the Home Office and a vast quantity of fire equipment had to be supplied, that department made a survey of all Government purchasing organisations and chose the Supplies Division of the Office of Works as the most appropriate machine to deal with this important service. This was but one side of its work. From about 1937 and throughout the war, that machine was enlarged and improved. When great quantities of canteen equipment were wanted by the Ministry of Food, it was through the agency of the division that these purchases were made. Later the introduction of school meals meant a further heavy purchase of canteen equipment. The Ministry of Works was charged, too, with the supply of all civil canteen requirements, and this duty again fell to the Supplies Division. Other important purchases for the Ministry of Works, carried out by the Supplies Division, included heavy canteen equipment, huts and doors.[2]

The Purchasing Branch was divided into sections, each under a Chief Purchasing Officer. Broadly, the functions of the purchasing sections—in part based on the delegated authority of the Director of Contracts—were to collect and classify forecasts of demands; to buy stores and equipment for meeting these demands; to place contracts so that the goods needed should be at the right place at the proper time; to administer contracts, including progressing, the consideration of claims and so forth; to allocate materials; to place individual orders; to certify accounts; and to keep a general watch on supply services.

The Supplies Division was the storekeeper not only for all divisions of the Ministry of Works, but it also held certain stocks for other departments (for example, medical stores for the Ministry of Health).

---

[1] Furniture for the Admiralty and certain barrack-room furniture for the War Office were important exceptions.

[2] In 1942 this side of the Purchasing Branch was transferred to a new division of the Directorate of Works.

By the end of the war some 180 storage buildings, totalling about three million feet super, were dispersed over the whole country.[1] Before the war the tendency had been to deliver direct wherever possible, but because of war-time conditions—such as the concentration of industry, the obligation to keep firms in full production and the need to purchase in advance all forecast requirements—many more deliveries had to be made from stores. The stores also held the reserve equipment for meeting demands for blankets, furniture and other goods for bombed-out civilians, and for furniture and other needs of the civil departments, hostels, and other accommodation. The load-on of stores was about 3,000 tons per week, including goods inwards and goods outwards to meet an average of 9,000 demands.[2]

(v)

Lands and Accommodation

When the Directorate of Lands and Accommodation took over the work hitherto carried out by the Supplies Division, as already noted, the housing estates formerly controlled by the Ministry of Munitions, the Admiralty and the Air Ministry were at the same time handed over to this directorate for management and disposal. At a later date certain accommodation services in the provinces were taken over.

The principal functions of the directorate, holding, as it did, the largest estate in the country, concerned the acquisition and requisitioning of land and buildings for civil departments, and headquarter staff of Service departments; the use and allocation of accommodation held by the Ministry; the settlement of claims for compensation for requisitioned land and buildings; negotiations of purchase price or rental for lands and buildings purchased or hired; co-ordination of executive divisions in carrying out accommodation schemes; advice and assistance to other divisions of the Ministry, other departments, allied Government and other bodies on Lands and Accommodation matters; the custody of Government premises in London and certain provincial towns; the requisitioning and compensation for open-cast coal; the Central Register of Accommodation; and the records of premises held by the Ministry.

The directorate was staffed initially by permanent officers of the department, together with temporary staff of various grades who had

---

[1] The total store space available at the outbreak of war was only about 300,000 feet.

[2] Categories of goods purchased by the Supplies Division and its principal services are shown in Notes and Appendices: Appendix XI, 'Supplies Division: Goods Purchased and Principal Services'.

entered during the First World War. Since 1928, the professional work was performed by a permanent grade of estate surveyors.

The estate surveyor was primarily a valuation surveyor, but to enable him to carry out the full range of duties of the division, he had to have some degree of knowledge of building construction. He had to judge the possibilities and limitations of buildings which he suggested for acquisition and to have a grasp of the law relating to real property, including war-time legislation and regulations. In addition, he had to know something about mineral valuation in dealing with compensation for open-cast coal; about agriculture in dealing with requisition and compensation for agricultural land; and about office and welfare organisation in dealing with allocation of accommodation for these purposes. Above all, however, he had to be temperamentally suited to make successful contact with representatives of departments and the outside public. No person likes his land to be requisitioned, and unless the requisitioning officer's approach was tactful the department was likely to receive bitter complaints of hardship and harsh treatment.

During the years 1920–37 the range of work of the directorate expanded steadily. In 1924 provincial accommodation was overhauled, inspected and re-allocated in order to ensure efficiency and economy. Several large programmes (such as, among others, employment exchanges, valuation offices, Assistance Board offices, and new post offices and telephone exchanges) were undertaken during the period.

In the rearmament period a scheme was prepared for the evacuation from London of the whole of the Civil Service and of other official bodies and services. The Central Register of Accommodation, designed to avoid overlapping in the war-time accommodation requirements both of central government and local authorities throughout the British Isles, was instituted in 1938, and by the outbreak of war some 33,000 premises were registered. Additional accommodation was found for expanding and new departments which had come into being as a result of war preparations, and for the storing of gas-masks and other air raid precaution equipment.

Under the terms of the Civil Defence Act, the directorate undertook the negotiations and financial arrangements with landlords of leased premises for the provision of air raid shelters, and similar shelters were provided in all new buildings erected during the period. The clearance of records often enabled existing basements to be used for shelter, and over 300,000 square feet of space was hired outside London for the storage of records so displaced.

On the outbreak of war, the department was given powers to requisition land (including premises) under the Emergency Powers Defence Act, and a branch was at once set up to deal with the compensation to be paid in respect of requisitioning. Throughout the war the Directorate of Lands and Accommodation carried a heavy burden. To cope with the additional work, its district offices in the provinces were rapidly expanded from the seven existing before 1939 to the twenty-one in existence at the height of the war. The evacuation scheme for the Civil Service was partially implemented, and evacuation offices were set up in Bath, Southport, Harrogate, and numerous other centres, to deal with the housing of staffs from London. Meanwhile the work of the Central Register of Accommodation increased rapidly. The number of ear-marking requests and enquiries rose steadily until November 1940 when they reached the peak of some 4,000 per week. Towards the end of the war there were approximately 200,000 live entries on the register (in addition to a large number 'invisibly' protected as excepted categories), and the weekly load of enquiries was some 2,000.

In addition to the settlement of rental compensation, the directorate was required to deal with compensation in respect of salvage of metals, petrol pipe-lines, war damage claims, and open-cast coal; and another of its burdens was the considerable amount of rehousing of Government staffs made necessary, both in London and the provinces, by air raid damage.

At its maturity the directorate was organised in five main groups (four professional and one clerical) which between them covered a vast and varied field. Thus, apart from normal Government needs for offices, stores, hostels, clubs, canteens, factories, open sites, and so on, the accommodation groups for London and the provinces met the requirements of Dominion and Allied Governments, American Red Cross (hostels, rest centres, doughnut bars), Women's Land Army hostels, seamen's clubs, hostels for Gibraltar refugees, school meal centres, etc. It had also to provide offices, studios and stations for the British Broadcasting Corporation and to find sites for temporary office buildings, hostels, cold stores, National Fire Force camps, timber dumps, static water tanks, prisoner-of-war camps, grain and other food stores, and many other services. The acquisition of a site often involved clearance from as many as twenty interested parties.

Accommodation was found for the Houses of Parliament, the Royal Courts of Justice, museums, art galleries, and kindred institutions, and an unusual service was to advise on sites under consideration for a mosque and cultural centre for the Moslem community in this country.

Other special services carried out during the war include surveys of accommodation available for the War Office in south-west England (30 million feet listed); vacant houses and flats in London (14 million feet listed in a week); occupation of country houses in certain areas by business firms; and a census of quarries and underground workings (excluding mines) throughout the country.

The activities of the compensation group fell under five main headings:

1. Negotiation of compensation payable under the Compensation Defence Act in respect of requisitioning of land and buildings required for Government occupation.

The Directorate of Lands and Accommodation was represented on the Valuation Sub-Committee appointed by Government to deal with the application of the Act and to secure uniform treatment of claimants by all departments. To apply the terms of compensation laid down by the Act to special types of premises or fixtures was not always a simple matter, and claimants from time to time submitted cases to the General Claims Tribunal for decision.

2. Settlement of certain claims arising out of the salvage of metal, and compensation in respect of the recovery of steel from blitzed buildings.

Claims (for example, in respect of railings and gates) which local authorities were unable to settle were referred to the Directorate of Lands and Accommodation for negotiation. One major difficulty was that the salvaged metal was often removed, and even melted down, before the claim for compensation reached the department. Claimants had the right of appeal to the General Claims Tribunal, whose decisions sometimes affected the basis of settlement.

3. Service of notices of entry and requisitioning of land and settlement of compensation in respect of the production of open-cast coal.

Compensation was negotiated both as to entry on the land for prospecting (including the boring of trial holes), and the subsequent requisitioning of the land for the removal of open-cast coal. The directorate settled royalties and payments for expectant profits, and special care had to be taken to avoid the unnecessary disturbance of owners and of agricultural land.

4. Requisitioning of land and settlement of compensation where petrol pipe-lines were constructed on behalf of the Ministry of Fuel and Power.

Estate surveyors worked side by side with engineers of the oil companies. Constant vigilance and co-operation were called for to avoid undue disturbance and damage to farm lands, and to ensure that contractors paid the compensation for which they became liable.

5. Preparation of claims on the War Damage Commission for war damage to buildings in Government occupation.

The Ministry of Works, through the Directorate of Lands and Accommodation, was the central Government department entrusted by the Cabinet with the task of co-ordinating and advising all other departments in matters of accommodation. Close liaison was maintained, especially with the Service departments, who consulted the directorate before requisitioning any occupied premises. The directorate, too, was responsible for advising the administrative side on all legislation affecting real property, such as Landlord and Tenant (War Damage) Bills, Landlord and Tenant (Requisitioning Land) Bill, Defence Regulations, Acquisition of Land Bill, and many others.

(vi)
The Contracts Directorate

The Contracts Directorate of the Ministry of Works was by no means the least notable of the group of divisions and directorates which grew from the modest establishment of the Office of Works to a scale appropriate to a fully-fledged Ministry; and its expansion was implicit in the development of the Government building programme, and therefore of the war effort as a whole.

The Directorate's war-time functions were partly administrative and partly executive. For many years the role of the Contracts Branch of the Office of Works had been in the main administrative, and before the formation of the Ministry it ranked as part of the department's secretariat. In its war-time role, however, the Contracts Branch took its place on the administrative side of the Ministry. The Director of Contracts, while responsible to the Deputy Secretary, kept in close touch with the Director-General on matters where contract policy might impinge on industry.

On the administrative side it was the business of the Contracts Branch to see that correct contracting principles were applied. In consequence, over a period of many years all matters of general contract policy and administration were its concern. The Branch had to consult and co-operate with other Government contracting departments, with public and professional bodies, and with associations of contractors, in order to ensure economy of purchase without loss of productive efficiency. The Branch was above all at pains to make certain that justice was done, and seen to be done, to all firms seeking a share in Government work. To that end it was incumbent upon it to examine and criticise contract proposals in the light of the principles laid down from time to time for the conduct of Government contracting business.

To help the Branch along this strait, and sometimes thorny, path progressive records were kept of firms eligible and ineligible to tender, of their characteristics and performance, and of all the works executed by individual contractors for some thirty years preceding the Second World War. All printed forms of contract were kept constantly under review or new issues were prepared to meet new needs. Agreements with supply authorities or for special services (such as, for example,

Royal Parks refreshment licences) were settled in the Branch, as were all questions involving departure from contract terms such as might well arise during the course of a contract. Claims for extra-contractual payments were examined and, if justified, were approved or submitted to higher authority.[1]

With the enormous expansion in activities and interests brought about by the defence programme, large blocks of works contracting were taken over from the Ministries of Supply, Aircraft Production and Fuel and Power. The development of the Contracts Directorate in the Ministry of Works, however, did not quite follow the pattern of development of these and other Government contracting departments; rather did it grow out of the earlier Office of Works organisation. Other departments had for many years found it expedient to work on a system under which the technical officer or production department formulated requirements and provided the contracts branch of the department with a specification or with details of appropriate firms to be asked for prices. The Office of Works Contracts Branch, and later the Ministry of Works Contracts Directorate, invited tenders or obtained prices, and on the recommendation of the production department placed an acceptance. Thereafter the ordering and progressing section carried on in the normal manner, but the Contracts Directorate remained responsible for all matters arising during the run of the contract. The system made for the observance of correct contracting principles, and ensured that only the Contracts Directorate could commit the Ministry for all purchases of consequence.

The Office of Works system had provided for many years a workable system which had proved generally satisfactory, and it was thought inexpedient, especially in war-time, to embark on major changes. With the commencement of the open-cast coal programme,[2] however, occasion was taken to introduce as an experiment a system of full control by the Directorate under which, apart from recommendations at appropriate stages by the technical officers, all contract operations for that programme were handled within the Directorate. The experiment proved successful, and strengthened the view held within the Ministry that the centralisation of all contracting

---

[1] For all routine operations, however, in such matters as issuing tender documents, copying specifications and bills of quantities and preparing draft contract documents, the executive divisions rather than the Contracts Branch were in the main responsible.

[2] The story of open-cast coal production is told elsewhere in this series. It begins in the Board of Trade, under which the Department of Mines then functioned. In 1943 the Ministry of Fuel and Power, which had meanwhile succeeded the Department of Mines, sought the advice of the Director-General of the Ministry of Works, as to a successor to Mr. (later Sir John) Gibson who had resigned. It was suggested instead that the whole work should be handed over to the Ministry of Works under the general direction of the Ministry of Fuel and Power. It might, no doubt, in any case have been transferred back to the Ministry of Fuel and Power; but it did actually go because the Minister of Works (Lord Portal) thought it put on him a responsibility that was unjustified.

work would show not only an increase in efficiency but a saving in staff and time.

Another step towards the complete control of contracting by the Directorate was taken when, from 1944 onwards, senior regional officers were allowed, under the direct authority of the Director of Contracts, to exercise certain powers in regard to contracts in excess of those possessed by executive officers. There was now a nucleus of delegated authority, on a regional basis both on the administrative and the executive side, under which a great volume of provincial contract work could be carried out without reference to headquarters.

Because of the close relations of the Ministry of Works with the building industry in war, the Ministry became more and more a centre of reference and a court of appeal on matters of contracting policy and procedure, as they affected not only Government but also general building and civil engineering works; and the Director of Contracts, as chairman of the Contracts Co-ordinating Committee Works Sub-Committee, was drawn into an orbit spreading far beyond the confines of contractual procedure.

*   *

*

In the next chapter we turn to see how far it became possible, under the stress of war, to formulate a building policy for the post-war future. Before we do so it seems appropriate to reflect on the total demand of the Government building programme, in terms of man-power and cost, on the nation's resources. This is summarised in the two tables at the end of this chapter.[1] They are extracted from the *Statistical Digest of the War*.[2]

---

[1] Annex to Chapter XVIII, Tables A and B.
[2] One of the volumes in this series.

ANNEX TO CHAPTER XVIII

(TABLE A)

MANPOWER

Number of Male Operatives Employed on Government Building Programme[1]

TABLE 26   End of Month   Thousands

	Total	Service and Supply Departments							Civil Departments[2][3]	New house construction (including site preparation)
		Total	Admiralty	War Office[2]	Air Ministry[2]	Ministry of Supply	Ministry of Aircraft Production[2]	Ministry of Transport[2]		
1941 July	541·8	342·6	34·2	55·1	109·3	100·5	32·8	10·7	199·2	—
August	543·8	341·0	33·2	55·7	109·3	100·0	32·1	10·7	202·8	—
September	557·8	347·2	32·2	55·5	109·9	108·1	30·6	10·9	210·6	—
October	560·9	348·5	32·6	56·5	108·7	105·9	32·3	12·5	212·4	—
November	537·7	346·0	31·0	56·5	106·7	106·4	34·3	11·1	191·7	—
December	517·6	333·7	29·5	55·9	99·3	103·0	34·9	11·1	183·9	—
1942 January	503·7	330·8	28·6	54·7	102·5	92·3	40·6	12·1	172·9	1·0
February	496·7	329·8	28·7	50·2	105·3	92·8	40·5	12·3	165·9	1·5
March	510·2	332·7	27·0	52·1	106·5	92·6	41·7	12·8	176·0	1·6
April	514·0	337·7	26·2	50·7	112·6	91·5	43·5	13·2	174·7	1·6
May	495·5	328·3	26·4	48·0	109·8	82·1	49·1	12·9	165·6	1·7
June	480·9	319·4	26·6	44·2	112·8	75·3	48·0	12·5	159·8	1·8
July	466·7	319·3	25·0	45·0	117·1	65·2	54·9	12·1	145·6	2·7
August	464·7	327·3	28·3	52·8	120·7	60·5	53·3	11·7	134·7	2·7
September	460·5	331·0	26·5	62·0	126·1	52·1	53·1	11·2	126·8	2·7
October	460·7	336·3	27·0	71·2	129·6	48·9	49·4	10·2	121·7	2·7
November	445·2	328·5	27·9	72·8	130·1	45·1	43·4	9·2	114·2	2·5
December	426·6	320·5	27·2	75·6	129·8	41·9	37·9	8·1	103·6	2·5

1943 January	425·3	323·5	27·7	78·3	130·2	38·9	39·7	8·7	99·7	2·1
February	419·9	319·9	30·0	76·9	127·8	37·7	39·0	8·5	97·9	2·1
March	405·7	312·4	32·2	72·5	124·5	37·5	37·7	8·0	91·2	2·1
April	388·7	296·4	31·4	61·3	123·8	36·2	35·3	8·2	89·9	2·4
May	372·3	280·3	32·2	51·4	119·1	35·6	33·7	9·1	89·7	2·3
June	356·1	263·1	31·9	44·9	109·8	34·7	32·6	8·9	90·7	2·3
July	347·1	247·1	31·8	38·2	103·9	34·1	29·6	9·4	96·1	3·9
August	351·4	244·4	31·4	37·8	102·2	33·0	29·6	10·0	101·0	6·0
September	344·8	235·8	31·8	36·9	99·0	31·5	26·6	10·4	101·7	7·3
October	335·4	224·9	31·9	34·4	94·5	29·4	25·2	9·6	101·6	8·9
November	330·5	221·4	30·8	33·2	87·6	35·0	24·7	9·0	100·3	8·8
December	316·7	215·6		34·1	78·3	40·1	23·9	8·4	91·5	9·6
1944 January	317·3	213·3	30·7	35·1	71·9	45·2	22·4	8·0	94·6	9·4
February	316·8	207·7	29·4	34·4	63·8	47·9	23·1	9·1	100·5	8·6
March	306·3	190·7	27·7	32·2	53·8	46·0	21·9	9·1	107·7	7·9
April	295·6	175·6	25·1	31·2	47·9	42·7	20·3	8·4	113·0	7·0
May	273·4	153·1	22·2	29·9	39·9	33·7	18·8	8·6	114·0	6·3
June	267·5	146·2	20·5	28·9	38·9	31·6	17·6	8·7	115·5	5·8
July	249·4	134·4	19·3	26·3	32·9	31·3	16·4	8·2	110·3	4·7
August	231·5	133·2	18·5	24·4	31·6	36·6	14·4	7·7	93·7	4·6
September	222·1	124·2	18·5	23·0	30·0	31·5	13·3	7·9	93·1	4·8
October	216·5	114·0	19·2	22·0	30·4	23·1	11·5	7·8	97·6	4·9
November	201·9	105·0	18·4	21·0	28·6	21·0	9·4	6·5	92·0	4·9
December	195·0	98·6	17·6	18·9	27·0	20·3	8·7	6·1	91·4	5·0
1945 January	189·7	93·8	16·3	17·6	26·9	20·3	7·2	5·5	90·5	5·4
February	198·2	94·5	16·4	17·6	26·5	21·2	7·1	5·7	95·3	8·4
March	200·1	92·3	15·1	17·0	25·9	22·1	6·4	5·8	94·7	13·1
April	207·1	91·0	15·3	16·7	25·6	21·5	5·7	6·2	99·6	16·5
May	218·1	91·9	15·0	15·9	25·4	23·0	5·6	7·0	105·7	20·5
June	219·9	87·0	14·4	15·0	23·3	23·6	4·3	6·4	106·3	26·6
July	242·5	87·4	14·6	14·0	22·8	24·2	4·5	7·3	122·8	32·3

Source: Ministry of Works

¹ Age sixteen and over.

² Labour employed on licensed work sponsored by War Office, Air Ministry, Ministry of Aircraft Production and Ministry of Transport is included under 'Civil Departments' before January 1943.

³ Including repair of houses made uninhabitable by war damage; salvage operations and war debris clearance; and first-aid repairs carried out by the Special Repair Service.

ANNEX TO CHAPTER XVIII

(TABLE B)

HOUSING AND BUILDING

Construction Activity[1]: Estimated Value of Work Done

TABLE 46   Great Britain   £ millions

		1940	1941	1942	1943	1944	1945
Estimated value of work done:							
Total		425	470	425	350	290	290
Military construction	Airfields, camps, and training establishments, defence works, storage depots, wireless telegraphy, etc.	140	120	125	122	49	12
Industrial facilities	Factories, storage, docks and harbour works	80	76	65	46	29	25
Civil Defence	Air raid precautions, public shelters, static water, etc.	⎫	42	23	12	9	—[2]
Residential building	Hostels and housing (new work)	⎪	22	16	6	13	30
Roads and streets	Strengthening, widening and major maintenance	88	2	3	3	3	2
Public and institutional buildings	Hospitals, schools, etc.	⎪	6	6	9	6	5
Public utilities	Electricity, gas, water, sewerage, railways, ports, canals, tramways, etc.	⎭	19	16	12	8	12
Mining	Mines and open-cast coal	⎫ 6	13	18	16	23	26
Air raid damage	Repairs, demolition and debris clearance	⎭	63	61	50	58	113
All other work	Including conversion, adaptation, repair and maintenance of houses	111	107	92	74	92	65

Source: Ministry of Works

[1] Building and civil engineering. Firms of working principals who employed no operatives are excluded, the estimated value of their output being £16 millions in 1946.

[2] For the purposes of this table it has been assumed that demolition work only was carried out under these headings in 1945.

CHAPTER XIX

PROSPECT

(i)

Post-War Building Policy

O
N Lord Reith's appointment as the first Minister of Works he was charged, as has been noted,[1] in the widest and most general terms to consult with 'the departments and organisations concerned with a view to reporting to the Cabinet the appropriate methods and machinery for dealing with the issues involved' in the reconstruction of towns and country after the war.[2] That responsibility, as the Lord Privy Seal (Mr. Attlee) stated in the House of Commons when the Ministry was set up, raised great problems and gave a great opportunity; but it was none the less an undefined responsibility that might well have distracted the new Minister from urgent war tasks that lay at hand.

The transfer of planning functions to the Ministry of Town and Country Planning in February 1943, the subsequent appointment of a Minister of Reconstruction, and the tendency of housing problems to be caught up in political controversy were all factors that ultimately narrowed the responsibility of the Minister of Works to the more technical aspects of post-war building policy. His responsibility in this respect was discharged through the Directorate of Post-War Building.[3]

(ii)

Housing

Much of the work of the Directorate had reference to house-building, and before we turn to examine more generally the Directorate's organisation, the housing position at the end of the war must be briefly described. Early in the war, as we have seen, the Ministry of

---

[1] See Chapter III.

[2] Statement by the Lord Privy Seal (Mr. Attlee). H. of C. Deb., 24th October 1940 Vol. 365, Col. 1152.

[3] The Directorate was set up in the autumn of 1941.

Health had cut short its housing programme[1] and the relatively few houses built during the war had been erected under stringent conditions and safeguards, and for specific reasons. Experiments in prefabricated houses, such as the Portal house sponsored by the Ministry of Works, were intended to provide temporary housing of adequate quality without calling, to any important extent, on labour from the building industry. The various aspects of prefabrication, in respect both of the shell of prefabricated houses and of the components, fittings and furnishings inside the houses, were studied, but the erection of temporary houses to accommodate those rendered homeless by the war had little direct bearing on the vast problem of permanent housing which awaited the end of hostilities. How limited was the extent of housebuilding from 1941 onwards is clearly shown in the annexed table, 'Number of Houses Built', extracted from the *Statistical Digest of the War*.[2]

At the end of the war authority was given[3] to spend up to £200 millions on temporary houses, and a programme was finally drawn up for the erection of 158,748 houses.[4] This number was made up as follows:

Authority responsible for production	Type			Number of houses
The Ministry of Works .	Arcon .	.	.	41,000
	Uni-Seco .	.	.	29,000
	Tarran .	.	.	19,015
	U.S.A. .	.	.	8,450
	Phoenix .	.	.	2,428
	Spooner .	.	.	2,000
	Universal .	.	.	2,000
	Orlit .	.	.	255
	Miller .	.	.	100
The Ministry of Supply .	Aluminium .	.	.	54,500
	TOTAL .		.	158,748

Plans to manufacture the Portal or a similar pressed steel house were dropped because factory capacity, labour and materials could not be released quickly enough from munitions production. A number of different types, less highly prefabricated and using such material as was available, had to be substituted.

The Ministry of Works undertook site works, including the construction of foundation slabs, and arranged the manufacture and erection of the houses. In the first annual report issued by the Ministry of Works since its creation in 1940[5] the difficult production problems

---

[1] See Chapter II.

[2] One of the volumes in this series.

[3] Under the Housing (Temporary Accommodation) Act 1944, as amended by Section 5 of the Building Materials and Housing Act 1945.

[4] The above figures include 2,000 houses intended for the Government of Northern Ireland.

[5] *Summary Report of Ministry of Works, 9th May 1945–31st December 1946* (Cmd. 7279).

HOUSING AND BUILDING
Number of Houses Built[1]

TABLE 45

	Total	Permanent houses built by local authorities[2]		Permanent houses built by private builders[2]		War-destroyed houses rebuilt		Houses built by Government departments[3]		Temporary houses erected by local authorities
		Assisted	Unassisted[4]	Assisted	Unassisted[4]	By local authorities	By private builders under licence	Permanent	Temporary	Number
England and Wales[5]:										
1935–38 (average)	334,405	48,579	12,336	1,177	272,313	—	—	—	—	—
1938–39	332,360	88,776	12,968	4,207	226,409	—	—	—	—	—
1939–40	195,962	40,231	10,221	2,849	142,661	—	—	—	—	—
1940–41	42,498	11,802	3,606	648	26,442	—	—	—	—	—
1941–42	9,841	1,676	1,237	118	5,483	—	—	—	1,327	—
1942–43	9,577	586	792	40	2,454	—	—	—	5,705	—
1943–44	5,768	1,437	1,102	12	1,067	—	—	—	2,150	—
1944–45	5,613	1,691	741	108	1,744	—	—	—	1,253	76
1945 (April to December)	10,384	366	—	—	901	142	36	—	—	8,939
Scotland:										
1935–38 (average)	24,426	15,850	990	5	7,581	—	—	..	..	—
1939	25,529	18,902	216	58	6,353	—	—	..	..	—
1940	14,206	10,357	117	228	3,504	—	—	..	..	—
1941	5,406	4,676	38	68	624	—	—	..	..	—
1942	3,206	3,034	38	21	203	—	—	..	..	—
1943	2,869	2,717	—	28	64	—	—	..	..	—
1944	2,553	2,383	—	36	134	—	—	..	..	437
1945	2,006	1,428	—	27	111	—	3	..	..	—
Northern Ireland[5]:										
1935–38 (average)	2,951	158	—	2,395	385	—	—	13	—	—
1938–39	1,334	1,110	16	—	207	—	—	1	—	—
1939 (April to December)	267	169	—	—	96	—	—	2	—	—
1940	400	400	—	—	—	—	—	—	—	—
1941	206	206	—	—	—	—	—	—	—	—
1942	—	—	—	—	—	—	—	—	—	—
1943	—	—	—	—	—	—	—	—	—	—
1944	27	—	—	—	10	—	—	17	—	—
1945	81	—	—	—	21	—	—	60	—	—

Source: Health Departments

[1] Including flats, each flat being counted as one unit.
[2] The Scottish National Housing Companies, Scottish Special Housing Association and the Northern Ireland Housing Trust are included in the figures for local authorities but other housing associations are included in the figures for private builders.
[3] Accommodation for the families of police, prison staffs, defence services and other Government employees and, in Northern Ireland, houses built on behalf of the Irish Sailors' and Soldiers' Land Trust.
[4] Excludes houses in England and Wales having a rateable value exceeding £78 (or £105 in the Metropolitan Police District).
[5] Years ended 31st March, from 1934–35 to 1944–45 for England and Wales, and from 1934–35 to 1944–45 for Northern Ireland. Thereafter calendar years.

inherent in the manufacture and erection of temporary houses are described. The principal types contained between 2,000 and 3,000 separate parts and components, all of which had to be manufactured in sufficient quantities by the right time and delivered to assembly and distribution depots for collection into sets ready for erection. From the end of 1945 the production of most of the fixtures and fittings was the responsibility of the Ministry of Supply, which was also charged with the manufacture, delivery and erection of aluminium temporary houses.

At the end of August 1945 the position was as follows:

Sites made ready by local authorities . .	41,000
Slab foundations under construction or completed	31,762
Houses in course of erection	4,228
Houses completed	2,524

In May 1946 a target was set for the completion of 96,000 houses by the end of 1946. When that date was reached 95,510 houses had been completed for local authorities in Great Britain. This total was made up as follows:

MINISTRY OF WORKS

	Types	*Aluminium*	*Total*
England and Wales . .	70,953	9,847	80,800
Scotland	12,226	2,484	14,710
	83,179	12,331	95,510

As these figures did not include 499 houses completed for the Government, and for the Government of Northern Ireland, the target was hit.[1]

The role of the Ministry of Works in regard to permanent housing was mainly in the field of experiment with non-traditional forms of construction, such as prefabricated houses, and the conduct of housing operations on behalf of the Minister of Health and local authorities under the provisions of the Building Materials and Housing Act, 1945.

If the Minister of Health considered that a new type of prefabricated house had merits, the promoter was licensed to erect a prototype. The scheme was then examined in detail by the Inter-Departmental Committee on House Construction, and in the light of the committee's report the Minister of Health decided whether a trial development group of houses was necessary before large-scale production could be approved. Contracts for development groups were placed by the Minister of Works. Habitable dwellings were provided by these experiments, and development groups were generally erected

---

[1] *Summary Report of Ministry of Works, 9th May 1945–31st December 1946* (Cmd. 7279).

on sites provided by local authorities, who had an option to purchase the completed houses at prices not exceeding the cost of comparable traditional houses.[1]

In Scotland the 1943 programme of 1,000 houses, and a second programme of 1,000 houses allocated early in 1944 among local authorities in whose areas needs were particularly urgent, together with a programme of 600 emergency houses undertaken in 1943 by the Scottish Special Housing Association in Clydebank, Greenock, Dumbartonshire, and Lanarkshire, were virtually the first steps towards the resumption of a regular housing programme, departmental arrangements for which had begun in the dark days of 1941 and 1942. In August 1942 the Scottish Housing Advisory Committee was reconstituted and three sub-committees were set up to consider housing design and lay-out, the furnishing and equipping of working-class houses and the measures to be taken to secure the best distribution of new houses in the immediate post-war period. The first two sub-committees reported in November 1942, and their report, published in 1944 as 'Planning our New Homes', not only set the standard for post-war houses built by local authorities but also aroused widespread interest in the general public. The other report was published later in the year as 'The Distribution of New Houses in Scotland'.

In 1943 all local authorities who did not already own enough land for one year's housing programme were asked to earmark the necessary land, and were told that they might proceed with its acquisition as soon as it was approved by the department for planning purposes. Early in 1944 local authorities were asked to co-operate in a scheme for the advance preparation of housing sites with the aid of civil engineering labour and plant to be released on the completion of airfield construction work. By the end of June 1945 sites had been approved for a total of over 128,000 houses, acquired for over 71,000 houses and serviced for over 14,000 houses. In April 1945 local authorities had been informed that the general embargo on new permanent house-building by them had been relaxed and that the department were ready to consider applications to invite tenders for houses as and when sites were serviced. As a result local authorities and the Scottish Special Housing Association had been authorised by 30th June to invite tenders for over 5,000 new houses as a first instalment of the post-war programme.

---

[1] Details of the number of the various prefabricated and other non-traditional types of houses under construction and completed are contained in the housing returns published by the Minister of Health and the Secretary of State for Scotland.

(iii)

The Directorate of Post-War Building

While the Directorate of Post-War Building[1] included in its organisation sub-committees dealing with the design and construction of houses and flats, its scope extended to all activities of the building industry. From the main committee, comprising representatives of Government, science, the professions and industry, derived three main 'policy and study' committees, the first concerned with design, the second with structure and the third with installation.[2]

The ground plan of the Directorate's work is seen in the list of the committees co-ordinated under each of the three policy and study committees[3] as shown below:

1. Under the Policy *Design* Committee there were eight committees, groups or sub-committees. Their field was the design of houses and flats; housing design (Scotland); house construction; school planning; business buildings; farm buildings; the architectural use of materials; and acoustics.

2. Five committees co-ordinated under the Policy *Structure* Committee were concerned respectively with steel structures; reinforced concrete structures; timber structures; walls, floors and roofs; and the fire-grading of buildings.

3. Under the Policy *Installations* Committee ten committees dealt respectively with lighting; heating and ventilation; mechanical installations; electrical installations; gas installations; plumbing; plastics; paint; non-ferrous metals; and standards.

Linked with the main structure committee were the Standards Committee[4] and Codes of Practice Committees, the British Standards Institution Committee[5] and a Publications Board for issuing reports and manuals.

By spring 1943 the Directorate of Post-War Building was able to report considerable progress in the study of building technique. Between October 1942 and March 1943 twelve of the twenty-three

---

[1] The Directorate at its inception was put under the general charge of Sir James West, Chief Architect to the Ministry of Works.

[2] The first chairmen of the three committees were respectively Sir Giles Scott, R.A. (Design); Mr. Ralph Freeman, M.Inst.C.E. (Structure); and Mr. Sydney Tatchell, F.R.I.B.A.

[3] As at 1st January 1943.

[4] The Standards Committee comprised representatives of the Government, local authorities, science, the professions and industry (including private enterprise housing). Later it became an independent committee linked with all study committees, and not attached to any one of the three co-ordinated policy committees.

[5] See Section (iv) of this chapter.

committees had already submitted first draft reports. All the study committees were conducting discussions with interested bodies of one kind or another. The Committee for Design of Houses and Flats, for example, had invited evidence from sixty representative organisations throughout the country (as well as from a number of prominent persons) and the Farm Buildings' Committee was collecting views and information by similar means. The Committee on House Construction (a joint committee of the two Health Departments and the Ministry of Works) was making a thorough examination of many types of houses built in unusual materials during the period 1919–1939. It was also considering new proposals not yet tried out and preparing the ground for practical experiments. Among the types of wall and roof considered by the Committee on House Construction some were partly fabricated while others were wholly assembled *in situ*. The committee did not report in detail on prefabrication as such; but it examined, among other things, the building components which resulted from the use of prefabrication methods. Those methods and their possibilities were being studied by the prefabrication section of the Standards Committee, especially with a view to determining what saving of labour and materials the system would make possible if it were widely applied.[1]

(iv)

Standardisation

War-time standardisation of design and construction was the responsibility of the Directorate of Construction (Economy) Design, of the Ministry of Works.[2] The Directorate had issued such documents as the War-Time Building Supplies Schedule, and had initiated war-time standard specifications published by the British Standards Institution. In addition to introducing various substitute materials, the

---

[1] It should be noted, however, that the Directorate of Works had already done much work in the standardising of prefabricated huts. In the spring of 1941 there were hundreds of huts of different types; these types were reduced to a dozen or so. Starting with fixed dimensional standards, it became possible to complete the foundations and site work generally in the knowledge that they would fit whichever type of hut was chosen. Another achievement of the Directorate of Works had been to obtain the agreement of other departments for a standard hostel lay-out ranging from a thirty-person hostel to a 1,000-person hostel or a 3,000-person camp. Considerable advance had also been made in the standardisation of canteen and kitchen equipment. See Chapter XVII.

[2] See Chapter V. The Directorate of Constructional Design was created with the object of promoting economy. Its duty was not to teach the other departments to design, but to persuade them to adopt minimum standards suitable to war conditions. For example, the Directorate issued Timber Economy Bulletins giving several substitutes for timber construction.

Ministry of Works had encouraged the economical use of existing materials by reducing or debasing standards. Many of these lower-grade standards would not have been acceptable before the war, but were necessary war-time expedients.

For post-war building, as we have seen,[1] a Standards Committee was set up by the Directorate of Post-War Building. It held its first meeting in August 1942.[2]

Every kind of standard applicable in building came within the committee's scope—minimum standards for consumer needs and for the performance of materials; standard dimensions and design intended to increase output, reduce costs, eliminate unnecessary types and secure interchangeability of units and parts; and, finally, standard terms and symbols intended to clarify specifications and instructions.

It was the function of the Standards Committee to draft proposals for standards, specifications and codes; but not to present them as final in form or to publish them. That was the work of the British Standards Institution and of the Codes of Practice Committee[3] set up by the Ministry of Works in collaboration with the Ministry of Health. To promote the closest scientific study of the whole field, and bring about intelligent and fruitful contact between the Standards Committee and the various study committees, the work of the committee was viewed as falling into the four categories: practice, design, materials and prefabrication.[4]

It is important to realise that the gospel of standardisation, as preached by the British Standards Institution, is not 'the apotheosis of all that is dull and monotonous . . . everything out of the same jelly mould . . . mass production at its dreariest', but the assessment of the suitability of many products for the purposes devised. As defined by the Institution, standardisation is of two kinds: functional and dimensional.

---

[1] See Section (iii) of this chapter.

[2] The committee's terms of reference were to study the application in building of standard plan elements, standard specifications and building components, and methods of prefabrication, with the particular object of ensuring (*a*) economy in the use of material in the post-war period, (*b*) simplified and speedier procedure and construction, and (*c*) wherever possible, improved quality and design. The committee was to make recommendations for such standards as well as for standards for terminology and consumer requirements; to collect, review and correlate recommended standards put forward by other study committees of the Directorate; and to draft material for the British Standards Institution and the Codes of Practice Committee of the Ministry of Works, to be used in the promulgation of official British Standards and Codes.

[3] See Section (v) of this chapter.

[4] 1. *Practice.* Requirements, plan elements, codes, terminology and other professiona matters with special reference to the activities of the Codes of Practice Committee. 2. *Design.* Manufactured parts, structural units, components and equipment. 3. *Materials.* All materials, with special reference to the British Standards Institution. 4. *Prefabrication.* Technical, economic and practical appraisal of the possibilities of prefabrication.

Functional standardisation covers all standards dealing with 'fitness for purpose', and has been classified under terms and definitions, quality, methods of test and methods of use.[1] Dimensional standardisation is carried out to achieve simplification, unification and interchangeability. By eliminating any unnecessary multiplicity of articles and appliances, such standards facilitate the processes of manufacture and replacement of parts and reduce stocks. Dimensional standardisation may also be used as an indirect method of specifying quality.

So far from industrial standardisation implying an arbitrary control, instituted by some mysterious governing body to frustrate the growth of new ideas in industry, it must rest, in order to be really effective, on general consent. With the growth of technical knowledge standards must be reviewed from time to time and kept up to date. In practice no British Standard is ever prepared unless a request for its issue has emanated either from the industry concerned, or from a Government department interested in the subject.

'Once these fundamental facts are clearly understood, public prejudice is likely to die. Standardisation will be seen in its proper perspective as working for the benefit of all . . . and as providing a basis for an equitable transaction between the seller and the buyer, or between the producer and the user'.[2]

(v)

Codes of Practice

The general policy of the Ministry of Works in regard to post-war preparedness embraced not only standardisation but the definition of what was, and what was not, good practice in building. It was for the Codes of Practice Committee, set up in September 1942, to certify good practice so as to make it almost as capable of being followed as the standard specification of the British Institution enabled good materials to be automatically used.

---

[1] *Terms and Definitions*—to secure accuracy of description and to clarify ideas. Terms and symbols are the alphabet of industry; obviously they must be in standard form, like any other language, if the possibility of misunderstanding is to be eliminated. *Quality*—to measure fitness for purpose. Standards under this heading can be based on composition or performance. *Methods of Test*—to establish uniformity in methods of measurement and test which diminish the chances of dispute and facilitate comparison of results. Such standards encourage a more general adoption of testing by industry. *Methods of Use*—(Codes of Practice)—to define the correct application of materials and appliances. These standards cover the methods of installation and are designed to secure adequacy of result and diminish the chances of accident. (*Standards Review*, Vol. 1 No. 1, May 1944.)

[2] *Standards Review*, Vol. 1, No. 1, May 1944, p. 6.

A code of practice was conceived as being a definition of the method in which materials could best be used to perform certain required functions. It was eventually a code of *good* practice and not necessarily the permissible minimum. It might obviously be a part of or linked with a specification of materials. There often could not be a sharp line of demarcation between a code of practice and a materials specification.

In considering the preparation of codes for constructional work it was essential to divide the field into a number of subjects, and these were ultimately linked together to form a coherent and logical code of building and engineering practice.

In practice two types of 'specification' were in use: (i) *what* materials were to be employed, and (ii) *how* the materials were to be employed in any specific job. A code of practice was mainly a generalised form of a portion of (ii) and was thus regarded as rather specially the responsibility of the engineer or architect.

The Codes of Practice Committee was the outcome of negotiations initiated by the Ministry of Works in consultation with the Ministry of Health and other Government departments, and consisted of nominees of the principal technical institutions, the British Standards Institution and the Building Industries National Council, with assessor members nominated by certain Government departments, and a chairman (Sir Clement Hindley) nominated by the Minister. Its terms of reference were to direct the preparation of codes of practice for civil engineering, public works, building and constructional work, as well as to settle general standards for safety and soundness of structure.

In the comprehensive codes of practice scheme for building, the design was to ensure that the various codes could be co-ordinated with each other and cover every operation used in building work. The work of drafting those codes was divided between the convenor institutions by suitable grouping of the subjects in the comprehensive scheme, and thus covered the whole field. The work of the various drafting committees was closely co-ordinated, not only to prevent overlapping but to ensure that the various parts of the code were in fact linked up. Although the plan of the comprehensive scheme was so designed that the relationship between the various building operations included was fairly obvious, care was necessary to avoid inconsistencies and to provide adequate cross-references. Under the general direction of the co-ordinating committee, a central technical group was set up which comprised representatives of the Department of Scientific and Industrial Research, the Ministry of Home Security, the Ministry of Works, the British Standards Institution and outside consultants. The object of the group was to draft the classification code, and at the same time keep under close review the work of all the drafting committees, making sure that the expansion of the subjects into suitable code headings was done systematically and in accordance with the general scheme.[1]

Three main codes were prepared by the Codes of Practice Committee: a Code of Functional Requirements of Buildings, and Codes of Building and of Civil Engineering. In the first report of the Codes of Practice Committee, presented to its constituent bodies on 29th January 1943, a comprehensive scheme of codes of practice for building was set out. Codes of practice for civil engineering and public works remained under consideration, since they rested on a somewhat different basis. In building practice, on the one hand, the code was applied to individual buildings which, although they varied in type, were all subject to many similar operations. In civil engineering, on the other hand, the works tended to be fewer and larger, with more diversity of function, and with variations imposed by local conditions; and there were consequently fewer operations of common application for a given volume of work or expenditure. Yet civil engineering works were such that the success of a scheme as a whole might well be jeopardised by the failure of a single part, or by the unsatisfactory execution of one of many kinds of operations. It follows that even though the number of operations of common application to civil engineering works might be few in number, and in any one project might form only a small proportion of the whole, great advantages could accrue from embodying these operations in codes.

For these reasons the Civil Engineering and Public Works Sectional Committee of the Codes of Practice Committee decided in May 1943 that the magnitude and diversity of the subject was such that it was impracticable and probably undesirable to attempt to produce a comprehensive scheme at that stage. Instead, a draft scheme was prepared, with reservations, under which an effective start could be made upon the task of code-drafting. The scheme was in three parts: first, a short general statement of civil engineering and public works; second, a schematic lay-out showing the extent to which the more important subdivisions of civil engineering were common to the several main branches of public works; and, third, suggested allocation of the work of drafting civil engineering and public works codes

---

[1] Code Committees were convened by the following institutions at the request of the Codes of Practice Committee: viz., the Institution of Civil Engineers; the Royal Institution of British Architects; the Institution of Mechanical Engineers; the Institution of Heating and Ventilating Engineers; the Institution of Electrical Engineers; the Institution of Municipal and County Engineers; the Institution of Water Engineers; the Institution of Structural Engineers; the Institution of Gas Engineers; and the Incorporated Association of Architects and Surveyors. The subjects covered were foundation and structures; site investigations; external walls and partitions; weather-resisting roof coverings; finishing series; lifts, hoists and escalators; fire-fighting installations, heating, ventilating with air conditioning and hot-water services; electrical equipment of buildings, sanitation, drainage, refuse disposal, load-bearing superstructures; water supply; earth-retaining structures; internal walls and partitions; heating, lighting, power and refrigeration (gas).

among the professional institutions as convenor bodies. There was also a full bibliography.

Ten chapters of the Code of Functional Requirements of Buildings and sixty-four Codes of Practical Building were published for comment. Comments on the draft codes were received from all over the world and considered by the committee.

(vi)
The Post-War Building Studies

The work initiated by the Directorate of Post-War Building, the Standards Committee and the Codes of Practice Committee, together with that of the complex network of professional sub-committees, groups, and organisations associated with them, bore fruit in a series of publications from 1944 onwards under the title *Post-War Building Studies*. The first of these valuable and timely studies was prepared by an inter-departmental committee appointed by the Minister of Health, the Secretary of State for Scotland and the Minister of Works, and was published under the title *House Construction*.[1] In a foreword the Minister of Works (Lord Portal) recalled that the Committee on House Construction had been appointed in September 1942, at his suggestion, and that after the submission of its report had been reconstituted on a broader basis as a standing advisory committee representative of the professions of architecture and engineering, and of all the elements of the building industry. Nevertheless, the reports were not official publications in the sense that the Government was responsible for or necessarily accepted the views expressed, but their contents were, as Lord Portal stated, authoritative and could not but be of great value to all concerned with prefabrication for building after the war.

In all, twenty-four separate post-war building studies were completed and published by the end of 1946. They were sponsored by various professional organisations or Government departments (among them the Building Research Board of the Department of Scientific and Industrial Research). In addition to the first report on housing, the series dealt with the standard construction for schools; plastics; plumbing; the painting of buildings; gas installations; steel structures; reinforced concrete structures; mechanical installations; solid fuel installations; electrical installations; the lighting of buildings; non-ferrous metals; sound insulation and acoustics; walls, floors and roofs; business buildings; farm buildings; the architectural use of

---

[1] S.O. Code No. 70-441-1*.

building materials; heating and ventilation; the fire-grading of buildings; school building for Scotland; farm buildings for Scotland; house construction (second report); and school furniture and equipment.

Besides sponsoring the study on House Construction, the Ministry of Works was associated with the Ministry of Health in the publication in 1944 of the *Housing Manual, 1944*,[1] intended for the guidance of local authorities and others concerned. The Ministry of Fuel and Power was consulted upon matters in which it had a direct interest, and the manual included material contributed by that department. The Ministry of Town and Country Planning advised on matters of site planning and lay-out.[2] Much of the information on materials and construction was prepared by the Building Research Station of the Department of Industrial and Scientific Research, which also undertook a general scrutiny of the technical appendices.[3]

(vii)
Scientific Research and Development

Linked with the work of the Directorate of Post-War Building and its satellite organisations was that of the Department of the Chief Scientific Adviser to the Ministry of Works.[4] Working in close co-operation with the Department of Scientific and Industrial Research, the Chief Scientific Adviser initiated and carried out research and experiments designed to improve the efficiency of the building and civil engineering industries.

Since, as previous chapters have shown, the building industry's importance in the national economy is outstanding, and a high proportion of the net capital investment in each pre-war year consisted of new building, it was clearly of importance to the community that this work should be carried out at the highest possible standards, particularly where it impinged upon the homes of the people.[5] In 1921 the Government of the day had accordingly set up the Building Research Station of the Department of Scientific and Industrial Research, in order to promote the application of science to the building

---

[1] H.M.S.O. Code No. 70–454*.

[2] Information on the lay-out and planning of houses had been given in previous manuals issued by the Ministry of Health, e.g. *Housing Manual on the Design, Construction and Repair of Dwellings* (issued in 1927 and reprinted in 1934) and the *Rural Housing Manual* (issued in 1938). In general, the guidance in those manuals still held good.

[3] These comprised materials and construction; lightweight concrete in cavity walls; the scientific use of timber; cooking and heating; flues; notes on specifications; private sewers; small sewage disposal works; British standards and British standard codes of practice.

[4] Dr. (later Sir) Reginald E. Stradling.

[5] Survey Report of Ministry of Works, 9th May 1945 to 31st December 1946.

industry for the benefit of the community. Between the First and
Second World Wars the station, with the help of the Forest Products
Research Laboratory, the National Physical Laboratory and some
research associations, amassed a great deal of data on the requirements which good buildings should satisfy and the properties of
materials and components used in their construction.[1] From this body
of knowledge day-to-day scientific advice on the problems of building
could be drawn, and critical appraisals made of new systems of
building construction or types of material.

The research organisation was strengthened when, in April 1945,
the Minister of Works appointed a group of leading scientists to form
a Scientific Advisory Committee to guide him on what research was
needed and on the manner in which it could best be carried out. The
committee delegated its more detailed work to a number of sub-
committees, and also co-opted to them persons likely to be able to
contribute to the consideration of particular aspects of problems. A
vast amount of detailed investigation was carried out by the Ministry's
own staff, with the co-operation of the Department of Scientific and
Industrial Research, of research departments in the universities, and
of the industry.

Among the numerous subjects of research special mention should
be made of investigations into some of the problems of mechanisation:
this was a necessary complement to the encouragement given to the
use of mechanical plant in the industry. Research and development
were concentrated on building processes in which mechanisation was
likely to yield the most useful immediate result.[2] New uses were found
for existing machines. New machines, particularly such as would be
suitable on small building sites, were developed; and it was arranged
that new machinery should be tried out by building contractors.
Where circumstances permitted, development and production contracts were placed with plant manufacturers.

The great and varying changes in the prices of building materials,
components and labour during the war led the Ministry of Works into
a new and significant field of investigation, namely, costing systems
applied to the process of house-building while the houses were in
course of erection. This was a method so far unknown in Great
Britain. The processes of traditional house-building were split up into
a series of separate operations for which the expenditure in man-
hours, materials and money could be measured continuously. On

---

[1] Survey Report of Ministry of Works, 9th May 1945 to 31st December 1946.

[2] Among the lines of inquiry pursued were *foundation construction* (mechanical excavation
of footings and the use of pile foundations); *drainage and services* (new kinds of soil-pipe,
easier to fit and more readily available than salt-glazed pipes, etc.); *material handling* (new
methods of transporting bricks and handling concrete, simple brick hoists, etc.); *erecting
and surfacing of walls* (scaffolding, mortar spreaders, building jigs, plaster extruders);
carpentry and joinery (new types of floors, roofs, stairways and cupboards, and the use of
power-driven hand tools).

eleven sites, each of fifty houses or more, situated in different parts of the country, this information was systematically collected by the Ministry's observers. The builders on the sites used their normal methods of construction and their own plans and specifications.

The records obtained in this way showed the amount of paid time expended on productive and non-productive work, and enabled estimates to be made of the real costs of building and of the costs of bad organisation or bad supervision, of guaranteed work, wet time, and so forth. In order to compare the old and the new systems, the same costing technique was also applied to sites on which non-traditional methods were used.[1]

(viii)

Building Apprenticeship and Training

The study of apprenticeship training, implicit in plans for the provision of something approaching full employment in the building industry, was the chief duty of the Education Committee of the Central Council for Works and Building.[2] No general survey of apprenticeship in the building industry had been made since that of the Ministry of Labour's Committee on Apprenticeship and Training in 1926. At that date it was found that in a typical group of young workers about twenty-nine per cent. were serving under written indentures, fifty-three per cent. as apprentices under verbal agreements, and eighteen per cent. as improvers. Three-quarters of all the young workers under twenty-one in the industry were classified as in one or other of these three categories; the remaining quarter were labourers.

According to the White Paper presented jointly by the Ministers of Labour and Works in 1943,[3] to which reference has already been made,[4] processes of change in the industry had not been wholly favourable to satisfactory apprenticeship. Generally speaking, the best opportunities for apprentice training were found in the smaller firms, provided they were large enough to give the young worker an all-round mastery of his craft. In the very large firms labour was apt to be highly specialised, and the admission of apprentices might well depend on whether or not the heads of the firms happened to interest themselves, on social grounds, in providing a thorough training.

---

[1] A special inquiry into costing was later carried out by a firm of chartered accountants (Messrs. Cooper Brothers & Co.) on the instructions of the Ministry of Works. See Working Party Report on *Building* (H.M.S.O. 1950, p. 36 and Appendix D).

[2] See Chapter XVIII.

[3] Report on *Training for the Building Industry* (Cmd. 6428).

[4] See Chapter XVIII.

After the outbreak of war, formal apprenticeship under a written indenture covered only a small proportion of junior entry into the industry, although verbal agreements were observed quite as faithfully as those which were legally binding. But for the most part there was a steady flow into the industry of men without any systematic training. This trend was derogatory to the status of the building worker himself, and gave grounds for the fear that a very high price might be paid for it, both by employers and by the public. Under war conditions apprenticeship thus became very flexible, if not haphazard, despite the efforts of employers' and operatives' organisations to bring in, over a number of years, schemes designed to secure better training for the young workers.

The Government's main decisions, as embodied in the White Paper of 1943, were:

1. The introduction of a post-war construction programme for ten to twelve years, which it was estimated would require the labour force in the building industry to be built up over a period to about one and a quarter million men.

2. The assumption by the Ministry of Labour of full responsibility for the special training, over a period of six months, of up to 200,000 trainees during the first three or four years after the war. (The Government to pay the cost of this training.)

3. The regulation of recruitment into the industry to correspond as closely as possible with estimated future demands, with the object of maintaining stability in the industry for the period of the programme.

4. The encouragement by the Government of arrangements by the building industry for a guaranteed period of employment each week. (The Government were prepared, at least during the immediate post-war period, to enforce such arrangements on all contractors if the industry as a whole desired it.)

5. The setting up of an Apprenticeship and Training Council as recommended by the Education Committee.

These decisions went as far as was practicable in war-time towards meeting the recommendations of the Education Committee. In the words of Sir E. D. Simon (later Lord Simon of Wythenshawe), who was closely associated with the work of the committee,

Government committees are often held to be a means of delaying action. In the case of the Education Committee there would have been some excuse for delay; the report dealt with a difficult and controversial issue which had to be discussed and agreed by the Ministry of Works, the Ministry of Labour, the Ministry of Health, the Scottish Office and the Treasury. Yet within two months of receiving the report the Government issued its White Paper, accepting all the recommendations of the report with minor modifications.

This was the first long-range piece of post-war planning to be officially adopted by the Government. It is a good augury for the energy and vision with which the Minister of Works and the Minister of Labour are preparing for the problems of peace.[1]

The Building Apprenticeship and Training Council was set up by the Minister of Works in 1943. Its composition included representatives of both sides of the industry, educationists and independent members; and its declared purpose was to advise on all matters concerning the recruitment, education and training of young persons for the industry, and to encourage the development of craft apprenticeship schemes and student apprenticeship schemes. On the educational side the Council strove to increase the number of full-time apprenticeship courses of two or three years' duration, and the annual intake to these courses in fact increased from 300 in 1942 to about 7,300 in 1946. They offered the attraction of a reduction in the period of apprenticeship for many of the boys who completed them.

The Council also emphasised the importance of training for management in the industry. As one of the most important steps towards that end it was urged that universities should have a degree course in building science.[2] After reviewing the standards of apprenticeship, the Council suggested to the industry that, as a minimum standard, there must be a written agreement providing for the apprentice to be taught the whole craft; for the oversight of the training by a Joint Apprenticeship Committee of the industry; and for release of an apprentice by the employer, for technical instruction at school, for one day a week or the equivalent.

The Council sought to guide not only recruitment but the distribution of recruits between the different crafts and regions. They recommended, for instance, that of the estimated annual requirement of 25,000 new entrants, at least 5,000 should be bricklayers, 1,750 plasterers, and 1,000 masons, because although total recruitment during 1945 was not far short of the normal annual intake required, there was a grave deficiency of recruits for these three crafts.

In addition to urging private employers, local authorities, and Government departments to play their full part in the training of recruits for the building industry, the Council promoted an apprentice-master scheme under which building work was carried out almost entirely by apprentices working under experienced craftsmen instructors. The work was done for Government departments and local authorities, and the Ministry paid the excess over the cost of doing the work by normal methods. At the end of 1946 there were approximately 2,500 boys employed in this way in different parts of the country.

---

[1] E. D. Simon, *Rebuilding Britain: A Twenty Year Plan*, 1945.

[2] There were already university courses at Manchester and Cardiff.

Training courses for adult building industry craftsmen were carried out by the Ministry of Labour, and consisted of six months' instruction at a centre, followed by fourteen months' practical experience with an approved employer. For civil engineering trainees, the courses of instruction at the centres varied from three to six months. Two methods of increasing the capacity of the centres were employed wherever possible. These were, first, to work double shifts at the centres themselves, and secondly, to send the trainees to building sites under the supervision of the centre instructors, during the last two months of the course.[1]

(ix)

Productive Efficiency

In all post-war plans for the building industry account had to be taken of the inevitable decline in productive efficiency. Comparison with pre-war standards is hardly possible in the absence of adequate statistical evidence, but it is probable that in 1945, as compared with 1938, the industry's productive efficiency had declined by at least one-third.[2] For this decline there were some obvious causes. During the war the industry lost a large part of its experienced labour force, and for six years the normal process of recruitment and training was interrupted. Many young craftsmen and apprentices were conscripted for national service before they had gained experience in the industry. Other men who left the industry during the war had lost much of their skill by the time they returned, while those who remained in the industry throughout the war were employed on work which usually differed markedly from that of peace-time. Immediately after the war the industry was required to expand very rapidly; the size of the labour force, which had fallen from nearly 1,362,000 in 1939 to just over half a million in 1945, rose to nearly a million in about eighteen months. It was inevitable that although the fully-trained worker retained his skill, the average level of skill was lower than that of pre-war days. In the rebuilding of the labour force after 1945 adult trainees were introduced in considerable numbers, and their necessarily low rate of output while they were gaining experience could not but reduce the average.[3]

It is also possible that payment by results adversely affected the post-war output, since workers tended to accept the basic rates as the measure of a reasonable output in normal times, whereas in fact these

---

[1] By 16th December 1946, 14,976 trainees had passed through the centres.
[2] Working Party Report, *Building* (H.M.S.O. Code No. 70–617*).
[3] *Ibid.*

rates were merely the result of a realistic appreciation of the exceptional circumstances existing between 1941 and 1947, when the Essential Work Order was in force.

By the end of the war the building worker's attitude to his work had undergone a change, and there were symptoms of declining morale and the abuse of privileges. A disproportionately large number of jobs, too, as compared with their distribution before the war, had been on war damage and other repairs, and these had given little opportunity for the highly-skilled craftsman trained for work of first-rate quality. Similarly the decline in the quality of materials had had a discouraging effect on craftsmen.

As to the employers, the large proportion of repair and maintenance work during and after the war kept very active the small firms which were suited to that type of work, but, on the other hand, there were few large building schemes of a type for which the bigger firms were best fitted. This had an adverse effect on average productivity. Moreover, the almost complete disappearance of speculative house-building removed one form of keen competition which had resulted in especially economical construction and a record of high productivity.

Among other factors contributing to lowered efficiency was the launching, immediately after the war, of a vast programme of building work without adequate planning beforehand.[1] The Government's estimate of the load of work that the industry could sustain was over-optimistic, and the programme fostered by official encouragement or direction made excessive demands on the industry's resources of labour, management, materials and professional services. The result was that these resources were very thinly spread, and the quantity of work started was only distantly related to the supply of building materials and labour then available. Hence, building schemes were unable to proceed with the regularity which is essential to efficiency in building operations.

What perhaps contributed more than any other single factor to the lowering of productive efficiency was the scarcity of building materials during and after the war. The shortage of traditional materials compelled the wider use of substitute materials; this often lowered productivity, sometimes because management and operatives were unfamiliar with the substitutes, and sometimes because operations were delayed while jobs designed for using one material were replanned to use another.

It was pertinent to post-war preparations that building methods in foreign countries should be investigated. Both the Government and the building industry were eager to learn at first hand what new techniques were being practised abroad, especially in the United

---

[1] Working Party Report, *Building* (H.M.S.O. Code No. 70–617*).

States, and whether they could be applied to British conditions. Missions and parties of inquiry visited the United States, both during and after the war. The first mission to visit the United States reported to the Minister of Works early in 1944. Among its members were Mr. A. C. Bossom, M.P., Sir G. M. Burt and Sir James West, at that time Chief Architect to the Ministry. Its recommendations formed the subject of detailed discussion at successive meetings of the Advisory Council of the Building and Civil Engineering Industries, but remained for the most part academic. More fruitful was the visit in July and August 1949 of a 'productivity team' of a more widely representative composition.[1] The team was one of a number, each concerned with a particular industry, sponsored by the Anglo-American Council of Productivity.

The report of the team comments particularly on the great speed of American constructional jobs and on their low cost in relation to the average rate of wages.[2] Of the factors which made for high productivity in the United States the most important, but not the only ones, were described as:

1. The complete pre-planning of the job by building owner, architect and contractor.
2. The proper co-ordination of sub-contractors' work and the effective collaboration between them and the general contractor.
3. The adequacy of supplies of labour and materials and the absence of restricting controls.
4. The general availability and use of mechanical aids.
5. The recognition of the importance of continuous research into the production of materials and into building techniques.
6. The nation-wide stimulus of the American industrial climate with its great effect on individual output.

It was to the last of these factors, which might be termed the psychological factor, that the report attached the greatest importance of all. Acceptance of the need for high productivity as an essential factor in industrial life, it stated, was universal in America, and it permeated the will and action of the operatives as well as of the professional and employer groups.

> The attitude of the individual towards his work must, in an industry like building, which depends so much on individual effort, be vital. At the same time, consciousness of forming part of a well-organised team moving at high speed has a definite effect upon productivity. There appears to be a real community of interest between all sections of the industry based on a realisation of their inter-dependence. Com-

---

[1] The team of seventeen was made up of three groups—management, professional and operatives. The team leader was Mr. Robert O. Lloyd, the secretary Mr. C. Gordon Rowlands, Secretary of the National Federation of Building Trades Employers.

[2] *Building* (The Anglo-American Council of Productivity, London 1950).

petition exists in full measure, but, once a job is started, the spirit of collaboration, inspired by the driving force of the general contractor, can be relied upon to secure the desired results.[1]

The report maintained that, apart from the adequacy of supplies of materials, all the influences towards high productivity mentioned above could be developed in the British building industry by its own efforts.

We believe that the prosperity and efficiency of the industry can be increased, its costs lowered and the earnings of its operatives raised, if the responsible industrial organisations, the Government departments concerned, individual building owners (private and public) and, above all, the individual members of the industry give due consideration to the picture which we have drawn, and if all strive to give effect to the recommendations we now make. Each one in his *individual capacity* must simultaneously make the necessary effort—architects, to plan better; contractors, to organise better; sub-contractors, to co-operate better; and operatives, to produce more.

$$\left(\text{x}\right)$$

Conclusion

It would be invidious to close this narrative with a citation which might be thought to imply that the building industry of Great Britain had been weighed in the balance and found wanting; or that in this, as in other great industries, Britain had everything to learn and the United States everything to teach. Comparisons, if they are to have any meaning or validity, can only be made between things that are in themselves truly comparable; and because the American industrial scene, both in peace and in war, is so different from the British—in its tradition, its atmosphere, its organisation, its social and psychological standards—the value of comparison between them lies as much in the contrasts that must remain contrasts as in commendable examples that might be followed. The British skilled building worker, whatever his post-war shortcomings, has been reared in a deeply rooted tradition of individual ability and craftsmanship which, if temporarily weakened or obscured as a consequence of the war, is none the less his particular heritage. His inherent qualities have in the past been suited to the scale and tempo of traditional British building methods; they would be inappropriate to the scale and tempo of most American building, which has had to meet the needs of a great and growing young nation spreading itself rapidly over a vast continent.

At the end of the war, and during the years that followed,[2] the

---

[1] *Building* (The Anglo-American Council of Productivity, London, 1950).

[2] That is, up to the end of 1951, when the writing of this narrative was completed.

position of the building industry remained undefined and its future course unsure. Any return to pre-war conditions of 'free enterprise', even were that goal accepted universally as a possible and desirable consummation, was barred by the political and economic circumstances of the time. It became apparent that such advantages as could accrue to the industry through the rapid restoration of its labour force to pre-war strength might well be offset by lowered standards of skill and integrity among the workers. Underlying this dilemma was a deeper one. Might not the industry, in the not too distant future, have to choose, or at least compromise on a large scale, between the traditional and the non-traditional techniques of building? As the war ended the weight of scientific research was already swinging against, rather than towards, traditional methods, and to its momentum the continuing house famine of the post-war years seemed likely to give an added impetus. Even in the 1930's, through the use of subcontractor specialists in house-building, a compromise between traditional and non-traditional methods had often been possible on the site. In the late nineteen-thirties specialists in single operations began to appear on the site, to pour the concrete, to lay the floors or the tiles, and then to pass on to the next site.[1] During the war the specialist, to a large extent, disappeared, and with him the ready-made and standard units which had begun to be used to simplify the work of house-building. Although the war-time experiments in temporary fabricated houses for a time bridged the gap between traditional brick houses and factory-made houses to be assembled on the site by building operatives plying a new craft and using new skills, the ultimate compromise, or perhaps the ultimate revolution, in building methods is not yet in sight. What is true of dwelling-houses is also true of other building on a greater scale. There is no augury; but there are portents whose light—or it may be whose shadow—falls upon cottage and palace alike.

---

[1] Dr. J. Bronowski in the *Observer*, 19th November 1950.

Notes and Appendices

NOTE I

The Functions of the Office of Works

1. As constituted at the outbreak of the Second World War, the Office of Works dated from 1852. It had already been separated from the Office of Woods (Commissioners of Crown Lands) chiefly in order to obviate the possibility of employing the Land Revenues for carrying on public works independently of votes of Parliament. The Board of Commissioners appointed under a Statute of William IV was now divided, with the first Commissioner as 'First Commissioner of H.M. Works and Public Buildings' and the two other Commissioners as 'Commissioners of H.M. Woods, Forests and Land Revenues'. At the same time, the principal Secretaries of State and the President or Vice-President of the Board of Trade were *ex officio* Commissioners of Works in conjunction with the First Commissioner, and by various enactments between 1852 and 1894 the powers of the Commissioners were extended and the procedure simplified.

2. The work of the department consisted, broadly, of the erection and finishing of any new buildings required for the civil (and to some extent the naval and military) services; the maintenance, repair, alteration, etc., of existing public buildings and of the Royal Palaces (including the furniture in such buildings, except in the case of the Royal Palaces) and the maintenance of the Royal Parks; the hiring of premises for the public services, wherever accommodation could be provided more conveniently and economically by this means than by the erection of new buildings; the administration and maintenance of the Osborne Convalescent Home for Naval and Military Officers; the administration of a number of non-voted and agency services; and public buildings overseas.

Since 1900 certain services were added to those previously undertaken by the Office of Works and others transferred from its charge to other departments; and its organisation, later absorbed into the Ministry of Works, comprised a secretariat and executive and advisory divisions. The executive and advisory divisions consisted of (*a*) the Architects' Division; (*b*) the Maintenance Surveyors' Division; (*c*) the Mechanical and Electrical Engineering Division; (*d*) the Quantity Surveyors' Division; (*e*) the Lands and Accommodation Directorate; (*f*) the Supplies Division; (*g*) the Office of the Controller of Accounts (Finance Division); (*h*) the Ancient Monuments Inspectorate; and (*i*) the Bailiff of Parks Division.

3. Limitations of financial powers of the Office of Works were prescribed by the Treasury. For works the total cost of which was estimated at less than £6,000, the approved estimate might be exceeded without express Treasury sanction by not more than ten per cent. or £300, whichever was the less. For works the total cost of which was estimated at more than £6,000, the approved estimate might be exceeded by not more than five per cent. or £1,000, whichever was the less. Minor works could be carried out without Treasury authority up to a limit of £500 and for Post Office services up to £1,000, with a margin of £50 and £100 respectively in

excess of the prescribed limit. Works up to an estimated cost of £50 were chargeable to maintenance.

Although it was the policy of the Office of Works wherever possible to carry out work in connection with buildings under its charge by means of contracts, direct labour was employed, for example, where work must otherwise necessarily have been carried out as day work under the supervision of officers of the department and the regular full-time employment of a staff of maintenance workmen was involved.

As an employer of direct labour the Office of Works could regulate at its discretion the wages of unpensionable employees of the workmen class whose posts were not detailed in the Estimates. Regard was given to the obligations placed on the contractor by the Fair Wages Clause, but due weight had to be given to the special conditions attaching to Government service.

4. The contract policy and procedure of the Office of Works provided for the normal method of purchase of both work and materials through competitive estimates. If for any reason it was considered in a particular instance impracticable or undesirable to obtain such estimates, and a purchase without competition was proposed, the final decision rested with the Contracts Division. Classes of contracts which were to be made the subject of open competition by advertisement in the press were determined from time to time. They normally comprised building and decoration works estimated to cover over £1,000; maintenance and periodical services in London and the larger provincial towns; privileges in the Royal Parks and elsewhere; furniture and similar stores, as well as engineering services, of an estimated value in excess of £500; and coal in towns where the consumption exceeded 500 tons per annum.

When resort was not had to open competition, competitive tenders were invited from selected firms on the list of contractors eligible to tender for contracts, usually a minimum of four firms for tenders up to £100, six firms for tenders from £100 to £400, and eight firms for tenders over £400. For building work estimated to cost over £1,000 in London and £750 in the provinces, bills of quantities were prepared, but the Contracts Division could give authority to dispense with them. Quantity surveyors were selected from an approved panel of surveyors who had agreed to abide by the standard conditions laid down by the department. Arrangements were made for maintenance contracts of various kinds up to prescribed limits; otherwise the previous sanction of the Contracts Division had to be obtained. Where the value of the work was over £3,000 prior Treasury approval was necessary. Routine building maintenance services in London and Edinburgh were carried out by direct labour. In London a periodical contract was also entered into covering certain services such as the supply of the materials and hire of the plant required for use by the direct employees (not including paint and grease); hauling; works of alteration or repair costing between £150 and £500; and works over £500 in exceptional circumstances where *ad hoc* tendering was impracticable or undesirable.

5. Measures were taken in the Office of Works to ensure the suitability of firms invited to tender. An alphabetical list and classified lists of those

eligible to tender were kept in the Contracts Division, together with notes of the records of the firms. Inquiries were made from other Government departments as to the character and capacity of firms who applied to be put on the list, and the executive division concerned was asked to report on them before they were added. A list of firms ineligible to tender was also kept by the Contracts Division. It was revised from time to time and copies were circulated to executive officers. In serious cases firms were 'black-listed' and other Government departments informed.

6. The furniture and general stores of the Office of Works, concentrated at Park Royal from 1932 onwards, served as a 'universal provider' for departments and comprised the sections dealing with furniture, general, engineering, builders' ironmongery, tools, carpets, window blinds and redundant furniture; and there were workshops for carpets, window blinds and repairs. There were also minor London stores and workshops (e.g. a clock store and workshop at King Charles Street, S.W.1, central work-shops at Scotland Yard and district workshops at Acton and elsewhere) as well as provincial small stores in Manchester and Edinburgh. Generally speaking, the workshops were used to carry out only such work as could not advantageously be made the subject of a contract. The cost of supplies passing through stores was charged in the first instance to the stores sub-head of the public buildings vote, the sub-head being relieved when the goods were actually issued by the transfer of the charge to the vote concerned. The stores overhead charges were recovered by means of fixed percentage additions to the value of the goods issued. These percentage additions varied for the different classes of goods supplied and normally ranged from about $7\frac{1}{2}$ per cent. to about $17\frac{1}{2}$ per cent.

The provision of fuel for Government departments fell to the Office of Works, and was carried out at its four London coal depots. Only a small reserve of coal was kept at these depots, their main purpose being the distribution of supplies purchased direct from collieries for the use of Government departments in London. The amounts to be charged to the respective votes for coal supplies were worked out weekly. An average price per ton was calculated for each class of coal: it covered, in addition to first cost, transport, handling and other supplementary charges incurred.

7. In 1924 the whole question of recoverable services carried out by the Office of Works, and of the method of accounting applied to them, was considered in detail with the Treasury. The decisions reached were on the following general lines:

(a) Services analogous to those ordinarily covered by Office of Works votes, hitherto carried out for civil and revenue departments on repayment terms, were now transferred as final charges to Office of Works votes. Treasury authority was to be obtained for any departure from this general rule.

(b) Works and services for certain bodies, etc., were now carried out on repayment terms. This ruling applied to the fighting Services; occupiers of Grace and Favour Residences; scientific societies and others housed in Government buildings for which they were liable under the terms of their occupation (e.g. the occupants of Burlington House); the Royal Household, etc.; Dominion Governments, the

Northern Natal Government and the Irish Free State; persons with whom the Office of Works was brought into relation either as landlord or tenant; Government departments or quasi-Government departments financed by grants-in-aid or by special funds (e.g. the Electricity Commission, the Road Fund, the Development Commission, etc.).

(c) Transactions in connection with repayment services were now always to be reflected in the Parliamentary accounts of the department.

(d) To cover the administrative expenses of the department a percentage addition was made to claims rendered in respect of recoverable services. This rate was subject to revision every three years.

NOTE II

Joint Negotiating Machinery in the Building and Civil Engineering Industries*

(i) England and Wales

1. For England and Wales the earliest agreement of a national character in the building industry was in 1899. It provided for the formation of local committees in the plastering trade to deal with trade disputes as they arose, and a central standing joint committee to consider cases which could not be settled locally.

In 1904 there was also set up by agreement a more elaborate scheme for conciliation in trade disputes in which bricklayers, stonemasons, carpenters and joiners were involved. The parties to the agreement were the employers' national federations and the trade unions catering for the trades concerned. Disagreements, if not settled locally, were referred to a Centre (or Area) Board, and from that, if necessary, to a National Conciliation Board. At any stage matters in dispute might be referred to arbitration by consent of the parties.

2. In the years immediately preceding the First World War the system of collective bargaining was already widely established, but the agreements were as a rule local in character (the locality being usually a single town) and unco-ordinated as between different occupations.

During the war years up to 1918 increases in rates of wages were made on the basis of purely local agreements by the addition of fixed awards which were usually the same for all classes of operatives. Apart from these increases little change was made in the pre-war system of agreements.

3. In order to remove anomalies in regard to wages, the two sides of the National Conciliation Board entered, in 1918, into a comprehensive wages agreement. Existing local agreements were to be maintained so long as they did not conflict with the new agreement, and provision was also made for co-ordinating general changes in wages. Later in the year, in order to secure greater uniformity of real wages and conditions, the employers' federations and the trade unions began a movement, which spread rapidly, for securing the regulation of wages and conditions on a regional basis by means of Regional Joint Councils.

4. In 1919 the national federations of employers and workers adopted the principle of national uniformity of hours of work; and in 1920 they agreed to regulate wages and other conditions on a national (but not necessarily uniform) basis.

This agreement resulted in the formation of the National Wages and

---

* The information contained in this Note is summarised from Ministry of Labour and National Service *Industrial Relations Handbook* (H.M.S.O. 1944).

Conditions Council for the Building Industry. It was a body charged with the regulation of wages and hours, the grading of towns for the purpose of wage regulation, and the regulation of allowances that were capable of national adjustment.

The Regional Joint Councils remained in existence to settle other matters and to assist the National Council in the work of grading and re-grading towns. This scheme, with minor modifications, remained in operation until 1932. In the interval the title of the National Wages and Conditions Council was altered to the National Joint Council for the Building Industry; and in 1932 an agreement was reached under which the duties of the National Conciliation Boards were transferred to the National Joint Council.

THE 1932 AGREEMENT

5. *Central and Regional Organisation.* The 1932 agreement is the basis of the machinery of negotiation in the building industry in England and Wales. It enunciates the principle that wages and conditions 'shall be determined on a national basis', but makes elaborate provision to secure that proper regard is had to local diversities of circumstance.

The machinery for giving effect to the agreement consists of a National Joint Council, and Regional, Area and Local Joint Committees. The National Joint Council consists of not more than forty members, half of whom are appointed by the National Federation of Building Trades Employers and half by the trade unions affiliated to the National Federation of Building Trades Operatives. It is the duty of the council to deal (in accordance with rules and regulations laid down in the constitution) with rates of wages, grading of towns, working hours, extra payments, overtime, night work, walking time, travelling and lodging allowances, and to settle any differences or disputes that may arise.

The council is required to appoint a grading commission and a conciliation panel as well as procedure and general purposes committees and must delegate certain functions to Regional, Area and Local Joint Committees.

The Regional Joint Committees[1] serve as connecting links between the National Council and the localities. The appointment and conditions of the Area Joint Committees are at the discretion of the Regional Joint Committees and their function is to serve as a further link in the chain of communication and procedure laid down by the agreement. The Local Joint Committees are provided for districts the extent of which is determined by themselves, subject to the overriding powers of the Regional Joint Committees to determine the boundaries of a district.

The membership of each type of committee consists of representatives of employers' organisations and trade unions in the region, area or district concerned.

6. *Wages Agreement.* To provide for the regulation of wages, various

---

[1] The nine regions are: North-Western, Northern, Yorkshire, Midland, Eastern Counties, Southern Counties, South-Western, South Wales and Monmouthshire, and London.

towns and districts outside London were classified, under the 1932 agree-ment, into ten 'grades' in respect of each of which 'datum standard rates' of wages were laid down as applicable to craftsmen. The rates for crafts-men in the inner and outer London areas respectively were determined by the addition of specified amounts to the highest of the grade rates; and the rate for labourers in any district was fixed at seventy-five per cent. of the rate for craftsmen in that district. These provisions were somewhat modi-fied under war and post-war conditions. The current standard rates were amended in April 1943, not by reference to the cost-of-living sliding scale, but by an amendment to the rules which varied the datum standard rates themselves.

Variation of the datum standard rates is the prerogative of the National Joint Council. The grading of towns and districts is performed 'nationally' by the Grading Commission, but it is permissible for any district to make application for a variation of its classification, such application being sub-mitted through the appropriate regional committee, which has power to make a recommendation to the Grading Commission.

Provision was also made under the agreement for departures from current standard rates by way of:

(i) 'exceptional margins' which apply to all occupations in the parti-cular locality and operate only for a prescribed period;

(ii) 'differential margins' which apply to a section of the industry only (e.g. a single occupation) in the particular locality, but continue for an indefinite period.

7. *Working Rules.* National Working Rules, annexed to the agreement, lay down the duration of the normal working week and working day and the rates of pay for overtime and night working and the allowances to be paid for walking time, travelling and lodging, together with a scale of extra payments to be made to workmen engaged on exceptional kinds of work, such as scaffolding, dirty work, hot work and work at an exceptional height, etc. It is open to any party in any district to initiate a proposal to vary the working rules, but no variation is possible unless and until the consent of the National Joint Council has been obtained.

8. *War-time Modifications.* The modifications of the normal arrange-ments in the building industry introduced during the Second World War are described in the main narrative. They comprised the following:

(1) As a war emergency measure, the consideration of variations of current standard rates of wages in accordance with changes in cost of living took place at intervals of months instead of annually.

(2) A Uniformity Agreement, between the parties to the National Joint Council of the Building Industry and the parties to the Civil Engi-neering Construction Conciliation Board, established a Joint Board to deal with wages and other questions on large sites where work of national importance was being carried out.

(3) Payment by results where practicable and desirable was made a condition of the scheduling of sites under the Essential Work (Building and Civil Engineering) Order 1942.

(4) Contracting undertakings under Defence (General) Regulation 56 AB, which provided that no person might carry out building or civil engineering work unless he held a certificate issued by the Ministry of Works, and such conditions as to hours of employment (including conditions as to Sunday work) were observed as the Minister might direct. The regulation also provided for the control of entry of new firms into the building and civil engineering industries.

(ii) Scotland

9. In Scotland there are separate employers' organisations, but many of the Scottish trade unions are affiliated to the National Federation of Building Trades Operatives. There is a Joint Agreement similar generally to that operating in England and Wales, but it does not cover all building trade occupations.

A separate Scottish National Joint Council for the Building Industry was set up in 1930; and a National Agreement, substantially similar to that for England and Wales, was adopted by the Council in 1932 but did not cover the plumbing, plastering, painting, or glazing trades. Machinery similar to that of the English agreement is provided for making constitutional and other amendments, but no provision was made for Regional or Area Joint Committees. The Council were, however, given authority to delegate certain powers to Local Joint Committees on questions of overtime, the fixing of grade district boundaries and the general regulation of the operation of the working rules.

10. The 1932 Scottish Agreement provided that various towns and districts should be classified into grades to which standard rates based on the official cost-of-living index would apply, the labourers' rate being seventy-five per cent. of the craftsman's rate in each grade. Under a temporary provision craftsmen and labourers both received war-time increases in full, so that the labourers' rate was eighty per cent. of that of craftsmen.

The grading of towns and districts is carried out by a Grading Committee. Any town or district may apply to the committee for an alteration in its grade, and provision is made for temporary alterations in grade classification by means of exceptional rates.

The National Working Rules are identical in many respects with those for England and Wales, but there are certain important differences, e.g. no provision is made as in England and Wales for the normal weekly hours to be extended during the summer months, the rules governing overtime are different, and in the rule relating to night-gangs there are regulations dealing with two-shift and three-shift systems which do not appear in the English agreement.

The war-time modifications for England and Wales applied equally to Scotland. A separate Joint Board for the administration of the Uniformity Agreement was, however, established under the title of the Scottish Joint Board with functions similar to those of the English Joint Board.

(iii) Joint Production and Site Committees

11. The great productive effort called for since the outbreak of war in 1939 gave a stimulus to collaboration and consultation between employers and workpeople. The Government actively supported these movements. In the building and civil engineering industries contractors and their workpeople were encouraged to improve production by closer co-operation on the sites of big works.

Before the war, in large employers' establishments or on building and civil engineering contracts of a considerable size, the trade unions concerned usually organised a Works Committee for the purpose of co-ordinating activities on the workers' side and bringing grievances to the notice of employers. Joint Works Committees were not common in this industry, but in 1942, by an amendment to the Essential Work (Building and Civil Engineering) Order the Minister of Labour and National Service was empowered to make or approve, after consultation with the parties concerned, arrangements for the consideration of cases of absenteeism or persistent lateness by a joint committee or other body established for a particular undertaking. In addition, the Ministry of Works encouraged the setting up of Site Committees with wider functions. These committees were representative of the management and organised workpeople, although not necessarily in equal numbers. They were mainly concerned with welfare, but could deal with purely local questions, including production, thus embracing the functions of Joint Production Committees, since it was competent for either side to raise any suggestions for improvement of production.

STANDING JOINT COUNCILS, COMMITTEES, ETC., ESTABLISHED BY VOLUNTARY AGREEMENT IN THE BUILDING AND CIVIL ENGINEERING INDUSTRIES

12. The bodies listed below have been established by voluntary agreement to provide machinery for negotiation, collective bargaining and the settlement of disputes and not infrequently the discussion of other matters of common interest. None the less, the settlement of wages and conditions of employment by negotiation between organisations of employers and workpeople is not necessarily dependent on the existence of voluntary standing joint machinery. Broadly speaking, three forms of machinery of negotiation, i.e. (i) standing joint bodies covered by this Note, (ii) a procedure of negotiation established by agreement, custom or practice, and (iii) statutory wage regulation machinery cover the whole industrial field.

Standing bodies in this list to which the description 'J.I.C.' is attached are constituted in accordance with the recommendations of the Whitley Committee. Bodies marked * are national bodies with which are associated regional, district or local bodies forming an integral part of the joint machinery of the industry.

The titles of trade unions abbreviated N.U.G.M.W. and T. & G.W.U. stand respectively for National Union of General and Municipal Workers, and Transport and General Workers' Union.

NATIONAL JOINT COUNCIL FOR THE BUILDING INDUSTRY — *Employers' associations represented:* Nat. Fedn. of Building Trades Employers; Nat. Fedn. of Plumbers and Domestic Engineers (Employers); Nat. Fedn. of Roofing Contractors.
Trade unions represented: Nat. Fedn. of Building Trades Operatives; Amal. Soc. of Woodworkers; Amal. Union of Building Trade Workers; N.U.G.M.W.; Nat. Soc. of Painters; T. & G.W.U. (Building Trade Workers' Section); Plumbers', Glaziers' and Domestic Engineers' Union; Nat. Builders' Labourers' and Constructional Workers' Soc.; Nat. Soc. of Street Masons, Paviors and Road Makers; Amal. Soc. of Woodcutting Machinists; Amal. Slaters' and Tilers' Provident Soc.; Nat. Assn. of Operative Plasterers.

SCOTTISH NATIONAL JOINT COUNCIL FOR THE BUILDING INDUSTRY — *Employers' association represented:* Scottish Nat. Building Trades Fedn. (Employers). *Trade union represented:* Nat. Fedn. of Building Trades Operatives.

CIVIL ENGINEERING CONSTRUCTION CONCILIATION BOARD FOR GREAT BRITAIN — *Employers' association represented:* Fedn. of Civil Engineering Contractors. *Trade unions represented :* T. & G.W.U.; N.U.G.M.W.

JOINT BOARD FOR THE BUILDING AND CIVIL ENGINEERING INDUSTRIES — *Employers' associations represented:* Employers' side of the Nat. Joint Council for the Building Industry; Employers' side of the Civil Engineering Construction Conciliation Board.
Trade unions represented: Employees' side of the Nat. Joint Council for the Building Industry; Employees' side of the Civil Engineering Construction Conciliation Board.

DEMOLITION INDUSTRY WAGES BOARD — *Employers' association represented:* Nat. Fedn. Demolition Contractors. *Trade union represented:* Nat. Fedn. of Building Trades Operatives.

SCOTTISH JOINT BOARD FOR THE BUILDING AND CIVIL ENGINEERING INDUSTRIES — *Employers' associations represented:* Scottish Nat. Building Trade Fedn. (Employers); Fedn. of Civil Engineering Contractors (Scottish Section). *Trade union represented:* Nat. Fedn. of Building Trades Operatives.

GLAZING (J.I.C.) — *Employers' association represented:* Nat. Council of Glazing Employers. *Trade union represented:* Plumbers', Glaziers' and Domestic Engineers' Union.

SCOTTISH PLASTERERS' NATIONAL JOINT COMMITTEE — *Employers' association represented:* Scottish Master Plasterers' Association
Trade union represented: Scottish Nat. Operative Plasterers' Protective and Benefit Federal Union.

*PLUMBING (J.I.C.) — *Employers' association represented:* Nat. Fedn. of Plumbers and Domestic Engineers (Employers).
Trade union represented: Plumbers', Glaziers' and Domestic Engineers' Union.

*NATIONAL JOINT COUNCIL FOR THE MASTIC ASPHALT INDUSTRY — *Employers' associations represented:* London Master Asphalters' Assn., Ltd.; Northern Master Asphalters' Assn.; Birmingham Area Asphalt Employers; South-Western Area Asphalt Employers; Newcastle Mastic Asphalt Employers.
Trade union represented: Amal. Union of Asphalt Workers.

CONCILIATION BOARD FOR ENGINE AND CRANE DRIVERS EMPLOYED BY MEMBERS OF THE LONDON MASTER BUILDERS' ASSOCIATION — *Employers' association represented:* London Master Builders' Assn.
Trade union represented: Nat. Union of Enginemen, Firemen, Mechanics, Motormen and Electrical Workers (section of T. & G.W.U.).

JOINT COMMITTEE OF THE LONDON AND SOUTHERN COUNTIES BRANCH OF THE NAT. FEDN. OF ROOFING CONTRACTORS AND THE AMAL. SLATERS' AND TILERS' PROVIDENT SOCIETY — *Employers' association represented:* London and Southern Counties Branch, Nat. Fedn. of Roofing Contractors.
Trade union represented: Amal. Slaters' and Tilers' Provident Soc.

NORTH-EAST COAST JOINT DIST. COMMITTEE OF EMPLOYERS AND OPERATIVES OF THE NATIONAL FEDERATION OF ROOFING CONTRACTORS — *Employers' association represented:* Nat. Fedn. of Roofing Contractors (North of England Branch).
Trade union represented: Amal. Slaters' and Tilers' Provident Soc. (Northern District).

JOINT COMMITTEE OF REPRESENTATIVES OF THE SCOTTISH TILE AND MARBLE CONTRACTORS' ASSN. AND THE SCOTTISH ASSOCIATED TILE FIXERS' UNION — *Employers' association represented:* Scottish Tile and Marble Contractors' Assn.
Trade union represented: Scottish Associated Tile Fixers' Union.

NATIONAL JOINT COMMITTEE FOR THE TERRAZZO MOSAIC INDUSTRY — *Employers' association represented:* Nat. Fedn. of Terrazzo-Mosaic Specialists.
Trade union represented: Amal. Union of Building Trade Workers.

NOTE III

Inter-departmental Committees for the Supervision of the Building Programme
1937–40

1. The Inter-departmental Committee on the Building Programme of Government Departments was set up at a conference of Ministers held on 2nd February 1937 with the following terms of reference:

'To ascertain the building programme of Government departments whether undertaken by departments direct or with financial assistance from the departments, and to consider possible measures, by priority or otherwise, for its completion.'

Any question of priority on which the committee were unable to reach agreement was to be referred to the conference of Ministers.

The committee met at the Ministry of Labour, under the chairmanship of the Permanent Secretary (Sir T. W. Phillips) and with representatives of the Treasury, Admiralty, War Office, Air Ministry, Ministry of Health, Board of Education, Ministry of Labour, Office of Works and the Scottish Office.

The committee held four meetings during 1937 and did not meet again until two years later, on 20th June 1939, when it was specially convened at the request of the Office of Works to consider a particular labour problem. The committee was not summoned again after this.

2. On 7th July 1939, at the request of the Minister for Co-ordination of Defence (Sir Thomas Inskip, later Viscount Caldecote), a Ministerial Building Priority Sub-Committee was set up and held its first meeting on 11th July. This was a sub-committee of the Committee of Imperial Defence. On 19th July the corresponding official sub-committee known as the Building Priority (Official) Sub-Committee was appointed, with Mr. Humbert Wolfe, of the Ministry of Labour, as chairman. The departmental representation was similar to that of the Inter-departmental Committee on the Building Programme of Government Departments.

3. The terms of reference of the official sub-committee were:

'To investigate and report on priority in the letting and execution of contracts for the various items of the building programme so far as the letting of such contracts is directly or indirectly under the control of Government departments and on any other matters arising therefrom.

'Decisions reached by agreement by this sub-committee, after confirmation by the chairman of the Ministerial Building Priority Committee, will be binding on departments. Points of dispute will be reported for decision to the Ministerial Priority Committee.'

4. After holding five meetings between 13th July and 9th September

1939 the sub-committee was given a new constitution and terms of reference. With the designation 'Works and Building Priority Sub-Committee' it was now brought into the general priority organisation, on exactly the same footing as the Materials, Production and Labour Sub-Committees of the Central Priority Department. Mr. Ralph Assheton, Parliamentary Secretary to the Ministry of Labour, was now appointed chairman and Mr. Humbert Wolfe deputy chairman, but the composition of the rest of the sub-committee remained the same. The new terms of reference were:

'Subject to the authority of the Ministerial Priority Committee to fix priority as between all classes of building and works of construction.'

The rulings and findings of the sub-committee were to go to the Central Priority Department for record.

5. The Works and Building Priority Committee, as it came to be known, remained in being until 25th September 1942 when, after having held forty-eight meetings, it was put in abeyance, its work being taken over by new committees under the direction of the Minister of Production. Meanwhile, on the creation of the Ministry of Works in October 1940, Mr. Ralph Assheton had given up his office as chairman of the sub-committee. His place was taken by Mr. George Hicks, Parliamentary Secretary of the new Ministry, with Mr. Hugh Beaver as deputy chairman.

6. Side by side with the official committees, Joint Consultative Committees, both for England and Wales and for Scotland, were set up in 1937. Their creation followed on conferences between the industry and the Minister of Labour. The committee for England and Wales met for the first time on 14th June 1937. With the Permanent Secretary of the Ministry of Labour as chairman, and with representatives of the Treasury, Admiralty, War Office, Air Ministry, Ministry of Health, Ministry of Labour and Office of Works sat four representatives of the National Federation of Building Trades Employers and four of the National Federation of Building Trades Operatives. Similar arrangements were made for the Scottish industry. In that case, however, the industrial representation of six employers (Scottish National Building Trades Federation) and eight operatives (National Federation of Building Trades Operatives) was augmented by a representative of the Scottish Master Plasterers' Association and one of the Scottish National Operative Plasterers' Federal Union. With the eight representatives of departments the committee numbered twenty-four.

7. The Joint Consultative Committee for England and Wales defined their own general objective. This was 'to assist in attaining and ensuring the most expeditious and efficient means for completing the Government's building programme, while at the same time avoiding or minimising any disturbing effects upon the efficient organisation of the building industry and/or upon the normal industrial and commercial development on which its long-term welfare largely depends'. This main subject was 'divided into two branches, both of which equally need attention at this time, these branches themselves being sub-divided, each into several items'. The sub-divisions were as follows:

A. WAGE RATES AND WORKING CONDITIONS

(1) Any questions requiring examination in relation to the process of fixing and adoption of appropriate wage rates and working conditions in respect of large Government building projects (*a*) in districts of a rural character; (*b*) in districts of an urban or industrial character.

(2) The question of the extent to which Government departments concerned could:

(*a*) avail themselves of the services of the National Joint Council for the Building Industry throughout their operations, e.g. (i) by giving the Council timely notice of new and considerable projects in order to enable suitable rates to be fixed (where necessary) after due inquiry; (ii) by enabling intending contractors for work in rural areas to be informed, prior to submission of tenders, of the standard rates (or exceptional margins in the case of large works in rural areas) prescribed by the National Joint Council; (iii) by reporting to the Council, for its attention, any difficulties which may come to their notice;

(*b*) in relation to the Fair Wages Clause, recognise and assist in securing compliance with joint decisions of the National Joint Council for the Building Industry on rates of wages and working conditions;

(*c*) factors as to the prices and availability of building materials.

B. SUPPLY OF LABOUR. SUPPLY OF MATERIALS

(1) The question of labour supply in its several aspects:

(*a*) Review of present position and likely requirements.

(*b*) Recruitment and training of skilled workers.

(*c*) Mobility of building workers (i) generally, in regard to possibly unequal distribution as between different parts of the country; (ii) in regard to the special cases of large projects in rural areas.

(*d*) Position likely to arise in 1940 when defence programme is completed.

(2) Factors relating to design, materials available and methods of construction, as bearing upon the question of any scarcity of certain classes of skilled labour.

(3) In the same connection as (2), factors in regard to any adjustments of the order of priority of different types of building works.

8. For the Scottish Joint Consultative Committee terms of reference were agreed as follows:

'(1) That a Joint Consultative Committee constituted of representatives of employers' and operatives' organisations and of Government departments shall be appointed. The general objective of this committee shall be to assist in attaining and ensuring the most expeditious and efficient means of completing the Government building programme and the housing programmes of local authorities in Scotland, while, at the same time, avoiding or minimising any disturbing effects upon the efficient organisation of the building industry and/or upon the normal industrial and commercial development on which its permanent welfare depends.

'(2) To recommend to the appropriate committees under the Scottish National Joint Council for the Building Industry to give sympathetic consideration to applications for overtime where necessity is proved.

'(3) That where it is proved in any district that there is a shortage oi labour, the matter should be dealt with by the appropriate Apprenticeship Committee under the Scottish National Joint Council for the Building Industry, in consultation with the Joint Consultative Committee if necessary, and the augmentation, if any, should be governed by a general quota of one apprentice to three journeymen in respect of each craft.'

9. The Joint Consultative Committee for England and Wales held nine meetings between 14th June 1937 and 21st December 1939; that for Scotland fifteen meetings between 29th September 1937 and 4th April 1940. When the Works and Building Priority Committee was brought into being the joint committees faded into the background, and the industrial element in the form of 'industrial advisory panels'[1] continued to collaborate with the official committee.

10. Apart from the committees set up during this period to deal specifically with the war-time building programme, there was in existence the Inter-departmental Works Committee consisting of representatives of the Service departments and the Office of Works. Its terms of reference were to ensure (1) free interchange of information and uniformity of procedure in respect of contracts, supply of stores for structural works, etc.; (2) co-ordination in methods of economical construction and design; (3) the study of the interests and convenience of all works branches when large programmes of work were undertaken by one of them; (4) the full use by the other Government works departments of the resources of each branch in respect of the technical matters for which it maintained an expert staff; and (5) to consider, before large building schemes in the United Kingdom were undertaken by Government departments, whether it would not be advantageous to entrust the execution of such schemes to the Office of Works.

---

[1] Of the building and civil engineering industries respectively.

NOTE IV
The Fair Wages Clause

The Fair Wages Clause, as embodied in Government contracts in the form in which it remained until 1937, was settled by a Resolution of the House of Commons of 10th March 1909.[1] It was recognised, however, after a number of years that the terms of the clause were no longer entirely appropriate in the changed circumstances of the day; and in 1937 the Minister of Labour appointed a committee, consisting of representatives of Government departments, trade unions and employers' organisations, with an independent chairman, to consider the wording of the Fair Wages Resolution.

In a White Paper[2] published in 1942 the Financial Secretary to the Treasury stated that as a result of discussions between the British Employers' Confederation, the Trade Union Congress and the Government, agreement had been reached on the draft of a new Resolution for submission to the House of Commons for its approval.

The principal changes shown by the new draft Resolution as compared with the existing Resolution were as follows:

'1. The standard of fair wages will no longer be solely the practice of "good employers" in the district. The employer will be required to observe such conditions as have been established for the trade or industry in the district by representative joint machinery of negotiation or by arbitration.

'2. The new Resolution specifically requires the contractor to observe "fair" conditions of labour as well as "fair" wages and to apply them to all persons employed by him in every factory, workshop or place where the contract is being executed. Contracting departments will require an assurance from a new contractor that to the best of his knowledge and belief he has complied with the general conditions of the Resolution for at least the previous three months.

'3. Under the old Resolution the Minister of the contracting department had, if called upon, to decide whether or not fair wages were being paid. Under the new Resolution any such questions will be reported to the Ministry of Labour and National Service and, if not disposed of by negotiation, will be referred to arbitration.

'4. The contractor shall recognise the freedom of his workpeople to be members of trade unions.'

The statement points out that while the Conditions of Employment and National Arbitration Order 1940 (made under the Emergency Powers (Defence) Act 1939) remained in force, the position of Government contractors with regard to wages and conditions of employment was governed by that Order. There was, accordingly, no immediate need for seeking to amend the existing Fair Wages Resolution, and before asking Parliament

[1] H. of C. Deb., Fourth Series of 28th Parliament, Vol. 2, Col. 415 *et seq.*
[2] Cmd. 6399.

466

to consider the terms of the new draft Resolution, it was desirable to have further experience of the administration of the Order and to allow opportunity for considering what changes might be necessary in view of any future developments with regard to the enforcement of industrial agreements. The Government, however, accepted the view of the Trades Union Congress General Council and the British Employers' Confederation that a statement should be made of the intention to submit to Parliament at the end of the war a new Resolution.

By a Resolution of the House of Commons of 14th October 1946 the draft terms of the Resolution were approved. Contractors for Government work were now required to observe and fulfil the obligations upon contractors as follows:

'1. (a) The contractor shall pay rates of wages and observe hours and conditions of labour not less favourable than those established for the trade or industry in the district where the work is carried out by machinery of negotiation or arbitration to which the parties are organisations of employers and trade unions representative respectively of substantial proportions of the employers and workers engaged in the trade or industry in the district.

'(b) In the absence of any rates of wages, hours or conditions of labour so established the contractor shall pay rates of wages and observe hours and conditions of labour which are not less favourable than the general level of wages, hours and conditions observed by other employers whose general circumstances in the trade or industry in which the contractor is engaged are similar.

'2. The contractor shall in respect of all persons employed by him (whether in execution of the contract or otherwise) in every factory, workshop or place occupied or used by him for the execution of the contract comply with the general conditions required by this Resolution. Before a contractor is placed upon a department's list of firms to be invited to tender, the department shall obtain from him an assurance that to the best of his knowledge and belief he has complied with the general conditions required by this Resolution for at least the previous three months.

'3. In the event of any question arising as to whether the requirements of this Resolution are being observed, the question shall, if not otherwise disposed of, be referred by the Minister of Labour and National Service to an independent tribunal for decision.

'4. The contractor shall recognise the freedom of his workpeople to be members of trade unions.

'5. The contractor shall at all times during the continuance of a contract display, for the information of his workpeople, in every factory, workshop or place occupied or used by him for the execution of the contract a copy of this Resolution.

'6. The contractor shall be responsible for the observance of this Resolution by sub-contractors employed in the execution of the contract, and shall, if required, notify the department of the names and addresses of all such sub-contractors.'

NOTE V
Forms of Contract

1. At the beginning of the rearmament programme the Treasury, in consultation with the Service departments, formulated the principles which should govern the placing of contracts under the abnormal conditions of the programme. Before these principles are examined, and their relevance to the building programme noted, changes in the normal contracts practice of the building industry itself in recent years must be briefly considered.[1]

Up to forty or fifty years ago, as has already been noted in the main narrative, building was carried on mainly by means of craftsmen and labourers employed by a 'builder' and the whole of the workshops and the organisation of work were laid out on the assumption that the builder had command of the building craftsmen in this personal way. Since, however, many new materials, new processes and mechanical services came to be used in the construction and equipment of building, it became impossible for any single architect or builder to have the specialised knowledge and experience to deal effectively with all of them. As a result the work of many specialist firms and sub-contractors had to be co-ordinated by the general contractor (whose own share of the contract might often be as small as perhaps a third of the whole job) and taken into account when deciding what type of contract should govern a particular job or method of construction.

2. The price to be paid to the building owner—whether a contract is let by competition or negotiated by the builder and the building owner—might be determined in one of two ways: either by a 'fixed price' or a 'cost reimbursement' contract. Of these two main types there are several variants.

Fixed Price Contracts. The contract price might be fixed in advance subject to variations and adjustment according to whether or not the work was in all respects carried out in accordance with the contract drawings and specifications. It might consist of a single sum or be the aggregate of various prices for different items of the work tendered by the contractor and accepted by the building owner.

Fixed price contracts might take several recognised forms, but are generally one of the following:

(a) *Lump Sum Contracts* in which the fixed price is a lump sum where no quantities have been prepared and the builder is responsible for carrying out all the works shown upon the drawings and described in the specification for this fixed price.

(b) *Bill of Quantities Contracts* based on fully detailed quantities prepared by a quantity surveyor to every item of which the builder has affixed a price. This was the fixed price contract most widely used in normal times. The aggregate of the quantities priced serves as the

---

[1] These are summarised in M.O.W. Report *The Placing and Management of Building Contracts.* H.M.S.O., 1944.

contract sum and the individual items provide a schedule for the valuation of any subsequent variations in design.

(c) *Schedule Contracts* based on a schedule either prepared *ad hoc* for the job or contained in a printed price schedule published by one or other of the Government departments. In such contracts the sum to be paid to the contractor is calculated when the work has been completed by application of the prices to the actual work done. Several departments used schedules of this sort freely during the war in order to enable them to place work promptly before particulars had been worked out and, therefore, before a bill of quantities in its proper sense could be prepared.

While these various types of contract are all known as fixed price contracts, during the Second World War and for some years after the First World War there was so much doubt and uncertainty about the cost of materials, rates of wages, lodging and travel allowances and other labour cost contingencies that the builders required the protection of 'rise and fall' clauses. Under these they received any increase and gave credit for any decrease in regard to these costs, according to whether they were above or below basic costs.

Such clauses, unless most carefully watched, might detract from the value of fixed price contracts as a means of ensuring keen buying of materials. They also prevent pre-contract determination of the total cost, and it is clear that the full advantage of placing contracts on the basis of fixed prices cannot be secured unless the general level of prices of building materials and of wages and other payments to the building operative is stabilised to enable the contract to be placed on a really fixed price basis.

3. *Cost Reimbursement Contracts.* In this type of contract the price to be paid is left to be determined at the time of entering into the contract, on the basis of the actual cost incurred by the contractor in carrying out the work, to which will be added an agreed amount as a fee to cover overheads and profits. Such contracts are used where the character or scope of the work is undetermined at the time of the contract, where time is not available for the preparation of particulars, and also where the builder might be unwilling to give fixed prices for work having regard to fluctuations in cost of materials, wages, output of labour and such other circumstances as make a fixed price contract difficult to negotiate.

Cost reimbursement contracts may take various forms, e.g.:

(a) *Cost plus percentage contracts*, commonly known as the *cost plus contracts*, under which the fee paid to the contractor is an agreed percentage of the actual cost of the building, as ascertained after the building is completed. It is the quickest way of arriving at an agreement and avoiding delay in starting operations and for that reason has been widely used (e.g. during the war 'cost plus' was the standard method of dealing with the repair of bomb damage). Under this system, however, higher costs mean higher fees; there is a direct financial incentive to extravagance; the inefficient contractor will make a larger profit than the efficient one.

(b) *Cost and fixed fee contracts.* Under this system a fixed lump sum fee, based on an estimate of the cost, is agreed between the architect or engineer on behalf of the owner and the contractor. Whatever the ultimate cost may be, the contractor receives this exact sum (subject only to allowances for any agreed variations in the job).

(c) *Value cost contracts.* In this case the normal fee is calculated as a percentage of a careful valuation of the work actually done, made on the basis of agreed schedules of prices. If the final cost is below the valuation then the fee is increased and *vice versa.* The contractor has, therefore, a definite financial incentive to economy.

4. Of the above three types of cost reimbursement contracts, little can be said in favour of the 'cost plus' contract, which can be justified only where circumstances render it unavoidable. It was regarded by the Ministry of Works as

'unsatisfactory and undesirable. Since work can be started almost as quickly under the "cost and fixed fee" system, we recommend that the "cost plus" system should never be used except in cases where the work is undetermined or is of utmost urgency, and that, when it is used, special care be taken to employ only reputable contractors and to provide effective supervision on behalf of the building owner.'[1]

In 'cost and fixed fee' contracts, when the work is finished the actual cost is checked against the estimated cost and the building owner is thus informed as to whether the contractor has carried out the work above or below the estimated cost. The contractor, therefore, is aware that if he is extravagant the building owner would know it and the contractor will suffer in prestige. The main advantage of this system, at all events in theory, is that if it is properly applied, the contractor's interests are very similar to those of the building owner; once the contract is fixed, nothing he does can affect his total remuneration, and his sole interest is to do a good job and to get it done quickly. In practice, however, other considerations might well take charge and the contract might well become indistinguishable from a cost plus percentage contract. It is indeed unlikely that any useful purpose would be served by comparing estimated costs with final costs except when the estimate is a target and the contractor has an opportunity to earn a bonus. Generally the circumstances which make a prime cost contract necessary preclude any estimate of cost worth the name.

The 'value cost' method is appropriate only for use by large organisations with highly competent staffs who have continuous programmes of work to carry out.

5. Local and public authorities, making use of 'direct labour' for carrying out building works, are sometimes able to build more cheaply and in any case to keep a check on the prices quoted by contractors. This type of labour organisation, with its own staff, plant and stores, grew up in the early period following the First World War and gave some protection against the excessive cost of house-building at that time; but it tended to disappear when the great building boom subsided and competitive prices became more normal. Encouraged by the Ministry of Health, direct labour organisations compete with industry in submitting estimates for particular works, basing costs upon prepared bills of quantities in competition with

---

[1] M.O.W. Report, *The Placing and Management of Building Contracts,* H.M.S.O., 1944.

contractors. But, although competition with the industry serves as a very valuable control and price regulator in regard to the contracts placed by the authority, it does not follow that an authority necessarily seeks or obtains more than a proportion of the building work so put out to tender. The usefulness of a direct labour organisation is greatest when its work is mainly of a repetitive character, preferably when it is confined almost entirely to housing, and when it is based on an independent costing department capable of ensuring that all proper costs, including all relevant overheads, are debited to the job, so that valid comparisons can be made between direct labour costs and contractors' prices.

6. The responsibility of the departments charged with the Government building programme for putting their building contracts on a basis which was at once fair to the industry and not disadvantageous to the public was shared with the Treasury. The normally accepted dividing line of responsibility between the Treasury and contracting departments was restated in 1936. On the one hand, it is the Treasury's responsibility to lay down the principles applicable to the placing of contracts, to regulate procedure, and to deal with any unusual conditions. On the other hand, it falls to departments themselves to take complete responsibility for contract administration in detail, to ensure that the conditions attaching to particular contracts are appropriate, and to see that the financial provisions are prudent and economical.

In the discharge of the defence programme as a whole it was inevitable that important questions of policy should arise on which there must be departures from accepted principles. The consideration of proposals for such departures was one of the main functions of the Treasury Inter-Service Committee. In appropriate cases contracts were submitted, usually in outline only, to the committee for discussion and criticism, without, however, impairing the responsibility of the Defence Minister concerned for the terms of individual contracts.

7. The normal method of purchasing Government supplies, where the Government shares the commercial market with private buyers,[1] is by competitive tender. This system, under which departments advertise for tenders, and accept the lowest, is apt to be modified under war-time conditions, to the extent that firms are selected and lists supplied to departments by their advisers as being suitable and competent to carry out work of appropriate extent and character. From the Government point of view competitive tender has been repeatedly endorsed by Parliament and its committees on account mainly of two supposed advantages: first, that the taxpayer secures the maximum value for his outlay; secondly, that it obviates any suspicion of collusion between the contracts departments and the contractors, thus providing a complete answer to any suggestion of favouritism in the allocation of Government work. On the other hand, the system has met with a good deal of criticism from industry. It is objected that the necessary formalities involve irritating delay: capital is locked up

---

[1] Different conditions govern the supply of (*a*) *technical stores* such as armaments and other special work for which the Government is the only customer; and (*b*) *general stores* (including building and similar constructional services) where the Government shares the commercial market with private buyers.

and chances of commercial work are lost during the long time spent by departments in examining tenders and placing contracts. Firms with good prospects of commercial work will not tender, or if they do the cost of carrying out the work may be enhanced to cover long options on materials and the risk of loss of commercial business. The delay in placing orders involves a corresponding delay in deliveries—a serious matter in a period of emergency. Further, even where competition is effective, especially in times of industrial depression, prices are often driven down to levels which do not provide a reasonable return on capital employed and in some cases cover no more than the contractor's out-of-pocket costs, with a partial contribution to overheads. For these reasons, eligible firms may refrain from tendering and this field of Government supply is consequently narrowed.

8. In the building industry especially is competitive tender open to serious abuses, the worst being that it may give advantage to firms which work to the lowest standards and seek occasion to avoid their responsibilities. Indiscriminate tendering, very low prices and bad building fall into a vicious circle; so that an unscrupulous firm, having quoted too low a price, may be faced with a heavy loss if it is properly to carry out the job, and will almost invariably cut the quality of its work. It is indeed a recognised and fundamental condition of good building that every contract shall be placed at a fair price with a responsible builder; and competitive tenders are therefore usually called from a limited number of firms carefully selected as being capable of and likely to do work of the required standard.

That view was endorsed by the Treasury in 1939 in so far as it commended that the system of competitive tender should not be abandoned entirely but should be used on a restricted basis compatible with the protection of the public purse. The entire absence of competition, it was contended, would present a serious difficulty, since in that respect the Government was peculiarly exposed to public criticism and any defence against such criticism was weakened when Government orders were not allotted by competitive tender.

9. The above conclusion on the subject of competitive tender was reached by the Treasury Committee on Contract Procedure, which had been appointed by Treasury Minute on 30th December 1938 to review the principles and methods of contract procedure already laid down by the Treasury Inter-Service Committee, and to make recommendation 'in the light of the practical experience gained by the defence programme'. The main part of the committee's recommendations, as applying to abnormal methods of contracting, is directly concerned with contracts for the production of munitions. Of more direct bearing on building costs was the experience of departments, as related to the committee, on the steps being taken to watch and control sub-contract prices.

10. A Treasury Inter-Service Committee Minute of 5th June 1936 had stated that it was clearly impossible to apply any general system of costings to sub-contractors, and had laid down that reliance was to be placed on the fact that from the point of view of their general business interests the main contractors would try to avoid paying excessive prices to sub-

contractors. That consideration, however, was not always applicable; and departments were to watch for instances in which contractors might appear to be paying excessive prices to sub-contractors, and also to keep in view the question of sub-contractors' profits. If it was found that main contractors tended to allow excessive profits to sub-contractors, steps were to be taken wherever possible to extend the practice of direct purchase by the State of components and their issue by the State to main contractors.

The departments, describing to the Treasury Committee their experience between 1936 and 1939, recalled that the problem in the past had been that the sub-contractor's price was an element in the contractor's costs, but that the department was not in contractual relationship with the sub-contractor and could not exercise the same control over the sub-contractor's prices as over the main contractor. But the departments had adopted the practice of ascertaining the sub-contractor's charges when the main contractor's price was being negotiated and could therefore take up negotiations with sub-contractors whose charges appeared *prima facie* excessive. The committee recommended that departments might more generally adopt the additional safeguard of requiring the main contractor to include a costings clause in important sub-contracts. In addition, the power to inspect books in the Ministry of Supply Act applied to sub-contractors as well as to main contractors. The contracting departments thus had at their disposal the machinery for securing fair sub-contract prices.

11. The general purport of the 1939 report of the Treasury Committee on Contract Procedure is to reaffirm the applicability of the principles laid down in the Treasury Inter-Service Committee's minute of 5th June 1939. While these principles apply mainly to contracts for the actual production of munitions, certain portions of the minute are relevant also to the erection of factories for such production. The following are to be noted:

(i) Since the State, in providing capital assets, could give no undertaking to buy the output of 'shadow' factories for more than a relatively limited period, the Government, in the long run, would have to meet a substantial part of the cost involved. That liability might be met either by including it as an element in the contract price of the article produced; or it might take the form of a claim for compensation on the expiry of Government orders. The balance of advantage therefore lay in the Government paying directly and at the outset for the new factories and acquiring ownership and control of them; and that course was to be adopted in all but exceptional circumstances, the freehold of the land, or at least a long leasehold, being obtained.

(ii) Where Government-owned factories were erected the normal procedure would be for the Government to entrust responsibility for the erection of the factory, and its subsequent management, to a firm chosen for their special experience of the type of production in question, the firm acting as agents of the Government. In fixing the profit (or management fee) no single hard-and-fast rule could be laid down. The guiding principle was that no more than fair and reasonable profits were to be allowed. Any attempt to prescribe a fixed percentage on the prices agreed for labour, material and on costs would lead to indefensible results.

(iii) The method likely to lead most directly to an equitable result was to assess profits by reference to a fair percentage upon the capital actually engaged for the time for which it was employed. In certain cases, however, difficulty might be experienced in obtaining particulars of the capital actually engaged and the time for which it was employed. In such cases, whether it was proposed to pay the profit as an ingredient in the price of the product or as a separate sum, contracting departments were to check the reasonableness of the profit proposed by considering its probable effect on the contractor's balance sheet. As close an estimate as possible was to be formed of the profit which would accrue to the contractor from the proposed contract and the period of time in which it would be earned; and of the extent to which the profits of the business would be affected. The weight which could be properly attached to this method of checking the reasonableness of the proposed profit would depend on a number of varying factors and in particular on the extent of the business placed by the State in relation to the total business of the contractor.

(iv) In all arrangements made for assessing profit (or management fee) provision might be made to give the firm concerned a reasonable incentive to efficiency and economy in production. That provision would in many cases take the form of allowing the firm to receive a percentage of the amount by which the actual cost of production was reduced below an agreed basic figure.

12. The problems of contracting in the defence programme engaged a good deal of attention in the first year of the war, and in January 1941 the Select Committee on National Expenditure reported on the subject.[1] This report was followed within a month by a further report (Fifth Report, 1940–41) dealing with militia camps in which the question of forms of contract was also raised. The Fourth Report is in great measure a description of, and commentary on, the problems of contracting in war-time, and on the general parts of the report the Treasury were in a large measure in agreement with the Select Committee. Some differences in point of view appear, however, in regard to the kernel of the contracts problem, that is the conflicting claims of fixed price and cost plus contracts. The Select Committee in the Fourth Report recommended that apart from special circumstances (such as the fact that a particular firm was highly efficient and had every indirect inducement to retain its economic efficiency) every effort should be made to place contracts on a fixed price basis. In the Fifth Report it was urged that cost plus contracts should not be made except in minor cases of extreme urgency.

13. The Select Committee condemned the cost plus form of contract because it could be justified only on grounds of speed and did not in fact achieve speed; and they thought it should be used only when it was essential

---

[1] Fourth Report of the Select Committee on National Expenditure, Session 1940–41.

to begin and complete a work in a matter of days. At all other times they favoured the use of fixed price contracts.

On the question of fixed price contracts the Treasury's comment was that the essence of its virtue seemed to inhere in confidence that the fixed price was a good price—that is, only likely to produce for the contractor a reasonable profit, but not more than a reasonable profit, if he executed the contract with due care and diligence. It was the difficulty of feeling that confidence (a difficulty felt sometimes by the department and sometimes by the contractor) which had led to the development of the several intermediate types of contract with varying emphasis of control as between cost and profit. While agreeing that the use of the cost plus contract should be strictly limited, a serious restriction to works of very short duration was impracticable.[1] There must inevitably be a considerable volume of contracting, particularly as regards repairs, and new construction of exceptional urgency[2] where payment on the basis of cost could not be avoided. Further, the uncertainties of war-time production and the novelty of war-time work to many contractors were serious disturbing factors which would lead in practice to a slower approach to a job and a more limited achievement under a fixed price contract. The intermediate types of contract, though more flexible, involved the disadvantage of flexibility; but they had the advantage of enabling agreement with the contractor to be more readily reached.

14. That during the rearmament period and for the first year of war the use of cost plus contracts had been more widespread than could be justified in principle cannot be denied. War Office experience of the militia camps had been unfortunate, and could be justified only by the extreme urgency of the circumstances which called the camps into being. The difference between the original estimates and he final cost, if not as great as the Select Committee suggested, was very considerable.[3] After allowing for such factors as exceptionally bad weather, overtime, increase in wage rates and price of materials, the erection of additional buildings of which the requirements were not known at the outset, and so forth, the War Office still had reason to feel compunction. The example of other Government departments which used cost plus contracts was quoted in vindication, but the War Office agreed that for the future cost plus was best avoided.

---

[1] The War Office in its comments on the report points out that no works contracts of any significance could be completed 'within a matter of days'.

[2] e.g. emergency repairs, etc., due to enemy action.

[3] The Select Committee concluded that the cost at the five camps which might be taken as typical examples varied from about two and a half times to nearly five times the estimate. The War Office replied that the original estimate for 35,000 militia was some £5¼ millions; but in fact 50,000 militia had to be accommodated in camps in 1939 and the corresponding estimate for this number was £7½ millions. The actual final cost of the militia camps was about £16 millions.

NOTE VI

The Central Priority Organisation

1. In the inter-war period the needs of the armed forces could be met without much central priority administration. The Government organisation consisted of the Supply Board, and the Board of Trade Supply Organisation.

2. The Supply Board derived its authority from the Committee of Imperial Defence and its functions were to find and allocate capacity for the war use of Service departments and to furnish estimates of the war demands of raw materials and labour to the Board of Trade and the Ministry of Labour. The Board worked through a number of Supply Committees concerned with various end products.

3. The Board of Trade Supply Organisation was responsible for making plans for the necessary war supplies of materials for public and private needs.

4. So long as capacity, labour and materials were in free supply, these arrangements worked satisfactorily and such clashes of interest as did arise were dealt with on the Supply Committees of the Supply Board; but the work of the Supply Committees was regarded primarily as preparation for war, and other arrangements had to be made to deal with the more numerous problems arising from expansion of the armament programme. After the Munich crisis the Cabinet had approved the following organisation:

(a) A Ministerial Priority Committee under the chairmanship of a Cabinet Minister without Portfolio and having as members Ministers of the Service and Supply departments, the President of the Board of Trade, and the Minister of Labour. The functions of this committee were 'to lay down the general principles of priority as between conflicting demands for manpower, raw materials, manufacturing capacity, transport services, etc., and to determine particular questions submitted to it'. It was planned that the committee should work largely through

(b) Priority Sub-Committees dealing with materials, labour, building, production, and any other subjects as was found to be necessary, the members being nominated by the departments interested.

5. The Ministerial Priority Committee was replaced as from 22nd May 1940 by the Production Council, which in turn was superseded by the Production Executive as from 30th December 1940. The Minister of Production assumed the functions of the Production Executive in February 1942.

Of the original Priority Sub-Committees, the Materials Committee alone survived the march of events.

For a time it met in joint session with the Production Committee; then the functions of allocating productive capacity and determining priority of

476

production were transferred to other committees. The Labour and Building Priority Committees drew their chairmen and secretariats from the Ministry of Labour and the Ministry of Works, and their functions were eventually absorbed into those Ministries.

The Central Priority Department was out-posted in the Ministry of Supply till the spring of 1941, when its accommodation was blitzed, and was then assigned to the War Cabinet secretariat (under the ægis of the Production Executive) and together with the secretariat of the Industrial Capacity Committee (then responsible, among other things, for the regional organisation) formed the nucleus of the Ministry of Production staff.

Principal Priority Officers and their departments became firmly established and played an increasingly important part in the work of solving problems both internal and inter-departmental.

The Priority of Work Order was never put into effect and no priority certificates as envisaged by that Order were ever issued. Except for Priority of Production Directions issued before and after Dunkirk and subsequently amended, the guiding principle became, in general, one of allocation, affecting materials, labour, machine tools, manufacturing capacity, building (largely labour and materials). In regard to materials, it proved possible to operate throughout on an allocation system; in regard to labour, particularly during the critical months of the build-up before D-Day, it was necessary to have within an allocation system a system of preference for the supply of manpower for designated products or services.

'It would be far from the truth to say that as from the end of 1942 there were no priority problems. They occurred in large numbers everywhere. They were settled by arbitration and agreement in the workshops, through Regional Board machinery, in London by discussion within departments and between departments, and, where necessary, by reference to the chairman of the Central Priority Committee. By and large, priority directions and priority certificates ceased to have significance, and conflicts were resolved by agreement on marginal changes to existing arrangements.

'Side by side with the diminishing emphasis on the value of "priority" in the sense in which it has been used above, there developed an entirely different type of "priority" problem relating to supply of labour. In circumstances in which the availabilities of buildings, plant and machine tools and materials were broadly satisfactory there arose, to an increasing degree, a need to secure a supply of labour sufficient to safeguard the production of vital requirements and essential services. Special action was required both to maintain the labour force engaged on vital work, i.e. by protecting labour from withdrawal or by replacing wastage, and in the case of expanding programmes to increase the labour force. The Ministry of Production and the Ministry of Labour, in collaboration with the other departments concerned, developed machinery for deciding at various levels from labour exchanges and regional offices up to Ministerial quarters the preference which should be accorded to the supply of labour for specified work.'

6. The Production and Materials Committees were merged into one Committee at the beginning of the war. This Committee shed its production functions in January 1941, and became simply the Materials Committee, with the following functions:

(1) To keep under review supply and requirements of materials in, or likely to be in, short supply.

(2) To determine allocations of materials where necessary.

(3) To consider any other questions referred to it on materials.

NOTE VII

Types of Brick

1. Although the term 'brick' is usually applied to material of burnt clay, its use is not restricted to this meaning (e.g. concrete brick, sand-lime brick, etc.). From the most ancient times burnt bricks have been in common use, but it was the Romans who established brick as a major material for construction.[1] So long as the Romans occupied Britain the art of brickmaking flourished, but on their withdrawal brickwork and masonry construction languished. The Saxons fell back on materials that lay to hand, like timber and thatch, and the Normans introduced from France excellent masonry, chiefly in stone. There was a revival of brickmaking in England in the thirteenth century, and considerable development in its use in the fifteenth century, but only for important edifices. During the reign of Henry VIII brickmaking was brought to high perfection, but it was the great Fire of London in 1666 that gave the greatest impetus to brick-building, and London was largely rebuilt of brick. From then on brick became the staple building material throughout the country, except for some special edifices or in those districts where good brick earth was not readily procurable.

2. The normal classification of clay bricks, recognised in the building industry, into the three broad classes of common, engineering and facing is primarily a division according to use, but by its very breadth this classification tends to conceal differences of considerable importance to the user.[2]

3. *Common bricks* are those which are serviceable for ordinary building construction and may be used either within the structure or, where a good finish is not required, as the exterior facing. Common bricks are made from a great variety of clays and by all the different processes used in the brickmaking industry. In many kinds, where the raw materials are worked primarily for common bricks, no particular care is exercised to ensure freedom from surface flaws and blemishes since the purchaser does not call for it. In other kinds the main object is to manufacture engineering or facing bricks, and any that do not conform with these requirements are sold as common. Common bricks therefore differ widely in quality; some possess high weather resistance and can be used satisfactorily under the severest conditions of exposure, while others have a lower weather resistance and can be relied upon to give satisfaction only in positions where the conditions of exposure are less severe.

4. *Engineering bricks* are those characterised by high compressive strength, low moisture absorption and high durability. They are used primarily

---

[1] For the history and place of bricks in building see *Building Research Special Report No. 20: Economic and Manufacturing Aspects of the Building Brick Industries* (H.M.S.O., 1933).

[2] The definitions of types of brick follow the description given in *Third Report of the Committee one the Brick Industry, Appendix II* (H.M.S.O., 1943). Notes on the properties of the bricks, particularly in relation to war-time uses, are given in *Building Research War-Time Bulletin No. 20* (H.M.S.O., 1942).

where the brickwork is designed to carry heavy loads or to resist severe conditions of exposure, as in tunnels and retaining walls, or where an impervious material is required, as in sewers and sewage works. Engineering bricks can be manufactured only from a limited number of the clays used for making common bricks.

5. *Facing bricks* are those manufactured or selected specifically to perform a decorative function. The greater proportion of facing bricks are manufactured in the same way as common bricks except that certain precautions are taken to avoid flaws and blemishes on the faces, while a minority are treated in the green state, e.g. by sand-blasting or rusticating, to give texture to the exposed face. A great variety of colours is obtained. Facing bricks vary in quality in a manner similar to common bricks, and provided that such special colours are not sought as can only be obtained at the expense of durability, they are, as a class, more durable.

6. In addition to these classes of clay bricks, two other types of bricks —*sand-lime bricks and concrete bricks*—should be distinguished.

Sand-lime bricks are covered by a British standard specification which sub-divided them into classes suitable for conditions of use of varying severity.[1] Their manufacture consists eventually in thoroughly mixing a suitable sand into five to ten per cent. of lime, moulding in a machine of the dry-press type, and hardening by exposure to high-pressure steam in autoclaves. The lime reacts in the autoclaves with the surfaces of the sand grains to form hydrated calcium silicates. The process is one that lends itself to a high degree of mechanisation.[2] The sand-lime process is technically distinct from all the processes followed in the manufacture of clay bricks. It is a comparatively recent development, and this gives to the part of the industry that operates it an initial advantage over the old-established sections of the clay-brick industry, particularly in respect of plant lay-out, mechanical haulage and conveyor systems. Although the relative simplicity of the process and the absence of kiln-firing are contributory factors, the fact that it has already secured a small but established place in the brick production of the country can be regarded as evidence of efficient working.

7. For external use in normal building the strength of a brick is generally of less importance than its durability, nor does strength by any means give an accurate measure of durability. It is only in certain classes of engineering and structural work that a high strength becomes as important as the durability. While the strength of a brick can be measured, no single measurable property of a brick can be used as a direct index of durability. To form an approximate estimate of the relative durability of different bricks one must rely on a complex of properties and consider them together.

8. Broadly, however, the main condition of decay of building bricks is the presence of water, and the assessment of the severity of the exposure to

---

[1] There is no similar specification for concrete bricks, which are generally sold for the same purposes as clay common bricks.

[2] For a detailed description of the process see *Building Research Special Report No. 21* (H.M.S.O., 1934).

which a brick may be subjected must therefore be related to the extent to which it will become liable to be saturated, for short or long periods. The great majority of common bricks possess a satisfactory durability under their normal conditions of use, but many common bricks, and a moderate proportion of facing bricks, cannot withstand more rigorous conditions. For severe exposure only a minority of common bricks, the majority of facing bricks, and practically all engineering bricks are usually found suitable.

Clay bricks cannot be used indiscriminately for all conditions and situations. It is necessary to consider the suitability of a particular product for the particular set of conditions prevailing, and it is from an inadequate appreciation of this that difficulties arise.

9. The main methods of testing clay or shale bricks are discussed in the third report of the Simmonds Committee.[1] These tests comprise sampling, compressive strength tests, water absorption tests and calculation of saturation coefficient, and tests for afflorescence.

---

[1] Appendix IV of the committee's report.

2H

NOTE VIII

Types of Cement[1]

1. The term 'cement' is used in the industry to cover a wide variety of materials. The types of cement mainly used in the building and civil engineering industries are Portland cement in its various forms, Portland blast furnace cement, and high alumina (or aluminous) cement.

Portland cement is made essentially from a calcareous material such as limestone or chalk and siliceous material such as clay or shale, or other materials such as marl or 'cement rock' containing both main groups of constituents. The ground and proportional raw materials are burnt at a temperature of 1,300–1,500 degrees Centigrade in large rotary kilns with pulverised coal, oil or natural gas as fuel. At this maximum temperature only some twenty to thirty per cent. of the mix becomes liquid and this causes the material to form nodules or balls known as Portland cement clinker. The latter is ground, with a small addition of gypsum to control the setting time, to a fine powder which forms the commercial product.

British Portland blast furnace cement, as well as the German Eisen Portland and Hochofen cements, are made from granulated blast furnace slags. Slag for use in the slag-containing cements is normally water granulated, dried and then ground into the Portland cement clinker. Air granulation has also been used in order to reduce the costs of drying, but it tends to produce a less active material, since the cementitious properties of slag are dependent upon obtaining the material in a glassy not a crystalline condition.

Aluminous cement is manufactured from bauxite and chalk or limestone. These are proportioned, ground and briquetted, and in modern practice usually burnt with pulverised coal fuel in open-hearth reverberatory furnaces, though electric furnaces are to be found where the circumstances are favourable. Rotary kiln burning is also used. The charge is completely fused and tapped continuously or intermittently into moulds of a size suited to the rate of cooling required. The product is ground to fine powder without any additions.

2. Portland cements of a number of different types are manufactured, notably normal, rapid-hardening, low-heat, sulphate-resistant, and white cements. The normal cement is a material which takes its initial set and ceases to be plastic within from one to a few hours after mixing with water. This setting time of a cement is measured in an arbitrary, but standardised manner. For testing purposes it is divided into an initial and final setting time, these representing in effect successive points on a time-stiffness curve. A clear differentiation has to be made between setting time and rate of hardening, or gain of strength, since the two are not related. Rapid-hardening Portland cement has a similar setting time to the normal variety,

---

[1] The information contained in this Note is for the most part based on a lecture (19th December 1944) on 'Cement and Concrete' by Dr. F. M. Lea, of the Royal Institute of Chemistry of Great Britain and Ireland.

but the subsequent gain in strength is more rapid. Low-heat and sulphate-resistant Portland cements are characterised respectively by a low heat of hydration and an increased resistance to attack by chemical agents, in particular solutions containing sulphates.

3. High-alumina cement is a material with a setting time comparable with that of Portland cements, but it gains strength very rapidly, and in addition has an outstanding resistance to attack by many chemical agents including sulphate solutions.

4. An important requirement for all cements is that of soundness, i.e. that the material shall not expand after setting and so disrupt a mortar or concrete of which it is the bonding agent. Two causes of unsoundness in Portland cement are excessive contents of uncombined calcium oxide or magnesia, both of which hydrate only slowly when in a dead-burnt condition, and expand on hydration. Another cause is an excessive addition of gypsum to Portland cement. Soundness is covered by a standard test to be found in the British Standard specification.

5. The use of aluminous cement was of great importance in certain special directions, and its use was restricted to work of national importance, including chemical resistance and refractory work for which there was no substitute.

Forms and Symbols used by Building Programmes Directorate

The nature of the works falling to the various departments is shown in Appendix 9. To enable the Building Programmes Directorate to prepare labour charts and forecasts for the programme of each department forms were devised when the allocation system was first introduced. With some modifications these forms were used throughout the war period. They were:

Form B.P.1. For advance notification by departments of all works over £5,000.

Form B.P.2. For providing more complete and accurate information by departments about the projects when the works were ready to commence.

Two forms of returns were devised at the same time and were also continued throughout the war period. They were:

Form W.B.1. A monthly return from every Government job over £5,000 in value, giving particulars of the labour employed, materials used and progress made on the last pay-day of each month.

Form W.B.S. A monthly summary prepared by each department showing the total labour employed by the department, including that on works below £5,000 in value.

In addition, by agreement with the Ministry of Labour and the Service and Supply departments, a weekly return was made on *Form E.D.622* of the position of every Service and Supply and Ministry of Works contract over £5,000. Initiated in April 1943, E.D.622 gave to the Ministry of Labour and to the chief and regional allocation officers of the Ministry of Works up-to-date information on the numbers of men employed on each of the important contracts, together with the number of additional men required and the number of men likely to be released in the following week. With this information it was possible to plan in advance the transfers of labour from one job to another, either locally or inter-regionally, with the minimum of delay and so to use the available labour to the best advantage.

Priority symbols, already in use when the Ministry of Works was set up, were continued throughout the war period. W.B.A. signified that the work was essential and urgent. During the Directorates period the additional symbols W.B.B. and W.B.Z. were used: W.B.B. for essential works not of the greatest urgency which could proceed in a relatively slow manner, with the use of local labour; W.B.Z. for jobs which after consideration could be postponed until labour was set free from the more urgent works. Both symbols were dropped when ceiling allocations were adopted in January 1943.

In the first allocation period the term 'super-priority' was at first used for a limited number of jobs to denote exceptional urgency. Later the term was changed to 'super-preference', which could only be accorded by the Minister of Works, on behalf of the War Cabinet, though the departments were encouraged to establish their own system of internal preference.

NOTE X

Committee organisation in the Ministry of Works 1940–45

1. The committee organisation of the Ministry of Works, from its creation in 1940 to the end of the war, was complicated, and was readjusted by each of the three Ministers (Lord Reith, Lord Portal, and Mr. Duncan Sandys) who were successively in office during the war years. The Works and Buildings Priority Committee[1] continued into 1942. Apart from this a network of councils and committees was set up within the new Ministry, of which the most important have been described in the text of this volume. The following list is mainly of councils and committees on which the building and civil engineering industries, and professional bodies, were represented:

The Central Council for Works and Building (including Committee on the Placing and Management of Building Contracts).

The Building Apprenticeship and Training Council (committees: 1. Consultative; 2. Education; 3. Registration; 4. Welfare).

The National Consultative Council for the Building and Civil Engineering Industries (formerly the Advisory Council of the Building and Civil Engineering Industries). Of this body the two main committees were: 1. The Building and Civil Engineering Joint Committee (formerly the Building Programme Joint Committee). 2. The Advisory Panel on Registration of Builders and Civil Engineering Contractors for (a) England and Wales; (b) Scotland.

Joint Advisory Panel for Scotland on the Building and Civil Engineering Industries.

Payment by Results Advisory Panel for England and Wales; and Sub-Committee for Scotland.

National Brick Advisory Council and Sub-Committees.

Codes of Practice Committee.

Standards Committee (Design Section, Materials Section, etc.).

War-Time Building Materials Standardisation Committee (and Canteen Equipment Sub-Committee).

Prefabricated Hut Design Committee.

Building Materials Co-ordinating Committee (Sub-Committee on (a) Supplies; (b) Price Control).

Scientific Advisory Committee.

Central Progress Committee on Bomb Damage Repairs.

Advisory Committee of Specialists and Sub-Contractors in the Building Industries (and Industrial Sub-Committee).

---

[1] See Note III, 'Interdepartmental Committees for the Supervision of the Building Programme, 1937–40'.

NOTE XI

The 'Garrison' Labour Force

1. Maintenance work not only absorbed a considerable volume of labour and materials but, because it was for long ill-defined and necessarily static, it also tended to complicate the labour supply position in many areas. The introduction of the allocation system in 1941 was the occasion for taking action to define and control so-called 'garrison' labour.

2. The method of control was to earmark the balance of the building labour not otherwise allocated ('garrison' labour), and to apportion it between the various regions so as to ensure that there was adequate labour for essential work—no more and no less. The control was needed, for as the Ministry of Works reduced the labour force as a whole, the margin to cover errors of estimating was also reduced; and the difficulties of regional and local distribution were increased. The garrison scheme, while serving to a large extent to earmark individual workers, gave maximum fluidity and mobility within very wide areas. The total garrison force was distributed over the whole country. For purely rural areas there were no special arrangements.

3. In submitting new allocations to the Production Executive in October 1941, the Minister of Works (Lord Reith) included for maintenance generally the figure 253,000 and defined its incidence as covering Government and local authority buildings, roads and services; first-aid repairs; salvage and demolition; public utilities; statutory companies; and private property. There was also 7,500 for private (civil licence) building, giving a total of 261,000 not covered by allocation to any department. In subsequent submissions to the Production Executive, Lord Reith made it clear that the garrison labour scheme, now approved in principle by the Ministers of Health and Home Security, comprised two sections:

Section A. Men scheduled in the employ of contractors and builders with definite contracts for local authorities, public utilities and Government departments. The contractors were settled by the departments concerned, and they sent lists of employees. The firms and men were then scheduled under the Essential (Building and Civil Engineering) Order 1942.

Section B. This comprised the balance of labour available for all work of garrison type. Such men were transferable between contractors in the area. Normally the transfer was through labour exchanges, but in each region the Works and Buildings Emergency Organisations directed the placing of labour where the normal labour exchange system was unable to do so.

4. These proposals were approved in principle by the Production Executive on 23rd December 1941. At that meeting a memorandum submitted by the Minister of War Transport asked for an assurance that the maintenance personnel in the employ of port authorities, railways and highways

authorities were not included in the proposals; and the Minister of Works explained that these dealt only with contractors' labour and not with permanent maintenance men employed by Government departments, local authorities, and public utility authorities.

5. The garrison labour scheme was unwelcome to the employers' federations, and their objections were set out in correspondence with the Ministry of Works. They contended that while the scheme sought to ensure that only a minimum of labour should be employed upon garrison work, it was in fact intended that there should always be an over-sufficiency of men in that category. That end, it was argued, would be attained by the following means:

(1) By the hoarding of labour.

(2) By setting up a one-way flow of labour (that is, non-garrison labour to garrison work, but not *vice versa*).

(3) By providing for guarantee payments to garrison labour, whether working or idle.

(4) By frequently obliging labour within the various small garrison areas to be idle and immobile.

It was urged, in brief, that the scheme approached the problems from the wrong end and that, far from arbitrarily fixed numbers of men being hoarded and immobilised in small garrison areas, no effort should be spared to make all men—including in particular the large numbers then in the direct employ of local authorities, public utility undertakings, etc.—mobile and available for any work within much larger and wider regions, and if necessary interchangeable between regions.

6. In meeting their criticisms, the fundamental points in the position taken up by the Ministry of Works were:

(1) The scheme earmarked elderly immobile labour—that is, men over military age.

(2) It was an allocation by regions and sub-regions, with full fluidity within the regions and full powers to secure fluidity over the regional boundary.

(3) No one outside the scheme was allowed to do garrison work; and there was no inflow unless there was an equivalent outflow, since the inflow was completely controlled.

(4) The Ministry of Works undertook the responsibility of seeing that the men were used, and any men not required for garrison work could be transferred temporarily to W.B.A. work.

(5) Although it was admitted that the volume of work varied, it was the intention of the Ministry of Works to reduce the garrison to a minimum. Since, in the difficult circumstances, the garrison labour could not be varied, it would always have to work to a minimum, but that minimum had to be adequate.

APPENDIX I

Activity and Capacity of the Building and Civil Engineering Industry in Great Britain (1932–45)

Year	Numbers of males insured at July (ages 16–64) ('000)	Numbers of unemployed January ('000)	Numbers of unemployed July ('000)	Cement output ('000 tons)	Bricks output (mns)	Average wage rates in 39 large towns (pence per hour) Craftsmen	Average wage rates in 39 large towns (pence per hour) Labourers	Average weekly earnings at July (s. d.)	Value of gross output (£ mn)
	(1)	(2)	(3)	(4)	(5)	(6)	(7)	(8)	(9)
1932	1,112	374	342	4,250	Not known	18·1	13·5	...	303
1933	1,125	446	293	4,400	7,300(b)	17·6	13·2	...	312
1934	1,162	355	265	5,200	7,310	17·6	13·3	...	332
1935	1,214	357	255	5,829	Not known	18·1	13·6	...	345
1936	1,267	406	228	6,661	7,300(a)	18·6	14·0	...	389
1937	1,287	294	212	7,245	7,320	19·1	14·3	...	421
1938	1,336	306	245	7,715	6,900(a)	19·7	14·8	66·0(d)	455
1939	1,362	370	212	8,212	Not known	20·2(c)	15·3(c)	...	442
1940	1,023	355	93	7,219	4,614	21·7	16·7	84·11	425
1941	919	70	21	7,097	2,982	22·7	17·8	97·1	470
1942	763	24	21	7,455	1,937	22·9	18·2	102·0	425
1943	592	15	12	7,002	1,426	23·9	18·9	108·4	350
1944	496	10	8	4,554	1,154(e)	24·2	19·1	107·11	290(h)
1945	572	8	6	3,648(e)		25·0(f)	20·0(f)	108·0(g)	..

NOTES: (a) Sales.
(b) Great Britain and Northern Ireland (output for sale).
(c) Wage rates for 1932–39 relate to 31st December of each year. Thereafter they represent the average for the year. The rates at August 1939 are the same as shown for December 1938.

(d) October 1938.
(e) Annual rate of the first six months.
(f) Average for first six months.
(g) Estimated.
(h) Provisional.

Sources: Ministry of Labour
Census of Production
Ministry of Works

Statistical Bulletin, October–November 1945

APPENDIX II

SCHEDULE A

Department

Particulars of Contracts of £10,000 and Over
(£5,000 and over in the case of the Office of Works)

Area, County or Town	Nature of Contract	Government department for which work is to be undertaken	Commencement	Completion	Total estimated cost	1937	1938	1939	Year	Carpenters	Bricklayers	Masons	Slaters and Tilers	Plasterers	Painters	Plumbers	All other workers except Navvies and Labourers	Navvies and Labourers	Total
			Actual or anticipated date of			Estimated works expenditure in				Estimated average number of workpeople required in the undermentioned occupations in 1937 and 1938									
					£	£	£	£	1937										
									1938										
									1937										
									1938										
County									1937										
Town									1938										
									1937										
									1938										

APPENDIX II *contd.*

SCHEDULE B

Particulars of Contracts Under £10,000
(Under £5,000 in the case of the Office of Works)

Department

Ministry of Labour Division (or other area as defined)	Total estimated cost £	Estimated works expenditure in 1937 £	1938 £	1939 £	Year	Carpenters	Bricklayers	Masons	Slaters and Tilers	Plasterers	Painters	Plumbers	All other workers except Labourers	Labourers	Total
					1937										
					1938										
					1937										
					1938										
					1937										
					1938										
					1937										
					1938										

Estimated average number of workpeople required in the undermentioned occupations in 1937 and 1938

APPENDIX III

Ministry of Labour

ADMINISTRATIVE AREAS

Division	*Area of Division*
London	Administrative County and City of London, and the County of Middlesex, and the areas in Essex, Kent and Surrey covered by the Employment Exchanges and Branch Offices at:— Barking, Bexleyheath, Bromley, Buckhurst Hill, Canning Town, Caterham Valley, Croydon, Dagenham, Dartford, East Ham, Epping, Epsom, Erith, Grays, Ilford, Kingston-on-Thames, Leyton and Walthamstow, Orpington, Penge, Redhill, Richmond, Sidcup, Stratford, Sutton, The Dittons, Tilbury, Westerham, Wimbledon.
South-Eastern	The Counties of Bedford, Bucks, Cambridge, Herts, Norfolk, Suffolk and Sussex, and the areas of Essex, Kent and Surrey not covered by the London Division.
South-Western	The Counties of Berks, Cornwall, Devon, Dorset, Gloucester, Hants, Oxford, Somerset and Wilts.
Midland	The Counties of Derby (except the Glossop and New Mills Districts), Hereford, Huntingdon, Leicester, Northampton, Nottingham, Rutland, Salop, Stafford, Warwick, Worcester, the Soke of Peterborough, and the Stamford District of Lincolnshire.
North-Eastern	The Counties of Lincoln (except the Stamford District) and Yorks (except the Cleveland District).
North-Western	The Counties of Cheshire, Lancs, and the New Mills and Glossop Districts of Derbyshire.
Northern	Cumberland, Durham, Northumberland (except Berwick), Westmorland and the Cleveland District of Yorks.
Scotland	Scotland and the Berwick District.
Wales	Wales and Monmouthshire.

APPENDIX IV

Summary by Departments of Estimated Expenditure on Building Works by Government Departments in the Four Quarters Ending 30th September 1940

Department	Total cost £	Estimated expenditure over the next four quarters:			
		31st Dec. 1939 £	31st March 1940 £	30th June 1940 £	30th Sept. 1940 £
Admiralty	25,048,000	2,437,000	2,584,000	2,373,000	2,257,000
War Office	40,599,000	11,076,000	8,955,000	5,076,000	3,742,000
Air Ministry	70,635,000	9,066,000	8,426,000	5,710,000	3,284,000
Air Ministry (factories and extensions to contractors' works)	22,712,000	7,458,000	5,122,000	5,989,000	4,134,000
H.M. Office of Works	25,595,000	7,180,000	5,117,000	4,668,000	4,670,000
Ministry of Supply	18,820,000	3,095,000	4,325,000	5,272,000	3,605,000
Home Office (Approved Schools and Prisons)	2,286,000	531,000	408,000	291,000	197,000
Home Office (Air Raid Precautions)	57,845,000	28,923,000	28,922,000	—	—
Board of Education	12,868,000	1,788,000	1,601,000	1,601,000	1,457,000
Ministry of Health:					
Ordinary Housing and Hospitals (including structural A.R.P. and first-aid posts)	6,050,000	2,850,000	1,716,000	1,033,000	450,000
Emergency Housing (first-aid and permanent repairs)	17,025,000	3,300,000	8,325,000	2,700,000	2,700,000
Essential Buildings (first-aid and permanent repairs)	8,800,000	1,600,000	4,400,000	1,400,000	1,400,000
Children's Camps	710,000	615,000	4,000	24,000	4,000
Water Supply, Sewage and Public Buildings	15,000,000	4,500,000	4,000,000	3,500,000	3,000,000
Ministry of Agriculture and Fisheries	200,000	49,000	30,000	36,000	20,000
Miners' Welfare Committee	1,011,000	186,000	148,000	140,000	124,000
Scottish Office:					
Department of Health	7,898,000	2,253,000	2,722,000	2,293,000	76,000
Education Department	3,100,000	39,000	197,000	304,000	410,000
Special Areas—Industrial Estate	965,000	91,000	101,000	101,000	62,000
Other departments	552,000	62,000	59,000	34,000	24,000
TOTAL	337,659,000	87,099,000	87,153,000	42,545,000	31,616,000

APPENDIX V

Summary by Counties of Estimated Expenditure on Building
Works by Government Departments in the Four Quarters Ending
30th September 1940

County	Total cost £	Estimated expenditure over the next four quarters			
		31st Dec. 1939 £	31st March 1940 £	30th June 1940 £	30th Sept. 1940 £
ENGLAND					
Bedfordshire .	1,859,982	409,829	328,095	35,595	9,418
Berkshire . .	2,683,048	681,585	470,961	210,961	119,476
Buckinghamshire .	622,315	204,741	156,852	28,352	12,882
Cambridgeshire .	1,587,393	190,964	319,103	428,103	347,823
Cheshire . .	5,194,752	1,661,215	1,254,609	338,609	115,559
Cornwall . .	1,025,204	303,197	177,188	128,588	87,648
Cumberland .	6,013,805	856,729	710,275	1,014,775	674,112
Derbyshire . .	1,772,028	625,659	569,728	45,728	31,613
Devonshire .	5,033,488	1,110,455	1,122,609	450,609	442,551
Dorsetshire .	2,040,681	379,115	201,273	259,273	278,617
Durham . .	4,729,034	1,776,014	1,718,071	362,571	230,250
Essex . .	5,584,199	1,961,209	1,724,115	145,615	78,968
Gloucestershire .	5,352,113	1,328,804	1,204,651	299,651	296,898
Hampshire .	10,568,795	2,102,207	2,011,012	1,177,512	777,393
Herefordshire .	739,226	312,883	131,741	73,741	23,881
Hertfordshire .	1,197,675	340,838	325,280	105,103	51,910
Huntingdonshire .	1,255,050	150,013	90,013	12	12
Kent . . .	6,029,356	1,595,910	1,489,164	389,164	315,733
Lancashire .	15,497,773	6,530,823	6,110,647	632,251	184,670
Leicestershire .	1,306,564	567,169	539,667	25,327	26,071
Lincolnshire .	5,723,214	755,460	872,677	626,177	411,468
London . .	11,489,849	4,817,703	4,772,049	654,579	568,163
Middlesex . .	6,141,836	2,494,228	2,395,690	247,890	169,964
Norfolk . .	4,926,883	776,517	662,122	332,122	249,951
Northamptonshire	957,802	289,641	277,385	125,385	126,479
Northumberland .	2,324,967	796,899	770,382	196,782	143,250
Nottinghamshire .	4,021,424	965,635	925,312	253,659	182,637
Oxfordshire .	1,690,439	301,139	213,154	67,154	66,544
Rutlandshire .	1,192,357	132,485	169,301	183,300	142,157
Shropshire .	4,907,152	1,008,286	856,194	539,194	195,034
Somersetshire .	3,374,728	463,231	433,778	503,778	577,069
Staffordshire .	10,453,312	2,348,334	2,971,743	2,104,743	1,177,895
Suffolk . .	3,187,393	541,328	363,858	23,358	16,537
Surrey . .	4,074,881	1,727,334	1,588,019	114,019	69,497
Sussex . .	1,812,092	441,283	253,248	161,248	124,176
Warwickshire .	4,990,352	1,862,478	1,857,656	403,656	232,561
Westmorland .	5,500	375	375	375	375
Wiltshire . .	6,362,504	1,225,612	1,248,103	1,142,603	827,373
Worcestershire .	2,371,920	549,237	392,844	162,844	111,044
Yorkshire . .	19,930,766	6,072,576	5,511,796	761,196	243,092
WALES					
Anglesey . .	134,940	60,738	70,655	655	591
Brecknockshire .	408,442	201,085	201,067	1,067	1,054
Caernarvonshire .	469,874	46,931	65,671	95,671	95,080
Cardiganshire .	37,169	25,320	10,284	284	255
Carmarthenshire .	476,126	178,982	62,641	32,641	2,375
Denbighshire .	4,266,627	178,284	282,029	609,529	804,330
Flintshire . .	770,258	304,240	183,517	25,517	3,129

County	Total cost £	Estimated expenditure over the next four quarters			
		31st Dec. 1939 £	31st March 1940 £	30th June 1940 £	30th Sept. 1940 £
Glamorgan .	6,046,276	2,266,839	1,101,299	258,949	159,390
Merioneth .	197,323	82,433	92,178	12,178	1,979
Monmouthshire .	3,189,074	1,437,210	527,684	235,484	193,975
Montgomeryshire	6,906	997	876	876	781
Pembrokeshire .	6,292,999	273,010	294,001	1,325,001	1,310,994
Radnorshire .	23,425	3,357	2,941	2,941	2,617
SCOTLAND					
Aberdeenshire .	1,309,660	266,092	301,804	237,976	131,340
Angus . .	2,539,866	431,218	532,820	398,746	270,075
Argyllshire . .	49,908	12,419	19,171	17,632	2,965
Ayrshire . .	1,112,717	308,191	299,219	236,387	30,405
Banff . .	56,950	7,139	12,700	11,570	1,400
Berwickshire .	331,860	82,860	82,420	81,850	77,730
Bute . . .	49,180	5,114	8,895	8,215	1,400
Caithness . .	414,364	83,306	85,100	74,674	560
Clackmannan .	26,600	312	1,200	1,700	2,300
Dumbartonshire .	1,618,789	401,084	506,707	341,110	94,600
Dumfries .	464,200	89,600	135,960	94,544	1,800
East Lothian .	699,265	164,699	160,540	138,884	124,300
Fifeshire . .	2,408,310	313,491	396,535	332,584	217,900
Inverness-shire .	493,177	53,479	90,530	118,725	97,180
Kincardineshire .	91,120	34,562	8,445	7,705	1,900
Kinross-shire .	1,582,025	21,445	32,410	82,170	130,000
Kircudbright .	7,925	1,386	2,135	4,050	3,250
Lanarkshire .	9,817,817	3,252,648	3,361,605	1,304,675	288,787
Midlothian .	2,689,869	828,658	801,780	243,002	119,520
Morayshire .	1,581,855	259,599	262,030	236,715	181,450
Orkneys . .	1,341,830	100,200	160,170	180,560	180,900
Peeblesshire .	74,605	301,162	3,140	3,030	2,110
Perthshire . .	911,795	174,685	189,775	55,295	13,400
Renfrewshire .	5,665,326	1,570,554	1,616,162	1,142,395	445,124
Ross and Cromarty	672,557	98,228	100,363	96,981	91,575
Roxburgh . .	34,608	6,342	9,017	8,026	1,810
Selkirk . .	26,580	3,165	5,852	5,467	2,000
Stirlingshire .	999,297	261,808	374,415	152,006	20,900
Sutherland .	9,580	1,667	2,930	3,050	1,070
West Lothian .	452,017	110,519	118,320	89,036	2,895
Wigtownshire .	168,815	47,334	48,910	20,185	2,650
Zetland . .	37,002	9,165	14,490	13,052	50
Scotland (area not stated) . .	1,206,200	241,200	191,400	71,900	68,700
Unspecified areas in Great Britain .	96,362,400	22,108,300	27,130,200	19,374,300	16,686,800
TOTAL .	337,659,360	87,099,194	87,152,723	42,544,592	31,615,747

APPENDIX VI

Statement by Lord Privy Seal on Ministry of Works and Buildings[1]

The Ministry of Works and Buildings will be responsible for the erection of all new civil works and buildings required by any other Government department. It will take over to begin with the whole organisation of His Majesty's Office of Works, including their present responsibilities for the erection of buildings for other Civil departments and for Service departments, and the work of the Ministry of Supply, including the new buildings section of the Ordnance Factories and the approval of plans of new private factories or extensions of existing private factories, to the cost of which the Ministry of Supply is contributing.

Highly specialised work at present carried out by the Service departments, either by direct labour or through contractors (such as the civil engineering works of the Admiralty; the construction of aerodromes or aerodrome buildings; fortification and defence works); and work overseas will remain with the Service departments.

The responsibility for maintenance and repairs of buildings and equipment in use by the Service departments or the Ministry of Supply will remain with those departments, except in so far as a transfer to the Ministry of Works and Buildings may be mutually agreed to be convenient.

The Ministry of Works and Buildings will be responsible for the licensing of private building, and for determining the priority of proposals for rebuilding buildings damaged by air raids.

The Ministry of Works and Buildings may arrange, by agreement with the Service departments or the Ministry of Aircraft Production, to erect on their behalf new works and buildings not of a highly specialised character, such as stores or depots or houses and buildings of an architectural nature, and for the supervision of contracts for the erection of new private factories or the extension of existing private factories required for war production.

The Production Council will lay down the general order of priority of building work. The Minister will be a member of the Production Council and responsible for the Works and Buildings Priority Committee. He will determine the application of the directions of the Production Council to the priority of particular buildings, subject to appeal, if necessary, to the Council.

The Minister will be empowered to call on all departments retaining responsibility for the erection and maintenance of buildings and works of construction (including departments concerned with work carried out by or on behalf of local authorities or public utility undertakings) to furnish from time to time such information as he may require as to the present and prospective demands of themselves and their contractors for labour and materials, and any points ancillary thereto.

---

[1] H. of C. Deb., 24th October 1940, Vol. 365, Col. 1150.

The Minister will be responsible for such control or central purchase of building materials not at present controlled as may be necessary.

The Minister will take steps to institute research into such questions as the adoption of substitutes for building materials which are in short supply, or the modification of designs and specifications with a view to expedition, and to ensure that the results of past and future research are promptly communicated to all concerned. For this purpose he will make full use of the Building Research organisation of D.S.I.R. He will be empowered to call on departments retaining responsibility for building to satisfy him that they are making full use of the results of research in this connection.

It is clear that the reconstruction of town and country after the war raises great problems and gives a great opportunity. The Minister of Works and Buildings has, therefore, been charged by the Government with the responsibility of consulting the departments and organisations concerned with a view to reporting to the Cabinet the appropriate methods and machinery for dealing with the issues involved.

APPENDIX VII

Tentative Order of Priority for Building and Construction

(It is realised that there may at any time be emergency defence or other such works to be carried out dictated by a change in the military or strategical situation.)

1. First-aid air-raid damage repairs to the military machine, gun emplacements, aerodromes, etc.
2. Clearance of air-raid damage, opening of roads and provision of public services.
3. First-aid air-raid damage repairs to any transport facilities, road, rail, port.
4. First-aid air-raid damage repairs to houses in industrial areas, including camps for re-housing; and repairs to war factories.
5. First-aid air-raid damage repairs to houses capable of quick repair, where they will be inhabited at once.
6. Essential maintenance and running repairs of services, transport, mines, etc.
7. Dispersal of war (particularly aircraft) factories, and any special protection of vital factories.
8. Protection of vital works against air attack, e.g., protection of oil tanks, dividing walls in machine shops, blast walls in power stations, duplication of water supplies, etc.
9. Aerodrome dispersals in stages (it is obvious all of these cannot be carried out at once).
10. Defence works (other than emergency defence works).
11. War factory extensions, or new war factories *capable of being brought into effective use in four months* (and for which the plant, machine tools, raw materials and components definitely are or will be available in time).
12. Extension of works producing materials for war factories, e.g., alloy and steel casting shops, etc., if capable of operating within six months.
13. W.B.A. jobs capable of being completed in four months.
14. Extensions of works to increase essential building materials, provided they can be effective in six months.
15. A.R.P. schemes for the larger and more vulnerable cities (total materials and labour for A.R.P. being limited to a maximum use of twenty per cent. of available labour and materials).
16. Air raid damage repair of non-war factories. (If the damage or demand for materials is not very great, such repairs should and could often be accelerated even if ranking low in the priority list.)
17. Army camps (in stages).
18. Storage, for such as ordnance stores, food.
19. All other existing W.B.A. jobs well in hand (but to be graded by departments in definite priorities).

20. Non-W.B.A. jobs in advanced stages of construction.

21. General industrial repairs and maintenance of an unavoidable nature.

All other works should be stopped unless there is some very special reason to the contrary, and no licences be given for any civil works unless of vital national importance.

N.B.: The term W.B.A. is used to refer to the Works and Buildings Priority Committee grading of first or 'A' priority. But after the adoption of some such priority as indicated above, the use of the symbol W.B.A. would be discontinued. The labour and material statistics which are now being established will assist in the closer direction of construction than has hitherto been possible; and works on the waiting list will be brought into activity as the position permits.

APPENDIX VIII

Lord Reith's Interim Report on Departments' Proposals for Curtailment

1. P.E.(41) 25th Meeting:—

All departments concerned to examine their building programmes with a view to the drastic curtailment of any projects which, however important in themselves, could be dispensed with. Lists of the works to be abandoned or curtailed should be submitted to the Works and Buildings Committee, where they could be co-ordinated and a report subsequently made to the Production Executive for incorporation in the reply to the Prime Minister.

2. We arranged for departments to submit their views, and a meeting of the Works and Buildings Committee yesterday considered them.

3. Departments' reports and proposals attached. They and this report are interim. An immense programme with such ramifications needs more scrutiny.

4. Since P.E.'s direction, a more detailed investigation was ordered by Lord President on factories. The detailed survey precedent to new six months allocations was also in hand.

5. Departments' proposals are mostly directed to curtailment of works not started.

6. Value of work stopped is about £2,500,000. Value of programmes curtailed at least £12,500,000. This means ultimately about 40,000 persons less in new allocations.

7. On the other hand, there are demands for increases of allocation amounting to more than that. It is unlikely that these will be accepted except such as arise from new policy decisions.

8. In addition to departments' proposals, a complete re-survey is in hand of programmes existing and proposed, on which new allocations will be based, and we will ask departments to reconsider certain works.

9. At the same time, as soon as we know the balance of building labour employed by commercial undertakings, local authorities, statutory companies, etc., we will consider with Ministry of Labour possibilities of reduction.

10. As to restriction of private work, a new draft Defence Regulation is to be circulated to Home Policy Committee, designed drastically to curtail demolition, repair, maintenance and interior decoration.

11. Discussions in progress on possibility of reducing standards. Report later.

APPENDIX VIII

SUMMARY OF DEPARTMENTS' PROPOSALS FOR CURTAILMENT OF PROGRAMMES

AIR MINISTRY

No curtailment possible.

The work in hand has the Prime Minister's approval.

There are approximately 120 further aerodrome stations, together with ancillary establishments still to be built.

WAR OFFICE

A reduction of the War Office Building Programme is being made through the curtailment of accommodation for troops. Works to the value of £10,000,000 have been cancelled.

The modified programme comprises:—
(a) Fixed Coast Defence Batteries.
(b) A.A. Batteries.
(c) Depots and workshops.
(d) Provision of essential accommodation.

MINISTRY OF AIRCRAFT PRODUCTION

It is impossible to abandon or curtail any building work now in progress without disastrous effects on the production programme and on the efforts now being made to meet the Prime Minister's own requirements as to the size and fighting power of the Air Force.

ADMIRALTY

The programme has been carefully scrutinised, no curtailment is possible except of a very minor character.

MINISTRY OF SUPPLY

The Engineering group of Ordnance factories is practically completed. Agency factories will be completed by the end of the year.

The present factory programme cannot be curtailed, factories for explosives and tanks are essential.

One proposed ordnance factory has been cancelled.

It is proposed to suspend certain filling factories in order that labour can be diverted to others to obtain early completion. They will not require an increased labour allocation.

MINISTRY OF WORKS AND BUILDINGS

Direct Programme

Curtailment of temporary office buildings.

Programme reduced from eleven schemes of twelve units to five schemes of six units.

Curtailment to the value of £400,000.

MINISTRY OF HEALTH

Hospital Programme

It is not possible to curtail this programme.

Water Schemes

Works abandoned value	£209,600
Works curtailed, value of curtailment	£313,500

Works under consideration for abandonment or curtailment,
value £161,000
Further curtailment possible if departments' programmes are reduced.

MINISTRY OF WAR TRANSPORT

Ports and Harbours

The Inland Sorting Depots are included in this programme.
No curtailment of any works is possible.

Railways

Minor curtailment may be effected if factories requiring railway services
are abandoned.

Highways

Certain major schemes are being curtailed or closed down.
No new schemes of road improvements are being approved unless they
relate to work of pressing necessity or on account of war requirements.
Highway works are less than contemplated in the programme.

Canals

A very small programme.
Two works are being abandoned value £16,000, but it is suggested that
additional wharves and jetties may be required in connection with the
food stores for Ministry of Food.

MINISTRY OF HOME SECURITY

A.R.P. shelter scheme, no curtailment possible.
Propose to press strongly for at least the renewal of present allocation.

HOME OFFICE

Static Water Schemes

Not possible to revise programme for which an allocation of 23,000 men
is asked. Further accommodation at stations will be required for the new
National Fire Services. Approximate value £1,000,000.

Approved Schools

Programme cannot be curtailed. Number of juveniles waiting admission to approved schools is rapidly increasing.

Police Buildings

Unable to curtail programme but are prepared to consider reduction of
labour allocation from 1,110 men to 900 men.

BOARD OF EDUCATION

Will attempt to make a reduction in the amount of A.R.P. provision.
Building programme not likely to exceed £30,000 to £40,000 value per
month.

MINISTRY OF LABOUR AND NATIONAL SERVICE

Headquarters Offices

No building projects are contemplated.

Regional and Local Offices

Building programme suspended.

Training Department

Minor adaptations only.
It is not anticipated that there will be additional works being brought
forward in the near future.

PETROLEUM DEPARTMENT

No curtailment appears possible.

It is claimed that the completion of schemes, particularly installation of main pipe lines, will result in reduction in both rail and road transport and that no operational labour is required in connection with works carried out by Petroleum department, therefore their projects do not come within the category of work covered by the Prime Minister's Minute.

They ask that their programme remains undisturbed.

GENERAL POST OFFICE

Curtailment of their duct and cabling programme is entirely dependent upon departments' requirements. They claim that in agreeing the labour force for their present allocation it was not appreciated that their work cannot be based on an output of £50 per man, and that their allocation should be increased for the next period to 6,000 men. The present one is 4,200 men.

It would appear that any question of curtailment will largely depend on curtailment of Service departments' works.

MINES DEPARTMENT

No works are being put in hand unless they are conducive to a substantial increase in output.

Coke Ovens. Coke ovens are showing signs of wear and tear, a certain amount of maintenance and repairs is visualised.

Canteens. A canteen programme for collieries of £1,300,000 is contemplated during the next period. In view of this latter item it is suggested that an increased allocation of some 500 men will be required.

DEPARTMENT OF HEALTH FOR SCOTLAND

Comprising:

Housing, emergency hospitals, other hospitals, first-aid posts, hostel camps, evacuation camps, water and drainage.

The programme is at present kept to the very minimum and all works carefully scrutinised, and no actual curtailment can be suggested other than stopping work involving sewerage purification.

BOARD OF TRADE

Gas Industry

Curtailment of departments' programmes should result in corresponding curtailment of this programme. No advance programme is made and no actual suggestions can be put forward.

I.C.I. Dyestuffs Expansion Scheme

The programme is under review in consultation with I.C.I. and the Board will advise Works and Buildings Committee as soon as this review is complete.

The Board of Trade will recommend a reduction.

Civil Buildings

In view of the necessity for drastic curtailment of work the Board feel that their revised instructions to Licensing Officers should give them only the most limited discretion to grant applications without reference to the Board of Trade but liberal power to refuse them.

ELECTRICITY COMMISSION

Curtailment of the programme is dependent on departments' programmes. 90,000 k.w. will be curtailed out of 300,000 k.w.—additional capacity required for operation by the autumn of 1943. This curtailment possible through the curtailment of Ministry of Supply work.

It will be possible to carry out their building programme to value rate of £600,000 per month in future. The present value allocation is at the rate of £840,000.

MINISTRY OF INFORMATION

B.B.C.

Overseas Expansion Programme

Not possible to curtail this programme, which is of the highest strategic importance.

The B.B.C. will, however, do everything in their power to exercise economy in detail and some lengthening of the time necessary for the work may be possible.

Broadcasting House

B.B.C. and Minister of Information have agreed reluctantly to postpone the extension of Broadcasting House.

The estimated value of this work is some £350,000.

Work on construction of specially protected accommodation must, however, proceed.

MINISTRY OF AGRICULTURE

Curtailment is not possible. The hostel programme is well advanced and the land drainage schemes are in connection with reclaiming land for agricultural purposes.

MINISTRY OF FOOD

No curtailment possible unless food was left in the ports. The dry stores programme, value £87,000 per month, could be curtailed if this was done.

APPENDIX IX

Maintenance Items

There was no precise definition of maintenance in Defence Regulation 56A, and generally the term was meant to cover such work as was necessary to maintain and preserve the structure of premises. For administrative purposes, maintenance was defined as covering the categories of work listed below:

1. Repairs to brick and stonework, pavings, drains, repairing and re-setting stoves and ranges. Repairing external woodwork, floors and internal woodwork generally, door furniture, fittings and builder's ironmongery, metal casements and ironwork. Repairing or replacing damaged tiles and slates to roofs, flashings, felted roofs, lead, zinc or asphalt flats, gutters, stack pipes, urinals, lavatories and other sanitary fittings, water services and fittings. Repairs to stucco, plaster-work and floors, tiled pavings and wall tiling. Repairs to roof glazing, windows and internal glazing. Repairs to gas, electricity and heating services, passenger and goods lifts and hoists.

2. Painting and redecoration.

3. Cleaning and other utility services, i.e., cleaning and flushing drains, manholes, gutters, etc.

4. The maintenance of privately owned railway track.

ANNUAL MAINTENANCE LICENCES

The granting of an annual maintenance licence comprising day-to-day work of maintenance avoided the need of having to make separate application for minor items of routine day-to-day work arising in commercial and industrial premises. These also included small alteration jobs occurring from day to day and structural alterations consequent on the transfer of existing machinery. In the case of minor decorative operations, they covered distempering, lime washing and colour washing of walls and ceilings in kitchens, bathrooms, lavatories, public waiting rooms and such work as might be required to comply with statutory obligations. (It is important to note that major repairs, other than day-to-day maintenance, did not come within the scale of maintenance work as defined for this purpose.)

APPENDIX X

Statement Giving Particulars of Contracts for Construction of R.O.F.s

Name of factory	Date work commenced	Anticipated date of completion	Approx. value of contract	Value of work done to date	Agents	Contractors	Remarks
FILLING FACTORIES							
2. Bridgend	4 Mar. 1938	February 1941	£3,646,000	£3,612,000	M.O.W.	Sir Lindsay Parkinson / Gee, Walker & Slater / Sir R. McAlpine & Sons / Nutthall & Son	
3. Glascoed	24 Feb. 1938	February 1941	£3,747,000	£3,622,000	M.O.W.	John Morgan, Ltd. / Bovis & Co.	
5. Swynnerton	18 Oct. 1939	March 1941	£7,630,000	£7,270,000	Sir A. Gibb & Partners	Mowlem & Co.	
6. Risley	13 Nov. 1939	March 1941	£8,430,000	£7,230,000	Sir A. Gibb & Partners	Sir Lindsay Parkinson	
7. Kirkby	27 Feb. 1940	March 1941	£5,672,000	£4,852,000	Sir A. Gibb & Partners	Holloway Bros.	
8. Aycliffe	18 May 1940	End July 1941	£3,590,000	£815,000	M.O.W.	Carmichael	
9. Thorp Arch	18 May 1940	End July 1941	£2,935,000	£656,000	M.O.W.	Higgs & Hill	
11. Brackla	26 Feb. 1940	End Dec. 1940	£890,000	£870,000	M.O.W.	Sir R. McAlpine & Sons	
NEW FILLING FACTORIES							
10. Queniborough	8 Nov. 1940	July 1941	£1,500,000	Starting	'55' Group	Holloway Bros.	
12. Swindon		July 1941	£1,500,000	Starting	'55' Group	John Laing & Son	Work should have started, but held up by War Agricultural Committee. Site being surveyed. Original site chosen had to be abandoned.
13. Macclesfield		End July 1941	£2,000,000		'55' Group	Sir Lindsay Parkinson	
14. Ruddington	1 Dec. 1940	End July 1941	£2,000,000	Starting	Sir A. Gibb & Partners	John Mowlem & Co. / Hy. Lovatt & Sons	
15. Walsall	1 Dec. 1940	End May 1941	£600,000	Starting	Sir A. Gibb & Partners	Sir A. McAlpine & Sons / James Crosby & Co.	
16. Elstow	25 Nov. 1940	End Aug. 1941	£1,500,000	£5,000	M.O.W.	E. Nutthall & Sons / Wm. Townson	
17. Featherstone	1 Dec. 1940	End July 1941	£2,000,000	Starting	Sir A. Gibb & Partners	Bovis & Co. / Pauling & Co.	

Name of factory	Date work commenced	Anticipated date of completion	Approx. value of contract	Value of work done to date	Agents	Contractors	Remarks
NEW FILLING FACTORIES (*contd.*)							
18. Burghfield	4 Nov. 1940	End July 1941	£2,000,000	Starting	Joint Engineers	Sir R. McAlpine & Sons	Site being surveyed. Several sites previously chosen had to be abandoned.
19. Tutbury (Derby)		End July 1941	£1,500,000	Nil	M.O.W.	Not settled	
20. Northampton		End July 1941	£1,600,000	Nil	M.O.W.	Not settled	
S.A.A. FILLING FACTORIES							
Southall	12 June 1940	End Feb. 1941	£404,000	£379,000	Joint Engineers	Kent & Sussex Contrs.	
Summerfield	27 Sept. 1940	End May 1941	£759,000	£20,000	Joint Engineers	John Cochrane & Son, Sir John Jackson, Ltd., Ford & Walton	
EXPLOSIVES FACTORIES							
Bishopton 1	11 Oct. 1937	December 1940	£2,800,000	£2,670,000	M.O.W.	Wimpey & Co.	
Bishopton 2	April 1939	April 1941	£1,689,000	£1,344,800	M.O.W.	H. Leggatt, Ltd., Jackson Brown, A. Stuart & Sons, C. Brand & Sons, H. Lovatt & Sons, Demolition & Construction Co.	
Bishopton 3	October 1939	April 1941	£2,684,000	£1,553,000	M.O.W.		
Bridgewater	5 Feb. 1940	End Mar. 1941	£1,567,000	£883,000	M.O.W.		
Drigg	24 Nov. 1939	End Mar. 1941	£1,200,000	£1,000,000	M.O.W.	Construction Co.	
Irvine	2 Dec. 1939	May 1941	£70,000	£5,000	M/S	A. M. McDougall & Co., Sir Wm. Lawrence & Son	
Pembrey	6 July 1938	End Feb. 1941	£1,200,000	£1,100,000	M.O.W.		
Wrexham	4 Nov. 1939	End May 1941	£3,913,000	£2,740,000	M.O.W.	Holborn Construction, Holland & Hannen & Cubitts, Ltd., Pauling & Co.	
RIFLES							
Fazakerley	April 1940	Beg. Mar. 1941	£323,735	£237,105	Handled direct by Woolwich	G. & J. Seddon, Ltd.	
Maltby	May 1940	Beg. Feb. 1941	£192,500	£170,500	Handled direct by Woolwich	W. G. Robson, Ltd.	

Name of factory	Date work commenced	Anticipated date of completion	Approx. value of contract	Value of work done to date	Agents	Contractors	Remarks
MEDIUM M/C SHOP							
Patricroft	June 1940	Beg. Feb. 1941	£125,000	£61,335	Handled direct by Woolwich	G. Gerrard & Sons	
S.A.A. FACTORIES							
Blackpole	July 1940	Mid-Feb. 1941	£90,000	£31,400	Handled direct by Woolwich	Sir A. McAlpine & Sons	
Radway Green	December 1939	End Feb. 1941	£944,140	£900,164	Handled direct by Woolwich	Trollope & Colls	
Southall	July 1940	End Feb. 1941	£150,000	£100,000	Handled direct by Woolwich	Kent & Sussex Contrs.	
Spennymoor	July 1940	End Mar. 1941	£301,316	£30,316	Handled direct by Woolwich	Sir Wm. Airey & Sons	
Steeton	July 1940	End Feb. 1941	£231,709	£106,828	Handled direct by Woolwich	Sir Wm. Airey & Sons	
ENGINEERING FACTORIES							
Cardiff	February 1940	Mid-Feb. 1941	£306,600	£203,250	M/S	Wm. Cowlin & Son	
Ellesmere Port	End Aug. 1940	Beg. Feb. 1941	£46,650	£10,140	M/S	A. Robinson / Sir A. McAlpine & Sons	
Hayes	June 1940	End Feb. 1941	£200,000	£132,281	M/S	Sir R. McAlpine & Sons	
Hooton	April 1940	End Jan. 1941	£203,300	£199,500	M/S	Taylor & Co.	
Leeds	August 1939	End Jan. 1941	£812,453	£787,453	M/S	Sir Wm. Airey & Sons	
Newport	March 1940	End Jan. 1941	£218,839	£201,597	M/S	Wm. T. Nicholls, Ltd.	
Nottingham (C.I.A.)	December 1940	February 1941	£20,000	Starting	M/S	Geo. Sands & Co. / Thos. Bow & Co.	
Poole	May 1940	February 1941	£170,000	£110,000	M/S	John Howard & Co.	
Radcliffe	March 1940	End Feb. 1941	£245,437	£196,169	M/S	Wm. Townson & Sons	
Theale	October 1940	March 1941	£100,000	£20,000	M/S	Wm. Cowlin & Sons	

APPENDIX XI

Supplies Division: Goods Purchased and Principal Services

I

CATEGORIES OF GOODS PURCHASED BY THE SUPPLIES DIVISION

(a) Furniture (residential, office, hospital, hostels, canteen, etc.) (generally in wood and metal).

(b) Manufactured woodwork and joinery, including special fittings for Post Offices, benches, racks, etc., for Royal Ordnance factories.

(c) Floor coverings.

(d) Beds, bunks and bedding.

(e) Building accessories, e.g., sanitary ware, ironmongery, etc.

(f) Engineering material which admits of centralised purchase.

(g) Fire-fighting equipment, pumping units, ancillary equipment, fire hose, relaying units, fire escapes, turntable ladders, steel water piping, etc.

(h) Chandlery, hardware, cleaning materials and domestic cloths.

(i) Crockery, glass and cutlery.

(j) Canteen equipment, light.

(k) Second-hand tentage.

(l) Tools (for training centres).

(m) Blinds, curtains and black-out materials and fittings.

(n) Stretchers, A.R.P. and first-aid and rescue equipment.

(o) Clocks and time recorders.

(p) Invalid tricycles, bath and Merlin chairs.

(q) Decontamination units and mobile gas cleansing stations.

(r) Operational equipment for factories.

(s) Miscellaneous clothing supplies for bombed-out civilians and hospitals (Ministry of Health). Protective clothing for training centres (Ministry of Labour).

(t) Fuel.

II

PRINCIPAL SERVICES

SERVICES PROVIDED UNDER MINISTRY OF WORKS VOTES

Supply and maintenance of office furniture for public departments generally including administrative offices of the Service and Supply departments, also Revenue buildings, Ministry of Labour buildings, Ministry of Health, etc.

Supply of showcases, fittings and furniture for the national museums, galleries and State repositories.

Supply and maintenance of furniture for all diplomatic and consular buildings, including the supply of plate for embassies.

Supply and maintenance of furniture for the State apartments in Royal palaces and furniture for the Houses of Parliament, the Osborne Convalescent Home for Officers, official residences, including Nos. 10 and 11 Downing Street, the First Sea Lord's residence, etc.

Supply and maintenance of furniture at Ministry of Pensions' hospitals, including supply of tricycles for disabled pensioners.

The Supplies Division is responsible for the furniture, including carpets, curtains, etc., required for State ceremonies, for example, Coronation, Silver Jubilee, etc. Also for arrangement of furniture and decoration of rooms for international conferences, receptions at Lancaster House, etc. The Supplies Division is also responsible for carrying out all internal and external removals, and for the supply of coal and coke, firewood and household articles, china, glass, cutlery, etc., to all the above departments.

Cleaning services are also controlled in a number of buildings in joint occupation of several departments. This service is carried out either by direct labour or under contract.

Supply of fire-fighting equipment, including pumps, hose and accessories of all descriptions, stirrup pumps, steel emergency water tanks, escape ladders, etc., required for the protection of Government buildings throughout London, the country and Scotland. In addition, steel tubes and fittings, electrical accessories, lamps, cables, etc., for all engineering services under the control of the Ministry are supplied by the Supplies Division.

Certain standard fittings which are required for the maintenance services of the Directorate of Works and which admit of bulk purchase are bought under contract by the Supplies Division.

SUPPLIES DIVISION SERVICES ON BEHALF OF OTHER MINISTRIES AND DEPARTMENTS

1. MINISTRY OF SUPPLY

(a) Royal Ordnance factories

Benches, various types, for workshops and process buildings in wood and metal.

Store racks, bins, cupboards, in wood and metal.

Canteen furniture, equipment and office furniture.

Chemical laboratory fittings.

Clothes lockers and shifting house or changing room fittings.

Linoleum and rubber floor covering with special cove surrounds.

Miscellaneous items for operational purposes in wood, metal, rubber and textiles.

Black-out blinds.

Air raid seating and equipment.

Fire-fighting equipment, including trailer pumps, mobile pumps, hose and ladders.

Surgery and welfare furniture and fittings.

Household materials, for example, domestic cloths, brooms, etc.

Beds and bedding.

Time-recording clocks.
Barrows and trucks.
First-aid and passive air defence equipment.
Bedroom furniture and canteen equipment for hostels.
(b) *Agent firms*
Office and canteen furniture and equipment.
Linoleum.
Time-recording clocks.
Fire-fighting equipment.
(c) *Hostels for industrial workers*
Furniture and equipment.

2. WAR OFFICE
(a) Furniture and fittings required by the Director of Fortification and Works for the hutment schemes quarters and hospitals, comprising:
Benches of various types.
Cupboards.
Tables.
Racking.
Carpets and curtains.
Fire-fighting equipment.
Domestic cloths.
(b) *Ordnance depots*
Office, school, mess, hospital and residential furniture.
Black-out material.
Fire-fighting equipment.
Linoleum.
Crockery.
Time-recording clocks.

3. ADMIRALTY
(a) *Fire-fighting equipment*
(b) *Time recording clocks*
(c) *Canteen equipment for:*
R.M. Police stations.
Industrial canteens.
(d) *Hostels for industrial workers*
Furniture and equipment.

4. MINISTRY OF HEALTH AND DEPARTMENT OF HEALTH FOR SCOTLAND
(a) *Emergency hospital supplies*
Beds and bedding, furniture, clothing, and equipment other than medical stores.
Stretchers for hospitals, first-aid posts, etc.
Steel and canvas dams.
Canteen equipment.
(b) *Children's evacuation scheme*
Beds and blankets.
(c) *Civil evacuation*
Furniture.

Beds and bedding.
Messing equipment.
Domestic cloths and stores.

(d) *Refugee reception depots*
Camp beds and blankets.
Household equipment.
Crockery and cutlery.
Domestic cloths and stores.

(e) *Temporary hostels and rest centres*
Furniture.
Crockery.
Cutlery.
Domestic equipment
Oil cookers.
Household articles.
Blankets, pallets, mattresses and camp beds.

(f) *Relief-in-kind schemes*
Emergency furniture.
Cooking utensils.
Cutlery.
Camp beds and bedding.
Household equipment.

(g) *Decontamination services*
Mobile decontamination units to be utilised for the cleansing of gas-contaminated persons where fixed stations were not available.
Equipment for special cleansing centres (hospitals and first-aid posts) for decontamination of gas casualties.

(h) *Public shelters*
Bunks.
Buckets and fire extinguishers.
Droplet masks.
Various equipment for first-aid posts in shelters.

(i) *Water undertakings*
Supply of fire-fighting equipment on prepayment terms.

(j) *War-time nurseries*
Furniture.
Beds and bedding.
Crockery and cutlery.
Kitchen equipment.
Cleaning materials.

(k) *Local authorities*
Bunks and Anderson shelters.

5. HOME OFFICE AND MINISTRY OF HOME SECURITY
(a) Supplies to the Emergency Fire Brigade organisation of pumping units and all ancillary gear. The principal items purchased were as follows:
Fire pumps of varying capacity from 120 to 1,400 gallons per minute on trailers and mobile chassis.

Two-man manual pumps.
Stirrup pumps.
Suction collecting heads, stand pipes, adaptors, nozzles, etc.
Suction and delivery hose and couplings.
Canvas and steel dams of various sizes, and deluge sets.
Extending ladders.
Turntable ladders.
50-feet escape units.
Hose-laying vehicles.
Hose-drying machines.
Miscellaneous gear, such as axes, crowbars, ropes, etc., for secure
work.
Fire extinguishers.
Haversacks for respirators and pouches for first-aid sets and oil-
skin clothing.
A.R.P. (local authorities).
Metal folding beds, camp beds and mattresses.
Rescue party equipment.
Stirrup pumps.
Decontamination hose, couplings and hose reels.
Steel water piping for emergency water mains.
Towing vehicles and general utility vehicles.
Articulated vehicles, tractors and low-loading trailers for carrying
water piping, dehydrators and mobile repair units.
Wheelbarrow pumps.
Fire floats.
Petrol-carrying lorries.
Motor and pedal cycles.
N.B.: The general contracts placed by the Ministry of Works for
this service also cover the needs of the Admiralty, War Office,
Air Ministry, Ministry of Supply, Home Office, Approved
Schools, Petroleum Department, Government of Northern
Ireland, Department of Defence for Dublin, Crown Agents,
including supplies to India, Burma, Australia, New Zealand,
Isle of Man.

(b) *National Fire Service scheme*
e.g., Regional reserve camps.
Fire force headquarters.
Divisional headquarters.
Training colleges.
Furniture.
Beds and bedding.
Kitchen equipment.
Household stores.

(c) *Ministry of Home Security*
Beds, bunks and bedding for fire-watchers (Compulsory Enrolment
Order).

6. AIR MINISTRY
(a) Supplies to Royal Air Force maintenance units:

Furniture and certain items of barrack equipment.
Domestic cloths, etc.
Crockery, glassware and electroplate.
Mattresses.
Hardware and holloware.
Carpets and rugs.
Linoleum.
Fire-fighting equipment.
Clocks.
Vacuum cleaners for operational services, home and overseas.

7. MINISTRY OF AIRCRAFT PRODUCTION
  (a) *Agent firms*
    Office and canteen furniture and equipment.
    Linoleum.
    Time-recording clocks.
    Fire-fighting equipment.
    First-aid and passive air defence equipment.
  (b) *Hostels for industrial workers*
    Furniture and equipment.

8. MINISTRY OF LABOUR
  (a) *Training centres*
    Furniture and benches.
    Supply of tools, drawing instruments and training materials.
    Protective clothing.
  (b) *Medical boards*
    Furniture.
    Medical equipment.
  (c) *Industrial concerns*
    Supply of fire-fighting equipment on prepayment terms.
    Canteen equipment.
  (d) *Hostels, rest-break centres, etc., for industrial workers*
    Furniture and equipment.
    Canteen equipment.

9. CROWN AGENTS FOR THE COLONIES
    Trailer fire pumps and equipment.
    Stirrup pumps.

10. MINISTRY OF PENSIONS
    Furniture.
    Clothing.
    Beds and bedding.
    Spinal carriages, Merlin chairs, bathchairs, invalid tricycles, etc.,
      for Service and civilian casualties.

11. DEPARTMENT OF DEFENCE, DUBLIN
    Trailer pumps and equipment, including hose and mobile units.
    Stirrup pumps.
    Canvas dams.

2K

12. NORTHERN IRELAND
Various equipment for hospital schemes, refugees, evacuees, etc.
Trailer pumps and equipment, including hose and mobile units.
Stirrup pumps.
Steel and canvas dams.
Disinfestation plant.
Rescue party and wardens' A.R.P. equipment.

13. PETROLEUM DEPARTMENT
Trailer pumps and equipment.
Foam compound for oil plants.

14. MINISTRY OF FOOD
(a) *British restaurants*
Light canteen equipment.
Furniture.
(b) *Buffer depots and cold stores*
Furniture, equipment and household stores.
De-infestation plant.

15. FOREIGN OFFICE
(a) Fire-fighting equipment, including pumps, for Egyptian Government.

16. MINISTRY OF AGRICULTURE
(a) *Women's Land Army hostels*
Furniture and equipment.
(b) *Farm workers' hostels*
Furniture and equipment.
(c) *Boys' harvest camps*
Oil cooking ranges.

17. BOARD OF EDUCATION
Light canteen equipment and canteen furniture for Board of Education school and nursery canteens.

18. MINERS' WELFARE COMMISSION
Light canteen equipment and canteen furniture for pit-head canteens.

19. BOARD OF TRADE
(a) *Gas and electricity undertakings*
Supply of fire-fighting equipment on prepayment terms.

20. MINISTRY OF WAR TRANSPORT
(a) *Railways, canals, docks and sea-going vessels*
Supply of fire-fighting equipment either as a charge on Votes or on prepayment terms.

21. FIRE-FIGHTING EQUIPMENT GENERALLY
Supplies to vital firms on instruction of parent departments.

22. GENERAL SERVICES

(a) Tentage—purchase of second-hand tents and marquees for all Service departments, Ministry of Food, Ministry of Agriculture, Ministry of Aircraft Production, etc.

(b) Fuel. Coal and coke supplied to War Department, Air Ministry, Ministry of Supply, Home Office, Approved Schools, Ministry of Labour training centres, etc.

(c) Supplies on prepayment to various voluntary welfare bodies.

(d) Supply of welfare and canteen equipment for contractors' staffs on Government building sites.

23. SUPPLIES TO DOMINION GOVERNMENT AND INDIA

(a) Fire-fighting equipment.

(b) Crockery.

24. ALLIED GOVERNMENTS IN BRITAIN

Furnishing of official accommodation.

25. AMERICAN GOVERNMENT: RECIPROCAL AID SUPPLIES

Furniture, bedding, etc., in bulk for United States forces.

Furnishing of leave centres, etc., for American Red Cross.

APPENDIX XII

Civil Engineering Works on Railways carried out on Ministry of War Transport Account

The main schemes carried out were:

Month work was completed	Company	Cost	Site and nature of works
Dec. 1939–Dec. 1940	G.W.	£68,000	OXFORD–DIDCOT. Loops, Kennington Junction, Radley and Didcot.
June 1940–Mar. 1942	L.N.E.	£158,000	Former Gt. C. main line. Marshalling yard extensions at Woodford and Annesley, loops at Charwelton, Rugby, Ashby Magna, Swithland, Loughborough, Ruddington and Hucknall.
July 1940–Jan. 1941	G.W.	£117,000	CARDIFF, NEWPORT, BARRY, SWANSEA. Sidings at docks.
Feb. 1941	Southern and G.W.	£91,000	READING. Junction.
Mar. 1941–May 1942	G.W.	£73,000	DIDCOT. Loops to Appleford Junction and Milton.
June 1941	G.W.	£67,000	TAVISTOCK JUNCTION. Loops and marshalling yard extension.
July 1941–Jan. 1942	G.W.	£51,000	SHREWSBURY–HEREFORD. Eight loops.
Aug. 1941–Nov. 1941	Southern	£86,000	READING – TONBRIDGE. Loops and sidings at Wokingham North Camp, Shalford, Gomshall and extension of marshalling yard at Tonbridge.
November 1941	G.W.	£257,000	NEWPORT–SEVERN TUNNEL JUNCTION. Quadrupling.
Dec. 1941–April 1942	L.M.S.	£84,000	DERBY–BRISTOL. Loops and sidings at five places.
April 1942–Sept. 1942	L.N.E.	£76,000	NORTHALLERTON–LEEDS. Eight loops.
June 1942–Oct. 1942	G.W.	£128,000	OXFORD. Loops to Woolvercote and Kennington Junction.
June 1942	Southern	£72,000	ROCHESTER. Strengthening disused bridge over Medway for emergency road or rail use.
July 1942–Mar. 1943	L.M.S.	£95,000	AYR–STRANRAER. Four loops.
August 1942	L.M.S.	£73,000	NORTHAMPTON. Loops and sidings.
August 1942	G.W.	£127,000	OXFORD. Marshalling yard.
Aug. 1942–May 1943	L.N.E.	£374,000	PILMOOR–THIRSK. Quadrupling.
August 1942	L.M.S. and G.W.	£500,000	GLOUCESTER–CHELTENHAM. Quadrupling.
October 1942	L.N.E.	£65,000	CONNINGTON (Peterborough). Marshalling yard.
December 1942	L.N.E.	£82,000	YORK. Reception sidings.
January 1943	L.N.E.	£58,000	CADDER. Marshalling yard.
February 1943	L.N.E.	£59,000	DONCASTER. Decoy yard extension.
March 1943	L.M.S.	£89,000	CARLISLE. Additional bridge over River Eden and quadrupling.

Schemes were also carried for control telephones and protection for telephone exchanges on various systems—total cost £527,000.

To deal with the influx of American troops into the United Kingdom, and later to provide for the large increase in rail traffic in connection with the invasion of Europe, further facilities had to be provided. The following were among the larger schemes:

Month work was completed	Company	Cost	Site and nature of works
Nov. 1942–July 1943	L.N.E.	£108,000	RESTON, AYTON, CHEVINGTON, PRESTON-LE-SKERNE and DONCASTER. Loops.
Jan. 1943–May 1943	G.W.	£153,000	NEWBURY–WINCHESTER. Crossing loops and chord to Southern Railway.
Mar. 1943–Oct. 1943	G.W.	£122,000	WITHAM, CASTLE CARY, SOMERTON and ATHELNEY. Loops.
March 1943	Southern	£90,000	SHAWFORD–EASTLEIGH. Loop and siding.
March 1943	Southern	£56,000	SOUTHAMPTON. Rail access from west to docks and loops at Romsey.
April 1943	G.W.	£248,000	DIDCOT–NEWBURY. Doubling of single line.
April 1943–Aug. 1944	G.W.	£54,000	PLYMOUTH–PENZANCE. Four loops, etc.
May 1943–Dec. 1944	G.W.	£91,000	BRISTOL–PLYMOUTH. Loops and sidings.
June 1943–Feb. 1944	Southern and G.W.	£51,000	LYDFORD. Junction and sidings.
July 1943	G.W.	£54,000	MORETON CUTTING. Marshalling yard extension.
Aug. 1943–Oct. 1943	Southern	£57,000	Additional sidings, etc., around Southampton, Eastleigh and Romsey.
October 1943	G.W.	£106,000	EXETER. Loops and reversing sidings.
September 1944	L.N.E.	£62,000	WELWYN GARDEN CITY. Marshalling yard.

Further information is contained on pp. 16, 23, 46, 47 and 125 and Appendix X of the *History of Inland Transport,* by M. P. Ashley; and Chapter 17 of the *History of the British Railways during the War, 1939–45,* by R. Bell.

Index

INDEX

(See Index to Place-Names following)

INDEX TO PLACE-NAMES

S.O. Code No. 63-111-3-7*